BELL LIBRARY
TEXAS A&M UNIVERSITY
CORPUS CHRISTI

RECEIVED AUG 3 1999

.M2
N67
1999

Norumbega Fault System of the Northern Appalachians

Edited by

Allan Ludman
School of Earth and Environmental Sciences
Queens College, City University of New York
Flushing, New York 11367-1597
and
Ph.D. Program in Earth and Environmental Sciences
City University Graduate School and University Center
365 Fifth Avenue
New York, New York 10036

and

David P. West, Jr.
Department of Geology
Earlham College
Richmond, Indiana 47374

Special Paper 331 erratum:
Enclosed is a color
replacement for page 68

SPECIAL PAPER
331
1999

Copyright © 1999, The Geological Society of America, Inc. (GSA). All rights reserved. GSA grants permission to individual scientists to make unlimited photocopies of one or more items from this volume for noncommercial purposes advancing science or education, including classroom use. Permission is granted to individuals to make photocopies of any item in this volume for other noncommercial, nonprofit purposes provided that the appropriate fee ($0.25 per page) is paid directly to the Copyright Clearance Center, 222 Rosewood Drive, Danvers, MA 01923, USA, phone (978) 750-8400, http://www.copyright.com (include title and ISBN when paying). Written permission is required from GSA for all other forms of capture or reproduction of any item in the volume including, but not limited to, all types of electronic or digital scanning or other digital or manual transformation of articles or any portion thereof, such as abstracts, into computer-readable and/or transmittable form for personal or corporate use, either noncommercial or commercial, for-profit or otherwise. Send permission requests to GSA Copyrights.

Copyright is not claimed on any material prepared wholly by government employees within the scope of their employment.

Published by The Geological Society of America, Inc.
3300 Penrose Place, P.O. Box 9140, Boulder, Colorado 80301

Printed in U.S.A.

GSA Books Science Editor Abhijit Basu

Library of Congress Cataloging-in-Publication Data
Norumbega fault system of the northern Appalachians / edited by Allan
    Ludman and David P. West, Jr.
        p.   cm. -- (Special paper ; 331)
    Includes index.
    ISBN 0-8137-2331-0
    1. Geology, Structural--Maine--Norumbega Fault Zone.   2. Geology,
Structural--Appalachian Mountains.   3. Norumbega Fault Zone (Me.)
I. Ludman, Allan, 1943- . II. West, David P., 1963- . III. Series:
Special papers (Geological Society of America) ; 331.
QE627.5.M2N67   1999
551.8'72'09741--dc21   99-22075
                                                    CIP

Cover: Photomicrograph showing muscovite fish (dextral sense of shear) from a high strain zone within the Norumbega fault system in south-central Maine. The thin section is cut parallel to the stretching lineation and perpendicular to foliation. Crossed polarized light. Width of field of view is 1.5 mm. Photo by David West.

10 9 8 7 6 5 4 3 2 1

Contents

Contents

Preface

INTRODUCTION

The Norumbega fault system of the northern Appalachians has been recognized recently as one of the most extensive and longest-lived structural features of the Appalachian orogenic belt. Although portions of the Norumbega system have been known for decades, it is only through recent multidisciplinary studies that its true magnitude and complexity have been appreciated, and it is only now beginning to receive the attention accorded its Southern Appalachian relative, the Brevard zone, or its modern west coast analogue, the San Andreas fault system. The goal of this volume is to provide a single venue for presenting a rapidly growing body of multidisciplinary research along the Norumbega fault system. The contributions contained in the volume provide the geological community with the most up-to-date views on the mechanics, timing, displacement history, and overall tectonic significance of the Norumbega system. Perhaps more important, however, these studies will introduce the Norumbega fault system to a broad audience and reveal its potential for understanding middle to shallow crustal processes in active fault systems throughout the world.

EVOLUTION OF IDEAS ABOUT THE NORUMBEGA FAULT SYSTEM

The history of work along the Norumbega fault system reveals a progressively deeper understanding of the full four-dimensional nature of the structure. Early mappers worked mostly in two dimensions to define its length and breadth, and concepts of its areal extent have changed significantly in the past two decades. Seismic and geochemical studies have now imaged its third dimension and allow us to discuss the depths to which it affects the northern Appalachian orogen. These types of studies continue today, but the most recent developments have been in understanding the system's fourth dimension—its longevity as an active fault system and the varied tectonic roles it played at different times during that history.

Early concepts

Field work in eastern and central Maine in the 1940s through the early 1970s revealed a significant metamorphic and structural discontinuity between low-grade and simply deformed rocks of central Maine and high-grade, intensely polydeformed strata of the mid-coastal region (Fig. 1; Doyle and Hussey, 1967; Griffin, 1973; Bickel, 1976). It is interesting that maps of this era did not define that discontinuity as a fault, although some small-scale faults were identified in mid-coastal Maine (Stoeser, 1966; Hatheway, 1969) and brittle faults were mapped along strike to the northeast on the basis of topographic lineaments and local lithologic offsets (Larrabee, 1964; Larrabee et al., 1965; Doyle and Hussey, 1967).

Stewart and Wones (1974) first used the name "Norumbega" to describe a fault zone 300 to 400 m wide that separated contrasting lithotectonic terranes in mid-coastal Maine just north of Penobscot Bay. The name Norumbega came from a small town in the area, but was also the mythical Indian city, rich in gold and jewels, that was the objective of sixteenth and seventeenth century European explorers along the coast of Maine. In some ways, this name was an unfortunate choice because many geologists at first considered the fault to be more myth than reality. In the middle to late 1970s, detailed mapping to the southwest (e.g., Pankiwskyj, 1976; Hussey and Newberg, 1977; and northeast (e.g., Wones, 1978; Wones and Thompson, 1979; Ludman, 1981) of the original type locality not only proved the reality of the Norumbega fault but also showed that it was a structure of regional significance.

Current concepts

Extent. The relatively narrow fault zone originally mapped by Stewart and Wones (1974) and subsequently mapped across the state by other workers is now regarded as one small component of a regional-scale Norumbega fault system that is at least

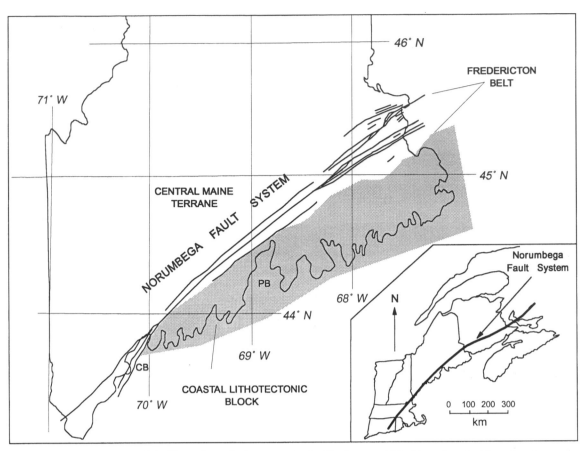

Figure 1. Extent of the Norumbega fault system in the Northern and Maritime Appalachians. Inset shows schematic trace of the system in the Northern Appalachians. Large map indicates complexity of the system where detailed mapping has been conducted. Shaded area outlines the Coastal lithotectonic block. CB = Casco Bay; PB = Penobscot Bay.

30–40 km wide. Detailed mapping unequivocally demonstrates the continuity of the Norumbega fault system for almost 450 km from Casco Bay in southwestern Maine to central New Brunswick (Hussey, 1988; Hussey et al., 1986; Newberg, 1985; Swanson, 1992, 1994; Swanson et al., 1986; West, 1993; Pankiwskyj, 1996; Ludman, 1991, 1998; Hubbard et al., 1995; McLeod et al., 1994; Potter et al., 1979). In addition, geophysical evidence (Durling and Marillier, 1990) and recent mapping summarized in this volume (Goldstein and Hepburn; Bothner and Hussey) suggest that the structure extends from southern Connecticut to the Gulf of St. Lawrence, a distance of nearly 1200 km (Fig. 1). Figure 2 provides a useful analogue for better visualizing the scale of the Norumbega system; the New England component of the Norumbega fault system is approximately the same length as the onshore segment of the San Andreas fault system in California.

The system is equally impressive at depth (the third dimension). Seismic reflection studies in central Maine (Stewart et al., 1986; Unger et al., 1987), eastern Maine (Doll et al., 1996), and the Gulf of St. Lawrence (Durling and Marillier, 1990) give some indication of the system's vertical extent. The U.S. Geological Survey–Geological Survey of Canada seismic reflection line from Quebec through Maine and into the Gulf of Maine (Stewart et al.,

1986) crossed the Norumbega system in an area of poor seismic reflectivity but suggested that the faults penetrate steeply to middle and lower crustal levels before becoming listric and flattening to the northwest. The marine reflection profile in the Gulf of St. Lawrence was interpreted similarly, except that flattening was to the southeast (Durling and Marillier, 1990). An exceptionally clear reflection image of the entire crust was obtained recently along a transect that crossed one Norumbega high-strain zone in east-central Maine (Doll et al., 1996). This image showed that at least one Norumbega fault strand penetrates the entire crust steeply, extending at least into the uppermost mantle. Doll et al. (1996) interpreted at least 1.5–2.5 km of dip-slip Moho offset on the Norumbega fault strand, and suggested that at least some Norumbega faulting post-dated the formation of the Moho in this region.

Timing and duration of faulting. The system's fourth-dimensional, temporal relationships have proved difficult to unravel and are the subject of a considerable amount of research. Detailed mapping of crosscutting relationships and thermochronological investigations have helped constrain the onset of Norumbega activity to Middle Devonian time (see Ludman et al. and West, this volume, for details). Segments of the system have been particularly fertile testing grounds for new methods of

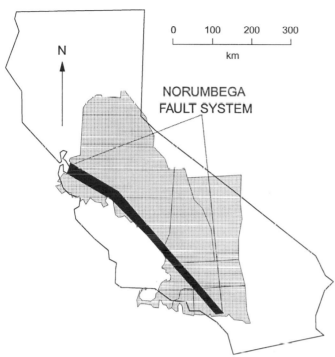

Figure 2. Comparison of the Norumbega and San Andreas fault systems. New England region (stippled) is flipped east-west to make the comparison.

dating fault motion, and at least two major periods of reactivation have been identified (late Paleozoic and Mesozoic; West et al., 1993; West and Lux, 1993; Doll et al., 1996). Detailed field and textural studies track a complex displacement history that may have been continuous for almost 100 m.y. at middle crustal depths exposed in mid-coastal Maine (West and Hubbard, 1997), but was more sporadic over that time span at epizonal levels exposed farther to the northeast (Ludman, 1998).

Previous uncertainties concerning its displacement history led to equally uncertain assignments to orogenic events in recent tectonic syntheses of the Appalachian orogen (e.g., Osberg et al., 1989; Hatcher et al., 1989). Evidence suggests that faulting associated with the Norumbega system may have spanned nearly 200 m.y., about six times the duration of activity in the San Andreas system (Weldon et al., 1993; Sims, 1993; James et al., 1993).

Tectonic significance. Because of the wide extent and longevity of the Norumbega system, a wide range of rock types has been subjected to faulting and shearing associated with the multiple stages of its activity. These include upper amphibolite facies polydeformed rocks of the Coastal lithotectonic block, less-intensely deformed greenschist to subgreenschist facies strata of the Central Maine and Fredericton belts (Fig. 1), large and small intrusive rock bodies of varied composition and age, and even the unmetamorphosed Carboniferous rocks of west-central and central New Brunswick. Relationships among these lithologies change along the strike of the system, precluding simple tectonic models.

In southern and south-central Maine, faults and shear zones of the Norumbega system locally juxtapose several contrasting lithotectonic belts (Fig. 3). In the easternmost part of the state, however,

the fault system is contained almost entirely within a single formation in the Fredericton belt (Osberg et al., 1985; Ludman, 1991). Faults now mapped within the Norumbega system, like those of the San Andreas, record a wide variety of motion, including dextral strike-slip, east- and west-vergent thrust, normal, and high angle reverse movements. These contrasting relationships, combined with its long and complicated history of reactivated movement, have clouded understanding of the tectonic significance of the Norumbega system and led to radically different concepts of its role(s) in northern Appalachian tectonism. Sparked by emergence of the exotic terrane model for the northwestern Cordillera (Monger and Irving, 1980; Coney et al., 1980), several early interpretations viewed the Norumbega system as a major transcurrent (sinistral) suture between ancestral North American rocks to the west and exotic terranes to the east (e.g., Kent and Opdyke, 1978; Keppie, 1989). Others have suggested that the system represents an important (albeit poorly understood) dextral break without calling upon significant offset (Rankin, 1994; Zen, 1983; Williams and Hatcher, 1983). A few tectonic syntheses have largely ignored the Norumbega system, apparently considering it a relatively late, tectonically insignificant feature that overprints structures which were far more significant in regional accretion history (e.g., Berry and Osberg, 1989). However, significant basement discontinuities across the Norumbega system were identified by gravity and magnetic modeling (Coblentz, 1988) and plutonic geochemistry (Andrew et al., 1983), suggesting that it was a significant structure at some time during its evolution.

SIGNIFICANCE OF THE NORUMBEGA FAULT SYSTEM FOR NEOTECTONIC AND ROCK MECHANICS STUDIES

Arguments about the amount and nature of displacement and the sequence, timing, and duration of faulting are reminiscent of similar debates concerning the San Andreas fault system—arguably the world's most intensely studied active fault system. Thus, while some pieces of the Norumbega puzzle can benefit from comparison with this modern analogue, both ancient and modern fault systems present some common problems that are as yet unresolved.

In a reversal of the traditional Uniformitarian approach, the Norumbega fault system may prove more valuable to understanding the modern San Andreas system than the modern fault will be to unraveling the Norumbega system. Figure 4 shows the regional metamorphic setting of rocks that host the Norumbega fault system. Metamorphic grade decreases steadily from southwest to northeast along the Norumbega system, from upper amphibolite facies between Casco and Penobscot Bays to lower greenschist and finally subgreenschist facies at the Maine–New Brunswick border. Farther east, unmetamorphosed Mississippian and Pennsylvanian redbeds are affected by the Fredericton fault, the eastern extension of the Norumbega system in New Brunswick. Crustal depths ranging from less than 5 km to about 18 km are inferred from these regional metamorphic conditions, and Hubbard et al. (1995) demonstrated that faulting was coeval at all depths during at least the first major displacement event in Devonian time. Differential

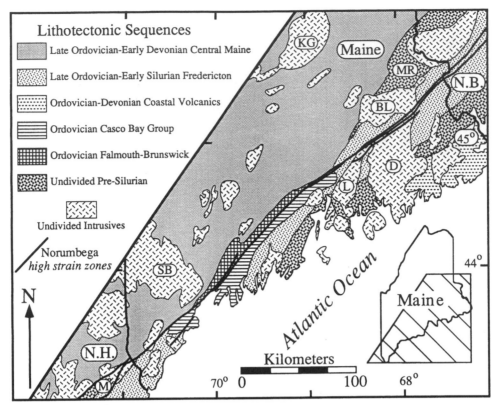

Figure 3. Generalized lithotectonic map of coastal northern New England and adjacent New Brunswick showing tectonic setting of the Norumbega fault system. (Modified from Osberg et al., 1985; McLeod et al., 1994.) Note that only selected high strain zones of the Norumbega system are shown: see the text for details. BL = Bottle Lake pluton; D = Deblois pluton; KG = Mount Katahdin granite; L = Lucerne pluton; M = Massabesic Gneiss Complex; MR = Miramichi anticlinorium; SB = Sebago batholith; N.B. = New Brunswick; N.H. = New Hampshire.

exhumation after the Devonian has since provided a window into the upper half of the crustal profile of this major transcurrent fault system. For example, rocks deformed at the 12–15 km depth at which current San Andreas earthquake foci are concentrated can be observed directly in east-central Maine; their deformation mechanisms can be analyzed and compared with deeper and shallower effects elsewhere along the Norumbega system.

The Norumbega system also presents experimentalists with an opportunity to field test their findings concerning the response of different lithologies to shear stresses at a wide range of crustal conditions. Experimental studies (e.g., Tullis and Yund, 1985, 1991) have given structural geologists abundant information about the deformational behavior of rocks under laboratory imposed conditions of, e.g., shear stress, strain rate, and temperature. However, because of the greater complexity of natural samples and the difficulties of extrapolating laboratory experiments over geologically meaningful periods of time, application of these experimental findings to natural systems remains tenuous at best.

Differential exhumation shown in Figure 4 has exposed the Norumbega fault system at what had originally been a range of pressure-temperature conditions corresponding to the upper half of the crust. Ambient temperatures and pressures associated with

Norumbega shearing can be identified from geobarometry and geothermometry of fault-generated mylonites and cataclasites and rocks that host the fault system, and detailed structural analyses can ascertain the roles of lithology and fluids during deformation (e.g., Ludman, 1998). Microfabric, scanning electron microscope, and transmission electron microscope analyses will eventually relate deformation mechanics to specific sets of conditions along the Norumbega system and thus provide experimentalists with the critical calibration needed to extend their work to actual fault systems. As even more detailed time-temperature-deformation histories are determined for different crustal levels, the Norumbega fault system may ultimately prove to be one of the best areas to field test experimental studies of deformation mechanics.

PERSPECTIVES CONTAINED IN THIS VOLUME

Figure 5 places the contributions to this volume in their geographic settings along the Norumbega fault system. The first three papers report on studies of deformation mechanisms and general rock behavior at the range of crustal levels encompassed by the entire system. Swanson examines features from the deepest level amphibolite facies rocks of southwestern Maine. His

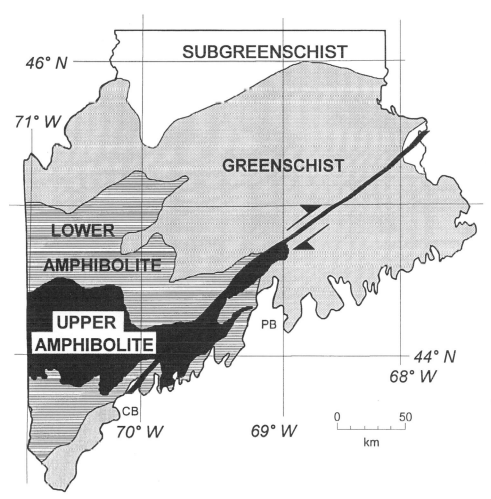

Figure 4. Regional metamorphic setting of rocks affected by the Norumbega fault system in Maine.
CB = Casco Bay; PB = Penobscot Bay.

study provides a detailed analysis of strain-related dextral shear fabrics and structures based on emplacement and subsequent fault deformation of small-scale veins and mesoscale and megascale granitoids. Hubbard and Wang examine quartz microfabrics in sheared rocks from a traverse along strike extending from amphibolite facies rocks in mid-coastal Maine to epizonal plutonic rocks near the Maine–New Brunswick border. Their analysis elucidates contrasting deformation mechanics at different crustal levels during a lengthy Norumbega history. Ludman and Gibbons provide the first comprehensive analysis of the effects of Norumbega shearing on plutonic rocks. They reconstruct a multistage deformation sequence in the Deblois pluton, the largest granitic batholith in eastern Maine, and describe microtextural evidence for deformation mechanisms associated with the shallow crustal segment of the fault system.

The next two papers address a question that has plagued regional mappers since the scale of the Norumbega system was fully appreciated. What structures in southern New England (if any) can be associated with this 30–40-km-wide fault system? Bothner and Hussey trace the Norumbega system southward

from the Casco Bay area, the southwesternmost point at which all mappers agree that the faults present can be confidently ascribed to the system. They use local mapping, regional potential field maps, fault mechanics, and deformation styles to track the system through the Gulf of Maine at least as far south as New Hampshire, and point the way for future mappers to identify its effects on land farther south. Goldstein and Hepburn pick up the trail from there; they catalogue the several potential candidates for Norumbega continuations in southern New England and suggest that the problem of identifying its southwestward extension may be more complex than previous workers have suspected. Their conclusion—that the system may well have affected different parts of Massachusetts, Rhode Island, and Connecticut, depending on which particular episode of motion is being considered—opens several interesting possibilities for future study.

Four papers examine the potential role(s) of the Norumbega system in the regional tectonic evolution of the Northern Appalachians. Swanson describes fault geometry in the deeper crustal segment in southwestern Maine and shows how regional-scale transpressional deformation has resulted from a large-scale restraining bend geome-

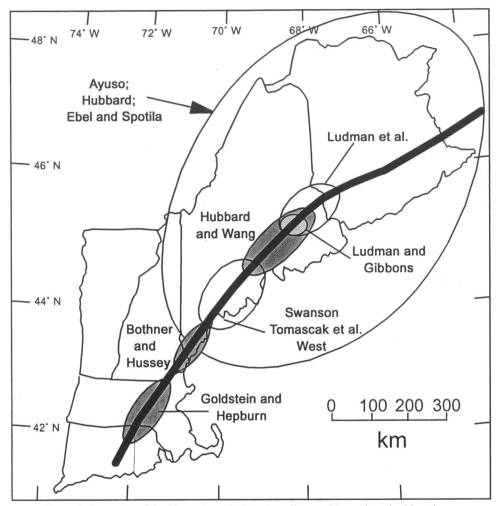

Figure 5. Segments of the Norumbega fault system discussed by authors in this volume.

try. The potential complexities of an adjoining releasing bend may also help to explain the wide range of fault movements that has been reported within the Norumbega fault system. Hubbard places the Norumbega system in a broader Northern and Maritime Appalachian context, comparing its orientation, displacement, and timing with those of other major transcurrent faults in Maine, New Brunswick, Nova Scotia, and Quebec. She proposes a broader scale view of the region, one comparable to the Himalayan collisional system, in which the effects of plate convergence extend for hundreds of kilometers across strike. Papers by Tomascak et al. and Ayuso compare the geochemical signatures of plutons in and across the Norumbega system. Tomascak et al. provide evidence that Norumbega faults juxtapose granites derived from isotopically distinct basement sources in southwestern Maine. Ayuso analyzes metallogenic provinces on both sides of the fault system in south-central and eastern Maine and comes to similar conclusions. These findings suggest that the Norumbega fault system may indeed represent a fundamental terrane boundary at depth in this region.

The last three papers discuss the most recent contributions to our understanding of the timing and displacement history along the Norumbega system. West outlines a protracted and polyphase history of Norumbega activity in south-central and southwestern Maine based on a synthesis of structural and geochronological information. His data from this region suggest ongoing dextral shear deformation from Middle Devonian to Early Permian time (~100 m.y.) during a prolonged period of slow regional exhumation. Ludman et al. present a comparable analysis for the shallowest segment of the fault system in eastern Maine based on crosscutting field relationships and new radiometric dating. They suggest that at least three progressively more brittle stages of faulting have occurred in that segment, possibly spanning a 200 m.y. history, and attempt to correlate measurable offset with individual fault stages. Ebel and Spotila conclude the volume with a modern seismic perspective, relating earthquakes recorded by the New England seismic network to the Norumbega system and evaluating the system's capability to produce a great earthquake. There is some evidence for modern fault motion within the area outlined by the Norumbega system, although the dominant sense of motion appears to be thrust faulting rather than strike-slip faulting.

FUTURE DIRECTIONS

This volume is not intended as a final summary of well-accepted conclusions, but rather as an interim report of the status of ongoing research into the evolution of this major transcurrent fault system. Several of the problems that plagued early investigations have been resolved. The Norumbega system is indeed a very real structure of regional significance; it was characterized by dominantly dextral strike-slip motion, but associated faults exhibited thrust, dip-slip, and oblique-slip displacement; its first demonstrable activity was during Early Devonian time, but several periods of reactivation suggest that it played roles in late Paleozoic regional accretion as well as later rifting through at least the middle of the Mesozoic Era.

Contributors to this volume have answered these early questions but have also raised new ones. The major problem—the tectonic role of the Norumbega system—is still unclear and several apparent contradictions must now be resolved. For example, although Hubbard's proposal that the system is but one component of a broad zone of plate convergence fits regional accretion models for the Devonian, the amount of measurable Devonian offset for this 40-km-wide system is much less than would be expected in such a setting. Tomascak et al. and Ayuso confirm that the deep segment of the Norumbega system locally separates crustal blocks with distinctly different geochemical signatures in southwestern Maine, but Ludman confirms its intraformational setting at shallow crustal levels in the eastern part of the state and in adjacent New Brunswick. Sinistral Late Silurian displacement has been described elsewhere in the Northern Appalachians as an important constituent of plate accretion in areas bracketing the Norumbega system (Hibbard and Hall, 1993; Holdsworth, 1994), but sinistral motion was either absent from the area affected by Norumbega deformation or evidence for it was obliterated by later shearing.

Detailed mapping along and across the Norumbega system in south-central Maine will eventually unravel the region's polydeformational history and show how the current juxtaposition of lithotectonic blocks was achieved. A better appreciation for the width of the orogen affected by Norumbega deformation will come from a careful hunt for effects of dextral shearing in the Central Maine belt, the strata of which have been largely ignored by those mapping deformation related to the Norumbega fault system. Southern New England mappers following suggestions by Goldstein and Hepburn will place the system in an even more comprehensive regional context and try to tie it better to the well-defined Alleghenian deformation in Rhode Island and Massachusetts. As more detailed Norumbega deformation timetables are constructed, information on slip rates, continuous vs. sporadic deformation, and amount of displacement during different fault stages will help resolve the question of whether the Norumbega system underwent motion comparable to that of modern interplate sutures.

ACKNOWLEDGMENTS

The Maine Geological Survey has sponsored detailed mapping of the Norumbega fault system and its host rocks for nearly four decades, including work by many of the contributors to this volume. We wish to express our appreciation for the interest and inspiration, as well as support, of State Geologists Robert G. Doyle, Walter Anderson, and Robert Marvinney. We are particularly indebted to Robert Marvinney and Mark Swanson for their helpful comments on an earlier version of this Preface. Contributions to this volume have benefited from insightful reviewers whose rigorous analyses and constructive comments contributed significantly to both the substance and presentation of its papers, including Sandra Barr, Henry N. Berry IV, Dwight Bradley, Patrick W. G. Brock, J. Dykstra Eusden, Alec Gates, Laurel Goodwin, Peter Gromet, MaryLouise Hill, John Hogan, Jerry Magloughlin, Michel Malo, Robert Marvinney, Peter Mattson, Daniel Murray, Philip Osberg, Carol Simpson, David B. Stewart, Jan Tullis, Joe Whalen, and Joe White.

REFERENCES CITED

Andrew, A. S., Loiselle, M. C., and Wones, D. R., 1983, Granitic plutonism as an indicator of microplates in the Paleozoic of central and eastern Maine: Earth and Planetary Science Letters, v. 66, p. 157–165.

Berry, H. N., IV, and Osberg, P. H., 1989, A stratigraphic synthesis of eastern Maine and western New Brunswick, in Tucker, R. D., and Marvinney, R. G., eds., Studies in Maine geology: Structure and stratigraphy: Augusta, Maine Geological Survey, p. 1–32.

Bickel, C. E., 1976, Stratigraphy of the Belfast quadrangle, Maine, in Page, L., ed., Contributions to the stratigraphy of New England: Geological Society of America Memoir 148, p. 97–128.

Coblentz, D. D., 1988, Crustal modeling in Maine through the simultaneous inversion of gravity and magnetic data [M.A. thesis]: Chestnut Hill, Massachusetts, Boston College, 82 p.

Coney, P. J., Jones, D. L., and Monger, J. W. H., 1980, Cordilleran suspect terranes: Nature, v. 188, p. 329–333.

Doll, W. E., Domoracki, W. J., Costain, J. K., Coruh, C., Ludman, A., and Hopeck, J. T., 1996, Implications of a seismic reflection profile across a part of the Norumbega fault system, east-central Maine: Geology, v. 24, p. 251–254.

Doyle, R. G., and Hussey, A. M., II, 1967, Preliminary bedrock geologic map of Maine: Augusta, Maine Geological Survey, scale 1:500,000.

Durling, P., and Marillier, F., 1990, Structural trends and basement rock subdivisions in the western Gulf of St. Lawrence, Northern Appalachians: Atlantic Geology, v. 267, p. 79–95.

Griffin, J. R., 1973, A structural study of Silurian metasediments of central Maine [Ph.D. thesis]: Riverside, University of California, 157 p.

Hatcher, R. D., Jr., Thomas, W. A., Geiser, P. A., Snoke, A. W., Mosher, S., and Wiltschko, D. V., 1989, Alleghanian orogen, in Hatcher, R. D., Jr., Thomas, W. A., and Viele, G. W., eds., The Appalachian-Ouachita orogen in the United States: Boulder, Colorado, Geological Society of America, Geology of North America, v. F-2, p. 273–318.

Hatheway, R. B., 1969, Geology of the Wiscasset quadrangle, Maine [Ph.D. thesis]: Ithaca, New York, Cornell University, 141 p.

Hibbard, J., and Hall, S., 1993, Early Acadian sinistral shear in north-central Maine: Geological Society of London Journal, v. 150, p. 815–818.

Holdsworth, R. G., 1994, Structural evolution of the Gander-Avalon terrane boundary: A reactivated transpression zone in the NE Newfoundland Appalachians: Geological Society of London Journal, v. 151, p. 629–646.

Hubbard, M. S., West, D. P., Jr., Ludman, A., Guidotti, C. V., and Lux, D. R., 1995, The Norumbega fault zone, Maine: A mid- to shallow-level crustal section within a transcurrent shear zone: Atlantic Geology, v. 31, p. 109–116.

Hussey, A. M., II, 1988, Lithotectonic stratigraphy, deformation, plutonism, and metamorphism, greater Casco Bay region, southwestern Maine, in Tucker, R. D., and Marvinney, R. G., eds., Studies in Maine geology: Structure and stratigraphy: Augusta, Maine Geological Survey, p. 17–34.

Hussey, A. M., II, and Newberg, D. W., 1977, Major faulting in the Merrimack Synclinorium between Hollis, New Hampshire, and Biddeford, Maine: Geological Society of America Abstracts with Programs, v. 10, p. 48.

Hussey, A. M., II, Bothner, W. A., and Thompson, J. A., 1986, Geological comparisons across the Norumbega Fault Zone, southwestern Maine, *in* Newberg, D. W., ed., Guidebook to field trips in southwestern Maine: New England Intercollegiate Geological Conference Guidebook, v. 78, p. 164–183.

James, E. W., Kimbrough, D. L., and Mattinson, J. M., 1993, Evaluation of displacements of pre-Tertiary rocks on the northern San Andreas fault, *in* Powell, R. E., Weldon, R. J., II, and Matti, J. C., eds., The San Andreas fault system: Displacement, palinspastic reconstruction, and geologic evolution: Geological Society of America Memoir 178, p. 257–272.

Kent, D. V., and Opdyke, N. D., 1978, Paleomagnetism of the Devonian Catskill redbeds: Evidence for motion of the coastal New England–Canadian Maritime region relative to cratonic North America: Journal of Geophysical Research, v. 83, p. 4441–4450.

Keppie, J. D., 1989, Northern Appalachian terranes and their accretionary history, *in* Dallmeyer, R. D., ed., Terranes in the Circum-Atlantic Paleozoic orogens: Geological Society of America Special Paper 230, p. 159–192.

Larrabee, D. M., 1964, Reconnaissance bedrock geology of the Wabassus Lake quadrangle, Washington County, Maine: U.S. Geological Survey Mineral Investigation Field Studies Map MF-282, scale 1:62,500.

Larrabee, D. M., Spencer, C. W., and Swift, D. J. P., 1965, Bedrock geology of the Grand Lake area, Aroostook, Hancock, Penobscot, and Washington counties, Maine: U.S. Geological Survey Bulletin 1202-E, 38 p.

Ludman, A., 1981, Significance of transcurrent faulting in eastern Maine and location of the suture between Avalonia and North America: American Journal of Science, v. 281, p. 463–483.

Ludman, A., 1991, The Fredericton trough and Norumbega fault zone in eastern Maine, *in* Ludman, A., ed., Geology of the Coastal lithotectonic block and neighboring terranes, eastern Maine and southern New Brunswick: New England Intercollegiate Geological Conference Guidebook, v. 83, p. 186–208.

Ludman, A., 1998, Evolution of a transcurrent fault system in shallow crustal metasedimentary rocks: The Norumbega fault zone, eastern Maine: Journal of Structural Geology, v. 20, p. 93–107.

McLeod, M. J., Johnson, S. C., and Ruitenberg, A. A., 1994, Geological map of southwestern New Brunswick: New Brunswick Department of Natural Resources and Energy Map NR-5, scale 1:250,000.

Monger, J. W. H., and Irving, E., 1980, Northward displacement of north-central British Columbia: Nature, v. 285, p. 289–294.

Newberg, D. W., 1985, Bedrock geology of the Palermo 7.5′ quadrangle, Maine: Maine Geological Survey Open-File Report 84-4, 21 p.

Osberg, P. H., Hussey, A. M., II, and Boone, G. M., 1985, Bedrock geologic map of Maine: Augusta, Maine Geological Survey, scale 1:500,000.

Osberg, P. H., Tull, J. F., Robinson, P., Hon, R., and Butler, J. R., 1989, The Acadian orogen, *in* Hatcher, R. D., Jr., Thomas, W. A., and Viele, G. W., eds., 1989, The Appalachian-Ouachita orogen in the United States: Boulder, Colorado, Geological Society of America, Geology of North America, v. F-2, p. 179–232.

Pankiwskyj, K. A., 1976, Preliminary report on the geology of the Liberty 15′ quadrangle and adjoining parts of the Burnham, Brooks, Belfast, and Vassalboro quadrangles in south-central Maine: Maine Geological Survey Open File Report 76-29, 16 p.

Pankiwskyj, K. A., 1996, Structure and stratigraphy across the Hackmatack Pond fault, Kennebec and Waldo Counties, Maine: Maine Geological Survey Open-File Report 96-2, 15 p.

Potter, R. R., Hamilton, J. B., and Davies, J. L., 1979, Geological map of New Brunswick: New Brunswick Department of Natural Resources Map NR-1, scale 1:500,000.

Rankin, D. W., 1994, Continental margin of the eastern United States: Past and present, *in* Speed, R. C., ed., Phanerozoic evolution of North American continent-Ocean transitions: Boulder, Colorado, Geological Society of America Continent-Ocean Transect Volume, p. 129–218.

Sims, 1993, Chronology of displacement on the San Andreas fault in central California, *in* Powell, R. E., Weldon, R. J., II, and Matti, J. C., eds., The San Andreas fault system: Displacement, palinspastic reconstruction, and geologic evolution: Geological Society of America Memoir 178, p. 231–256.

Stewart, D. B., Unger, J. D., Phillips, J. D., Goldsmith, R., Poole, W. H., Spencer, C. P., Green, A. G., Loiselle, M. C., and St. Julien, P., 1986, The Quebec–western Maine seismic reflection profile: Setting and first year results, *in* Barazangi, M., and Brown, L. D., eds., Reflection seismology: The continental crust: American Geophysical Union Geodynamics Series, v. 14, p. 189–199.

Stewart, D. B., and Wones, D. R., 1974, Bedrock geology of the northern Penobscot Bay area, *in* Osberg, P. H., ed., Geology of east-central and north-central Maine: New England Intercollegiate Geological Conference Guidebook, v. 66, p. 223–239.

Stoeser, D. B., 1966, Geology of a portion of the Great Pond quadrangle, Maine [M.A. thesis]: Orono, University of Maine, 88 p.

Swanson, M. T., 1992, Late Acadian–Alleghenian transpressional deformation: Evidence from asymmetric boudinage in the Casco Bay area, coastal Maine: Journal of Structural Geology, v. 14, p. 323–341.

Swanson, M. T., 1994, Minimum dextral shear estimates in the Casco Bay area of coastal Maine from vein reorientation and elongation: Geological Society of America Abstracts with Programs, v. 26, p. 75.

Swanson, M. T., Pollock, S. G., and Hussey, A. M., II, 1986, The structural and stratigraphic development of the Casco Bay Group at Harpswell Neck, Maine, *in* Newberg, D. W., ed., New England Intercollegiate Conference Guidebook, v. 78, p. 350–370.

Tullis, J. A., and Yund, R. A., 1985, Dynamic recrystallization of feldspar: A mechanism for ductile shear-zone formation: Geology, v. 13, p. 238–241.

Tullis, J. A., and Yund, R. A., 1991, Diffusion creep in feldspar aggregates: Experimental evidence: Journal of Structural Geology, v. 13, p. 987–1000.

Unger, J. D., Stewart, D. B., and Phillips, J. D., 1987, Interpretation of migrated seismic reflection profiles across the Northern Appalachians in Maine: Royal Astronomical Society Geophysical Journal, v. 89, p. 171–186.

Weldon, R. J., II, Meisling, K. E., and Alexander, J., 1993, A speculative history of the San Andreas fault in the Central Transverse Ranges, California, *in* Powell, R. E., Weldon, R. J., II, and Matti, J. C., eds., The San Andreas fault system: Displacement, palinspastic reconstruction, and geologic evolution: Geological Society of America Memoir 178, p. 161–198.

West, D. P., Jr., 1993, Nature, timing, and extent of dextral shear deformation in south-central Maine [Ph.D. thesis]: Orono, University of Maine, 228 p.

West, D. P., Jr., and Hubbard, M. S., 1997, Progressive localization of deformation during exhumation of a major strike-slip shear zone: Norumbega fault zone, south-central Maine, USA: Tectonophysics, v. 273, p. 185–202.

West, D. P., Jr., and Lux, D. R., 1993, Dating mylonitic deformation by the $^{40}Ar/^{39}Ar$ method: An example from the Norumbega fault zone, Maine: Earth and Planetary Science Letters, v. 120, p. 221–237.

West, D. P., Jr., Lux, D. R., and Hussey, A. M., II, 1993, Contrasting thermal histories across the Flying Point fault, southwestern Maine: Evidence for Mesozoic displacement: Geological Society of America Bulletin, v. 105, p. 1478–1490.

Williams, H., and Hatcher, R. D., 1983, Appalachian suspect terranes, *in* Hatcher, R. D., Williams, H., and Zietz, I., eds., Contributions to the tectonics and geophysics of mountain chains: Geological Society of America Memoir 158, p. 33–53.

Wones, D. R., 1978, Norumbega fault zone, Maine: U.S. Geological Survey Summary of Technical Reports VIII, p. 108–111.

Wones, D. R., and Thompson, W., 1979, The Norumbega fault zone: A major regional structure in central eastern Maine: Geological Society of America Abstracts with Programs, v. 11, p. 60.

Zen, E., 1983, Exotic terranes in the New England Appalachians: Limits, candidates, and ages, *in* Hatcher, R. D., Williams, H., and Zietz, I., eds., Contributions to the tectonics and geophysics of mountain chains: Geological Society of America Memoir 158, p. 55–81.

MANUSCRIPT ACCEPTED BY THE SOCIETY JUNE 9, 1998

Geological Society of America
Special Paper 331
1999

Kinematic indicators for regional dextral shear along the Norumbega fault system in the Casco Bay area, coastal Maine

Mark T. Swanson
Department of Geosciences, University of Southern Maine, Gorham, Maine 04038

ABSTRACT

Late Paleozoic deformation in the Casco Bay area of coastal Maine is focused at a restraining bend along the southwestern end of the Norumbega fault system. Regional dextral strike slip expressed as the Casco Bay shear-zone system has produced a variety of distinct kinematic indicators on the microscopic, outcrop, and regional scales. Structures on the outcrop scale include asymmetric feldspar, quartz, and pyrite clasts, and quartz, pegmatite, and amphibolite boudins, backward-rotated shear-band boudins, forward-rotated competent-layer and foliation boudinage and related transgressive boudin strings, as well as synthetic shear bands, antithetic Reidel (R′) kinks, Z folds, and related imbricate packets. Sheath folds, indicative of high levels of shear strain, are common but difficult to use as shear-sense indicators without full exposure. Larger scale indicators include pegmatite megaboudins and associated flanking isoclinal flow folds, oblique en echelon cataclastic faults, and large, 30-m-wide, R′-type sinistral kinkbands. Similar structures on the microscopic scale include asymmetric, tailed porphyroclasts and porphyroblasts, asymmetric quartz aggregates, rotated and/or displaced grain fragments, rotated garnets, mica fish, shear bands, and oblique fabrics. On a more regional scale the oblique orientation of prominent F2 folds in rocks on the southeast side of the fault zone also indicate significant regional dextral shearing. Fold tightening, reorientation, and more intense shearing are focused at the Casco Bay restraining bend.

INTRODUCTION

Regional dextral shear of Late Devonian to Permian age in the Casco Bay area can be related to the southwest continuation of the Norumbega fault system (Stewart and Wones, 1974; Hubbard et al., 1995) into this coastal Maine area (Fig. 1). The Casco Bay segment of the fault creates a restraining bend (Swanson, 1993a, 1995, this volume) in this dextral strike-slip system. The main restraining segment, locally the Flying Point fault, serves as a major tectonic boundary, locally separating the Central Maine and Falmouth-Brunswick sequence on the northwest from the Coastal lithotectonic belt and Saco-Harpswell sequence of the Casco Bay Group on the southeast (Hussey, 1988; Osberg et al., 1985). Recent field studies in the Casco Bay area show that ductile dextral shear strain is not only concentrated along the fault traces of the Casco Bay shear-zone system shown in Figure 1, but is also distributed in the intervening rocks. The distribution of kinematic indicators helps to delineate the regional pattern of strain accommodation associated with deformation at this restraining bend.

Kinematic indicators

Work by Simpson and Schmid (1983) sparked interest in the use of kinematic indicators to determine the movement history of major fault zones such as the Norumbega. Coupled with foliation and lineation relationships, these kinematic indicators have proved invaluable in deciphering the role of strike-slip shearing for rocks within exhumed orogenic terrains such as the Grenville province (Nadeau and Hanmer, 1992; Hanmer, 1988; Hanmer and McEachern, 1992), the Canadian Rockies (Hansen, 1989), and the southern Appalachians (Gates et al., 1988).

Kinematic indicators, particularly asymmetric boudinage,

Swanson, M. T., 1999, Kinematic indicators for regional dextral shear along the Norumbega fault system in the Casco Bay area, coastal Maine, *in* Ludman, A., and West, D. P., Jr., eds., Norumbega Fault System of the Northern Appalachians: Boulder, Colorado, Geological Society of America Special Paper 331.

helped to delineate the widespread effects of Norumbega shearing in the Casco Bay area (Swanson, 1992, 1995). Lithologic contrasts and the progressive introduction of orthogonal features (boudin partings, veins, and pegmatites) during a lengthy shear history result in a richly detailed suite of kinematic indicators. These structures help to define the extent of regional shear and permit the refinement of a structural model for the Casco Bay area that includes both vertical and strike-slip components for this complex transpressional environment (Swanson, this volume).

Structural setting

Late collisional interactions involving oblique convergence in the Northern Appalachians created a late Paleozoic system of dextral strike-slip faults that includes the Norumbega fault zone. Shearing along the Norumbega fault zone in the Casco Bay area tightly folded older structures in metasedimentary and metavolcanic rocks of the Casco Bay Group (F2 structures of Hussey, 1988) and produced a prominent horizontal elongation parallel to F2 fold hinges (Swanson, 1993b). This elongation is expressed as an L2 stretching lineation with boudin partings, quartz veins, and pegmatite intrusions orthogonal to the mineral lineations (Swanson, 1989, 1992). The horizontal elongation is attributed to ductile dextral strike-slip shearing that effected the rotation of initially oblique F2 folds. Extensive clockwise reorientation of these folds, particularly near major high-strain zones of the Casco Bay area, led to a dextral layer-parallel shear regime. The distribution of hinge-parallel lineations and kinematic indicators indicates dextral shear within a 30-km-wide Casco Bay shear-zone system as the southwestern continuation of the Norumbega fault (Swanson, 1993a).

This regional deformation was also contemporaneous with widespread quartz veining and granitic intrusion in the form of pegmatite veins, dikes, and small plutons. Most of these veins and intrusions occur in both deformed and undeformed varieties, so veining and intrusion were synchronous with regional transpression. Layer-parallel elongation during shear led to initially orthogonal orientations for boudin partings, quartz veins, and pegmatite intrusions. Once in place, these orthogonal features were subjected to clockwise reorientation and elongation during shear (Swanson, 1992, 1994). The intermittent introduction of these new structural markers during shear helped to produce a wide variety of kinematic indicators throughout the Casco Bay area.

KINEMATIC INDICATORS

This report examines a variety of asymmetric structures within rocks of the Casco Bay area that can serve not only as kinematic indicators, but as evidence for the general level of shear strain. These strain and kinematic indicators can be found at various scales of observation from the microscopic to the regional map scale. However, outcrop scale features are the first encountered during field surveys.

Outcrop-scale indicators

Outcrop-scale structures include features such as high-strain layering produced by disaggregation and grain-size reduction; reoriented orthogonal boudin partings, veins, and intrusions; oblique boudin strings; isolated asymmetric pods and clasts; asymmetric folds and crenulations; noncylindrical folds; oblique shear bands; and antithetic kinks.

High-strain layering. The presence of sheath folds, extensive asymmetric boudinage, and intense stretching lineations in upright flow-layered metamorphic rocks within the Casco Bay area indicates significant layer-parallel shearing. Such high-strain flow layering in deep crustal gneisses, for example, plays an important role in deformation in the Grenville province (Davidson, 1984; Hanmer, 1988; Nadeau and Hanmer, 1992; Hanmer and McEachern, 1992) where "straight planar gneisses" are interpreted as tectonically significant ductile shear zones. Similarly, in southernmost Maine and New Hampshire, work by Hussey (1980) in the Rye Formation gneisses presented a reinterpretation of these lithotectonic units that emphasized the effects of ductile shear. Locally within the Casco Bay area, the strongly lineated planar gneisses with fine-grained uniform layering also require a high-shear-strain interpretation.

Common throughout the Cushing Formation of the Casco Bay area, as described by Hussey (1971a, 1971b, 1985) are fine-grained, uniformly layered granofels and quartzo-feldspathic gneisses. These flow-layered rocks (Figs. 2 and 3) have textural characteristics similar to those of the "straight planar gneisses" and exhibit fine-grained homoclastic (uniform grain size) mylonitic textures (Hanmer, 1987). Examples of heteroclastic (varied grain size) mylonitic textures (Hanmer, 1987) are also found (Fig. 2, B and C, and 3D) and include porphyroclastic gneisses that vary from fine-grained uniformly textured units (Figs. 2D and 3A) within the core of the Flying Point fault zone to heterogeneous, coarsely porphyroclastic units common along the northwest side (Fig. 2). Fine-grained, flow-layered marble units

Figure 1. Structural setting for the Casco Bay area: A: Casco Bay shear-zone system along the southeast side of the main Flying Point fault zone showing major high strain zones and syntectonic to post-tectonic intrusions (after Osberg et al., 1985; Hussey and Bothner, 1995). B: Regional fault-zone configuration showing restraining bend geometry in the Casco Bay area along the southwest end of the Norumbega fault zone (after Osberg et al., 1985) and the location of the study area. As a guide to localities mentioned in the text, the Casco Bay exposures can be subdivided into northeast-trending bands that extend through the inner, middle, and outer sections of the bay area. Inner Casco Bay localities (from southwest to northeast) include Mackworth Island, Falmouth, Yarmouth, South Freeport, Wolfe's Neck, Flying Point, Merepoint, and Simpson's Point. Middle Casco Bay localities (from southwest to northeast) include the Spring Point and Fort Williams exposures of Cape Elizabeth (CE), and Sturdivant, Cousins, Little John, Moshier, French, Sow and Pigs, Pettengill, Sister, and Goose Islands. Outer Casco Bay localities (from southwest to northeast) include the Two Lights (TL) and Richmond Island exposures of Cape Elizabeth, Stave and Bates Islands, and Harpswell Neck (HP).

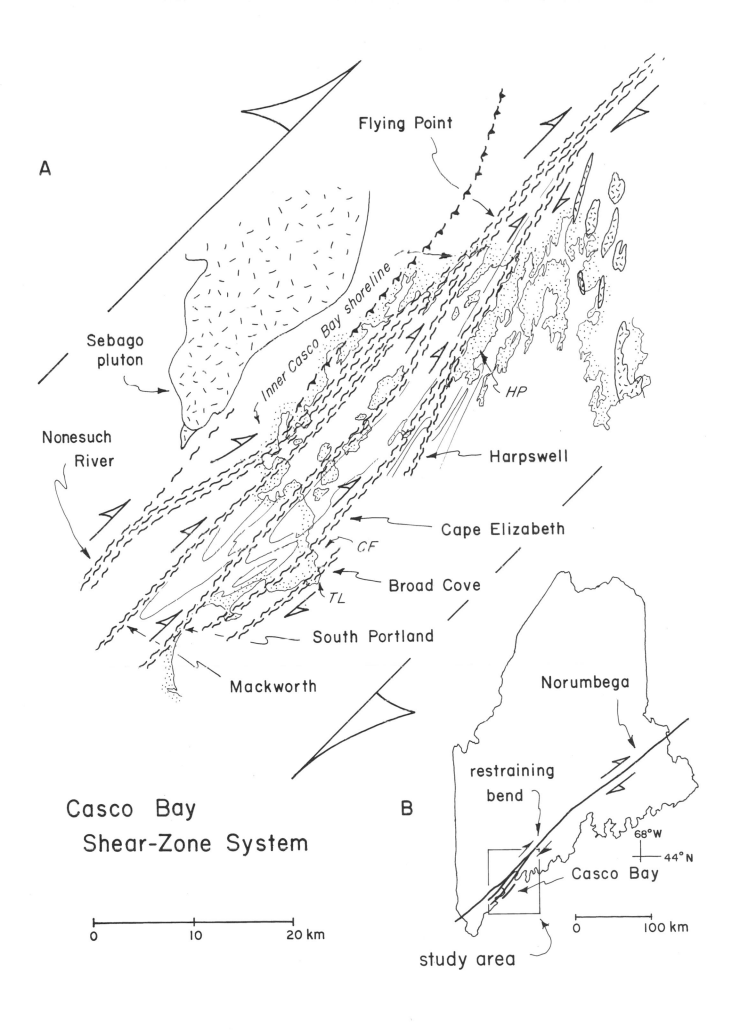

A

Flying Point

Sebago
pluton

Inner Casco Bay shoreline

Nonesuch
River

HP

Harpswell

Cape Elizabeth

CF

Broad Cove

TL

South Portland

Mackworth

Casco Bay
Shear-Zone System

B

Norumbega

restraining
bend

Casco Bay

68°W

44°N

study area

0   10   20 km

0   100 km

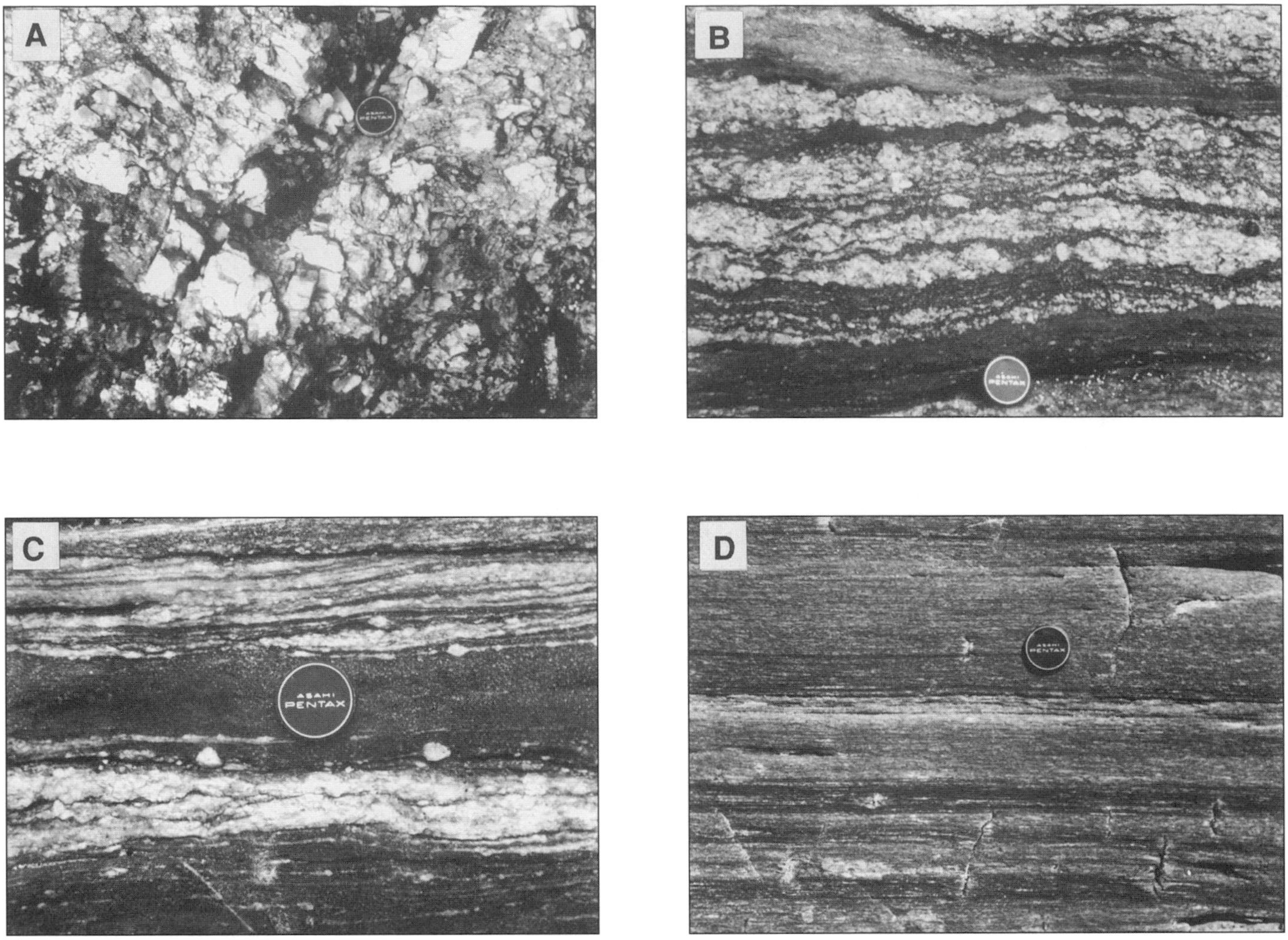

Figure 2. Stages in grain-size reduction during dextral strike-slip shearing; outcrop textures show progressive disaggregation of granitic pegmatites and the development of flow layering in porphyroclastic mylonitic gneisses (from inner and middle Casco Bay localities). A: Coarse, clastic texture within mildly deformed pegmatite intrusion (Little John Island). B: Coarsely porphyroclastic texture (Yarmouth) in more sheared rocks. C: Finer-grained flow texture (Falmouth) and isolated porphyroclasts. D: Finely flow-layered texture (Flying Point). Lens cap for scale is 5.4 cm in diameter.

(Fig. 3D) derived from the Spurwink marble and other carbonate units within the Cushing Formation are also developed, and commonly contain coarse lithic fragments disaggregated by shear.

Feldspathic porphyroclastic units resulted from mechanical disaggregation of pegmatite-injected rocks during shear. Protomylonitic fabrics within coarse granitic pegmatites can be shown to progress from coarsely homoclastic textures during bulk grain reduction, by fracturing of the feldspar framework, to coarsely heteroclastic textures as the disaggregated feldspar fragments were dispersed by shear. This strain-related progression (Fig. 2) can be easily seen in coarsely porphyroclastic units where clearly derived from pegmatitic protoliths. With sufficient shear these units may have been transformed into the fine homoclastic textures of straight planar gneisses (Figs. 2D and 3A) such as can be found along the Flying Point fault zone. Many of the quartzofeldspathic units are likely to represent highly sheared pegmatite intrusions. Quartz-veined units also progress from multiple discordant vein arrays to deformed transgressive boudin strings, isolated asymmetric boudin lenses, and eventually fine-grained, thinly ribboned units (Fig. 3, A and B). Schistose upper Casco Bay units such as the Scarboro and Jewell Formations that have phacoidal or shear-banded textures and the strongly lineated quartz-ribboned phyllonite (after Pollock, 1993) of the Diamond Island Formation were also modified by shear.

L2 orthogonal partings. Planar extensional fractures perpendicular to the local L2 stretching direction are common features in these rocks, reflecting the coaxial component of this transpressive deformation. Initially orthogonal extensional features (rather than oblique as modeled by Maher, 1987; Hudleston, 1989) within sheared rocks do not appear to be common. They

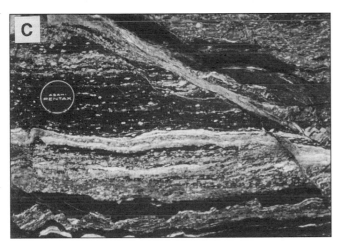

Figure 3. Outcrop-scale shear textures showing effects of high shear strains from the inner Casco Bay exposures. A: Straight planar flow layering in quartzo-feldspathic granofels. B: Highly-strained phyllonite with nearly foliation-parallel quartz lenses from the Mackworth Formation (Sturdivant Island). C: Mylonitic textures within felsic-veined and deformed amphibolites (Sturdivant Island). D: Localized coarsely porphyroclastic band of marble tectonite (Moshier Island). Lens cap for scale is 5.4 cm in diameter.

have been reported in only a few other areas: as thin orthogonal veins and fractures in various tectonites (Hansen, 1989; Hanmer, 1982; Holm et al., 1989), as syntectonic gash veins in fault zones of eastern China (Xu et al., 1986), and as the initiation mechanism for asymmetric foliation and bone-shaped boudin structures in sheared gneisses (Lacassin, 1988; Malavieille and Lacassin, 1988). Mawer (1987) also described late orthogonal veins in sheared rocks of the Meguma terrane in Nova Scotia. This initially orthogonal geometry for veins and intrusions may be characteristic of the transpressive regime but difficult to recognize due to extensive shearing common in these zones.

Orthogonal structures (relative to lineation and foliation) in the Casco Bay area form partings for both competent-layer and foliation boudinage (Fig. 4A), and on a larger scale distinct mineralized veins and granitic pegmatite intrusions. Partings and veins

(quartz, calcite, ankerite, chlorite, actinolite, and pyrite) range from fabrics of micro-veinlets to distinct puckers in the 1–10-cm-length range and longer veins in the 1–10-m-length range. Boudin partings of competent layers, with sufficient separation and mineralization, can produce meter-thick, blocky masses of quartz as the rectangular partition or gap mineralization (Fig. 5C) similar to the blocks of quartz in bone-shaped boudins described by Malavieille and Lacassin (1988). Longer fractures, where mineral filled, are veins that formed perhaps as partings of thicker, more competent units. Longer veins as wide as 10 cm may reach tens of meters in length. Planar undeformed granitic pegmatites (quartz, feldspar, biotite, muscovite, tourmaline, and garnet) also occur in this orientation and were emplaced along L2 orthogonal fractures. Undeformed planar pegmatites may be several meters in width and have probable lengths in the 100 m range.

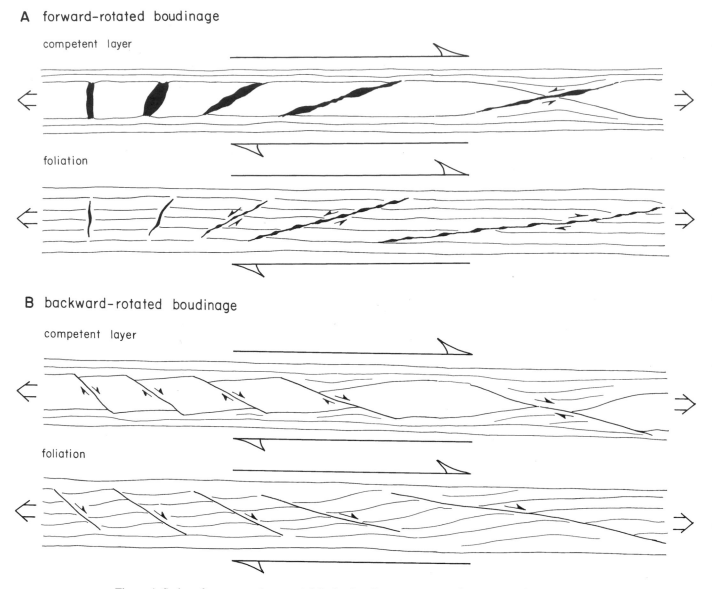

Figure 4. Styles of competent-layer and foliation boudinage accompanying transpression with initiation during layer-parallel elongation and modification by dextral shear. A: Forward-rotated, competent-layer and foliation boudinage (tension fracture boudinage) from initial orthogonal partings and veins to oblique quartz lenses with antithetic slip during reorientation. B: Backward-rotated, competent-layer and foliation boudinage (shear-band boudinage) from initial oblique shear zones with antithetic rotation during extension and shear.

Reoriented orthogonal structures. Continued dextral shear resulted in the clockwise reorientation of the initially orthogonal structures described here. The resulting asymmetry is useful in recognizing the effects of dextral shear. Modification of initially symmetric (orthogonal to lineation and foliation) features into sheared asymmetric geometries was described by Hanmer (1986) as his type I asymmetric pullaparts and by Malavieille and Lacassin (1988) as modified partings in their bone-shaped boudins.

In the Casco Bay rocks initially orthogonal structures can be seen in various stages of reorientation (Fig. 5) due to clockwise rotation during dextral shear. The resulting forward-rotated asymmetric boudinage (Fig. 4A) (Swanson, 1992, 1997) was used to infer a general transpressive style of deformation. A selection of outcrop structures can used to infer a sequence of reorientation, from initially orthogonal to oblique to the flow foliation (Figs. 5 and 6) for thin boudin partings as well as the thicker partition mineralizations, each giving a distinct asymmetry as dextral shear and reorientation progressed. The orientation of these planar and deformed features can be used in equal-area plots to verify the sense of rotation during shear and that the stretching lineation represents the shear direction (Fig. 6B).

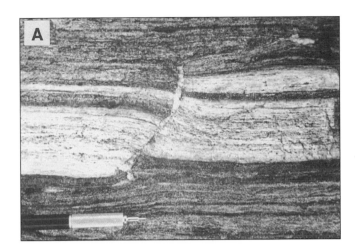
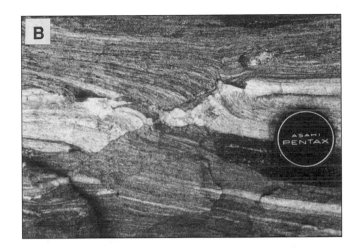

Figure 5. Forward-rotated boudins as thin partings and blocky quartz-filled gaps showing effects of low to moderate levels of continued shear strain. A: Thinly mineralized boudin partings in quartzo-feldspathic flow layer with slight clockwise rotation and antithetic slip (Simpson's Point, inner Casco Bay). Pencil is 0.8 cm thick. B: Continued shear results in rotation of the parting surface to lower angles and increased antithetic slip (Simpson's Point, inner Casco Bay). C: Thick boudin partition with distinct asymmetry due to initial stages of clockwise rotation (Harpswell Neck, outer Casco Bay). D: Thick oblique lens showing distortion and streamlining of the partition mineralization (Harpswell Neck, outer Casco Bay). Lens cap for scale in B is 5.4 cm in diameter. Hammer in C and D is 28 cm long.

Transgressive quartz boudin strings and deformed pegmatite intrusions. Clockwise rotation during dextral shear, as described here, yields a distinctive and consistent geometric pattern (Fig. 6A). Deformed veins and intrusions occur as variably transgressive, planar elements, oblique to the flow foliation with a consistently more northerly trend than the northeast-trending metamorphic layering. These veins and intrusions develop a vein-parallel or intrusion-parallel antithetic slip during rotation (Figs. 5A and 6A) as described by Hudleston (1989) and Swanson (1992) for both natural and experimental examples. Longer mineralized partings, i.e., quartz-filled veins and pegmatitic intrusions, due to their relative competence, also are elongated during rotation. The angle of the transgressive veins and boudin strings

(Fig. 6A) relative to the flow layering (B-angle) decreases and elongation increases with increasing shear, both of which can serve as an estimate of minimum shear strain (Swanson, 1992, 1994, this volume) assuming a simple shear model for the deformation. Transgressive boudin strings as remnants of syntectonic intrusion are part of the structural fabric of high-strain gneisses exposed in the Ailao Shan–Red River shear zone of southeast Asia (Leloup et al., 1993), for example, where measurements of layer-parallel elongation from leucocratic boudin trails were used as an estimate of minimum shear strain (Lacassin et al., 1993).

Reoriented planar structures also typically develop flanking folds in the adjacent wall rocks as has been described for metadolerite dikes reoriented by Caledonian thrusting in Nor-

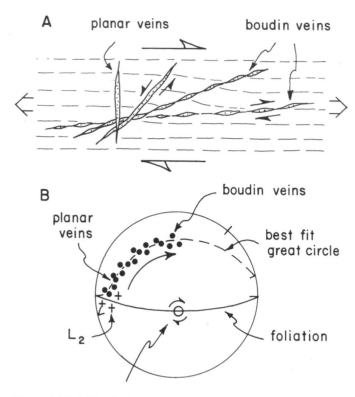

Figure 6. Model for the forward rotation of initially orthogonal partings and veins. A: Initial orthogonal extension, rotation with antithetic slip, and vein-parallel elongation producing low-angle transgressive boudinage quartz sheets or pegmatite intrusions. B: Stereonet representation of the forward rotation model due to shear and extension parallel to steeply dipping foliation surfaces typical of the Casco Bay area. Horizontal lineations within the foliation coincide with the poles to undeformed planar partings or veins with subsequent clockwise rotation as indicated. Best-fit great circle determines the rotation axis for the deformation, perpendicular to lineation and contained within the plane of the foliation.

way (Gayer et al., 1978) and for reoriented ice-filled fractures in glaciers (Hudleston, 1989). Similar folds are found associated with reoriented quartz veins and pegmatite intrusions in the Casco Bay area and are discussed in more detail in the following text.

Asymmetric clasts and pods. Individual pods or lenses of quartz and pegmatite that make up these transgressive boudin strings often have a distinct asymmetry, having offset tails in a stair-stepping geometry (Simpson and Schmid, 1983; Passchier and Simpson, 1986) within the metamorphic flow layering. Single pods and clasts maintain their asymmetry even after considerable separation and isolation. These asymmetric pods vary from centimeter-scale quartz aggregates or feldspar clasts to meter- and 10-m-scale pegmatite pods (Fig. 7) that usually have well-developed subhorizontal shear lineations diverging along their flanks. Similar pods in the Kennebecasis fault zone of southern New Brunswick were described as "mega-augen" (Park et al., 1994) where both the foliations and lineations were deflected during shear flow around these more competent inclu-

sions. Fields of tapered, disaggregated, pegmatite pods are also described from the Central Britt shear zone of the Grenville province, Ontario (Culshaw et al., 1994).

Individual, 1–2-cm-wide feldspar clasts from initial veins in metavolcanic gneisses (Fig. 7, C–E) on Stave and Upper Goose Islands show geometries with tapered, stair-stepped tails (Fig. 7C), and some with flanking asymmetric flow folds. Fractured and rotated clasts (Fig. 7F) show separate clockwise rotation and intervening antithetic slip. The quartz and/or feldspar grains and grain aggregates dominate the observed asymmetric clasts and pods; other distinctive asymmetric grains include pyrite clasts to ~2 cm in width found at Little John Island. These pyrite clasts also have a tapered, sigmoidal shape modified from original cubes as a result of ductile deformation at relatively high temperatures. A quartz-tourmaline clast ~4 cm in diameter showing clear dextral asymmetry was found along the Goslings.

Shear bands and shear-band boudins. Late-stage shear typically develops synthetic shears at low angles to the metamorphic flow layering. These oblique synthetic shears or shear bands are referred to as C-surfaces in S-C mylonitic rocks or as C′ surfaces where they cut dominant shear planes (C-surfaces) within shear zones (Weikjermars and Rondeel, 1984; Weikjermars, 1987; Williams and Price, 1990; Leger and Williams, 1986). Banded types of fabrics (Blenkinsop and Treloar, 1995) are most common in the Casco Bay area and are illustrated in Figure 8 (A–C). Shear band fabrics in the Two Lights exposures of Cape Elizabeth were important in the initial recognition of regional dextral shear in the Casco Bay area. Here, quartz-rich rocks record relatively low shear strains yet show dextral shear expressed as a distributed, finely-textured, shear-band fabric (similar to Fig. 8A), as well as larger scale oblique fault zones (Fig. 9A). Shear bands commonly pervade the outcrop as millimeter or centimeter-scale shears with slight flexures of the layering adjacent to each shear band element. Individual shear band elements range from 0.5 cm to 10 cm. Shear-banded textures are also common in schistose units of the Scarboro and Jewell Formations (Fig. 8C), particularly along the Cape Elizabeth and Broad Cove fault zones where they develop the typical foliation fish geometries originally described by Hanmer (1986).

These shear bands typically dissect the flow layering into distinctly asymmetric lenses, fish or phacoids, particularly within the schistose or phyllitic host-rock lithologies (8, B and C) as an asymmetric foliation boudinage (Hanmer, 1986, 1988; Stock, 1992) or as shear-band boudins of competent layers (Fig 4B). These boudin geometries were described by Hanmer (1986) as his type II, where early necking of layers is modified by shear, and by Goldstein (1988) as a type III, where the layers are cut by oblique shears to form the boudins. Dissection by oblique shears and eventual separation imparts a doubly-tapered asymmetric geometry to the lenses and leads to the backward or antithetic rotation of the layer-parallel segments (Fig. 8B). This antithetic rotation was modeled by Jordan (1991) and used by Hanmer (1986) to indicate transpressive deformation. Backward-rotated shear-band boudins such as these can be found on Sturdivant

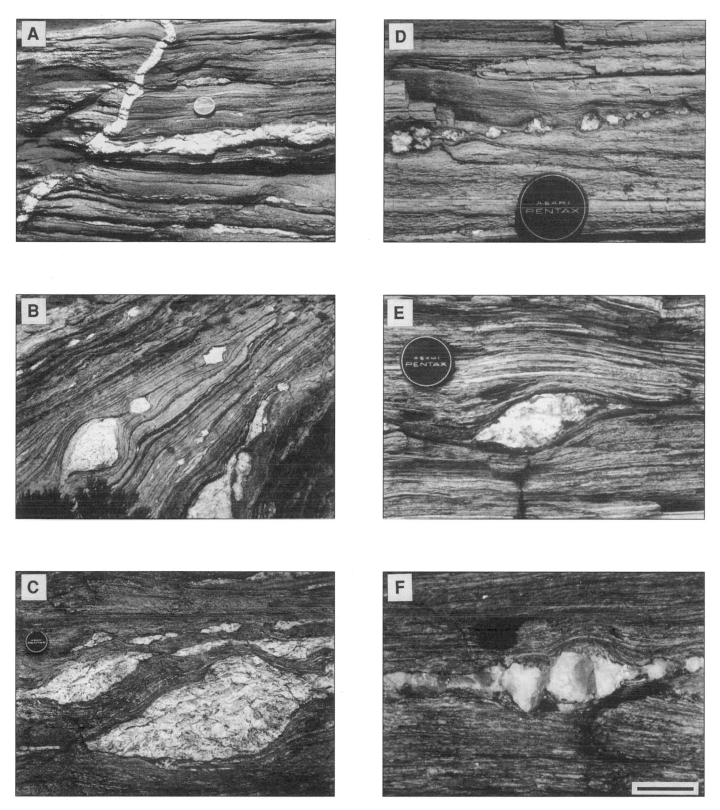

Figure 7. Pegmatite (A–C) and quartz-vein (D–F) geometries resulting from progressive dextral shear. A: Crosscutting relations showing slightly transgressive orientation for the lower angled, more deformed granitic intrusion (Wolfe's Neck, inner Casco Bay). B: Highly attenuated pegmatite boudin strings and pods (Merepoint, inner Casco Bay) showing considerable intrusion-parallel elongation during shear. C: Asymmetric geometries of multiple pegmatite boudins in dextral shear (Sow Island, inner Casco Bay). D: Breakup of quartzo-feldspathic veins into strings of individual clasts upon rotation and elongation during shear (Upper Goose Island, middle Casco Bay). E: Streamlined asymmetric quartz clast (French Island, middle Casco Bay). F: Single feldspar clast showing early stages of breakup, rotation, and intervening antithetic slip (Upper Goose Island, middle Casco Bay). Scale bar in F represents 1 cm. Lens cap for scale in A–E is 5.4 cm in diameter.

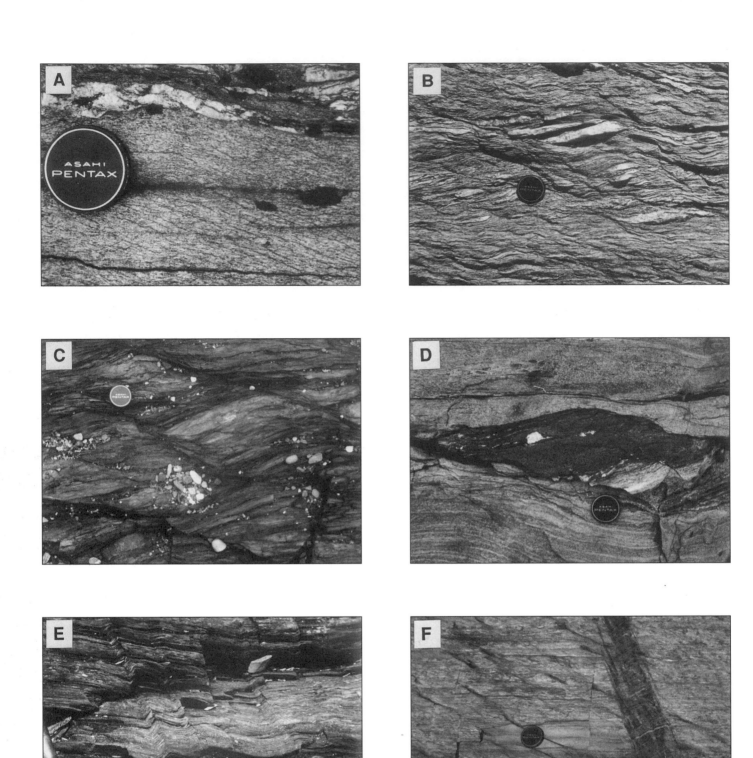

Figure 8. Shear bands and antithetic kinks. A: Finely textured shear-band fabric only locally developed in quartz-rich layer (Little John Island, inner Casco Bay). B: Separate quartz lenses defined by dextral shear bands (French Island, middle Casco Bay). C: Widely spaced shear bands in phyllites delineating distinct foliation fish with antithetic rotation of the foliation (Two Lights area, outer Casco Bay. D: Isolated, asymmetric boudin pod of sheared amphibolite, bounded by extensional shears and exhibiting antithetic rotation of the internal amphibolite layering (Bustins Island, middle Casco Bay). E: Multiple antithetic kink bands (Harpswell Neck, outer Casco Bay). F: Conjugate relation showing low-angle dextral shear bands and high-angle zone of en echelon sinistral kink bands (Richmond Island, outer Casco Bay). Lens cap for scale is 5.4 cm in diameter; hammer is 28 cm (only half shown).

Island within the highly sheared Mackworth phyllites, within thin amphibolite layers at Little John Island within the Flying Point shear zone, and along the outer Casco Bay exposures of Stave and Bustins Islands (Fig. 8D). Gaudemer and Tapponier (1987), in their study of extensional shear in a metamorphic core complex in Nevada, estimated that gamma shear strains of ~20 were necessary for separation of boudin segments by extensional shears. Boudin separation can also be seen in the Casco Bay examples (Fig. 8D), suggesting a similar level of shear strain.

Larger scale versions of these shear bands are represented by the en echelon cataclastic fault-zone array in the Two Lights exposures of Cape Elizabeth (Fig. 9A), where individual faults may be over 1 km in length. An oblique fabric alignment within pelitic lithologies is also found at the south end of Chebeague Island. This discordant fabric zone was originally interpreted as a normal-type cross fault by Hussey (1985) on the basis of the apparent offset of lithologic units, but the fabric orientation along with steeply plunging z-crenulations suggests oblique dextral shear. A similar shear band structure within the Ailao Shan–Red River fault zone of southeast Asia was reported by LeLoup et al. (1993) and described as a large-scale extensional shear band.

Sinistral kinks. Antithetic sinistral kink bands at high angles to the metamorphic flow layering are also common throughout the Casco Bay area (Fig. 8, E and F). These were recognized by Hussey (1985, 1988) as a late stage of northwest-trending kink banding. These high-angle antithetic structures are valuable kinematic indicators for late-stage regional dextral shear where they function as outcrop scale R′ shears. High-angle antithetic R′ shears such as these have been reproduced in simple clay shear experiments (Riedel, 1929) and in the deformation of foliated materials (Williams and Price, 1990) where they develop as kink bands.

High-angle antithetic kink bands are a part of wall-rock deformation associated with the Two Lights and Richmond Island fault zones (Figs. 8F and 9B), both as discrete fracture surfaces within the fault array and as distributed kink banding associated with dextral shear-band fabrics within the adjacent host rocks (Fig. 8F). The association of high-angle, sinistral kink bands with low-angle dextral shear bands (Figs. 8F) supports a conjugate R-R′ Riedel interpretation for regional shear (Fig. 9B). The Casco Bay high-angle kink bands vary in width from millimeter-scale crenulations to centimeter-scale kink bands in finer-grained schistose rocks to larger kinks, several meters to tens of meters in width. A larger scale version is found at Cousins Island and may extend across the inner Casco Bay area to Little Whaleboat Island. This kink band is more than 35 m wide and is possibly 6 km long. Other antithetic structures along Harpswell Neck (Swanson et al., 1986) are sinistral strike-slip faults at high angles to the local upright foliation. These faults initiated as kink bands and evolved toward discrete brittle faults upon continued shear.

Asymmetric Z-shaped folds, kinks, and crenulations. Perturbations in uniform layer-parallel shear flow also give rise to intrafolial folds, kinks, and crenulations having a Z-shaped asymmetry reflecting the dextral shear sense (Fig. 10). Kinks and crenulations develop in the more mica-rich or schistose units, and the Z-shape flow folds are better seen within rocks that have layer-parallel quartz veining (Fig. 10, A–C). These late asymmetric folds have steeply plunging axes at high angles to the stretching lineations that mark the shear direction.

Asymmetric folds evolve during progressive deformation (Mies, 1991); fold amplification and rotation into the extension direction occur with increasing shear strain. Axial planes are initially inclined at moderate angles to the flow layering; this angle tends to decrease with increasing shear strain, approaching parallelism with the flow foliation (cf. Fig. 10, A–E). Likewise, the hinge lines are also rotated and converge toward the lineation or shear direction, forming sheath folds (discussed in more detail in the following text). The amplification of the folds and rotation of the axial planes result in the attenuation of the short or inverted limbs of the Z-folds. A common feature within the Casco Bay rocks is the development of a series of Z-folds as "trains" or "pileups" where the sequences of individual folds become imbricated along the attenuated limbs. Excellent examples of these imbricated fold packages can be found on Little John and Cousins Islands (Fig. 10B). This imbrication gives rise to isolated packets of inclined fold limbs that become isolated and streamlined in the flow layering as in some of the higher strain rocks on Cousins Island (Fig. 10D) and Harpswell Neck (Swanson et al., 1986). Similar structures from blastomylonitic gneisses of the Øygarden complex of Norway were described as compressional tectonites (Fossen and Rykkelid, 1990) or contractional composite structures (Rykkelid and Fossen, 1992), referring to intrafolial fold trains imbricated by reverse-type shear zones along the inverted limbs. Rykkelid and Fossen (1992) attributed these contractional structures to local slip transfer across the shear layers, so these may be of only local significance.

Asymmetric differential flow folds are also commonly associated with the more competent pods and clasts. These vary from small asymmetric flexures that flank individual feldspar clasts along Upper Goose Island, to larger, 10-m-scale pegmatite pods on Wolf Neck and Merepoint (Fig. 11, A and B) to kink-type folds associated with tapered quartz boudins in Cape Elizabeth, to larger scale isoclinal folds that have possible "sheath" or noncylindrical geometries elongated in the lineation or shear direction found adjacent to pegmatite pods on Sister Island (Fig. 11). These flow folds develop from simple flexures along the flanks of discordant veins and intrusions to isoclinal folds along the separated boudin pods under greater shear strain. Folds localize along the pod flank facing the shear flow, due to flow perturbation around the more competent asymmetric pods. Experimental studies of folds due to flow perturbations about inclusions during shear by Van Den Driessche and Brun (1987) show gamma shear strains of ~6–8 are needed for the development of folds with this geometry.

Noncylindrical "sheath" folds. Noncylindrical folds aligned parallel to the stretching lineation or shear direction, as indicators of high shear strain, are common throughout the Casco Bay area (Fig. 10, E and F). These sheath folds are easy to recognize in

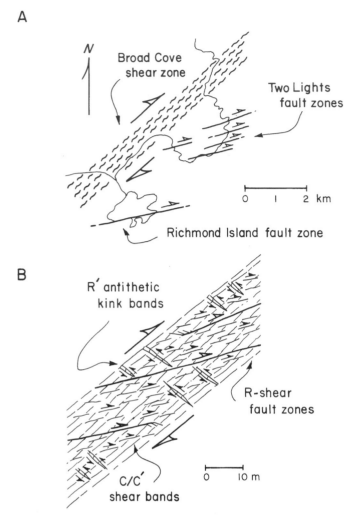

Figure 9. Geometry of low-angle strike-slip faults and high-angle kink bands in relation to regional dextral shear. A: Oblique orientation and en echelon pattern of discrete, cataclastic, dextral strike-slip faults (including the Two Lights and Richmond Island faults, Cape Elizabeth, outer Casco Bay), interpreted as R-shears, related to shearing along the nearby Broad Cove fault zone. B: Conjugate relation between low-angle extensional shear bands and individual oblique fault zones (R-shears) and the high-angle, antithetic kink-bands (R'-shears) as seen in the Two Lights and Richmond Island exposures (Cape Elizabeth, outer Casco Bay).

cross-section by the closed or "eye" fold pattern (Fig. 10E) or by the "anvil" geometry at the base of the sheath (Mies, 1993). On the foliation surface the distinctly curved and attenuated fold noses (Fig. 10F) clearly delineate their noncylindrical nature. High shear strains can take Z-folds, for example, as described herein that have initially steeply plunging hinge lines (perpendicular to the L2 lineation and shear-flow direction) and modify them into noncylindrical "sheath" folds (Fossen and Rykkelid, 1990; Mies, 1993), the sheath being parallel to the lineation and shear flow direction. The fold noses become stretched and attenuated into the elongation and shear direction. Flanking edges of these flattened, stretched tubes develop the typical hinge-parallel lineation so common within the Casco Bay and other areas of

orogen-parallel shear. Gamma shear strains greater than 20 are required to form sheath-fold geometries (Mies, 1991, 1993), on the basis of numerical modeling.

The Casco Bay examples exhibit clear eye (Fig. 10E) and anvil geometries as well as foliation-plane views (Figs. 10F and 12) that show the shapes of the attenuated fold noses. Several examples exhibit other secondary fold complications; one from the Broad Cove shear zone at Trundy Point in Cape Elizabeth shows a complex cross-sectional profile that suggests refolding of an already highly attenuated sheath fold. Attenuation of the limbs during sheathing of quartz layers produces detached quartz hinge zones that can survive as rods aligned parallel to the lineation direction. One such example at Little John Island is strongly lineated and has a distinct spiral geometry. The sense of asymmetry of this spiraled quartz rod matches what is expected for dextral shear as illustrated by Mawer and Williams (1991) for the shear modification of a fold hinge zone.

Sheath folds can be used to determine shear sense, assuming a reoriented Z-fold model, if one side of the flattened sheath is distinctly thinned and the closure direction of the sheath tip can be delineated (Fossen and Rykkelid, 1990; Mies, 1993). Use of the sheath folds as kinematic indicators, however, is difficult in that eye fold exposures may show the thinner limb but closure directions are difficult to interpret. Foliation-plane exposures make it easy to determine the closure direction but only one of the flanking limbs is typically exposed. Two examples of hand-sized sheath fold tips at Trundy Point (Fig. 12) show varied flanking limb thicknesses relative to closure directions that could be used to support the interpretation of dextral shear in the Broad cove shear zone. However, the geometries are not clear with evidence for formation from initial S-folds (Fig. 12A) rather than Z-folds in the model of Fossen and Rykelid (1990) and Mies (1993) and of the formation of sheath upon sheath structures (Fig. 12B).

Many of the smaller folds with lineation-parallel hinge lines may be interpreted as the upper or lower flanks of larger flattened sheath folds. The larger scale interpreted map pattern of lithologic units in the middle Casco Bay area (Hussey, 1985), for example, also exhibits an apparent anvil-type structure with opposing asymmetric folds typical for cross sections at the base of sheaths (Mies, 1993). This suggests the possibility of large 10-km-scale sheath folds within the deformed Casco Bay rocks, again reflecting high shear strain. However, not all lineation-parallel folds can be attributed to such extreme reorientation and attenuation of initial steeply plunging Z-folds.

Other asymmetric folds. Lineation-parallel folds, termed "a-type" folds (Mattauer, 1975; Malavieille, 1987), may have formed in situ due to constrictions across the plane of shear (Mattauer, 1975), shearing of layers oblique to the shear zone (Malavieille, 1987), or flank effects of shear-flow variations (Holdsworth, 1990). These a-type folds are best seen in cross section, perpendicular to the lineation direction. In this view, these asymmetric folds suggest a general vertical or horizontal constriction across the shear zone depending on geometry. Hori-

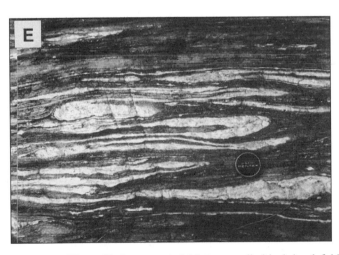

Figure 10. Asymmetric folds to noncylindrical sheath folds. A: Broad, kink-like, steeply plunging Z-fold in quartz-ribboned garnet schist (Cousins Island, middle Casco Bay). B: Tight Z-folds in foliation-parallel quartz layer with highly attenuated and inverted limbs; note the apparent imbrication of the thicker limbs at thrust-type surfaces along the attenuated, inverted limbs, (Cousins Island, middle Casco Bay). C: Z-fold pile-ups in tight contractional packets in mylonitic gneisses (Falmouth, inner Casco Bay). D: Remnant Z-folds in thin quartz layers preserved as a tight imbricate packet, streamlined by shear flow (Cousins Island, inner Casco Bay). E: Flattened "eye" fold (just above lens cap) and isolated fold hinges in deformed granitic layers in the Flying Point fault zone (Falmouth, inner Casco Bay). F: Foliation—plane view (looking southeast) of an attenuated sheath fold showing the lineation-parallel hinge lines, Broad Cove fault zone (Cape Elizabeth, outer Casco Bay). Lens cap for scale in A–E is 5.4 cm in diameter; pencil in F is 14 cm long.

A   early geometry for pegmatite intrusion

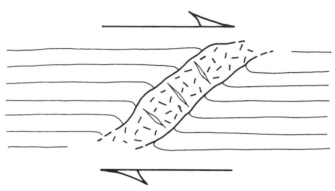

B   intermediate geometry - Wolfe's Neck

C   late geometry - Sister Island

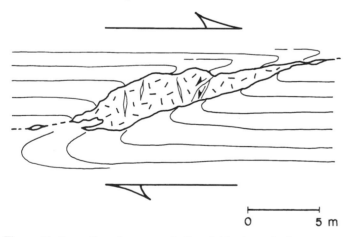

0   5 m

Figure 11. Formation of asymmetric flow folds about the larger pegmatite intrusions in the inner Casco Bay exposures. A: High-angle, planar, granitic pegmatite intrusion with early, open, asymmetric folds
along flank (as seen at Wolfe's Neck). B: Continued reorientation and
beginning of segmentation into boudins by orthogonal quartz veins and
the development of tighter, asymmetric, flow folds (Merepoint). C: Continued reorientation and streamlining of pegmatite pod with asymmetric, tapered tails and isoclinal, flanking flow folds, most likely with
sheath geometry; note continued extension reflected in orthogonal quartz
veins and extensional shears (Sister Island).

zontal constriction on steeply inclined planes during shear would
induce the formation of upward-verging folds with a reverse-slip
component (Figs. 13A and 14A). Vertical constriction would
induce downward-verging folds with a normal-slip component
(Figs. 13B and 14B).

S-folds are also not uncommon in these dextrally sheared
Casco Bay rocks. Some lineation-parallel asymmetric folds
exhibit apparent S geometries, but these depend on the direction
of plunge and the orientation of the exposure surface. Gently
plunging hinge-parallel folds will show either S or Z geometries
depending on the angle of exposure. Other clear S-folds that have
steeply plunging axes (Fig. 14, C and D), would seem to indicate
sinistral shear. Sinistral shear interpretations from such structures
are not corroborated by additional kinematic evidence in the
same outcrop. Other interpretations are likely.

Whereas dextral shear and layer-parallel elongation dominate the deformation, occasionally layer-normal shortening is
expressed as the crumpling of initially orthogonal structures. This
shortening is most often seen in the thinner tails of tapered veins
and intrusions that have tight, often ptygmatic buckle folds (Figs.
14C and 15). During shear of these intrusions and reorientation
by clockwise rotation (Fig. 15B) these tightly folded tails are
modified, which imparts an S geometry to the fold sets, yet this
has no kinematic significance for sinistral shear. S-folds such as
these can be seen in the inner Casco Bay area along Williams
Island (Fig. 14D) and Merepoint Neck (Fig. 14C), in association
with sheath folds and transgressive pegmatite intrusions. In the
Pemaquid Point and Ocean Point areas 20–30 km to the east outside of the higher strain zones of Casco Bay, thin (~10 cm),
crumpled orthogonal granitic intrusions and thinner (to ~1 cm),
quartz veinlets register significant layer-normal shortening but
have undergone little reorientation due to shear.

Other problematic folds that don't fit into the regional dextral
shear model include centimeter-scale chevron folds that have horizontal fold axes and axial planes at Trundy Point, Cape Elizabeth,
normal dip-slip kink bands that have horizontal rotation axes
throughout the inner Casco Bay area, as well as millimeter-scale
crenulations within the more phyllitic units having horizontal
intersection lineations. The geometry of these small-scale chevron
folds, kinks, and crenulations is indicative of vertical shortening of
the steeply inclined flow foliation, a surprising but not unlikely
feature of the Casco Bay shear-zone system. These structures are
most likely related to collapse of localized uplift due to transpression along this section of the fault system (Swanson, 1997a).

Microscopic-scale indicators

Kinematic indicators in thin section as the microscopic
expression of dextral shear are also abundant and varied in rocks
of the Casco Bay area. The microscopic-scale indicators contain
the usual range of asymmetric clasts and fabrics and fully support the field interpretation of dextral shear based on outcrop-
scale structures. Microscopic-scale structures include asymmetric
grain aggregates, tailed or winged porphyroclasts, rotated

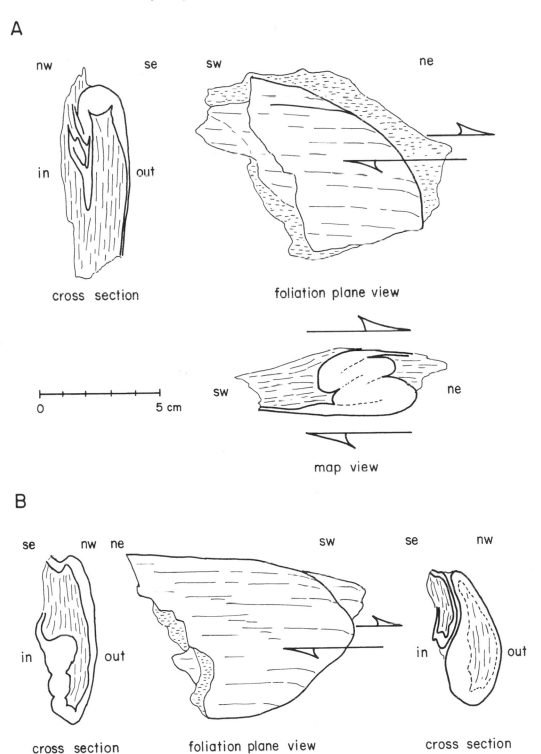

Figure 12. Sheath-fold development from flattened and attenuated Z-folds (after Fossen and Rykkelid, 1990; Mies, 1993) should show distinctly thinned limbs relative to the closure direction for use as kinematic indicators. Sheath fold noses from Broad Cove fault zone (Cape Elizabeth, outer Casco Bay) show clear closure directions but complex limb geometries in cross section. Note that both examples should be showing their thinned-limb flanks, as indicated in the attenuated Z-fold model for dextral shear. A: Foliation—plane view (looking northwest) of a broad sheath fold nose in quartz layers within schistose unit, clearly showing the noncylindrical nature; note the horizontal stretching lineations along the partially exposed flank, the complex limb geometries and the apparent S geometry as seen in the map-view section. B: Foliation—plane view (looking southeast) of an attenuated sheath fold showing both lineation-parallel hinge lines and complete hinge-line profile along the closure tip and the development of a double flanking sheath structure toward the tip.

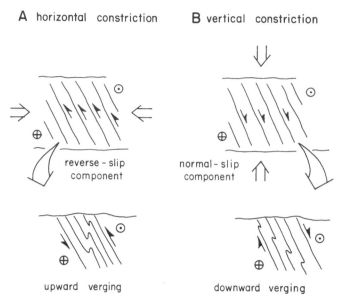

A horizontal constriction   **B** vertical constriction

reverse - slip
component

normal - slip
component

upward verging   downward verging

Figure 13. Effects of constriction in the development of lineation-parallel folds. A: Horizontal constriction during dextral strike-slip shearing induces upward-verging asymmetric folds along inclined shear layers, reflecting a reverse-slip component to shear. B: Vertical constriction during shear would induce downward-verging asymmetric folds along inclined shear layers, reflecting a normal-slip component to the shear deformation.

garnets, rotated fractured grains, mica fish, and various shear bands and crenulations (Figs. 16 and 17).

Grain-size reduction. Microscopic structures can be used to assess the extent of textural modification brought about during regional dextral shearing. Thin-section examination of lineated, fine-grained planar gneisses and finely layered granofels was found to corroborate the field interpretations that they record high levels of shear strain (Fig. 16). Fine-grained, uniformly layered granofels (Fig. 16D) reveal an internal quartz lens and ribbon structure. Grain-size reduction and flow-layer development is expressed in aggregates of elongate to more equant recrystallized quartz grains accentuated by grain shape and grain aggregate alignments.

Elongation. Strong elongation in these rocks is expressed as elongate mineral and mineral aggregate alignments as well as asymmetric strain shadows and quartz beards about more rigid grains and clasts. Elongations can be extreme. Quartz-filled strain shadows adjacent to millimeter-wide pyrite grains in Diamond Island phyllonites (Fig. 17F), for example, have grown to ~0.5 cm in length on either side, indicating elongations of 1100%. Asymmetric quartz strain shadows about ilmenite grains in schists of French Island (Fig. 17E) indicate elongations of ~800%. The grains may have been fibrous at one time but have been recrystallized.

Asymmetric grains and grain aggregates. Thin elongate lenses within the ribbon layering are often slightly transgressive, reflecting transposition into the flow plane during the deformation. Transgressive lenses would be subjected to pinch and swell

type boudinage and separation into individual grain clusters. Some of these quartz-grain aggregates occur as inclined "fish" with asymmetric tapered tails (Fig. 17A) that can serve as clear kinematic indicators. Higher shear-strain levels, however, produce flow-layered quartz ribbons (Fig. 16D) and are difficult to use as kinematic indicators.

Distinctly porphyroclastic and porphyroblastic units yield abundant kinematic indicators with asymmetric geometries due to shear flow. Feldspar occurs as the principal porphyroclast mineral, and garnet as the dominant porphyroblast mineral encountered in the inner Casco Bay area. Feldspar clasts (Fig. 17A) that have asymmetric tails range to several centimeters in diameter for the coarsely porphyroclastic textures; there are finer size ranges in the higher strain units. The coarser textured lithologies represent deformed pegmatites (Fig. 16, A and B), the large-diameter feldspars being remnants of the initial pegmatite textures. The finer, more uniform, well-layered homoclastic textures (Fig. 16D) represent the more highly strained units in a probable sequence of grain-size reduction.

Porphyroblastic garnets to 3 mm in diameter are common in certain lithologies of the Casco Bay area. The garnets typically occur with ragged grain outlines and asymmetric tails (Fig. 17, C and D). Distinctive mica mats (quarter mats of Hanmer and Passchier, 1991) are also developed along the compressional flanks of the garnet porphyroblasts (Fig. 17C), due to pressure solution of quartz and recrystallization of the remaining micas. Inclusion patterns vary from nearly straight inclusion trails at angles to the foliation showing evidence of rotation only within the outer garnet layers to more sigmoidal inclusion trails showing evidence of rotation during garnet growth (Fig. 17D). The asymmetry of the sigmoidal trails in these "helicitic" garnets (after Spry, 1969) serves as a useful kinematic indicator. Garnets from biotite schist units at Lower Goose and Whaleboat Islands show rotations of nearly 180°. The sigmoidal inclusion trails suggest that prograde metamorphism (garnet growth) was, in part, synchronous with dextral shearing.

Porphyroblastic minerals that yield asymmetric geometries in thin section also include staurolite, pyrite, and ilmenite. The staurolite in moderately sheared rocks in the Bailey Island area shows some oblique orientations and asymmetric tails. Pyrites in the Diamond Island Formation at Spring Point and the ilmenites of the Cushing Formation at French Island show spectacular strain shadows (Fig. 17, E and F) consisting of recrystallized quartz beards with some asymmetry attributed to dextral shear. Centimeter-sized pyrite porphyroblasts at Cushing Island display distinct wings resulting from ductile deformation of the pyrite flanks.

Well-developed mica fish (Lister and Snoke, 1984) occur in the Casco Bay area rocks, but were not a dominant microstructure. Muscovite is the dominant mineral phase, occurring as fish with minor biotite as well as amphibole. The muscovite most often occurs as shredded aggregates and thin foliations, aligned parallel to the flow foliations. Only a few samples were found with the oblique orientations needed to serve as clear kinematic indicators.

Figure 14. Enigmatic fold geometries include lineation-parallel asymmetric folds (A and B) seen in cross section, looking down-plunge of steeply dipping shear flow layers and steeply plunging apparent S-folds (C and D) seen in map view in pegmatite intrusions reoriented by dextral shear. A: Granitic vein showing reverse-slip component (Merepoint Neck, inner Casco Bay). B: Quartz vein and/or layer suggesting normal-slip component to shear deformation (Goose Island, middle Casco Bay). C: Tightly folded granitic vein tip modified by dextral shear (Merepoint, inner Casco Bay). D: Apparent S-fold in granitic vein as a possible remnant of early shortening phase (Williams Island, inner Casco Bay). Lens cap for scale is 5.4 cm in diameter.

Microshears. Shear bands, or microshear surfaces that cut obliquely across the main mylonitic fabric, are common in some of these rocks (Fig. 17G). Here, small flexures and offsets of foliation surfaces to several millimeters in length can be seen. Foliation surfaces drag into these microshears and are in places delineated by aligned recrystallized chlorite and/or fine-grained carbonate mineralization. These micro-shear bands correlate with the larger outcrop-scale structures as a late semibrittle overprint to the overall ductile shear and are interpreted as essentially C′ surfaces within strongly flow-layered rocks.

Microscopic scale kink bands and crenulations at high angles to the shear direction and showing antithetic slip are interpreted as R′-shears. These are similar to the outcrop-scale sinis-

tral kink bands whose geometry and orientation relative to the flow layering can indicate regional shear. These microstructures are common where associated with a normal dip-slip reactivation in the Mackworth Formation along the Flying Point boundary. Lineated quartz sheets show a late-stage normal dip-slip reactivation expressed as microscopic kink bands that cut the fine-scale flow layering in the recrystallized quartz sheets.

Oblique fabrics. Secondary oblique foliations representing the plane of flattening under noncoaxial strain are only found locally in the Cape Elizabeth area as solution cleavages in garnet-rich lithologic layers. Oblique solution cleavages within the quartz-mica matrix anastamose around the more rigid garnet porphyroblasts (Fig. 17H). The oblique orientation at ~15° counter-

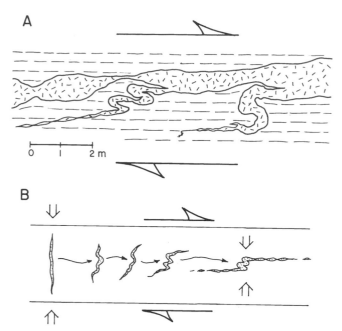

Figure 15. Formation of apparent S-folds due to early layer-normal shortening and later dextral shear. A: Outcrop sketch of deformed granitic pegmatite intrusions modified by dextral shear from Pettengill Island, inner Casco Bay. B: Interpreted sequence of early folds due to layer-normal flattening and subsequent reorientation by dextral shear.

clockwise to the flow layering supports the dextral shear interpretation for these rocks. A more evolved example of similar solution cleavages that are essentially parallel to the shear zone can be found in the southwestern exposures of the Cape Elizabeth fault zone along the Spurwink River.

Regional map scale

Early estimates of displacement along the Norumbega fault zone were ~30 km (Wones and Stewart, 1976) on the basis of offset plutons, but did not attempt to account for earlier ductile dextral shear. The recognition of regional strain accommodation associated with this shearing suggests that much larger magnitudes of displacement could be possible across the system. More recent estimates based on distributing minimum shear strains (estimated from reoriented quartz veins and pegmatites) across the 30-km-wide Casco Bay shear-zone system were ~150 km (Swanson, 1992, 1994). Detailed mapping along the northeastern segment of the fault system by Ludman (1998) gave similar estimates of ~125 km on the basis of reconstruction of lithologic contacts. With the wide distribution of indicators for regional shear throughout the Casco Bay area and the possibility of large-magnitude displacements, there should be evidence for dextral shearing on the regional scale. Larger, regional-scale structures reflecting this dextral shear include oblique regional fold patterns and the geometry of intrusions.

Oblique F2 fold orientation. The regional pattern of upright F2 folds on the southeast side of the Norumbega fault system is delineated on the tectonic inset for the State bedrock geologic map (Osberg et al., 1985). These folds have an oblique orientation to the trend of the fault zone (Fig. 18A) and anastamose into the trace of the fault as it is approached. Several regional fold hinges can be followed along a curving trace as they anastamose into the trend of the main fault zone (Osberg et al., 1985; Kaszuba and Simpson, 1989). The geometry of these oblique folds is typical for shear-related deformation (Sylvester, 1988; Jamison, 1991; Bürgmann, 1989). The oblique orientation and sigmoidal pattern indicate regional dextral strike slip (Swanson, 1992, 1993a). The intensity, tightness, and degree of reorientation also suggest transpression against a restraining bend section of the fault in the Casco Bay area, described in more detail in a separate chapter (Swanson, this volume).

Geometry of intrusions. The numerous igneous intrusions within the coastal zone on the southeast side of the regional fault system have a variety of shapes (Fig. 18B). The Late Devonian ages for most of these intrusions also indicates some involvement in regional strain accommodation about the developing Norumbega fault zone (Swanson, this volume). The more circular undeformed intrusions are to the east away from the main fault zone, suggesting little regional shear-related strain. The distinctly elongated intrusions are restricted to a broad 30–40-km-wide zone along the fault. Elongate pluton shapes have been shown to be the result of intrusion along evolving shear-fabric orientations, pluton deformation prior to complete crystallization, or simply postsolidification modifications (Brun and Pons, 1981; Hutton and Reavy, 1992; Paterson and Fowler, 1993). Similar relationships were outlined by Speer et al. (1994) for granitoids in the Southern Appalachians where many were interpreted as indicators of regional dextral shear. In the coastal Maine area (Fig. 18B) the restriction of the elongate intrusions to the areas adjacent to the fault and their oblique orientation can be used to indicate the degree and extent of early distributed ductile shear associated with the development of the Norumbega fault system.

DISCUSSION

The structures and geometric relationships described herein are useful indicators for direction and sense of shear within the rocks of the Casco Bay area. The general pattern of strain can be characterized as transpressional, including both layer-parallel shear and elongation. Strain partitioning of deformation into translational and compressional (or contractional) components is enhanced by the strong planar anisotropies produced by oblique F2 folding in this area. The rotation of these folds with their upright limbs into the trend of the shear zone produces a generally heterogenous strain distribution controlled by the orientation and competence of the limb lithologies. Strain localization can be seen within the study area in the splaying pattern of the Casco Bay shear-zone system, where high shear-strain zones separate lower strain areas of upright folded rocks that still reveal some dextral shear but are dominated by hinge-parallel elongation.

The varied lithologies of the Casco Bay area also contribute

Figure 16. Thin-section textures in high shear strain. A: Coarse feldspar porphyroclast within sheared granitic bands (Freeport). B: More even-textured, medium-grained, sheared granitic band (Freeport). C: Finer grained, porphyroclastic texture with quartz bands, asymmetric clasts, and grain aggregates (Flying Point). D: Finely layered texture with thinned quartz grain aggregates (Flying Point). The scale bar represents 1 cm.

to a heterogenous strain distribution. Less-competent rocks such as the Spurwink marble and other carbonate lenses within the Cushing Formation, the pelitic schists of the Scarboro and Jewell Formations, as well as the phyllonitic Diamond Island Formation have accommodated greater shear relative to the adjacent more competent gneisses, amphibolites, and intruded granitic pegmatites. The broader anticlines within the Cape Elizabeth area, for example, are cored by metavolcanic rocks of the Cushing Formation and are dominated by tight upright folding and hinge-parallel elongation. The intervening synclinal axes where composed of the more pelitic upper Casco Bay rocks became the focus of shear-strain localization, as in the Cape Elizabeth and Broad Cove shear zones.

While most areas show intermittent orthogonal fracturing followed by dextral shear, an intriguing sequence can be seen in boudinage of a 1-m-thick amphibolite layer within the Scarboro Formation on Bates Island (Fig. 19). This layer shows evidence for an early history of layer-parallel dextral shear as transgressive strings of asymmetric quartz lenses. Later layer-parallel extension produced strictly symmetric partings in simple to complex "fishmouth" geometries, showing no reorientation due to dextral shear. Dextral shear in these rocks was apparently terminated and overprinted by a late stage of layer-parallel elongation. This transition to pure shear may be correlated to a general strain localization of dextral shear components to the major shear-zone boundaries within the inner Casco Bay system.

CONCLUSIONS

The kinematic indicators discussed in this chapter can be used to decipher the strain history of the Casco Bay area in relation to the regional Norumbega fault system. The wide variety of

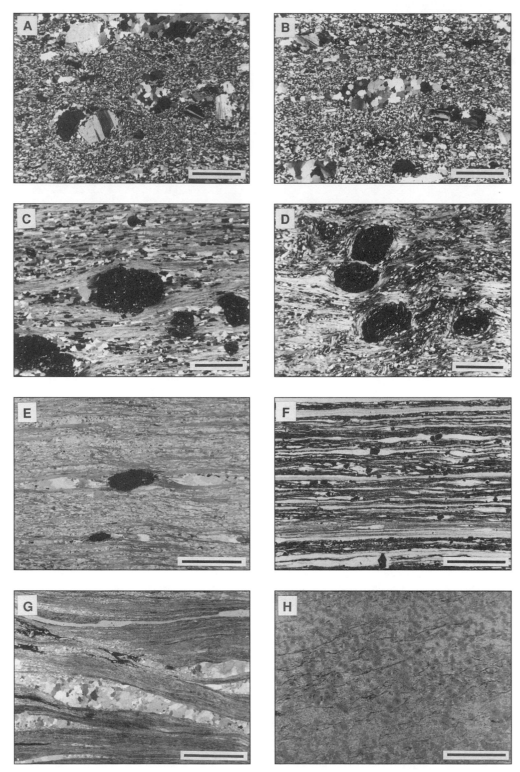

Figure 17. Microscopic kinematic indicators. A: Rotated displaced feldspar porphyroclasts from Flying Point (inner Casco Bay). B: Asymmetric quartz-grain aggregate (same location). C: Garnet porphyroblast with asymmetric tails of recrystallized quartz (Goose Island, middle Casco Bay). D: Garnet porphyroblasts with sigmoidal inclusion trails (Flying Point, inner Casco Bay). E: Ilmenite grains with long asymmetric quartz shadows (French Island, middle Casco Bay) F: Pyrite grains with extreme quartz-filled pressure shadows but no clear sense of asymmetry (Spring Point, middle Casco Bay). G: Oblique dextral shear band and tapered asymmetric geometry of isolated quartz lenses (Higgins Beach, Cape Elizabeth, outer Casco Bay). H: Oblique solution cleavage in garnetiferous units at Trundy Point (outer Casco Bay). The scale bar represents 1 mm.

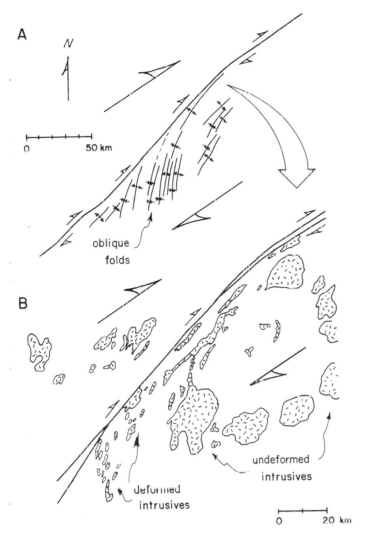

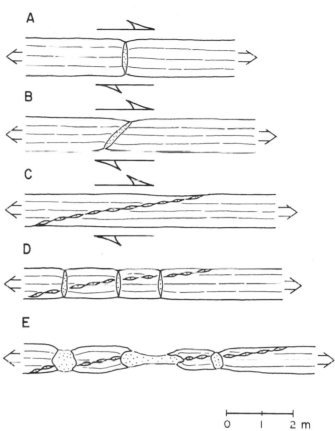

Figure 18. Regional map relations in the Casco Bay area (after Osberg et al., 1985) suggesting dextral shear. A: Prominent F2 folds on the southeast side of the fault show progressive reorientation from east to west toward the main Flying Point fault and anastamose into the trend of the fault as they are traced to the north. B: Pattern of syntectonic intrusion in the northern restraining bend area shows undeformed intrusives to the east of the fault zone and deformed intrusives subparallel to oblique upright foliations adjacent to the main fault segment.

Figure 19. Interpreted sequence of strain for the complex boudinage of a 1-m-wide amphibolite layer (Bates Island, outer Casco Bay). A: Initiation of orthogonal fracture and symmetric competent-layer boudinage. B: Subsequent dextral shearing results in clockwise rotation and sinistral slip along planar parting. C: Reorientation to lower angles and vein-parallel boudinage into low angle strings of tapered quartz lenses. D: Cessation of dextral shear with the initiation of a second phase of layer-parallel extension reflected in early symmetric boudin partings. E: Continued layer-parallel elongation in the absence of dextral shear leads to the development of curled-lip, fishmouth-style of boudinage with wide quartz and/or chlorite mineralized gap areas. This late layer-parallel elongation without modification by dextral shear may correlate with shear localization into the higher strain zones of the inner Casco Bay.

lithologies in the Casco Bay rocks and the continuous introduction of secondary materials as orthogonal quartz veins, boudin partings, and granitic pegmatite intrusions lead to a rich assemblage of multiscale kinematic indicators. The regional pattern is clearly dextral and widely distributed, the overall geometry reflecting regional strain accommodation along a restraining segment of the Norumbega fault system. Dextral shear strain is also concentrated along high-strain zones within the Casco Bay shear-zone system. An understanding of the range of possible kinematic indicators, from microscopic, to outcrop and regional scales, will help in the recognition of regional dextral shear, and transpression throughout the northern Appalachians.

ACKNOWLEDGMENTS

Research for this project was initially undertaken during sabbatical leave from the University of Southern Maine in 1989. Field research was subsequently funded by National Science Foundation grant EAR-9104575 for 1991–1992. My thanks to Allan Ludman, Dwight Bradley, and an anonymous reviewer for their comments and suggestions that helped improve the manuscript.

REFERENCES CITED

Blenkinsop, T. G., and Treloar, P. J., 1995, Geometry, classification and kinematics of S-C' and S-C' fabrics in the Mushandike area, Zimbabwe: Journal of Structural Geology, v. 17, p. 397–408.

Brun, J. P., and Pons, J., 1981, Strain patterns of pluton emplacement in a crust undergoing non-coaxial deformation, Sierra Morena, southern Spain: Journal of Structural Geology, v. 3, p. 219–229.

Bürgmann, R., 1989, Transpressional strain along the southern San Andreas fault, Durmid Hill, California: Geological Society of America Abstracts with Programs, v. 21, no. 6, p. 264–265.

Culshaw, N. G., Ketchum, J. W. F., Wodicka, N., and Wallace, P., 1994, Deep crustal ductile extension following thrusting in the southwestern Grenville Province, Ontario: Canadian Journal of Earth Sciences, v. 31, p. 160–175.

Davidson, A., 1984, Identification of ductile shear zones in the southwestern Grenville Province of the Canadian Shield, in Kröner, A., and Greiling, R., eds., PreCambrian tectonics illustrated: Stutgart, Germany, E′, Schweizerbart'sche Verlagsbuchhandlung, p. 263–279.

Fossen, H., and Rykkelid, E., 1990, Shear structures in the Øygarden area, West Norway: Tectonophysics, v. 174, p. 385–397.

Gates, A. E., Speer, J. A., and Pratt, T. L., 1988, The Alleghanian Southern Appalachian Piedmont: A transpressional model: Tectonics, v. 7, p. 1307–1324.

Gaudemer, Y., and Tapponier, P., 1987, Ductile and brittle deformation in the northern Snake Range, Nevada: Journal of Structural Geology, v. 9, p. 159–180.

Gayer, R. A., Powell, D. B., and Rhodes, S., 1978, Deformation against metadolerite dykes in the Caledonides of Finnmark, Norway: Tectonophysics, v. 46, p. 99–115.

Goldstein, A. G., 1988, Factors affecting the kinematic interpretation of asymmetric boudinage in shear zones: Journal of Structural Geology, v. 10, p. 707–715.

Hanmer, S., 1982, Vein arrays as kinematic indicators in kinked anisotropic materials: Journal of Structural Geology, v. 4, p. 151–160.

Hanmer, S., 1986, Asymmetric pull-aparts and foliation fish as kinematic indicators: Journal of Structural Geology, v. 8, p. 111–122.

Hanmer, S., 1987, Textural map units in quartzo-feldspathic mylonitic rocks: Canadian Journal of Earth Sciences, v. 24, p. 2065–2073.

Hanmer, S., 1988, Ductile thrusting at mid-crustal level, southwestern Grenville Province: Canadian Journal of Earth Sciences, v. 25, p. 1049–1059.

Hanmer, S., and McEachern, S., 1992, Kinematical and rheological evolution of a crustal-scale ductile thrust zone, Central Metasedimentary Belt, Grenville orogen, Ontario: Canadian Journal of Earth Sciences, v. 29, p. 1779–1790.

Hanmer, S., and Passchier, C. W., 1991, Shear sense indicators: A review: Geological Survey of Canada Paper 90-17, 72 p.

Hansen, V. L., 1989, Structural and kinematic evolution of the Teslin suture zone, Yukon: record of an ancient transpressional margin: Journal of Structural Geology, v. 11, p. 717–733.

Holdsworth, R. E., 1990, Progressive deformation structures associated with ductile thrusts in the Moine Nappe, Sutherland, N. Scotland: Journal of Structural Geology, v. 12, p. 443–452.

Holm, D. K., Norris, R. J., and Craw, D., 1989, Brittle and ductile deformation in a zone of rapid uplift: Central Southern Alps, New Zealand: Tectonics, v. 8, p. 153–168.

Hubbard, M. S., West, D. P., Jr., Ludman, A., Guidotti, C. V., and Lux, D., 1995, The Norumbega fault zone, Maine: A mid- to shallow-level crustal section within a transcurrent shear zone: Atlantic Geology, v. 31, p. 109–116.

Hudleston, P. J., 1989, The association of folds and veins in shear zones: Journal of Structural Geology, v. 11, p. 949–957.

Hussey, A. M., II, 1971a, Geologic map of the Portland 15′ quadrangle, Maine: Maine Geological Survey, Geology Map Series GM-1, scale 1:62,500.

Hussey, A. M., II, 1971b, Geologic map and cross sections of the Orrs Island 7.5′ quadrangle and adjacent area, Maine: Maine Geological Survey, Geology Map Series GM-2, 18 p, scale 1:24,000.

Hussey, A. M., II, 1980, The Rye Formation of Gerrish Island, Kittery, Maine: A reinterpretation: Maine Geologist, v. 7, p. 2–3.

Hussey, A. M., II, 1985, Geology of the Bath and Portland 1° × 2° sheets: Maine Geological Survey, Open-file rept., 85-87, 82 p.

Hussey, A. M., II, 1988, Lithotectonic stratigraphy, deformation, plutonism and metamorphism, greater Casco Bay region, southwestern Maine, in Tucker, R. D., and Marvinney, R. G., eds., Studies in Maine geology,

Volume 1, Structure and stratigraphy: Augusta, Maine Geological Survey, p. 17–34.

Hussey, A. M., II, and Bothner, W., 1995, Geology of the coastal lithotectonic belt, southwestern Maine, in Hussey, A. M., II, and Johnston, R. A., eds., Guidebook to field trips in southern Maine and adjacent New Hampshire: New England Intercollegiate Geologic Conference Guidebook, v. 87, p. 211–228.

Hutton, D. H. W., and Reavy, R. J., 1992, Strike-slip tectonics and granite petrogenesis: Tectonics, v. 11, p. 960–967.

Jamison, W. R., 1991, Kinematics of compressional fold development in convergent wrench terranes: Tectonophysics, v. 190, p. 209–232.

Jordan, P. G., 1991, Development of asymmetric shale pull-aparts in evaporite shear zones: Journal of Structural Geology, v. 13, p. 399–409.

Kaszuba, J. P., and Simpson, C., 1989, Polyphase deformation in the Penobscot Bay area, coastal Maine, in Tucker, R. D., and Marvinney, R. G., eds., Studies in Maine geology, Volume 2: Structure and stratigraphy: Augusta, Maine Geological Survey, p. 145–161.

Lacassin, R., 1988, Large-scale foliation boudinage in gneisses: Journal of Structural Geology, v. 10, p. 643–647.

Lacassin, R., Leloup, P. H., and Tapponnier, P., 1993, Bounds on strain in large Tertiary shear zones of SE Asia from boudinage restoration: Journal of Structural Geology, v. 15, p. 677–692.

Leger, A., and Williams, P. F., 1986, Transcurrent faulting history of southern New Brunswick, in Current research, Part B: Geological Survey of Canada Paper 86-1B, p. 111–120.

Leloup, P. H., Harrison, T. M., Ryerson, F. J., Wenji, C., Qi, L., Tapponier, P., and Lacassin, R., 1993, Structural, petrological and thermal evolution of a Tertiary ductile strike-slip shear zone, Diancang Shan, Yunnan: Journal of Geophysical Research, v. 98, p. 6715–6743.

Lister, G. S., and Snoke, A. W., 1984, S-C mylonites: Journal of Structural Geology, v. 6, p. 617–638.

Ludman, A., 1998, Evolution of a transcurrent fault system in the upper crust: The Norumbega fault zone, eastern Maine: Journal of Structural Geology, v. 20, p. 93–107.

Maher, H. D., Jr., 1987, Kinematic history of mylonitic rocks from the Augusta fault zone, South Carolina and Georgia: American Journal of Science, v. 287, p. 795–816.

Malavieille, J., 1987, Extensional shearing deformation and kilometer-scale "a"-type folds in a Cordilleran metamorphic core complex (Raft River Mountains, northwestern Utah): Tectonics, v. 6, p. 423–448.

Malavieille, J., and Lacassin, R., 1988, "Bone-shaped" boudins in progressive shearing: Journal of Structural Geology, v. 10, p. 335–345.

Mattauer, M., 1975, Sur le mécanisme de formation de la schistosité dans l'Himalaya: Earth and Planetary Science Letters, v. 28, p. 144–154.

Mawer, C. K., 1987, Mechanics of formation of gold-bearing quartz veins, Nova Scotia, Canada: Tectonophysics, v. 135, p. 99–119.

Mawer, C. K., and Williams, P. F., 1991, Progressive folding and foliation development in a sheared coticule-bearing phyllite: Journal of Structural Geology, v. 13, p. 539–555.

Mies, J. W., 1991, Planar dispersion of folds in ductile shear zones and kinematic interpretation of fold-hinge girdles: Journal of Structural Geology, v. 13, p. 281–297.

Mies, J. W., 1993, Structural analysis of sheath folds in the Sylacauga Marble Group, Talladega slate belt, southern Appalachians: Journal of Structural Geology, v. 15, p. 983–993.

Nadeau, L., and Hanmer, S., 1992, Deep-crustal break-back stacking and slow exhumation of the continental footwall beneath a thrusted marginal basin, Grenville orogen, Canada: Tectonophysics, v. 210, p. 215–233.

Osberg, P. H., Hussey, A. M., II, and Boone, G. M., 1985, Bedrock geologic map of Maine: Augusta, Maine Geological Survey, scale 1:500,000.

Park, A. F., Williams, P. F., Ralser, S., and Léger, A., 1994, Geometry and kinematics of a major crustal shear zone segment in the Appalachians of southern New Brunswick: Canadian Journal of Earth Sciences, v. 31, p. 1523–1535.

Passchier, C. W., and Simpson, C., 1986, Porphyroclast systems as kinematic indicators: Journal of Structural Geology, v. 8, p. 831–843.

Paterson, S. R., and Fowler, T. K., 1993, Re-examining pluton emplacement processes: Journal of Structural Geology, v. 15, p. 191–206.

Pollock, S. G., 1993, Terrane sutures in the Maine Appalachians, USA and adjacent areas: Geological Journal, v. 28, p. 45–67.

Riedel, W., 1929, Zur mechanik geologischer Brucherscheinungen: Zentralblatt fur Mineralogie, Geologie und Palaeontologie, v. 1929B, p. 354–368.

Rykkelid, E., and Fossen, H., 1992, Composite fabrics in mid-crustal gneisses: Observations from the Oygarden Complex, West Norway Caledonides: Journal of Structural Geology, v. 14, p. 1–9.

Simpson, C., and Schmid, S. M., 1983, An evaluation of criteria to deduce the sense of movement in sheared rocks: Geological Society of America Bulletin, v. 94, p. 1281–1288.

Speer, J. A., McSween, H. Y., Jr., and Gates, A. E., 1994, Generation, segregation, ascent and emplacement of Alleghanian plutons in the southern Appalachians: Journal of Geology, v. 102, p. 249–267.

Spry, A., 1969, Metamorphic textures: Oxford, Pergamon Press, 350 p.

Stewart, D. B., and Wones, D. R., 1974, Bedrock geology of the northern Penobscot Bay area, *in* Osberg, P. H., ed., Geology of east-central and north-central Maine: New England Intercollegiate Geologic Conference Guidebook, v. 66, p. 223–239.

Stock, P., 1992, A strain model for antithetic fabric rotation in shear band structures: Journal of Structural Geology, v. 14, p. 1267–1275.

Swanson, M. T., 1989, Mesoscale Acadian deformation mechanisms during regional horizontal extension and distributed dextral strike-slip simple shear strain: Geological Society of America Abstracts with Programs, v. 21, no. 6, p. 66.

Swanson, M. T., 1992, Late Acadian–Alleghenian transpressional deformation. Evidence from asymmetric boudinage in the Casco Bay area, coastal Maine: Journal of Structural Geology, v. 14, p. 323–341.

Swanson, M. T., 1993a, The Casco Bay restraining bend on the Norumbega fault zone: A model for regional deformation in coastal Maine: Geological Society of America Abstracts with Programs, v. 25, no. 6, p. 478.

Swanson, M. T., 1993b, Stretching lineations, shear zone kinematics and dextral transpression along the Flying Point/Norumbega fault zone, Casco Bay, Maine: Geological Society of America Abstracts with Programs, v. 25, no. 2, p. 82.

Swanson, M. T., 1994, Minimum dextral shear strain estimates in the Casco Bay area of coastal Maine from vein reorientation and elongation: Geological Society of America Abstracts with Programs, v. 26, no. 3, p. 75.

Swanson, M. T., 1995, Distributed ductile dextral shear strain throughout the Casco Bay area, *in* Hussey, A. M., II, and Johnston, R. A., eds., Guidebook to field trips in southern Maine and adjacent New Hampshire: New England Intercollegiate Geologic Conference Guidebook, v. 87, p. 1–13.

Swanson, M. T., 1997, Asymmetric boudinage in mylonitic gneisses, *in* Snoke, A. W., Todd, V. R., and Tullis, J. A., eds., Atlas of mylonites and fault-related rocks: Princeton, New Jersey, Princeton University Press.

Swanson, M. T., Pollock, S. G., and Hussey, A. M., II, 1986, The structural and stratigraphic development of the Casco Bay Group at Harpswell Neck, Maine, *in* Newberg, D. W., ed., Guidebook for field trips in southwestern Maine: New England Intercollegiate Geologic Conference Guidebook, v. 78, p. 350–370.

Sylvester, A. G., 1988, Strike-slip faults: Geological Society of America Bulletin, v. 100, p. 1666–1703.

Van Den Driessche, J., and Brun, J.-P., 1987, Rolling structures at large shear strain: Journal of Structural Geology, v. 9, p. 691–704.

Weijermars, R., 1987, The Palomares brittle-ductile shear zone of southern Spain: Journal of Structural Geology, v. 9, p. 139–157.

Weijermars, R., and Rondeel, H. E., 1984, Shear-band foliation as an indicator of sense of shear: field observations in central Spain: Geology, v. 12, p. 603–606.

Williams, P. F., and Price, G. F., 1990, Origin of kink bands and shear band cleavage in shear zones: An experimental study: Journal of Structural Geology, v. 12, p. 145–164.

Wones, D. R., and Stewart, D. B., 1976, Middle Paleozoic regional right lateral strike-slip faults in central coastal Maine: Geological Society of America Abstracts with Programs, v. 8, p. 304.

Xu, J., Wang, P., Ching, R., and Ye, Z., 1986, Ductile deformation and regional strain field in the southern segment of the Tancheng-Lujiang fault zone, eastern China: Pure and Applied Geophysics, v. 124, p. 337–364.

MANUSCRIPT ACCEPTED BY THE SOCIETY JUNE 9, 1998

Printed in U.S.A.

Geological Society of America
Special Paper 331
1999

Temperature variability during shear deformation: An interpretation of microstructures along the central Norumbega fault zone, Maine

Mary S. Hubbard
Department of Geology, Kansas State University, Manhattan, Kansas 66506-3201
Hui Wang
Department of Geological Sciences, University of Maine, Orono, Maine 04469

ABSTRACT

The central portion of the Norumbega fault zone is ~30 km wide and exhibits considerable strain variability across this width. Shear-sense indicators across the entire width of the zone are consistent with dextral shear. In an effort to better understand the nature of deformation and deformational mechanisms in this segment of the fault zone, quartz and some feldspar microstructures were analyzed in order to distinguish between differences in deformational conditions both along and across the strike of the shear zone. Observations of quartz microstructures along an ~30 km length of the Norumbega fault zone suggest fairly uniform temperatures of deformation (300–350 °C). Feldspar microstructures in these rocks suggest higher temperatures (450–500 °C), on average, than the quartz microstructures. This apparent temperature discrepancy is probably due to inherited feldspar microstructures that developed during an earlier higher temperature deformational episode. Samples collected across the strike of the fault zone show variability in interpreted deformation temperatures in quartz. Across the portion of the fault zone that exhibits moderate strain, interpreted temperatures are higher (400–450 °C) than temperatures within the high strain zone (300–350 °C). The moderate strain region most likely represents an episode of older deformation that occurred at deeper crustal levels than the apparently lower temperature high strain zone. Analysis of quartz c-axis fabrics across the central Norumbega fault zone shows a variation in c-axis patterns that coincides with the variability in strain and interpreted deformational temperatures. The highest strain samples exhibit single-girdle c-axes patterns, whereas samples from successively lower strain zones exhibit asymmetric crossed girdles and symmetric crossed girdles. Our observations lead us to conclude that differences in microstructures across this major shear zone are due to different episodes of deformation under different temperature conditions or evolving temperature conditions during localization of deformation.

INTRODUCTION

Geologic studies of the Norumbega fault zone have shown this zone (1) to have undergone protracted dextral shear coeval with intrusive activity, (2) to be characterized by a heterogeneous distribution of strain across its 5–30 km width, and (3) to have a history of differential exhumation along its >300 km length. Most of these characteristics are recognized to some degree in both active and ancient transcurrent regimes around the world. For example, the San Andreas fault system in California exhibits a heterogeneous distribution of strain and has been active for the past 30–40 m.y. (Wallace, 1990). The Atacama fault zone of

Hubbard, M. S., and Wang, H., 1999, Temperature variability during shear deformation: An interpretation of microstructures along the central Norumbega fault zone, Maine, *in* Ludman, A., and West, D. P., Jr., eds., Norumbega Fault System of the Northern Appalachians: Boulder, Colorado, Geological Society of America Special Paper 331.

northern Chile consists of two strands of a sinistral ductile system across which strain differentially localized during exhumation in the Jurassic and Early Cretaceous (Scheuber and Andriessen, 1990). In southern Chile, Hervé et al. (1993) suggested a relationship between granitic intrusion and dextral strike-slip displacement along the Liquiñe-Ofqui fault zone in the Miocene. In Morocco microearthquake seismicity is evidence for the distributed nature of active sinistral movement across a 40–50-km-wide zone adjacent to the Nékor fault (Hatzfeld et al., 1993). Although these features of distributed shear, strain localization or partitioning through time, exhumation during deformation, and coeval intrusion are recognized in many places, the details of the absolute or relative timing and the interrelation of these processes are unclear. A strike-slip zone that underwent a degree of exhumation during deformation should show evidence of different deformation temperatures along strike within the zone. If there had been a component of variable localization of deformation across the zone through time, then there should be evidence for different deformation temperatures across the strike of the fault zone. If one could determine that deformation temperatures interpreted from the rock record were variable across or along strike, and if one could determine the pattern of temperature variability, then we would be able to better understand the crustal levels at which various parts of a shear zone were active and how deformation localizes or distributes itself during the life of a major shear zone.

In this study we investigate the utility of using quartz and feldspar microstructures as indicators of temperature (assuming that strain rate and water content are constant) and as proxies for relative crustal level during deformation in an effort to better understand the evolution of strain distribution during the exhumation history of the Norumbega fault zone in central Maine. This approach relies heavily on comparisons of microstructures in field samples with microstructures from experimentally deformed samples presented in the literature. Because there are multiple unconstrained variables in the field and because field samples are likely to have undergone multiple deformation events, comparisons with experimental studies must be made carefully; therefore, our study should be considered a preliminary effort at extracting relative deformation temperatures from microstructures. Interpreted temperatures can be compared from samples along and across the fault zone in order to understand how deformation was partitioned in time and space. An understanding of how strain is distributed in the middle to shallow crustal levels of an ancient strike-slip zone is important to our understanding of the deformation processes at the inaccessible subsurface levels of modern strike-slip systems.

GEOLOGIC BACKGROUND

The Norumbega fault zone and the surrounding regions (Fig. 1) have been studied by many researchers for the past 20 years (e.g., Stewart and Wones, 1974; Wones, 1978; Hussey and Newberg, 1978; Pankiwskyj, 1976; Ludman, 1981; Osberg et al.,

1985; Newberg, 1986; Swanson et al., 1986; Kaszuba and Simpson, 1989; Swanson, 1992; West, 1993; Hubbard et al., 1995). During this time there have been many interpretations regarding the geometry, sense of movement, and tectonic significance of this structure. The Norumbega fault was first named by Stewart and Wones (1974) for exposures north of Bucksport, Maine. Wones (1978) described the Norumbega fault as a 3–4-km-wide zone of multiple, dextral strike-slip faults. Subsequent work (Pankiwskyj, 1976; Hussey and Newberg, 1978; Ludman, 1981; Osberg et al., 1985; Newberg, 1986) has shown that this fault zone is continuous from eastern New Brunswick, where it is known as the Fredericton fault, south possibly to New Hampshire. Hubbard et al. (1991) recognized a wide zone of distributed dextral shear fabrics and used the name "Norumbega fault zone" to designate the previously mapped Norumbega fault and other fault segments in south-central Maine, as well as the wide (>20 km) zone of distributed shear in a variety of lithologic units between and around these segments. Swanson (1992) and West and Hubbard (1997) also described a wide zone of distributed ductile, dextral shear deformation as part of the Norumbega fault zone in south-central and southwestern Maine.

West (1993) discussed the timing, structural features, geographic extent, and tectonic significance of dextral shear defor-

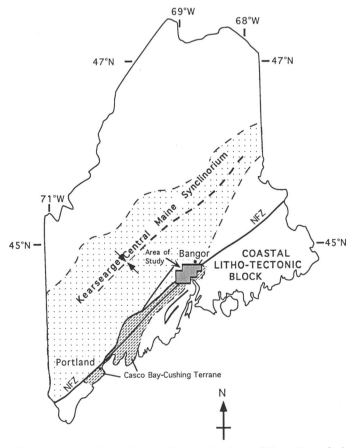

Figure 1. General tectonic map showing location of Norumbega fault zone (NFZ) and study area.

mation of the Norumbega fault zone in south-central Maine. On the basis of detailed structural observations as well as $^{40}Ar/^{39}Ar$ thermochronology, he proposed two different styles of dextral deformation, a wide zone (>20 km) of heterogeneously distributed shear structures, and a localized zone (~1 km) of high strain mylonitization. West interpreted the wide zone of dextral shear to reflect a major episode of Late Devonian to Early Carboniferous transcurrent tectonism related to the later stages of the Acadian orogeny. West and Lux (1993) presented evidence that the relatively narrow zone of high strain mylonitization occurred in latest Carboniferous–earliest Permian time.

In eastern Maine, Ludman (1995) mapped the Norumbega fault zone as a series of subparallel, dominantly brittle fault strands distributed across an ~20 km width in greenschist facies metasedimentary rocks and granitic intrusive rocks. A few exposures of ductile shear fabric suggest either locally higher temperatures or, perhaps, lower strain rates.

For the purposes of investigating the variability of deformation temperatures, this study targeted an area of the northeast-striking, central Norumbega fault zone that represents a transitional region between rocks of generally amphibolite grade metamorphism to the southwest and upper greenschist grade rocks to the northeast. Detailed structural observations and bedrock mapping were conducted along a 30-km-long and 5–20-km-wide, cross-strike transect (Fig. 2). The Norumbega fault zone in this study includes the original Norumbega fault (Stewart and Wones, 1974) and several previously mapped discrete faults in central Maine, including the Hackmatack Pond fault, the Sennebec Pond fault, and the wide area between these faults.

In the study area and along much of its strike, the Norumbega fault zone separates two distinct tectonic domains: the Kearsarge Central Maine synclinorium (Lyons et al., 1982) to the northwest and the Coastal lithotectonic block (Osberg et al., 1985) to the southeast (Fig. 2). Lithologies within the Norumbega fault zone are generally included with the stratigraphy of the Coastal lithotectonic block. The Hutchins Corner formation is the only unit of the Kearsarge Central Maine synclinorium that is exposed in the study area. Units of the Coastal lithotectonic block that compose the Norumbega fault zone in the study area include the Cushing Formation, the Cape Elizabeth Formation, the Passagassawakeag Gneiss, and the Bucksport Formation.

Lithologies of these formations include metapelite, quartzite, metagraywacke, phyllite, mafic and felsic metavolcanic rock, calc-silicate rock, and quartzo-feldspathic gneiss. Because each of these rock types accommodates deformation differently, we have tried to limit our study to just two of the lithologies. Pelite and quartzo-feldspathic gneiss are the most common lithologies across the Norumbega fault zone, and typically contain quartz-rich layers, so we chose samples from within these lithologies for our study of microstructures. There are still likely to be differences in the accommodation of deformation between these two rock types, so this must be considered in any interpretations of the data.

The stratified rocks of the study area have been metamorphosed in a low-pressure facies series; conditions of meta-

morphism ranged from greenschist to amphibolite facies (Novak and Holdaway, 1981; Osberg, 1988). The metamorphic grade is lowest on the northwest sides of the Norumbega fault zone in the Hutchins Corner Formations (Bickel, 1976).

There are two kinds of intrusive rocks in the study area: (1) strongly foliated gneissic granitoid; (2) weakly to nonfoliated granitoids and pegmatite. Strongly foliated granitoid rocks are generally found in narrow, elongate bodies within the Norumbega fault zone. The best example is the Winterport gneissic granite, a light gray plagioclase-quartz-biotite gneissic granite characterized by a strong penetrative foliation. This foliation is oriented parallel to the main shear fabric of the adjacent gneissic and schistose rocks, suggesting pretectonic to syntectonic intrusion.

The relatively undeformed Mount Waldo granite is located within the central section of the Norumbega fault zone and is a light gray, medium-grained, muscovite-bearing, biotite granite. The weighted mean $^{207}Pb/^{206}Pb$ age of four zircon analyses from this granite is 371 ± 2 Ma (Stewart et al., 1995). Deformation fabrics appear to be deflected around this pluton, suggesting that shear deformation postdated or continued after pluton emplace-

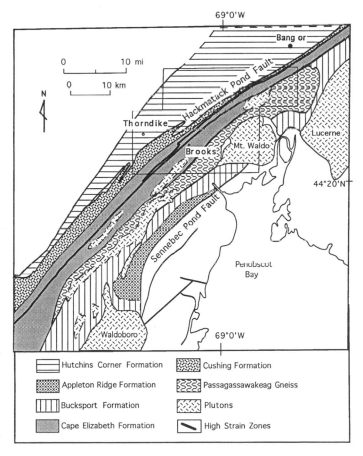

Figure 2. Simplified tectonic map of central Maine showing major geologic units and location of study area. The Norumbega fault zone encompasses the width between the Hackmatack Pond fault and the Sennebec Pond fault (modified from Osberg et al., 1985). The white areas represent undivided peri-Gondwanan sequences.

ment. This deflection is seen in a strike change of nearly vertical fabrics from N40–50E to N20–30E on the west side of the pluton and from N40–50E to N50–60E on the north side of the pluton (this study).

The shear deformation features in the central section of the Norumbega fault zone can be divided into two different types: (1) several zones of localized high strain superimposed on a wide zone of heterogeneously distributed structures with penetrative dextral shear fabrics; and (2) a narrow zone of significantly higher strain mylonitization. This variation in strain is similar to that observed by West (1993). The narrow zone of high strain mylonitization in this study area may be continuous with the high strain zone that West studied. Rocks of the wide zone (20–25 km) of distributed deformation exhibit some degree of grain-size reduction. Ductile shear deformation was heterogeneously distributed across this zone. On the basis of a greater degree of grain-size reduction, several localized zones of higher strain were recognized within this distributed shear zone. This relation of grain-size reduction to strain is not quantifiable, but has also been assumed in a qualitative manner by other workers (Newman and Mitra, 1993; Van der Pluijm, 1991; Pryer, 1993). Most pelitic and quartzo-feldspathic rocks of moderate to low strain within the zone of distributed shear show a range in average grain size from 0.1 to 5.0 mm. Higher strain zones within the zone of distributed shear show a smaller range in grain size from 0.1 to 0.5 mm.

The degree of grain-size reduction also distinguishes the narrow high strain zone from the wide zone of distributed shear. Within the high strain zone the average grain size is <0.1 mm. The high strain zone is composed of dark-colored, fine-grained mylonitic and ultramylonitic rocks. The degree of grain-size reduction limits recognition of the protolith. Detailed mapping has shown that the 1-km-wide high strain zone consists of heterogeneously distributed bands of mylonitic and ultramylonitic textures in pelitic and quartzo-feldspathic rocks.

The planar shear fabric and compositional layering across the Norumbega fault zone in east-central Maine are generally nearly vertical, striking N30–60°E (Fig. 3A). The shear fabric within the distributed shear zone is defined by schistosity, i.e., preferred orientation of elongate aggregates of quartz and concentrations of dark minerals in thin layers. On the basis of the ubiquitous presence of asymmetric shear features, this planar fabric is interpreted to be the product of noncoaxial shear deformation. The mylonitic foliation within the high strain zone is also defined by schistosity, layers of feldspar porphyroclasts, and the presence of planar, sheared quartz-rich layers.

Several types of lineations are present in the study area, including stretched quartz rods, elongate boudins, intersection lineations, and mineral cluster lineations. The most common lineations, however, are the well-developed mineral cluster lineations defined by elongate concentrations of quartz, feldspar, and biotite. The bearing of the lineation is generally subparallel to the strike of the foliation in this region, trending N22–N50°E. The majority of these linear features plunge shallowly to the northeast or southwest and suggest a subhorizontal northeast-southwest

stretching direction, interpreted to represent tectonic transport during strike-slip deformation (Fig. 3B).

There are two general types of folds in the field area: (1) open, asymmetric folds with nearly vertical fold axes and (2) upright isoclinal folds. The upright isoclinal folds are well displayed in the Passagassawakeag Formation (Fig. 4). Both limbs of the upright folds show evidence for dextral shear sense, suggesting that these folds formed during or prior to strike-slip movements (Hubbard, 1992). Axial surfaces of the asymmetric folds strike N5–20°E and dip steeply. The asymmetry of these z-shaped folds is consistent with dextral shear.

Across the Norumbega fault zone in the study area ubiquitous asymmetric fabric elements facilitated the use of modern methods for kinematic analysis (Simpson and Schmid, 1983; Hanmer and Passchier, 1991). The asymmetric features observed include intrafolial folds, boudinage (Fig. 5A), composite planar fabric, pressure shadows, porphyroclast tails, trails of inclusions in porphyroclasts, mica fish (Fig. 5B), shear bands, intragranular faults, and crystallographic preferred orientation of minerals. The interpretation of movement sense based on these indicators is consistently dextral relative to the northeast-striking foliation.

In monomineralic horizons the obliquity of elongate grain shapes relative to the planar shear fabric, also known as grain-shape preferred orientation, may also be used as a shear-sense indicator (Bouchez et al., 1983; Simpson and Schmid, 1983; Hanmer and Passchier, 1991). Along the Norumbega fault zone there is common grain-shape preferred orientation in quartz-rich domains. The grain-shape alignments were formed by elongate recrystallized grains, subgrains, and sheared and rotated porphyroclasts. The sense of obliquity between shear fabric and quartz grain-shape alignment for the quartz-rich samples indicates dextral shear.

MICROSTRUCTURES AND DEFORMATION TEMPERATURES

Physical conditions such as temperature, pressure, and the presence or absence of fluids influence the processes by which a rock and its constituent minerals deform when subjected to stress. Other factors such as strain rate, rock composition, and grain size also have some impact on deformation processes. Deformation mechanisms are the grain-scale processes that act to accommodate stress with rock deformation as the result. For a particular mineral, different deformation mechanisms are operative under different physical conditions and each of those deformation mechanisms will result in different microstructures. Microstructures are textural features and grain-boundary relationships observed at the thin-section scale. Because temperature may have a dominant control on which deformation mechanism becomes active, one can use microstructures for some minerals as a relative geothermometer for deformation. Many researchers have considered this relation between microstructures and temperature in the study of both experimentally and naturally deformed rocks (Tullis and Yund, 1985; Simpson, 1985; White and Mawer, 1986;

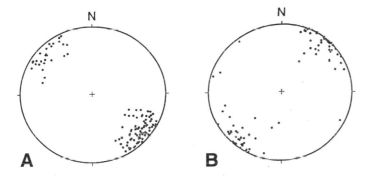

Figure 3. Equal-area, lower-hemisphere projections of fabric data from the study area. A: Plot of poles to planar shear fabric in mylonitized rock. B: Plot of stretched mineral lineations.

Figure 4. Upright fold in feldspathic gneiss of the Passagassawakeag Formation near North Searsmont. Photo taken looking toward N45°E. Outcrop is ~1 m in height.

Knipe, 1989; Hirth and Tullis, 1992; Pryer, 1993; Srivastava and Mitra, 1996). We have utilized quartz and feldspar microstructures from samples both along and across strike of the central Norumbega fault zone in order to compare the variability of interpreted temperatures of deformation. We have followed the nomenclature presented by Hirth and Tullis (1992) of "regime 1–3" for a relative comparison of lower, moderate, and higher temperature conditions of deformation for dislocation creep processes. Because of crystallographic and rheologic differences,

these regimes for quartz represent lower absolute temperatures than the same regimes for feldspar.

Temperature regimes

Hirth and Tullis (1992) experimentally deformed quartz aggregates under different conditions. On the basis of microstructural observations of these deformed aggregates and the interpreted relative rates of grain-boundary migration, dislocation climb, and dislocation production, they divided the field of dislocation creep for quartz into three regimes.

Regime 1 microstructures were produced at the lowest temperatures or faster strain rates. Under these conditions dislocation production is too fast for diffusion-controlled dislocation climb to accommodate deformation effectively. Grain-boundary migration recrystallization is the dominant recovery mechanism, and subgrains do not form. The original grains exhibit irregular and patchy undulatory extinction at the optical scale. Original grains may be inhomogeneously flattened.

Regime 2 occurs at higher temperatures than regime 1 or slower strain rates. The rate of dislocation climb is rapid enough to accommodate recovery. Recrystallization occurs mostly by progressive rotation of subgrains. Original grains are homogeneously flattened and characterized by a sweeping undulatory extinction and optically visible subgrains. Core and mantle structure is common and the recrystallized grains that constitute the mantle are similar in size to subgrains in the core grain.

Regime 3 is produced at even higher temperatures or slower strain rates, where the rate of climb is still high but the migration at grain boundaries is also rapid. Recrystallization, therefore, occurs by both grain-boundary migration and progressive subgrain rotation. In regime 3 recrystallized grains are much larger than subgrains, and complete recrystallization occurs at low strain.

Experimental studies such as that of Hirth and Tullis (1992) and the results of microstructural studies for field situations in which the deformation conditions are constrained by other means have led to a basic understanding of the relationship of microstructures for quartz and feldspar and deformation temperatures (Simpson, 1985; Pryer, 1993; Srivastava and Mitra, 1996). The onset of crystal plasticity for quartz is ~300 °C in naturally deformed rocks (Schmid and Haas, 1989). Crystal plastic deformation of feldspar generally occurs at higher temperatures than for quartz (upper greenschist grade [450 °C] to granulite facies) (Debat et al., 1978; Hanmer, 1982; Tullis, 1983; Bell and Johnson, 1989). Experimental studies have shown that dislocation climb in feldspar is very difficult. Due to this phenomenon, and the relatively slow rate of grain-boundary migration during deformation, large original feldspar porphyroclasts remain generally undeformed but are slowly replaced at their margins by smaller recrystallized grains in regime 1 (Tullis and Yund, 1985). Because feldspars deform plastically at higher temperatures than quartz, they may preserve microstructures from early, high-temperature deformation events. During later lower temperature deformation feldspar may deform in a brittle manner or not at all,

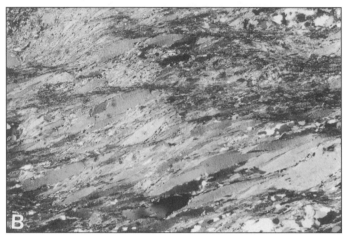

Figure 5. Shear-sense indicators. A: Boudinaged quartz vein from Cape Elizabeth Formation with asymmetry indicative of dextral shear. Photo taken looking down on outcrop. Northeast is on right. Lens cap for scale is 50 mm. B: Photomicrograph of mica fish from pelitic horizon of Passagassawakeag Formation. Asymmetry of fish is consistent with dextral shear. Northeast in on right. Width of area in photo is 6 mm. Crossed nicols.

while quartz deforms plastically and incorporates lower temperature microstructures. Because of these differences in deformation behavior there may be problems in using both quartz and feldspar microstructures for interpreting deformation temperatures of polydeformed rocks.

In order to understand the variability of temperatures possibly related to differential exhumation from southwest to northeast along the Norumbega fault zone, we examined microstructures from pelitic and quartzo-feldspathic samples collected along strike. We also analyzed the microstructural variability across strike with the goal of determining whether strain localization may have migrated across the fault zone through time, thus producing deformational features at different moments in an evolving thermal history (i.e., producing a record of variable deformation temperatures across strike). We base our temperature estimates on a compilation of interpreted correlations between temperature and microstructures from the literature (Table 1).

Because rocks of the Norumbega fault zone have undergone multiple deformation episodes, we focus attention on quartz microstructures that should record the later, lower temperature deformation, which is most likely related to fault zone dextral shear. Some feldspar microstructures are described for comparison, but our final interpretations are drawn from quartz.

Textural Features

Observations along strike. In an effort to observe a systematic variation in deformation temperature along strike of the Norumbega fault zone, samples were collected within the core of the high strain zone. Starting in the southwest, quartz in sample 94W20c1 (quartzo-feldspathic gneiss, Fig. 6) has undergone extensive dynamic recrystallization to form fine, roughly equant, recrystallized grains (Fig. 7A). These recrystallized grains have straight or slightly wavy boundaries and some relict ribbon grains remain (Fig. 7B). The presence of ribbons together with recrystallized grains at the grain boundary indicates that dislocation climb was active, and recrystallized grains formed by subgrain rotation with minor grain-boundary migration, as in regime 2 of Hirth and Tullis (1992). New recrystallized quartz grains have a moderate grain-shape preferred orientation oblique to the long axis of relict ribbon grains and an apparent lattice-preferred orientation, indicated with insertion of a wave plate.

Feldspars from sample 94W20c1 (Fig. 6) show some undulatory extinction that is either a product of crystal plastic deformation or possibly cataclasis (Fig. 7C). Twins and kink bands in plagioclase are also present. Feldspar porphyroclasts exhibit core and mantle structures (Fig. 7D). The mantle grains around the sutured core grain boundary are significantly smaller than the patches of differential extinction within the core, but could be the product of strain or metamorphic reaction. Fracturing of feldspar is also very common and irregular and recrystallized grains are commonly found within fractures, suggesting that both fracturing and dynamic recrystallization acted to reduce the feldspar grain size.

Estimates for the deformation temperature based on quartz microstructures described here are ~300–350 °C (Simpson, 1985; White and Mawer, 1986; FitzGerald and Stunitz, 1993; Pryer, 1993; Srivastava and Mitra, 1996). This is the likely temperature regime for fracturing the feldspars. If other feldspar microstructures in this sample are truly the product of crystal plastic processes they are likely to be relicts from earlier, higher temperature deformation episodes (Tullis and Yund, 1985).

Sample 94W20d2 was collected from the same outcrop as 94W20c1 (Fig. 6), but is slightly coarser grained and may represent a lower strain version of the same quartzofeldspathic lithology. Sample 94W20d2 was used for quartz c-axis analysis and is discussed in the following. Quartz microstructures are similar to 94W20c1, and have straight grain boundaries and relict ribbons (Fig. 8). Sample 94W20d2 shows more grain-shape preferred orientation than 94W20c1. The deformation temperature interpreted from quartz microstructures in this sample is also

TABLE 1. CORRELATION OF MICROSTRUCTURES AND DEFORMATION TEMPERATURES

Estimated deformation temperature (°C)	Quartz microstructure	Feldspar microstructure	References
~250–300	Patchy, undulatory extinction, recrystallization around rims of original grains to form smaller grains with sutured boundaries. Regime 2 of Hirth and Tullis, 1992.	Fracturing. Reaction to white mica.	White, 1976; Mitra, 1978; Simpson, 1985; Hirth and Tullis, 1992.
~300–350	Flattened original grains, core-and-mantle structure, deformation bands, recrystallized grains same size as subgrains with curved boundaries. Regime 2 of Hirth and Tullis, 1992.	Fracturing, patchy, undulatory extinction, reaction to white mica.	Mitra, 1978; Law et al., 1986; Simpson, 1985; FitzGerald and Stunitz, 1993; Hirth and Tullis, 1992.
~350–450	Some oblique, elongate recrystallized grains, quartz recrystallized to equant, polygonal grains with straight grain boundaries. Regime 3 of Hirth and Tullis, 1992.	Fracturing, undulatory extinction, twinning, kink bands, large feldspar grains exhibit sutured grain boundaries, myrmekite.	Simpson and Wintsch, 1986; Law et al., 1990; Hirth and Tullis, 1992.
~450–500	Complete recovery. Strain-free equant grains with 120° triple junctions.	Fracturing, twinning, kink bands, myrmekite, core and mantle structure as in Regime 1 of Hirth and Tullis, 1992.	Simpson and Wintsch, 1986; Srivastava and Mitra, 1995; FitzGerald and Stunitz, 1993; Hirth and Tullis, 1992.
~500–550	Complete recovery, quartz in ribbons has grain boundaries perpendicular to ribbon margins, straight grain boundaries.	Fracturing, twinning, kink bands, subgrain rotation, recrystallized grains are the same size as subgrains, myrmekite.	Simpson and Wintsch, 1986; Srivastava and Mitra, 1995; FitzGerald and Stunitz, 1993.
~550–650	Complete recovery, recrystallized grains larger than original grains.	Twinning, kink bands, complete recovery, rotation recrystallization.	Hanmer, 1981; Simpson and Wintsch, 1986; Srivastava and Mitra, 1995; FitzGerald and Stunitz, 1993.

~300–350 °C. Farther northeast, quartz grains in sample 94W10a (Fig. 6) are recrystallized to small, roughly equant, polygonal grains. The recrystallized grains have straight or slightly wavy boundaries, and occupy ribbon-shaped regions suggestive of regime 2 of Hirth and Tullis (1992). We interpret the quartz microstructures to have formed at temperatures of ~300–350 °C. Feldspar grains in sample 94W10a exhibit microstructures similar to those described here for sample 94w20c1: irregular undulatory extinction, twins, kink bands, and core and mantle structures (Fig. 9). We interpret the feldspar microstructures to be relict from an earlier deformation event. Sample 94W5i1 came from the Brooks area, northeast of the sample site for 94W10a. Quartz from 94W5i1 recrystallized by both grain boundary migration and progressive subgrain rotation to form elongate core and mantle structures. The ribbon-like cores are up to 0.2 mm wide and 0.5 mm long and lensoid in shape (Fig. 10A). The lensoid cores contain subgrains of the same size as the recrystallized grains in the mantle, indicating climb-accommodated dislocation creep, as in regime 2 of Hirth and Tullis (1992).

Feldspar porphyroclasts in sample 94W5i1 are 5–8 mm wide, but have recrystallized to form equant, polygonal smaller grains and subgrains (Fig. 10B). A few plagioclase porphyro-

clasts show evidence of grain-boundary migration recrystallization. Other feldspar grains are brittlely fractured. Most of these fractures are perpendicular to the foliation and filled with quartz or mica grains. Some of the recrystallized feldspar grains exhibit strong undulatory extinction, suggesting that they have been further deformed. Twinning of feldspar is also common.

We interpret the deformation temperature to be ~300–350 °C on the basis of quartz microstructures. Feldspar microstructures suggest higher temperatures, but this temperature difference is likely to be due to an earlier, high-temperature deformation followed by a later, lower temperature deformation that correlates with quartz microstructures and the brittle fracturing of the feldspars.

Sample 94W6a came from the vicinity of Monroe, Maine (quartzo-feldspathic gneiss, Fig. 6), northeast of sample 94W5i1. Quartz grains show both a grain-shape preferred orientation (Fig. 11) and a crystallographic preferred orientation, as discussed in a following section. Grain boundaries are straight to irregular and are locally pinned by muscovite. Most feldspar grains are the same grain size as quartz. Feldspar grains show some reaction textures. Interpreted temperature from quartz is 300–350 °C.

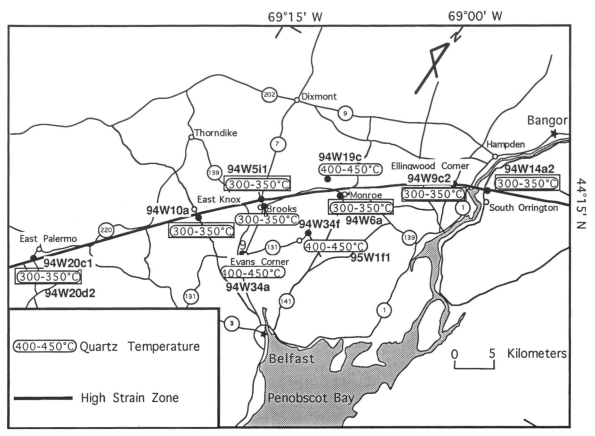

Figure 6. Map of study area showing locations of samples used for microstructural analysis both along and across the strike of the Norumbega fault zone and showing deformation temperature ranges interpreted from the quartz microstructures. Bold numbers are sample numbers and black dots are sample locations. Temperatures enclosed in a rectangle are for samples discussed in terms of their variation along strike. Temperatures without a rectangle are the across-strike samples.

Farther northeast, sample 94W9c2 (calc-pelite, Fig. 6) is largely an ultramylonite. However, a few coarse quartz grains (2–3 mm in diameter) are preserved. Quartz grains in quartz-rich layers show recrystallization to fine, roughly equant, polygonal grains (<0.1 mm). Relict quartz ribbons in these layers contain subgrains of the same size as the recrystallized grains (Fig. 12), suggesting that rotation recrystallization, as in regime 2, was the operative deformation mechanism (Hirth and Tullis, 1992). Ultra fine-grained calcite and mica constitute most of the matrix in the ultramylonite. Quartz microstructures are consistent with a deformation temperature of about 300–350 °C (Simpson, 1985).

Sample 94W14a2 (quartzo-feldspathic gneiss, Fig. 6) was collected at the northeast end of the study area. This sample contains numerous fractured feldspar porphyroclasts (Fig. 13). Either crystal plastic deformation or cataclasis played a role in the formation of undulose extinction in the feldspars. Feldspar grains also exhibit twinning and kinking. These porphyroclasts are surrounded by finely recrystallized quartz and mica grains, which are possibly reaction products. There are some relict elongate quartz ribbons, suggesting that quartz deformation was regime 2. On the basis of the fractured feldspar grains and quartz micro-

structures, we interpret the deformation temperature to have been in the range 300–350 °C. Although many of the quartz textures from along-strike samples appear different optically, our analysis of microstructures leads us to conclude that temperatures of deformation were not significantly different along the 30 km length of the Norumbega fault zone that we studied.

Observations across strike. We aimed our study of microstructures across the strike of the Norumbega fault zone at understanding the role of variable localization of deformation through time. Assuming that exhumation of the Norumbega fault zone was synchronous with strike-slip deformation, one would expect to see lateral migration of the locus of deformation across the fault zone expressed as localized zones that deformed at different temperatures. We based temperature estimates on quartz microstructures from four samples of pelitic or quartzo-feldspathic rocks collected across the strike of the central Norumbega fault zone.

Sample 94W34a (pelite, Fig. 6) was collected in the southeast part of the Norumbega fault zone and is texturally representative of samples from that area. Recrystallized quartz grains have lobate or sutured grain boundaries, indicative of progressive subgrain rotation and climb-accommodated dislocation creep, as

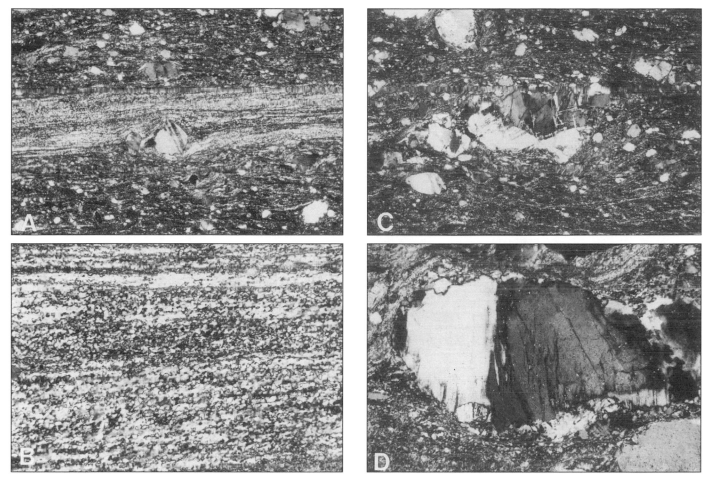

Figure 7. Photomicrographs of sample 94W20c1. Northeast is on the right side in all images. A. Recrystallized quartz in quartz-rich horizon. Length of crossed nicols image is 6 mm. B: Close-up of quartz shown in Figure 7C. Recrystallized grains show weak grain-shape preferred orientation. Grain boundaries are straight to wavy. Length of image is 1.5 mm. C: Feldspar grain is fractured and is surrounded by finer recrystallized grains. Course feldspar grain also shows twinning. Crossed nicols photo is 6 mm long. D: Close-up of feldspar showing core and mantle structure and minor twinning. Length of crossed nicols image is 1.5 mm.

in regime 3 of Hirth and Tullis (1992) (Fig. 14A). Most of the recrystallized grains exhibit strong undulose extinction, suggesting that they have been further deformed. These new grains are 0.2–0.5 mm in diameter. Quartz from this sample also has a lattice-preferred orientation and is discussed in the next section. Feldspar porphyroclasts are recrystallized on their margins and exhibit undulose extinction and deformation twinning (Fig. 14B). There may be some reaction products on the margins of feldspar porphyroclasts as well. We interpret feldspar and quartz microstructures to represent a deformation temperature of ~400–450 °C.

Farther northwest but still south of the high strain zone, sample 95W1f1 (quartzo-feldspathic gneiss, Fig. 6) contains quartz that occurs as large recrystallized grains located in ribbon-shaped regions with some smaller recrystallized grains (Fig. 15). Individual mica grains control some of the quartz grain shapes. Lobate quartz grain boundaries suggest that grain-boundary migration may have occurred together with rotation recrystalliza-

tion, suggesting possible regime 3 deformation. Feldspar grains exhibit reaction to muscovite and quartz, and myrmekite development (Fig. 15). We interpret the deformation temperature for both quartz and feldspar to have been ~400–450 °C.

Sample 94W34f (Fig. 6) came from an outcrop just south of the high strain zone. Quartz grains in sample 94W34f show a core and mantle structure with extremely elongate cores (Fig. 16A). These ribbon-like cores are 2 mm long and as wide as 0.5 mm. Some of the cores show subgrains similar in size to the recrystallized new grains in the mantle. The combination of core and mantle structure and a high axial ratio for quartz cores is consistent with rotation recrystallization, as in regime 2 of Hirth and Tullis (1992). Plagioclase porphyroclasts (larger than 5 mm) show reaction textures and, in places, strain-induced dynamic recrystallization of regime 1 (Fig. 16B). Fine-grained feldspars (grain size <0.5 mm) are also present in the matrix of this sample and elongate grains are oriented subparallel to the foliation. Tem-

Figure 8. Photomicrograph of sample 94W20d2 showing grain-shape preferred orientation. Length of crossed nicols image is 1.3 mm. Northeast is on the right side.

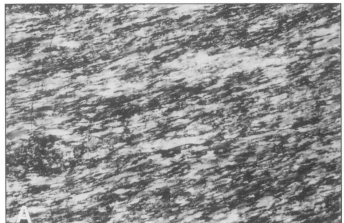

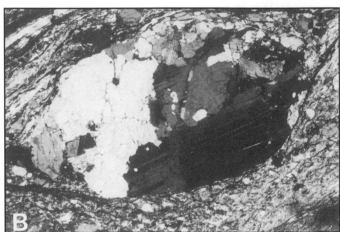

Figure 9. Photomicrograph of sample 94W10a showing fracturing, twinning, and recrystallization of feldspar clast. Length of crossed nicols image is 6 mm. Northeast is on the right side.

Figure 10. Photomicrographs of sample 94W5i. Images are with crossed nicols and the length of each image is 6 mm. In both cases northeast is on the right. A: Elongate quartz grains recrystallized at margins. Subgrain rotation is the likely recrystallization mechanism. B: Relict feldspar clast now consists of recrystallized grains and subgrains.

perature of deformation interpreted from quartz is 300–350 °C, and temperature interpreted from feldspar textures is 400–450 °C and most likely represents earlier conditions. This sample was used for quartz c-axis analysis discussed in the following.

Sample 94W19c (Fig. 6) was collected 1 km north of the high strain zone. Quartz occurs both as porphyroclasts and as finer grains in the matrix (Fig. 17). This variation in quartz grain size may be inherited from a poorly sorted sedimentary protolith. Quartz porphyroclasts are ~1.5–2 mm in diameter and exhibit subgrains. Finer grains in the matrix have irregular, cuspate grain boundaries, suggesting a component of grain-boundary migration. The combination of subgrains and cuspate grain boundaries suggests that rotation recrystallization and grain-boundary migration were active processes, as in regime 3 of Hirth and Tullis (1992). Feldspar porphyroclasts are rare in this sample. Where present, they are <0.5 mm long and are irreg-

ular in shape. We estimate the deformation temperature to be ~400–450 °C from quartz microstructures. Quartz from this sample also exhibits a crystallographic preferred orientation as discussed in the next section.

Variations in Quartz C-axis Orientations. Analysis of crystallographic preferred orientation is a powerful tool for studying the conditions and processes of ductile deformation. Quartz deformation experiments (Tullis et al., 1973), numerical models (Lister, 1977; Lister and Williams, 1979), and textural analysis (Starkey, 1979; Schmid and Casey, 1986; Law et al., 1984) have contributed much toward the understanding of quartz c-axis fabrics. Although a great deal of controversy still remains in this field, researchers generally agree that quartz c-axes tend to fall into a few well-defined pattern groups (Schmid and Casey, 1986; Lister and Williams, 1979). For example, asymmetrical single-girdle patterns are the most common in zones of high strain with a strong simple shear component dominated by basal slip (Schmid and Casey, 1986; Law et al., 1994), whereas asymmetrical crossed girdles are

Figure 11. Photomicrograph of sample 94W6a showing grain-shape pre-ferred orientation. Length of crossed nicols image is 1.3 mm. Northeast is on the right side.

Figure 13. Photomicrograph of sample 94W14a2 showing fracturing, kinking, and twinning of feldspars. Length of crossed nicols image is 6 mm. Northeast is on the right side.

Figure 12. Photomicrograph of sample 94W9c2 showing subgrains in relict quartz ribbon and recrystallized grains of same size as subgrains. Rotation recrystallization is likely deformation mechanism. Length of image is 1.5 mm. Northeast is on the right side.

found in shear zones with components of both simple and pure shear (Lister, 1977; Lister and Williams, 1979). Symmetrical crossed girdle textures are usually found in pure shear zones or zones that have undergone only a small magnitude of simple shear strain (Law et al., 1984; Schmid and Casey, 1986).

Analytical Techniques. Petrofabric analyses of quartz c-axis preferred orientation were carried out on five of the samples dis-cussed herein, using an automated universal stage mounted on a petrographic microscope. We measured at least 200 c-axes in each thin section. Section planes were oriented perpendicular to the foli-ation and parallel to the stretching lineation. The c-axis data are presented on equal-area, lower-hemisphere projections; the planes of projection contain the lineation and pole to foliation (Fig. 18).

C-axis results. Adopting the single-girdle and crossed-girdle fabric classification introduced by Lister (1977), samples

94W20d2 and 94W34a can be classified as single girdles, sample 94W34f can be regarded as an asymmetric crossed girdle, and samples 94W6a and 94W19c may be described as symmetric cross girdles. There is a general correlation between the measured c-axis pattern and the degree of strain interpreted for each sample.

The samples that yielded a single-girdle pattern were collected from the zones of high strain. Samples 94W20d2 is from the narrow zone of highest strain, and sample 94W34a is from a local-ized zone of high strain within the zone of distributed shear. Using the orientation of asymmetry for these single girdles as a kinematic indicator (Lister and Williams, 1979; Simpson and Schmid, 1983), these c-axis measurements confirm the dextral sense of shear inter-preted from other kinematic indicators (Fig. 18).

Sample 94W34f was collected from a zone of moderate strain just south of the narrow zone of high strain. This sample yielded an asymmetric cross-girdle pattern of quartz c-axes (Fig. 18). By comparison with experimental studies (Dell'Angelo and Tullis, 1989) and simulation studies of quartz c-axis fabric development associated with simple shear deformation (Lister and Hobbs, 1980; Jessell, 1988), asymmetrical crossed girdles can be used as shear-sense indicators. The orientation of asym-metry for the girdle pattern indicates the sense of movement for the simple shear component (Behrmann and Platt, 1982). The asymmetry of sample 94W34f is consistent with dextral shear, but may indicate a larger component of pure shear than samples 94W20d2 and 94W34a.

C-axis plots for samples 94W6a and 94W19c2 can be regarded as symmetrical crossed girdles (Fig. 18). These sam-ples are from moderate to low strain segments of the distributed shear zone. Although the symmetrical girdle patterns suggest that these samples came from zones of pure shear, the presence of numerous asymmetric fabric features seen both in the field and in thin section confirm that either these samples were sub-jected to some component of dextral simple shear deformation, or that there was partitioning of deformation in simple and pure

Figure 14. Photomicrographs of sample 94W34a. Northeast is on the right side in both crossed nicols images. Both images are 6 mm long. A: Recrystallized quartz with sutured grain boundaries. B: Recrystallization and twinning of feldspar clast.

DISCUSSION

Quartz microstructures from samples collected along strike within the high strain zone show regime 2 characteristics and therefore yield uniform estimates of deformation temperature 300–350 °C (Fig. 6). It has previously been suggested that the Norumbega fault zone was differentially exhumed during or following deformation, the southwestern part of the zone having been exhumed from deeper crustal levels and therefore higher temperatures than the northeastern part (Hubbard et al., 1995). If this was the case we should see decreasing temperatures of deformation toward the northeast. Several explanations are possible for the uniformity of microstructures along strike in this study area: (1) there has not been differential exhumation from southwest toward northeast; (2) the differential exhumation predates the phase of deformation recorded by the quartz; or (3) the study area did not include a sufficient along-strike length to see a decrease in deformation temperatures toward the northeast. Because quartz microstructures are easily "reset" and therefore represent only the last phase of deformation, we favor an explanation where the differential exhumation predates the phase of deformation recorded by the quartz. We suggest, however, that future work along strike should include a larger area in order to better distinguish between explanation 2 and 3.

Quartz microstructures from samples collected across strike show a degree of variability with the interpreted higher temperatures (quartz regime 3) from south of the Norumbega fault zone and from a locality just north of the high strain zone. Quartz microstructures from within the high strain zone are all interpreted as regime 2. This suggested variability in deformation temperature is most likely due to either true variability in temperature across the Norumbega fault zone during the last deformation phase or to a difference in timing of deformation from the higher temperature locations to the lower temperature locations. Localized small intrusive bodies could be the source of temperature variability across the zone; however, because of the consistency of regime 2 quartz microstructures within the high strain zone, we favor an interpretation for which the high strain zone represents a later phase of deformation that took place under lower temperature conditions. An interpretation of a separate phase of deformation for the high strain zone is further supported by the difference in c-axis patterns for that zone. This interpretation is also consistent with the geochronologic results of West and Lux (1993) that suggested later (ca. 290 Ma) dextral shear along the high strain zone when compared to the surrounding zone of distributed shear. The possibility of other variables that could affect microstructures such as strain rate and the presence or absence of fluids must also be considered. We have assumed these variables to be constant throughout the study area, but this assumption is difficult to substantiate in the field.

CONCLUSIONS

Field observations and microstructural analysis along the Norumbega fault zone in east-central Maine provide insights into

shear zones. The observed correlation of quartz c-axis fabric to the degree of strain across the central Norumbega fault zone is consistent with reports of c-axis pattern variations in other shear zones. Carreras et al. (1977) documented the progressive development of the c-axis fabric of recrystallized grains with increasing shear strain in the Cap De Creus mylonite zone (northeast Spain). They argued that the quartz c-axis fabric at zones of low strain is characterized by a weak and variable preferred orientation, indicating the influence of original grain control. They suggested that the intensity of the preferred orientation increases from outside toward the middle of the mylonite zone, through symmetrical crossed girdles, to asymmetric crossed girdles, to asymmetric single girdles. The implication is that the middle of the mylonite zone is the highest strain section and exhibits the asymmetric single-girdle quartz texture, thus correlating amount of strain and the c-axis pattern. Another possibility, however, is that the high strain zone of the Norumbega fault zone is the product of a separate episode of deformation that had a greater noncoaxial component.

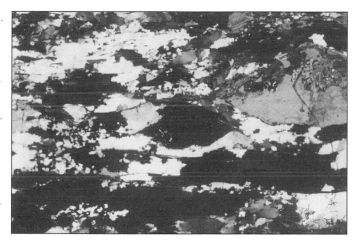

Figure 15. Photomicrograph of sample 95W1f1 showing quartz in ribbon-shaped regions with some grain boundaries pinned by muscovite. Feldspar is recrystallized and has myrmekite formation. Length of crossed nicols image is 6 mm. Northeast is on the right side.

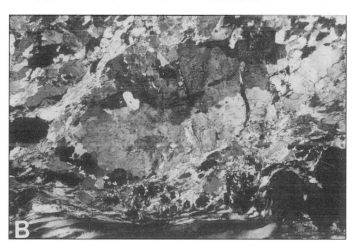

Figure 16. Photomicrographs of sample 94W34f. Northeast is on the right side in both crossed nicols images. Both images are 6 mm long. A: Relict quartz grains are extremely elongate and have partially recrystallized at their margins. B: Plagioclase porphyroclast shows both recrystallization and reaction textures.

shear-zone characteristics for middle crustal levels of strike-slip deformation. We interpret the fault zone at this study area to be a 30-km-wide zone on the basis of the presence of shear fabric across this width. Ubiquitous asymmetric textural features confirm a dextral sense of shear across the entire width of this zone. Grain-size variability across the zone is interpreted to be the product of strain variability and localization during deformation. For samples studied along strike within the high strain zone there is no difference in interpreted deformation temperatures from quartz microstructures. We attribute this lack of variation in temperature to deformation that may have followed differential exhumation that was suggested by Hubbard et al. (1995). Samples collected across strike exhibit microstructures which we interpret to represent higher temperatures (400–450 °C) outside of the high strain zone and lower temperatures (300–350 °C) within the high strain zone. One plausible explanation is that high strain deformation localized during a later phase, when rocks were at a shallower crustal level than during the time of distributed Norumbega fault zone deformation (West and Hubbard, 1997). Quartz c-axis measurements yielded patterns of symmetric single girdles, asymmetric crossed girdles, and symmetric crossed girdles. The asymmetric patterns of preferred orientation are consistent with the interpretation of dextral shear. The variation in c-axis patterns correlates with the variation in strain deduced from grain-size differences, but also suggests the greatest degree of noncoaxial deformation within the high strain zone.

The data presented here support the notion that strain is distributed at depth in a strike-slip system and that the strain localization is heterogeneous within a system and could be due to differences in lithology, protolith, grain size, or presence of fluids. The heterogeneous distribution of strain may also be a function of variable localization through time. Studies of deformation temperatures in other shear zones around the world will help further elucidate the variability of deformation conditions along and across shear zones in other settings. Within a single zone such as the Norumbega fault zone, further studies should also consider expanding analysis to a greater length of the fault zone or extending the analysis to a greater number of samples within a smaller area to better understand local variations. We emphasize, however, the importance of the microscopic features to an understanding of the large-scale processes.

ACKNOWLEDGMENTS

We thank the following for useful discussions of Norumbega fault zone geology and microstructural analysis: C. Simpson, J. Tullis, A. Hussey, D. Stewart, C. Guidotti, D. Lux, D. West, A. Ludman, M. Brown, G. Solar, and M. Yates. We thank A. Ludman and D. West for their comments and for being willing to compile this volume. Reviews by J. Tullis and J. C. White greatly improved the manuscript. This study was supported by National Science Foundation grant EAR-9218833.

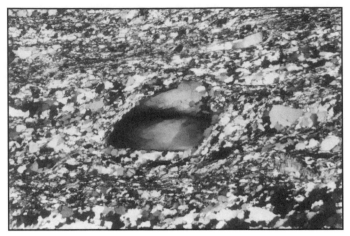

Figure 17. Photomicrograph of sample 94W19c showing subgrains in quartz porphyroclast and cuspate grain boundaries on matrix quartz (bottom of image). Crossed nicols image is 6 mm long; northeast on the right side.

REFERENCES CITED

Behrmann, J. H., and Platt, J. P., 1982, Sense of nappe emplacement from quartz c-axis fabrics: An example from the Betic Cordilleras (Spain): Earth and Planetary Science Letters, v. 59, p. 208–215.

Bell, T. H., and Johnson, S. E., 1989, The role of deformation partitioning in the deformation and recrystallization of plagioclase and K-feldspar in the Wooddroffe thrust mylonite zone, central Australia: Journal of Metamorphic Geology, v. 7, p. 151–168.

Bickel, C. E., 1976, Stratigraphy of the Belfast quadrangle, Maine, *in* Page, L. R., ed., Contributions to the stratigraphy of New England: Geological Society America Memoir 148, p. 97–128.

Bouchez, J.-L., Lister, G. S., and Nicolas, A., 1983, Fabric asymmetry and shear sense in movement zones, Geologische Rundschau, v. 72, p. 401–419.

Carreras, J., Estrada, A., and White, S., 1977, The effects of folding on the c-axis fabrics of a quartz mylonite: Tectonophysics, v. 39, p. 3–24.

Debat, P., Soula, J.-C., Kubin, L., and Vidal, J.-L., 1978, Optical studies of natural deformation microstructures in feldspars (gneiss and pegmatites from Occitania, Southern France): Lithos, v. 11, p. 133–145.

Dell'Angelo, L. N., and Tullis J., 1989, Fabric development in experimentally sheared quartzites: Tectonophysics, v. 169, p. 1–21.

FitzGerald, J. D., and Stunitz, H., 1993, Deformation of granitoids at low metamorphic grade. I: Reactions and grain size reduction: Tectonophysics, v. 221, p. 269–297.

Hanmer, S. K., 1981, Segregation bands in plagioclase: Non-dilational en-echelon quartz veins formed by strain enhanced diffusion: Tectonophysics, v. 79, p. 53–61.

Hanmer, S. K., 1982, Microstructure and geochemistry of plagioclase and microcline in naturally deformed granite: Journal of Structural Geology, v. 4, p. 197–213.

Hanmer, S., and Passchier, C. W., 1991, Shear sense indicators: A review: Geological Survey of Canada Paper 90-17, 72 p.

Hatzfeld, D., Caillot, V., Cherkaoui, T. E., Jebli, H., and Medina, F., 1993, Microearthquake seismicity and fault plane solutions around the Nékor strike-slip fault, Morocco: Earth and Planetary Science Letters, v. 120, p. 31–41.

Hervé, F., Pankhurst, R. J., Drake, R., Beck, M. E., and Mpodozis, C., 1993, Granite generation and rapid unroofing related to strike-slip faulting, Aysén, Chile: Earth and Planetary Science Letters, v. 120, p. 375–386.

Hirth, G., and Tullis, J., 1992, Dislocation creep regimes in quartz aggregates: Journal of Structural Geology, v. 14, p. 145–159.

Hubbard, M. S., 1992, Fold development in a strike-slip shear zone, the Norum-

bega Fault system, Maine [abs.]: Eos (Transactions, American Geophysical Union), v. 73, p. 534.

Hubbard, M. S., West, D. P., Jr., Lux, D. R., Orifice, J., Guidotti, C. V., Higgins, K., and Yanasak, J., 1991, Major dextral strike-slip deformation in the Northern Appalachians: The Norumbega fault zone, Maine, Geological Society of America Abstracts with Programs, v. 23, no. 5, p. A311.

Hubbard, M. S., West, D. P., Jr., Ludman, A., Guidotti, C. V., and Lux, D. R., 1995, The Norumbega fault zone, Maine: Mid shallow level crustal section within a transcurrent zone: Atlantic Geology, v. 31, p. 109–116.

Hussey, A. M., II, and Newberg, D. W., 1978, Major faulting in the Merrimack synclinorium between Hollis, N. H., and Biddeford, Maine, Geological Society of America Abstracts with Programs, v. 10, p. 48.

Jessell, M. W., 1988, Simulation of fabric development in recrystallizing aggregates—II. Example model runs: Journal of Structural Geology, v. 10, p. 779–794.

Kaszuba, J. P., and Simpson, C., 1989, Polyphase deformation in the Penobscot Bay area, coastal Maine, *in* Studies in Maine Geology, Volume 2: Augusta, Maine Geological Survey, p. 145–161.

Knipe, R. J., 1989, Deformation mechanisms—Recognition from natural tectonites: Journal of Structural Geology, v. 11, p. 127–146.

Law, R. D., Knipe, R. J., and Dayan, H., 1984, Strain path partitioning within thrust sheets: Microstructural and petrofabric evidence from the Moine Thrust Zone at Loch Eriboll, Northwest Scotland: Journal of Structural Geology, v. 6, p. 477–497.

Law, R. D., Casey, M., and Knipe, R. J., 1986, Kinematic and tectonic significance of microstructures and crystallographic fabrics within quartz mylonites from the Assynt and Eriboll regions of the Moine thrust zone, NW Scotland: Royal Society of Edinburgh Transactions, Earth Science v. 77, p. 99–126.

Law, R. D., Schmid, S. M., and Wheeler, J., 1990, Simple shear deformation and quartz crystallographic fabrics: A possible natural example from the Torridon area of NW Scotland: Journal of Structural Geology, v. 12, p. 29–45.

Law, R. D., Miller, E. L., Little, T. A., and Lee, J., 1994, Extensional origin of ductile fabrics in the Schist Belt, Central Brooks Range, Alaska—II. Microstructural and petrofabric evidence: Journal of Structural Geology, v. 16, p. 919–940.

Lister, G. S., 1977, Discussion: Crossed girdle c-axis fabrics in quartzites plastically deformed by plane strain and progressive simple shear: Tectonophysics, v. 39, p. 51–54.

Lister, G. S., and Hobbs, B. E., 1980, The simulation of fabric development during plastic deformation, the effects of deformation history: Journal of Structural Geology, v. 2, p. 355–370.

Lister, G. S., and Williams, P. F., 1979, Fabric development in shear zones: Theoretical controls and observed phenomena: Journal of Structural Geology, v. 1, p. 283–297.

Ludman, A., 1981, Significance of transcurrent faulting in eastern Maine and location of the suture between Avalonia and North America: American Journal of Science, v. 281, p. 463–483.

Ludman, A., 1995, Strain partitioning, timing, and amount of offset in the Norumbega fault zone, eastern Maine: Geological Society of America Abstracts with Programs, v. 27, no. 1, p. 65.

Lyons, J. B., Boudette, E. L., and Aleinikoff, J. N., 1982, The Avalonian and Gander zones in central eastern New England, *in* St. Julien, P., and Beland, J., eds., Major structural zones and faults of the northern Appalachians: Geological Survey of Canada Special Paper 24, p. 43–66.

Mitra, G., 1978, Ductile deformation zones and mylonites: The mechanical processes involved in the deformation of crystalline basement rocks: American Journal of Science, v. 278, p. 1057–1084.

Newberg, D. W., 1986, The Norumbega fault zone between Bath and Freedom, Maine, *in* Newberg, D. W., ed., Guidebook for fieldtrips in southwestern Maine, New England Intercollegiate Geological Conference Guidebook, p. 80–97.

Newman, J., and Mitra, G., 1993, Lateral variations in mylonite zone thickness as influenced by fluid-rock interactions, Linville Falls fault, North Carolina:

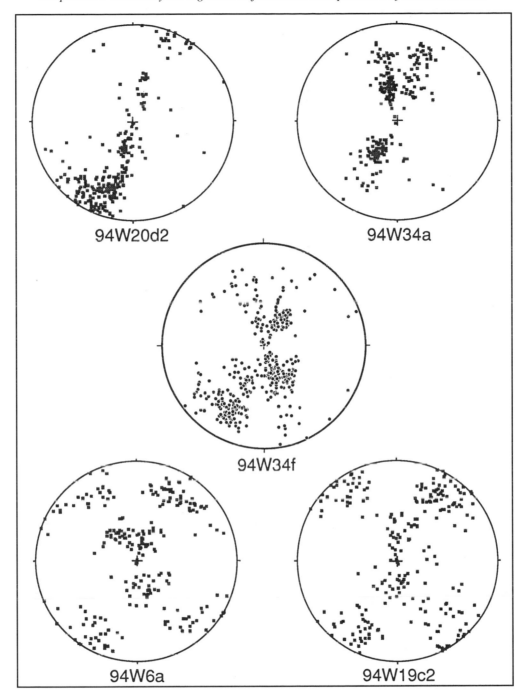

Figure 18. Equal-area, lower-hemisphere projections of quartz c-axis for five samples. All samples were cut perpendicular to foliation and parallel to lineation. The equators of each plot represent orientation of trace of foliation along the lineation. In each case northeast is on the right side of the projection. Samples 94W20d2 and 94W34a are interpreted to be asymmetric single girdles. Sample 94W34f is interpreted to be an asymmetric crossed girdle. Samples 94W6a and 94W19c2 are interpreted to be symmetric crossed girdles. All asymmetries are consistent with dextral shear.

Journal of Structural Geology, v. 15, p. 849–863.

Novak, J. M., and Holdaway, M. J., 1981, Metamorphic petrology, mineral equilibria, and polymetamorphism in the Augusta quadrangle, south-central Maine: American Mineralogist, v. 56, p. 51–69.

Osberg, P. H., 1988, Geologic relations within the shale-wacke sequence in south-central Maine, *in* Tucker, R. D., and Marvinney, R. G., eds., Studies in Maine Geology, Volume 1: Augusta, Maine Geological Survey, p. 51–73.

Osberg, P. H., Hussey, A. M., II, and Boone, G. M., 1985, Bedrock geologic map of Maine: Augusta, Maine Geological Survey, scale 1: 500,000.

Pankiwskyj, K. A., 1976, Preliminary report on the geology of the Liberty 15′ quadrangle and adjoining parts of the Burnham, Brooks, Belfast, and Vassalboro quadrangles in south-central Maine: Maine Geological Survey Open File Report no. 76–29, 8 p.

Pryer, L. L., 1993, Microstructures in feldspars from a major crustal thrust zone:

The Grenville Front, Ontario, Canada: Journal of Structural Geology, v. 15, p. 21–36.

Scheuber, E., and Andriessen, P. A. M., 1990, The kinematic and geodynamic significance of the Atacama fault zone, northern Chile: Journal of Structural Geology, v. 12, p. 243–257.

Schmid, S. M., and Casey, M., 1986, Complete fabric analysis of some commonly observed quartz c-axis patterns, *in* Hobbs, B. E., and Heard, H. C., eds., Mineral and rock deformation: Laboratory studies: American Geophysical Union Geophysical Monograph 36, p. 263–286.

Schmid, S. M., and Haas, R., 1989, Transition from near-surface thrusting to intrabasement decollement. Schlinig thrust, Eastern Alps: Tectonics, v. 8, p. 697–718.

Simpson, C., 1985, Deformation of granitic rocks across the brittle-ductile transition: Journal of Structural Geology, v. 7, p. 503–511.

Simpson, C., and Schmid, S. M., 1983, An evaluation of criteria to determine the sense of movement in sheared rocks: Geological Society of America Bulletin, v. 94, p. 1281–1288.

Simpson, C., and Wintsch, R. P., 1986, Evidence for deformation-induced K-feldspar replacement by myrmekite: Journal of Metamorphic Geology, v. 7, p. 261–275.

Srivastava, P., and Mitra, G., 1996, Deformation mechanisms and inverted thermal profile in the North Almora Thrust mylonite zone, Kumaon Lesser Himalaya, India: Journal of Structural Geology, v. 18, p. 27–39.

Starkey, J., 1979, Petrofabric analysis of Saxony granulites by optical and X-ray diffraction methods: Tectonophysics, v. 58, p. 201–219.

Stewart, D. B., and Wones, D. R., 1974, Bedrock geology of northern Penobscot Bay area, *in* Osberg, P. H., ed., Geology of east-central and north-central Maine, New England Intercollegiate Geologic Conference Guidebook, v. 66, p. 223–239.

Stewart, D. B., Tucker, R. D., and West, D. P., Jr., 1995, Genesis of Silurian composite terrane in northern Pennobscot Bay, *in* Hussey, A. M., II, and Johnson, R. A., eds., Guidebook for fieldtrips in southwestern Maine: New England Intercollegiate Geological Conference Guidebook, v. 87, p. 29–49.

Swanson, M. T., 1992, Late Acadian–Alleghenian transpressional deformation: Evidence from asymmetric boudinage in the Casco Bay area, coastal Maine, Journal of Structural Geology, v. 14, p. 323–342.

Swanson, M. T., Pollock, S. G., and Hussey, A. M., II, 1986, The structural and stratigraphic development of the Casco Bay Group at Harpswell Neck, Maine, *in* Newberg, D. W., ed., Guidebook to field trips in southwestern Maine, New England Intercollegiate Geological Conference Guidebook, v. 78, p. 350–370.

Tullis, J., 1983, Deformation of feldspars, *in* Ribbe, P. H., ed., Feldspar mineralogy: Washington, D.C., Mineralogical Society of America, p. 297–323.

Tullis, J., and Yund, R. A., 1985, Dynamic recrystallization of feldspar: A mechanism for ductile shear-zone formation: Geology, v. 13, p. 238–241.

Tullis, J., Christie, J. M., and Griggs, D. T., 1973, Microstructures and preferred orientations of experimentally deformed quartzites: Geological Society of America Bulletin, v. 84, p. 297–314.

Van der Pluijm, B. A., 1991, Marble mylonites in the Bancroft shear zone, Ontario, Canada: Microstructures and deformation mechanisms: Journal of Structural Geology, v. 13, p. 1125–1135.

Wallace, R. E., 1990, The San Andreas fault system, California: U.S. Geological Survey Professional Paper 1515, 283 p.

West, D. P., Jr., 1993, Nature, timing, and extent of dextral shear deformation in south-central Maine [Ph.D. thesis]: Orono, University of Maine, p. 228.

West, D. P., Jr., and Hubbard, M., 1997, Progressive localization of deformation during exhumation of a major strike-slip zone: Norumbega fault zone, south-central Maine, USA: Tectonophysics, v. 273, p. 185–201.

West, D. P., Jr., and Lux, D. R., 1993, Dating mylonitic deformation by the ^{40}Ar-^{39}Ar method: An example from the Norumbega fault zone, Maine: Earth and Planetary Science Letters, v. 120, p. 221–237.

White, S. H., 1976, The effects of strain on the microstructures, fabrics and deformation mechanisms in quartzites: Royal Society of London Philosophical Transactions, ser. A, v. 283, p. 69–86.

White, J. C., and Mawer, C. K., 1986, Extreme ductility of feldspars from a mylonite, Parry Sound, Canada: Journal of Structure Geology, v. 8, p. 133–143.

Wones, D. R., 1978, Norumbega fault zone, Maine: U.S. Geological Survey Summary of Technical Reports VIII, National Earthquake Hazards Reduction Program, p. 108–111.

MANUSCRIPT ACCEPTED BY THE SOCIETY JUNE 9, 1998

Geological Society of America
Special Paper 331
1999

Multistage shearing of the Deblois granite in the Kellyland fault zone, eastern Maine

Allan Ludman
Department of Geology, Queens College, City University of New York, Flushing, New York 11367-1597, and Ph.D. Program in Earth and Environmental Sciences, City University Graduate School and University Center, 365 Fifth Avenue, New York, New York 10036
Susan Gibbons*
Department of Geology, Queens College, City University of New York, Flushing, New York 11367-1597

ABSTRACT

Effects of shallow-crustal shearing on granite are revealed by a 3.5-km-wide transect through the Kellyland fault zone, one of three high-strain zones of the Norumbega fault system in eastern Maine. The epizonal Deblois pluton underwent four stages of shearing, the first two of which accompanied significant mid-Paleozoic dextral displacement. Stage 1 converted homogeneous megacrystic granite to a strongly foliated rock by a combination of ductile (quartz) and brittle (microcline, albite) processes. The disparate behavior of these phases suggests low temperatures (≤300 °C) and pressures in accord with the epizonal character of the pluton. Fine-grained granitic dikes intruded before and during stage 1, and in a strain-free period that separated it from later deformation. Stage 2 was a mostly brittle event evidenced by cataclasite veins that offset stage 1 foliation. A narrow zone of stage 2 mylonite and ultramylonite suggests either extreme cataclasis and cataclastic flow or a combination of strain, temperature, pressure, and fluid activity capable of supporting ductile deformation at temperatures even lower than those associated with stage 1. Stage 3 (dextral) and stage 4 (sinistral) strike-slip activity did not produce significant displacement, although stage 3 faults have a strong topographic expression enhanced by glacial erosion.

The same events are recorded in adjacent metasedimentary rocks, but lithic and textural contrasts reveal differences in detail. Anisotropy in the interbedded wacke-pelite section caused stage 1 strain localization, but strain was more homogeneously distributed in the granite. Phyllosilicate content controlled deformation in the stratified rocks, whereas the behavior of quartz determined the effect of deformation in the granites.

INTRODUCTION

The Norumbega fault system is one of the largest strike-slip fault systems of the northern Appalachians, extending at least 400 km from the high-grade metamorphic terrane of southwestern Maine, through the low-grade rocks of eastern Maine, and into the unmetamorphosed Carboniferous strata of west-central New Brunswick (Fig. 1). Nearly all studies of the Norumbega fault system (e.g., Hussey et al., 1986; Swanson, 1992, 1995; West, 1993, 1995) have focused on the high-grade segment where most faulting occurred at mid-crustal conditions (Hubbard et al., 1995; West and Hubbard, 1997). The only previous study of the Norumbega fault system at shallow crustal levels described its evolution in low-grade metasedimentary rocks in eastern Maine (Ludman, 1998), but the system also affects two epizonal granite batholiths there—the Bottle Lake complex and the Deblois pluton (Fig. 2)—requiring that the nature of shearing in

---

*Present address: 7307 Foxside Lane, Humble, TX 77338.

Ludman, A., and Gibbons, S., 1999, Multistage shearing of the Deblois granite in the Kellyland fault zone, eastern Maine, *in* Ludman, A., and West, D. P., Jr., eds., Norumbega Fault System of the Northern Appalachians: Boulder, Colorado, Geological Society of America Special Paper 331.

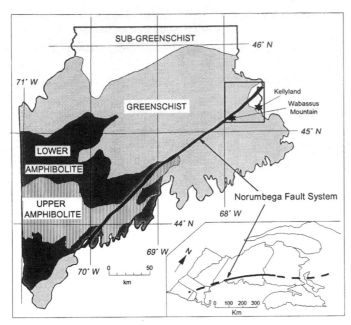

Figure 1. Extent and crustal setting of the Norumbega fault system (NFS). Inset shows extent (solid) and possible extensions (dashed) of the NFS in the northern Appalachians. Modified from Osberg et al. (1985). Main map shows variation in regional metamorphic grade along the NFS in Maine (after Guidotti, 1985).

these bodies be determined for full characterization of the shallow-crustal segment of the fault system.

The Kellyland fault zone is the southernmost high-strain zone of the Norumbega fault system in eastern Maine, and is unusually well exposed where it cuts the Deblois pluton in the vicinity of Wabassus Mountain (Fig. 2). This chapter describes multistage Kellyland fault zone shearing in that pluton and compares faulting in the granite with that in the adjacent metasedimentary rocks to construct a model for the Norumbega fault system at shallow crustal levels. This report is the first detailed description of Norumbega shearing in plutonic rocks, at any crustal level.

Geologic setting

The Norumbega fault system is ~40 km wide in eastern Maine and is hosted mostly by chlorite- and subchlorite-grade metasedimentary rocks of the Fredericton belt, a locus of Late Ordovician through Middle Silurian(?) turbidite deposition (Fig. 2). These strata were folded during Middle to Late Silurian time and then intruded by several plutons before the region was affected by Norumbega fault system faulting (Ludman, 1991; Ludman et al., 1993). Low-grade regional metamorphic assemblages in early to middle Paleozoic strata and unmetamorphosed Carboniferous fault slivers in the Norumbega fault system indicate shallow crustal levels throughout all Norumbega activity in eastern Maine (Ludman, 1991, 1998). Miarolitic cavities in plutons that intrude the Fredericton suite and metamorphic assemblages in their contact aureoles show more precisely that the Bottle Lake, Deblois, and Pocomoonshine plutons (see Fig. 2) were emplaced at pressures ≤1.5–2.5 kbar (Ayuso, 1984; Ludman

et al., 1989). Similar epizonal levels are reported for other Late Silurian and Early Devonian batholiths in eastern Maine and western New Brunswick, including the Lucerne (Wones and Ayuso, 1993) and Pokiok (Rast and Lutes, 1979) plutons. The eastern Maine segment of the Norumbega fault system thus records deformation in the uppermost crust, in contrast with the upper amphibolite regime of south-central and southwestern Maine where mid-crustal depths are documented for most Norumbega fault system shearing (West, 1993, 1995; Swanson, 1992, 1995; Hubbard et al., 1995; West and Hubbard, 1997).

The Norumbega fault system underwent a complex history of recurrent and reactivated dextral strike-slip faulting in eastern Maine, most displacement occurring in two major pulses (Ludman, 1995; Ludman et al., this volume; Ludman, 1998). Stage 1 produced bed-parallel, north-northeast–trending (010°–025°) shear zones that are widely distributed in the Fredericton belt, but strain was strongly localized in pelitic horizons and along bedding planes. Stage 1 spanned the transition from ductile to brittle shearing, apparently accompanying dehydration of the metasedimentary rocks (Ludman, 1998). Stage 2 faults trend more easterly (040°–065°) and formed by mostly brittle processes. Stage 2 strain was partitioned into three high-strain zones here named the Codyville, Waite, and Kellyland fault zones (Fig. 2). Each is 2–5 km wide, contains numerous anastomosing fault strands (Fig. 2), and is separated from the others by broad areas exhibiting little stage 2 strain. It is these stage 2 faults that are generally shown as the Norumbega fault system on regional-scale maps. For example, the geologic map of Maine (Osberg et al., 1985) depicts the system in eastern Maine as two parallel faults now recognized as part of the stage 2 Waite high-strain zone.

The Kellyland fault zone was named after extensive outcrops at the Grand Falls of the St. Croix River at Kellyland (Ludman, 1998). A prominent topographic lineament highlights the Kellyland fault zone for more than 100 km, despite thick glacial deposits that mask lithologic contacts and other structures. In an area where most lakes, sculptured bedrock, and glacial deposits are aligned at 140°, the northeast-trending lowland occupied by the Big Lake flowage stands out dramatically for more than 40 km from the type locality of the Kellyland fault zone to the margin of the Deblois pluton (Fig. 3). A prominent cliff formed by differential erosion of sheared granite and metasedimentary rocks traces the Kellyland fault zone from the north face of Wabassus Mountain to Nicatous Lake, another 60 km to the southwest. It is interesting that the faulted rocks are more resistant to erosion and underlie the higher elevations along this segment.

Geology of the Wabassus Mountain area. Larrabee (1964) and Larrabee et al. (1965) mapped several plutons in eastern Maine and proposed a stratigraphic and structural framework for the region. Most of their interpretations have been revised substantially, but they correctly identified northeast- and northwest-trending faults in the plutons and their host rocks. Ayuso (1984) described the evolution of the Bottle Lake complex, more accurately defined its limits in the Wabassus Mountain area, and recognized a fault contact (now viewed as part of the Waite fault

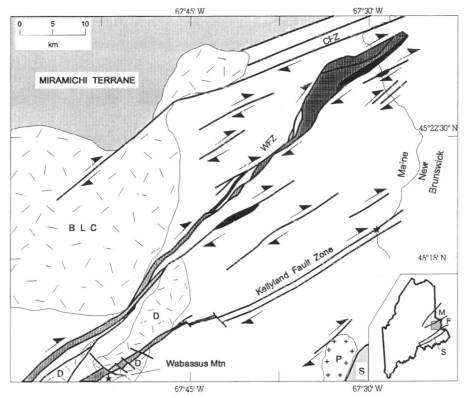

Figure 2. Geologic setting of the Norumbega fault system (NFS) in eastern Maine. Inset shows local lithotectonic framework. Terranes: S—St. Croix: F—Fredericton: M—Miramichi. The NFS in eastern Maine is mostly contained within the Fredericton belt. Main map shows three NFS high-strain zones and individual faults in areas of broadly distributed strain. White area = Fredericton belt, light stipples = pre-Silurian terranes, random dash areas = granite, plus pattern = mafic rocks, dark stipples = NFS mylonites and phyllonites, black = post-Acadian redbeds. BLC = Bottle Lake plutonic complex, D = Deblois pluton, P = Pocomoonshine gabbro-diorite. NFS high-strain zones, Kellyland fault zone: CFZ = Codyville fault zone, WFZ = Waite fault zone.

zone) between it and the Fredericton belt. He assigned granite at Wabassus Mountain to the Lead Mountain pluton and suggested that it was separated by a fault (now the Kellyland fault zone) from yet another granitoid, the Wabassus Lake quartz monzonite. These two bodies were subsequently interpreted as components of the Deblois pluton, the largest post-Acadian batholith in southeastern Maine (Osberg et al., 1985).

Figure 4 is a detailed map of the Wabassus Mountain area based on 1:24,000 scale mapping from 1993 through 1997. The area is underlain by variably calcareous quartzofeldspathic wackes and subordinate slates of the Flume Ridge Formation that have been intruded and thermally metamorphosed to biotite (± actinolite) grade by the Bottle Lake and Deblois plutons. The pluton–host rock contacts shown in Figure 4 are modified significantly from earlier geologic maps, and the cataclasite and mylonite zones in the Waite and Kellyland high-strain zones had not been reported previously. A small sliver of unmetamorphosed red conglomerate in fault contact with the Bottle Lake complex is similar to post-Acadian (Carboniferous?) molasse found elsewhere along the Waite fault zone by Higgins (1992) and Ludman (1991, 1998)

Unusually extensive exposures along lumber roads on the southwest shoulder of Wabassus Mountain provide a nearly complete transect through the Kellyland fault zone where it cuts the northeasternmost apophysis of the Deblois pluton (Fig. 4). Unsheared Flume Ridge hornfels at the south end of this transect was intruded by coarse-grained Deblois granite exhibiting a typical hypidiomorphic granular texture. Strain related to the Kellyland fault zone increases to the north, and progressively more deformed granite passes into ultracataclasite and/or ultramylonite and then into highly deformed Flume Ridge strata. This report describes the mechanics and history of shearing in the Deblois granite, as revealed by a nearly completely exposed portion of the transect (solid line segment in Fig. 4).

Methods

The indicated segment was mapped by pace and compass at a scale of 1:1200 during the summer of 1994; additional detailed mapping was done in adjacent areas in 1995 and 1996. Representative specimens were collected for petrographic analysis and 60 oriented thin sections were prepared,

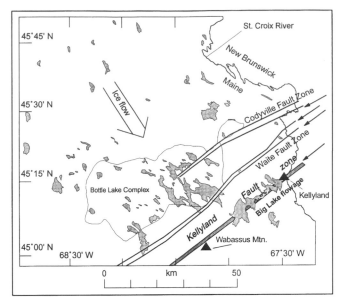

Figure 3. Topographic expression of the Kellyland fault zone. The north-east-trend of the Big Lake flowage differs markedly from the regional northwest-southeast topographic lineaments. Bottle Lake complex is outlined for location in Figure 2. Arrows indicate sharp changes in course of St. Croix River at Norumbega fault system high-strain zones. Shaded areas are lakes.

with pairs made for most specimens perpendicular to foliation and both perpendicular and parallel to the dominant lineation. Selected samples were stained to determine the amount and distribution of potassic feldspar, particularly in fine-grained cataclasite.

KELLYLAND FAULT ZONE AT WABASSUS MOUNTAIN

The study area is underlain almost entirely by the Deblois pluton and by fault rocks generated during shearing. Crosscutting relationships among the granite, fine-grained granitic dikes, cataclasites, and mylonites reveal complex, multistage deformation along the Kellyland fault zone.

Granite of the Deblois pluton. The Deblois pluton in the Wabassus Mountain area is a coarse- to very coarse grained (1.5–6 cm) leucocratic hornblende-biotite granite composed mostly of pink perthitic microcline, white sodic plagioclase, and interstitial quartz. Plagioclase occurs as subhedral to euhedral crystals, as large subhedral inclusions within microcline megacrysts, and as rapakivi rims around microcline. Biotite and hornblende make up as much as 15% of the rock, and biotite is more abundant in the study area. Principal accessory minerals are apatite, zircon, and titanite.

Textural variations permit separation of the pluton near Wabassus Mountain into rim and core facies (Fig. 4) comparable to divisions of the Lucerne pluton to the southwest (Wones and Ayuso, 1993). The rim facies has a coarse grained (1.5–3 cm) hypidiomorphic granular texture and the core facies has a coarse- to very coarse grained (2.0–6.0 cm) appearance with megacrysts of microcline, locally with rapakivi rims, and smaller euhedral crystals of plagioclase. The rim facies grades into the core facies along the transect shown in Fig. 4. The core facies is truncated by the Kellyland fault zone at Wabassus Mountain and does not reappear on the opposite side of the fault zone. Megacrystic Deblois granite crops out in a separate fault-bounded sliver across

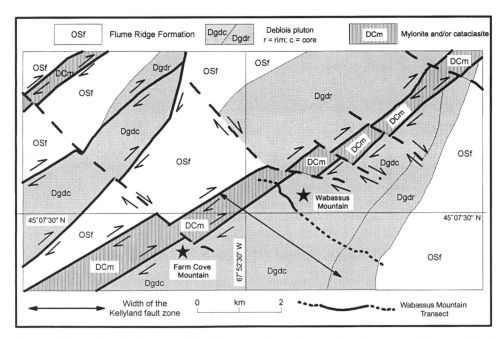

Figure 4. Detailed geologic map of the Wabassus Mountain area. Double arrow indicates width of Kellyland fault zone. Dashed-solid line indicates Wabassus Mountain transect: solid portion is area shown in Figure 9. White (OSf) = Flume Ridge Formation. Coarse stipple (Dgd) = Deblois pluton. Diagonal ruled pattern (DCm) = mylonite and/or cataclasite of Kellyland and Waite fault zones.

the Kellyland fault zone northwest of the study area, apparently on a minor Norumbega fault system fault strand that connects the Kellyland fault zone and Waite high-strain zone (Fig. 4).

Granitic dikes. Two different types of granitic dikes are present, a single pegmatite at the southern margin of the pluton, and several fine-grained dikes. Neither type is abundant in the Deblois pluton, but both have been observed at several places along the eastern margin of the body south of the study area. These dikes appear to be typical late-stage granitic differentiates with chilled margins flanking coarser interiors.

The fine-grained dikes are important in unraveling the deformation history of the Kellyland fault zone because of their relationships with features produced during the multiple fault episodes discussed in the following section (Fig. 5). These dikes are composed of fine-grained (0.5–4 mm), light gray granite and are typically only a few centimeters thick, but one dike 3 m wide crops out in the core facies on Wabassus Mountain. All dikes dip steeply to vertically and their generally random strikes at Wabassus Mountain and elsewhere throughout the pluton suggest little structural control during intrusion. The dikes resemble coarser grained Deblois granite mineralogically, with a few differences: biotite is the only ferromagnesian phase in some specimens; potassic feldspar is gray rather than pink; and plagioclase occurs only as discrete crystals, never as inclusions or as rapakivi rims mantling the microcline.

Fault rocks. Effects of both brittle and ductile shearing are evident in the Deblois pluton. Several varieties of cataclasite crop out in narrow zones throughout the study area, and are distinguished by grain size, orientation, and relationships with the granite and the dikes. Coarse breccias contain porphyroclasts, to 5 mm in diameter, of polymineralic granite fragments, microcline, plagioclase, and ribbon quartz, set in a sparse, fine-grained cataclastic matrix (Fig. 6A). With greater comminution, rocks develop equal amounts of matrix and porphyroclasts, and a distinctive "terrazzo floor" texture (Fig. 6B). Mylonites and ultramylonites at the granite–Flume Ridge contact contain feldspar and ribbon quartz microporphyroclasts in an extremely fine grained matrix (Fig. 6C). More detailed descriptions of these rocks are given in the following, where they are related to individual stages in Kellyland fault zone evolution.

Faults

More than 300 fault and shear surfaces have been measured at Wabassus Mountain, although the two-dimensional nature of the glaciated outcrops makes it difficult to accurately determine more than the trend of many of those surfaces (Fig. 7A). Fault trends define four distinct populations, three of which are also recognizable in a stereonet showing poles to those fault surfaces for which full three-dimensional attitudes could be measured (Fig. 7B). The pavement outcrops make it difficult to find lineations indicating the sense of fault motion, but a few have been identified. These demonstrate dominantly strike-slip motion on three of the four sets of faults (Fig. 7C), and evidence from the

Flume Ridge Formation shows that the fourth set also involved dominantly horizontal movement. Kinematic indicators (discussed in the following), offset foliation, dikes, and cataclasite veins indicate that populations 1, 2, and 3 are dextral strike-slip faults, and that faults of the fourth group are sinistral.

Consistent crosscutting relationships show that the four groups of faults represent distinct events (stages 1 through 4) in the evolution of the study area. The evidence is summarized in Figure 8, a photograph of an outcrop (the Wabassus Mountain "Rosetta Stone") in which the critical age relationships are readily observed. The unfoliated dike in Figure 8 intrudes Deblois granite exhibiting typical 020° trending stage 1 foliation. A narrow stage 2 fault zone, trending 045° and filled with fine-grained cataclasite, offsets the granite-dike contact dextrally. Finally, the stage 2 fault was offset dextrally by a 290° trending stage 3 fault zone that contains mostly very fine grained cataclasite containing pods with coarser "terrazzo floor" fabric. The dike thus predates stage 2, and the absence of foliation indicates that it is postkinematic with respect to stage 1. It is inferred to have been emplaced during a static, strain-free interval separating the two fault episodes. This interval was long enough for the core facies granite to cool from conditions permitting the partly ductile, partly brittle stage 1 deformation to those requiring totally brittle shearing during stage 2 (see following).

Different strain gradients for stages 1, 2, and 3 in the best-exposed part of the transect confirm that these stages were separate events (Fig. 9). Although both stage 1 and stage 2 strain increase northward along the transect from the contact with the Flume Ridge Formation, the readily discernible differences are shown in Figure 9. The stage 3 gradient was subsequently superimposed across the stage 1 and stage 2 gradients. Different fault mechanisms characterize each stage of faulting, and will be described in detail in the next sections.

Stage 1. Initial shearing in the Wabassus Mountain area produced the penetrative foliation that characterizes the Deblois pluton along the strike of the Kellyland fault zone. The granite was converted from the homogeneous material typical of the batholith to a strongly anisotropic rock with a penetrative foliation defined by quartz ribbons that flow around the feldspar megacrysts and, to a lesser extent, by aligned biotite flakes (Fig. 10A). Quartz microfabrics in these ribbons, the lack of foliation in the rim facies at the Flume Ridge contact, and the irregular intensification of foliation northward from the contact into the core facies demonstrate clearly that the foliation is the result of faulting rather than a primary igneous contact phenomenon. The intensity of stage 1 foliation varies across the Kellyland fault zone but its orientation remains relatively constant, striking within a few degrees of 020° (Fig. 7A). Exceptions occur in small-scale drag folds adjacent to stage 2 and stage 3 shear zones and in larger folds near the fault contact with the Flume Ridge Formation. Two-dimensional outcrops and its anastomosing nature make it difficult to measure the dip of the foliation, but it appears to be steep, deviating only about 15° from vertical.

Fine-grained granite dikes crop out in areas of moderate and

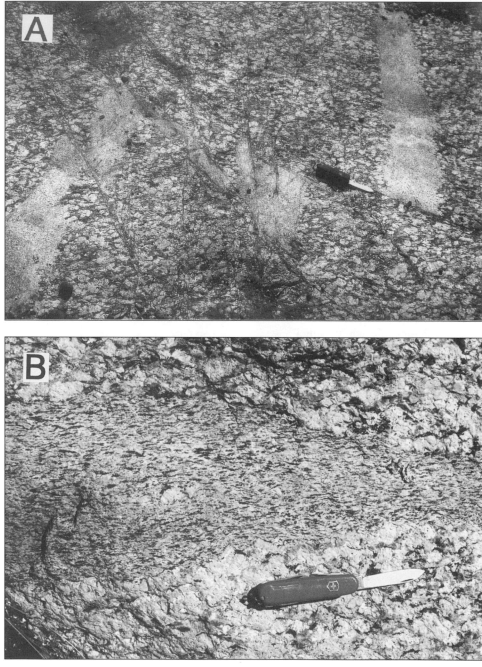

Figure 5. Fine-grained granitic dikes at Wabassus Mountain. A: Unfoliated (post-stage 1) dike cutting stage 1 foliation. Knife is 15.5 cm long. B: Mylonitized dike with foliation parallel to foliation in host granite: interpreted as synkinematic with respect to stage 1 shearing. Knife is 15.5 cm long.

high stage 1 strain on Wabassus Mountain, and have diverse relationships with stage 1 fabric (Fig. 5). Dikes that are unfoliated and cut sharply across stage 1 foliation are clearly postkinematic with respect to stage 1 shearing (Fig. 5A). Others that are oriented randomly but have a strong foliation parallel to stage 1 fabric in the host granite are interpreted as prekinematic with respect to stage 1 (Fig 5B). A few dikes having margins parallel to stage 1 foliation are also strongly foliated. These may have

been synkinematic, their intrusion partially controlled by already existing stage 1 foliation and their foliation imparted by continued stage 1 shearing. The varied relationships with foliation suggest that dike emplacement began prior to stage 1, persisted throughout stage 1 activity, and continued after that activity had ceased (see Ludman et al., this volume).

Stage 1 strain distribution. Stage 1 strain gradients are indicated by changes in fabric along the transect, particularly in the

Figure 6. Fault rocks in the Deblois pluton associated with the Kellyland fault zone. A: Coarse-grained cataclasite. B: Fine-grained cataclasite. C: Mylonite and ultramylonite. Coin is 8 mm.

appearance of quartz. Strain is partitioned inhomogeneously, with local zones of high strain interspersed with low strain areas. Figure 9B shows the map-scale variations; small-scale fluctuations, on the order of 1 m, can only be shown schematically. Three levels of increasing stage 1 strain are identified in the

granite, corresponding to progressively more intense stages of deformation as described by Hirth and Tullis (1992) and dePaor and Simpson (1993).

Interstitial quartz in the deformed rim facies granite shows development of a few subgrains by irregular sweeping extinction, but exhibits neither grain-shape- nor lattice-preferred orientation (Fig. 10B). These low-strain stage 1 features are typical of lower regime 2 quartz microfabrics as described by Hirth and Tullis (1992). Feldspars are unchanged from their original igneous textures. With increased (moderate) strain, quartz grains coalesce to form ribbons in which relatively coarse domains display strong grain-shape-preferred orientation but lack any lattice-preferred orientation (Fig. 10C). These ribbons anastomose around microcline and plagioclase crystals that show little evidence of deformation, although some albite twin lamellae are brittlely offset or kinked. More extensive layer-normal shortening has occurred in zones of highest stage 1 strain, with striking grain-shape preferred orientation and the beginnings of lattice-preferred orientations in ribbon quartz (Fig. 10D). Elongate domains in the ribbons display the sweeping extinction of higher strain realms of regime 2 of Hirth and Tullis (1992). Feldspars are also elongated and some develop polycrystalline fabrics leading to incipient corona structures. The small recrystallized grains visible along many domain boundaries in the quartz ribbons suggest partial recovery by dynamic recrystallization and/or healing along late-stage fractures.

A few anomalous zones of apparently entirely ductile deformation are associated with the narrow stage 1 high-strain zones shown schematically in Figure 9B. Grain size is greatly reduced, the tiny biotite flakes are strongly foliated, and both quartz and feldspars appear to have been deformed ductilely to produce a fine-grained mylonitic fabric. These bands of more ductile deformation are typically discontinuous, only a few centimeters across, and parallel the dominant stage 1 foliation. Like the foliation, they are truncated by stage 2 and stage 3 cataclasite. The small mylonite bands pass gradationally into the foliation with a gradual increase in grain size, suggesting that they represent atypical stage 1 conditions. The particular combination of strain rate, fluid pressure, and temperature that produced these zones is not known, but is the subject of ongoing research.

A covered area ~100 m wide separates granite on Wabassus Mountain from phyllonite to the north generated from the Flume Ridge Formation. Exposures on Farm Cove Mountain to the southwest fill this gap and complete the transect through the Kellyland fault zone (Fig. 4). The southernmost outcrops at Farm Cove Mountain are a continuation of the south to north sequence of moderate- and high-strain stage 1 fabrics seen on Wabassus Mountain. These persist until the north face of Farm Cove Mountain, where they are dragged into a more easterly orientation and then overprinted by stage 2 mylonite and ultramylonite that separate the granite from the Flume Ridge Formation.

Nature of stage 1 deformation. Stage 1 strain was broadly distributed in granite across the 3.5 km width of the Kellyland fault zone, generally increasing toward the contact with the Flume

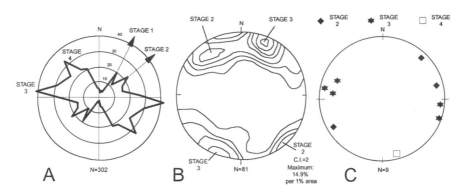

Figure 7. Faults and fault-related lineations at Wabassus Mountain. A: Rose diagram showing trends of all shear surfaces identified at Wabassus Mountain (solid line segment in Fig. 4). B: Contoured (C.I. = contour interval) stereonet (lower hemisphere) showing poles to measurable shear surfaces. C: Stereonet of lineations on shear surfaces, demonstrating subhorizontal nature of motion during shearing stages 2, 3, and 4.

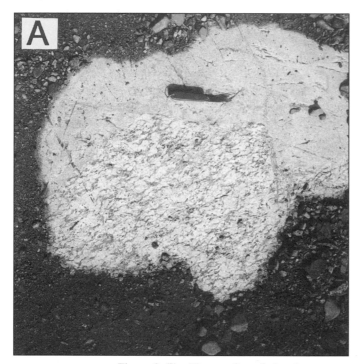

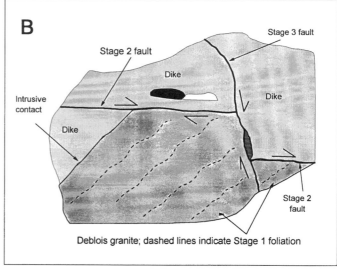

Figure 8. The "Rosetta Stone" showing sequence of fault events. A: Photograph. B: Interpretation (see text for explanation).

Ridge Formation. The most dramatic foliation is in rocks of the core facies, but low-strain stage 1 features are also observed in the rim facies at the southern part of the transect, showing that strain distribution was not controlled by textural variations. Apparently coeval stage 1 faulting along the Kellyland fault zone in the metasedimentary rocks was episodic (Ludman, 1998), and the complex dike history at Wabassus Mountain suggests similarly sporadic stage 1 deformation in the Deblois pluton.

The strikingly different behaviors of quartz and feldspars during stage 1 indicate shearing near the brittle-ductile transition for the Deblois pluton. Experimental studies of quartz

aggregates by Hirth and Tullis (1992) suggest relatively dry conditions, low temperatures, and high strain rates for the stage 1 quartz microfabrics. Ambient temperatures of ~250–350° C are estimated for stage 1 shearing based on estimated temperature calibration of these fabrics by dePaor and Simpson (1994), and were probably in the lower part of this range (possibly below 300 °C; J. Tullis, personal commun., 1996). Thus, enough time had elapsed after intrusion for even the core facies of the granite to cool to these temperatures before faulting began. Because the pluton intruded at very shallow levels of the crust where cooling was presumably rapid, the age of the

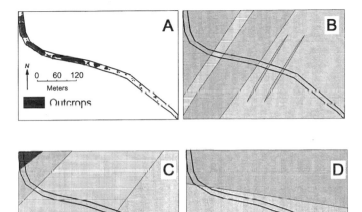

Figure 9. Kellyland fault zone strain gradients at Wabassus Mountain. A: Outcrop control for following maps. B: Stage 1 strain (increasing darkness indicates increasing strain). C: Stage 2 strain. D: Stage 3 strain.

Deblois pluton thus approximates the onset of stage 1 (see Ludman et al., this volume).

Outcrop- and microscopic-scale kinematic indicators, including asymmetric (σ) microcline and plagioclase porphyroclasts, dextral shear bands, and dextrally deformed lenses of granite, confirm dextral shear for stage 1 throughout the transect. Although widely distributed, these indicators are not very abundant and most porphyroclasts are symmetrical. This fact and intense foliation-normal shortening evidenced in the high- and moderate-strain zones suggest that stage 1 deformation may have had a large component of coaxial strain.

The rarity of late-stage veins, absence of hydrothermally altered host rock, and the low degree of deuteric alteration in both facies of the pluton suggest that fluids did not play a significant role in stage 1 deformation. The feldspars and ferromagnesian minerals of the sheared Deblois pluton are remarkably unaltered and are more pristine than minerals in many other undeformed granitoids in southeastern Maine. If fluids were abundant, they did not interact with the rock during either cooling or stage 1 shearing.

The cool, dry, shallow conditions indicated for this earliest activity along the Kellyland fault zone serve as a reference point for the environment of subsequent fault stages. In the absence of evidence for tectonic overthrusting, deep burial beneath Carboniferous molasse, or additional plutonism along the Kellyland fault zone, stages 2, 3, and 4 must have taken place during continued post-Acadian exhumation at even cooler and lower pressure conditions than stage 1.

Stage 2. The second stage of activity created the Kellyland fault zone, sensu stricto. The most intense stage 2 effects in the fault zone are recorded at the northern end of the transect, northwest of Wabassus and Farm Cove Mountains (Fig. 4). They include offset of the Deblois pluton, deformation of stage

1 foliation, and overprinting stage 1 fabrics with cataclasite, mylonite, and ultramylonite. Most of the study area, however, underwent only low to moderate stage 2 strain, and its effects on the granite are less impressive than the widespread stage 1 foliation. Thus, evidence for stage 2 shearing on most of the Wabassus Mountain transect consists of narrow cataclasite-filled shear zones ranging from a few millimeters to a few centimeters wide. These zones maintain a nearly constant attitude along the transect, striking within a few degrees of 040° and dipping very steeply to vertically. Exceptions are in small-scale drag folds adjacent to stage 3 faults.

Most outcrop-scale stage 2 faults are straight, planar features that truncate stage 1 foliation and some granitic dikes as shown in Figure 8. Their dextral strike-slip character is confirmed on the regional scale by ~8 km of dextral separation of the eastern margin of the Deblois pluton (Fig. 2; see Ludman et al., this volume). Small-scale stage 2 faults in the pluton mirror this sense of motion with dextrally dragged stage 1 foliation, particularly where it is caught between two stage 2 shear zones, dextrally offset dikes and foliation surfaces, and a few asymmetric or rotated microporphyroclasts in the cataclasite and mylonite.

Stage 2 shear zones are typically filled with fine-grained (0.5 mm to 10 μm cataclasite; Fig. 11A), although coarser varieties are also common, with porphyroclasts of feldspar, stage 1 ribbon quartz, and polymineralic granite fragments (Fig. 11B). Alternating light (coarse) and dark (fine) layers shown in Figure 11A indicate grain-size variation rather than compositional segregation. Cataclasite typically occurs in coherent veins traceable for several meters, but many splay into complex horsetail terminations or pass into spidery zones of diffuse strain in which microveins anastomose irregularly through the host granite (Fig. 11C). In the more coherent zones, subsidiary hairline faults and cataclasite microveins show Riedel shear relationships to the main cataclasite. Interaction between stage 2 cataclasite and stage 1 foliation locally creates what appears to be an S-C fabric (Fig. 11A), but different fault mechanics (ductile behavior to form stage 1 quartz ribbons, brittle deformation to form ribbon quartz porphyroclasts in the catclasite) show that these are more appropriately attributed to separate fault episodes.

Stage 2 strain distribution. Unfoliated granite and Flume Ridge hornfels at the south end of the transect show no evidence of stage 2 shearing. Low-strain stage 2 effects first appear within the zone of lowest stage 1 strain as sparse, irregularly spaced brittle faults and very rare cataclasite veins 1–5 mm thick. A few stage 2 fault surfaces in this zone are polished and contain subhorizontal slickenlines. Thicker cataclasite-filled bands (5 mm to 2.5 cm) become more abundant and more close-spaced toward the north, cutting low- and high-strain stage 1 domains. Stage 2 strain increases northward like that associated with stage 1 but, as indicated earlier, the stage 2 strain gradient overprints different levels of stage 1 strain (Fig. 9C).

Moderate strain is inferred where stage 2 cataclasite packages as wide as 1 m (Fig. 12) occur near the boundary between high and moderate stage 1 strain. Farther north, in the zone of

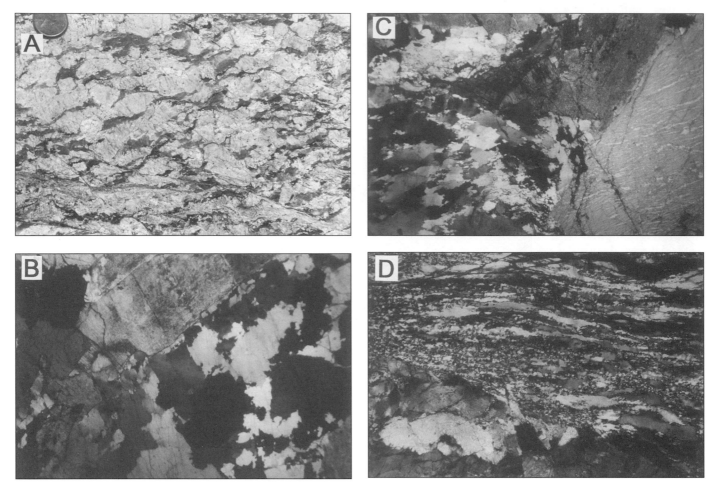

Figure 10. Fabrics indicating stage 1 strain. A: Photograph showing stage 1 foliation in high-strain region; stage 2 cataclasite is at bottom of photograph. B–D: Photomicrographs of quartz microfabrics showing increasing stage 1 strain. Crossed polarizers and 8.5 mm field width in all. B: Subgrains and domains in quartz from lowest stage 1 strain realm lacking grain-shape-preferred orientation. Note brittle behavior of adjacent feldspars (width = 8.5 mm). C: Strong grain-shape-preferred orientation but little change in feldspars (width = 8.5 mm). D: Intense grain-shape-preferred orientation and moderate lattice-preferred orientation in quartz, flattening and fracturing in feldspar. Small recrystallized grains indicate partial recovery in ribbon quartz bands.

chaos created by intersection of stage 2 and 3 shear zones, stage 2 cataclasites are even more abundant and closely-spaced, but individual shear zones are more diffuse and are cut by equally diffuse stage 3 cataclasites, resulting in the weblike pattern shown in Figure 10C. Moderate strain persists less chaotically northwestward to the mylonites at Farm Cove Mountain.

The most intense stage 2 strain is restricted to a narrow zone of mylonite and ultramylonite, locally as wide as 100 m and as narrow as 25–50 m, in contact with Flume Ridge phyllonite at the north end of the transect (Fig. 4). The mylonite is a dense, thinly laminated rock containing light (pale gray to white) and dark (gray) laminae 1–4 mm thick (Fig. 13A). The lighter (coarser) bands contain microcline and albite porphyroclasts and strongly elongate quartz ribbons and ribbon fragments with a moderate to strongly developed lattice-preferred orientation (Fig. 13B). The larger porphyroclasts are highly fractured and typically angular;

the smaller ones are better rounded. Darker laminae are much finer grained (1–5 µm) with a well-developed foliation that wraps around smaller, generally more rounded feldspar porphyroclasts.

The ultramylonite is a very dense, vitreous rock that fractures conchoidally, is strongly foliated and very finely laminated, and contains only a few microporphyroclasts embedded in an extremely fine grained matrix (Fig. 13, C and D). Color is more uniform than that of the mylonite, generally dark greenish-gray, but darker gray laminae only fractions of a millimeter thick are discernible in the field and in thin section. This color variation is in part compositional, the dark laminae containing concentrations of anhedral carbonate, and in part textural, dark laminae being finer grained than the lighter bands. Microporphyroclasts are typically well rounded and some have developed σ-type asymmetric tails.

Interlayered on a microscopic scale with the ultramylonites are thin bands of relatively coarse grained cataclasite (Fig. 13D) that would be considered typical of fine-grained stage 2 cataclasite elsewhere along the transect. Neither the angular microporphyroclasts of feldspars and ribbon quartz nor the fine-grained matrix exhibit the foliation or flow pattern of adjacent mylonite and ultramylonite laminae in the same thin section. These microbreccias are tentatively interpreted as representing seismic events in these shallow crustal rocks.

Nature of stage 2 deformation. Widespread brittle behavior of all minerals is indicated for low- to moderate-strain stage 2 shearing in the Deblois granite. Quartz that had responded ductilely in forming stage 1 ribbons was broken into coarse porphyroclasts and comminuted further to produce the fine-grained cataclasite matrix. All fine-grained dikes responded brittlely to stage 2 faults, including the synkinematic mylonitized varieties that had behaved ductilely during stage 1. This is what would be expected for recurring shearing in a pluton undergoing progressive cooling and exhumation.

Stage 2 mylonite and ultramylonite exhibit the combination of ductile and brittle features characteristic of what Passchier and Trouw (1996) termed low-grade mylonites, including stepped fragmented grains exhibiting both synthetic and antithetic microfaults (Fig. 13D). Some ductile fabric elements were clearly inherited from stage 1, e.g., the oriented subgrains of ribbon quartz bands and porphyroclasts. In general, the finer the grain size, the more ductile the appearance. Small porphyroclasts and the matrix in the darker mylonite bands appear to have undergone bulk ductile behavior, as have asymmetric (σ) porphyroclasts and matrix in the ultramylonite, but interlayered coarser cataclasite is clearly brittle. Large feldspar and ribbon quartz porphyroclasts in light bands of the mylonite are fractured and offset, reflecting the brittle behavior characteristic of the lower strain environments.

The question arises as to the degree to which grain size reduction in the mylonite and ultramylonite was accomplished by ductile recrystallization, a requirement in most recent definitions of these terms (e.g., Tullis et al., 1982; Passchier and Trouw, 1996). Brittle comminution dominated the low- and intermediate-strain realms during stage 2 shearing, and it is possible that the rocks called mylonites and ultramylonites in the field were also produced brittlely, and should therefore be more accurately called cataclasites and ultracataclasites. Continued milling of the original granite may have produced an ultra-fine-grained cataclasite matrix capable of supporting cataclastic flow and rounding the remaining porphyroclasts. The low temperatures and pressures interpreted for stage 1 and subsequent stage 2 shearing make this an attractive hypothesis, but identification of the deformation mechanism(s) in these very fine grained rocks is beyond the scope of petrographic studies. Scanning electron microscopy will be utilized in an attempt to resolve this question.

Similar problems of "cold" mylonitization are reported from the mid-crustal segment of the Norumbega fault system, where narrow zones of mylonite and ultramylonite were superimposed on older strain gradients (West, 1993, 1995; Ludman and West, 1996). West (1993) and West and Lux (1993) demonstrated that the narrow zones of most intense mylonitization were not coeval

with the broad region of earlier (ductile in that area) Norumbega fault system deformation, but formed as much as 80 m.y. later. On the basis of the brittle aspects of the high-strain mylonites, West and Hubbard (1997) suggested that mylonitization occurred after exhumation, at much shallower levels than the initial Norumbega shearing in that region.

A similar picture has emerged in eastern Maine. Multiple reactivation of faults correlated with stage 2 shearing is well documented in turbidites in the Kellyland fault zone and in the Waite fault zone (Ludman, 1998; Ludman et al., this volume). Some of the late-stage events are clearly post-Carboniferous, as the faults offset rocks of Pennsylvanian age in New Brunswick (McLeod et al., 1994). It is thus possible that, as in the deeper segment of the Norumbega fault system, the mylonite and ultramylonite may not have been coeval with the brittle deformation that defines stage 2 shearing throughout most of the study area. This does not resolve the mylonitization problem, but exacerbates it, because an additional 80 m.y. of exhumation would presumably move the granite even farther from conditions under which ductile mylonitization is expected.

Fluids were not important in the stage 2 brittle shearing that characterizes most of the area, but may have been a factor in the ductile behavior adjacent to the Flume Ridge Formation. Minimal alteration of stage 2 cataclasite veins indicates that zones of stage 2 cataclasis were not pathways for fluid during or after stage 2 shearing. As discussed herein, an environment cooler (i.e., <300 °C), higher in the crust, and apparently as dry as that associated with stage 1 is indicated for stage 2 shearing in the granite.

Stage 3. Stage 3 shear zones are widely spaced, thin bands of cataclasite that cut and offset stage 1 foliation, stage 2 cataclasite bands, and granitic dikes. Stage 3 cataclasite zones are typically finer grained and darker than those of stage 2, although the relatively coarse "terrazzo floor" fabric is best developed in stage 3 faults. Very fine grained, almost black stage 3 cataclasite crops out near the northern end of the traverse. Stage 3 cataclasites in the zone of chaos are unique in that they are green as the result of extensive alteration in which chlorite has not only replaced all biotite and hornblende, but has also grown as tiny crystallites in areas bordering cataclasite veins.

Stage 3 cataclasite-filled shear zones are typically mappable for tens of meters along strike and range in strike from 270°–325°, but most cluster around 290°. In the zone of chaos, however, short coherent segments <1 m long pass rapidly into diffuse patches and can not be traced continuously. Northwest-trending map-scale faults shown by Larrabee (1964) and Larrabee et al. (1965) are assigned to stage 3, and parallel several large elongate lake basins excavated by glaciers in the Deblois and Bottle Lake plutons. The alignment of these lakes deviates by about 20° from regional glacial striation patterns, suggesting that they result from preferential erosion along stage 3 faults.

Stage 3 strain distribution. Stage 3 faults and cataclasite-filled shear zones are found throughout the traverse and have also been recognized in the otherwise unfaulted Deblois granite outside the Kellyland fault zone. They increase in abundance toward

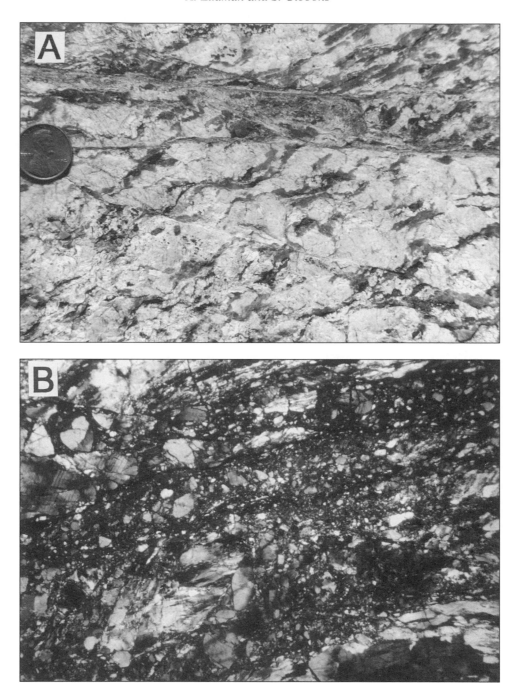

Figure 11 (above and opposite page). Stage 2 cataclasite. A: Fine-grained cataclasite vein cutting stage 1 foliation. Lens cap is 5.0 cm. B: Photomicrograph of stage 2 cataclasite containing porphyroclasts of ribbon quartz, feldspars, and lithic fragments. Width of field = 8.5 mm, crossed polarizers. C: Photograph of the "zone of chaos" resulting from intersection of diffuse stage 2 and 3 cataclasite veins. Hammer is 33 cm long.

the north (Fig. 9D) and are most common in the zone of chaos, leading to the diffuse weblike pattern of microveins that permeates the granite. This pattern suggests an approach to a high-strain stage 3 shear-zone, located just northeast of the transect where phyllonites derived from the Flume Ridge Formation appear to have been displaced (Fig. 4). Larrabee et al. (1965) also

mapped a (stage 3) fault in precisely this location, locating it along steep-walled lowlands that parallel stage 3 trends.

Nature of stage 3 faulting. Cataclasite fabrics described here indicate entirely brittle processes for stage 3 shearing. Progressive milling from foliated granite to the "terrazzo floor" texture, to increasingly fine grained cataclasite and ultracatacl-

asite represent brittle deformation under progressively increasing shear strain.

Stage 4. Stage 4 faults are ubiquitous throughout the study area, appearing in most exposures as steeply dipping hairline fractures and brittle faults trending 335°–350° that crosscut and offset all lithologies and structures. Although widespread and abundant, they are not as prominent as features of stages 2 and 3 shearing because they lack the cataclasite produced by those events and displace the earlier structures by only a few millimeters to a few centimeters. Their sinistral sense of displacement distinguishes stage 4 faults from other structures in the region. They appear to postdate the other episodes and may be totally unrelated to the Kellyland and Norumbega fault zones.

SUMMARY OF KELLYLAND FAULT ZONE HISTORY IN THE DEBLOIS PLUTON

The Deblois pluton intruded previously folded strata of the Flume Ridge Formation and cooled from its liquidus temperature to ~300 °C before the first dextral faulting began. Stage 1 shearing then converted the otherwise massive granite to an anisotropic, strongly foliated rock with foliation increasing in intensity toward the northwest. Granitic dikes intruded the foliated pluton during and after stage 1 shearing. The pluton then cooled further, to temperatures lower than those at which it and the dikes could deform ductilely (although the mylonites and ultramylonites may suggest otherwise). Stage 2 shearing was initiated only after the youngest dikes had cooled to this threshold. Although the environment was one of dextral strike slip, the shear couple had rotated to a more easterly direction than that involved in stage 1 shearing and the lithic anisotropy produced during stage 1 did not significantly affect stage 2 fault geometry or strain localization.

After additional exhumation, stage 3 shearing affected all lithologies brittlely, including cataclasites produced during stage 2 shearing. Stage 4 faulting followed later.

Faults observed in the Flume Ridge Formation in the Waite fault zone parallel those of stages 3 and 4, but are mutually crosscutting and have been interpreted as a conjugate set associated with northwest-southeast compression. Stage 3 and 4 faults in the granite might be a conjugate set, but their grossly different abundances, state of development, and consistent age relationships argue against this interpretation.

Fluid-rock interaction was apparently insignificant during most of this history, with only minor alteration of ferromagnesian minerals in the granite during stage 3 faulting. This is in marked contrast to extensive effects of fluids in the Bottle Lake pluton where it is cut by the (stage 2) Waite fault zone, including widespread saussuritization of plagioclase, kaolinization of potassic feldspar, and injection of epidote-rich veins into phyllonite and ultracataclasite.

DISCUSSION

Figure 14 summarizes the episodic evolution inferred for the Kellyland fault zone in the Deblois granite and compares it with that deduced for metasedimentary rocks along strike at the Kellyland type locality (Ludman, 1998). Constraints on the absolute ages and duration of these events are presented elsewhere in this volume by Ludman et al.

Marked similarities in Kellyland fault zone evolution in the Deblois granite and its metasedimentary host rocks permit direct correlation of its early stages, and thus make it possible to assess the effects of shearing on the different lithologies in the shallow crustal environment of eastern Maine. In both pluton and host

Figure 12. Isolated zone of intense stage 2 strain. Part of a meter-wide zone of very fine-grained cataclasite bands within area otherwise typical of low-strain stage 2 features. Unfoliated dike is at bottom of photograph. Coin is 8 mm.

The different lithologies at the two localities led to different behavior during faulting, particularly with regard to stage 1; e.g., stage 1 shearing created anisotropy in the Deblois pluton at Wabassus Mountain, but strain was broadly distributed across the pluton in the Kellyland fault zone and its gradient directly reflects regional-scale strain. At Kellyland, strong anisotropy existed in the interbedded metawackes and metapelites prior to stage 1 shearing, and controlled strain distribution in the Fredericton belt so that most strain was accommodated along bedding planes and in pelitic horizons. Pressure solution was an important mechanism in stage 1 deformation in mica-rich wackes and pelites but not in the granite, where crystal plastic deformation of quartz (dislocation climb and/or creep) and brittle deformation of feldspars occurred. Thus, the abundant phyllosilicate minerals at least partially controlled stage 1 strain localization and deformation mechanisms in the metasedimentary rocks, whereas the behavior of quartz ultimately controlled deformation in granite.

Grain-size differences also caused different behavior in granite and stratified rocks. Stage 1 foliation in the granite anastomoses on a small scale around individual microcline megacrysts, whereas the anastomosing stage 1 shear zones at Kellyland are controlled by larger scale bedding features. Thrust faulting associated with stage 1 transpression at Kellyland was not recognized at Wabassus Mountain, but this may result from the two-dimensional nature of the outcrop.

Stage 2 effects were similar in granite and metasedimentary rocks. Cataclasite bands and sharply defined faults developed in both, and previously existing anisotropy—bedding, stage 1 foliation, or shear zones—had little effect on the orientation, geometry, or mechanics of shearing. The most intense stage 2 strain produced phyllonite from Flume Ridge strata and mylonite and/or ultramylonite from the granite. The stage 2 cataclasites differ mineralogically, as would be expected from the different protoliths. Those in the metasedimentary rocks are calcareous and are more soluble than the wackes and pelites from which they formed. Granite-derived cataclasite is noncalcareous and some is more resistant to erosion than the undeformed pluton. This differential erodability of cataclasites caused the stage 2 topographic lineament that traces the Kellyland fault zone for more than 100 km.

Shearing attributed to stages 3 and 4 at Wabassus Mountain was not recognized as such at Kellyland. There are no west-northwest–trending (stage 3) dextral shear zones at the latter locality, perhaps because strain at that stage of development was accommodated along previously existing stage 1 or stage 2 shear zones. Several late northwest-trending fractures were measured there, but these displayed neither the dextral stage 3 nor sinistral stage 4 offset seen at Wabassus Mountain.

The intimate association of brittle and ductile features in stage 1 and stage 2 remains problematical. Although similar relationships are reported from many fault zones, they are typically attributed to late-stage brittle deformation superimposed on early ductile shearing or to deformation at conditions at the brittle-ductile transition, where both types of behaviors are possible

rock, early (north-northeast–trending stage 1) shearing was accomplished by a combination of ductile and brittle processes and was followed by more easterly trending brittle faulting. A static, strain-free period separated these two stages of deformation in both rock types (Ludman, 1998; Ludman et al., this volume). Further similarities in strain distribution and sense of displacement indicate that deformation stages 1 and 2 at Wabassus Mountain are equivalent to the two main shearing events at Kellyland, and can be ascribed to the entire Kellyland fault zone.

The composite picture is more complete than one derived from either lithology. For example, metasedimentary rocks at Kellyland more clearly document the episodic nature of stages 1 and 2, and the localized strain heating and changes attributed to progressive dehydration permit more detailed understanding of stage 1 shearing than is possible at Wabassus Mountain (Ludman, 1998). The longer Wabassus Mountain transect, however, provides more complete insight into the range, maximum intensity, and partitioning of stage 2 strain.

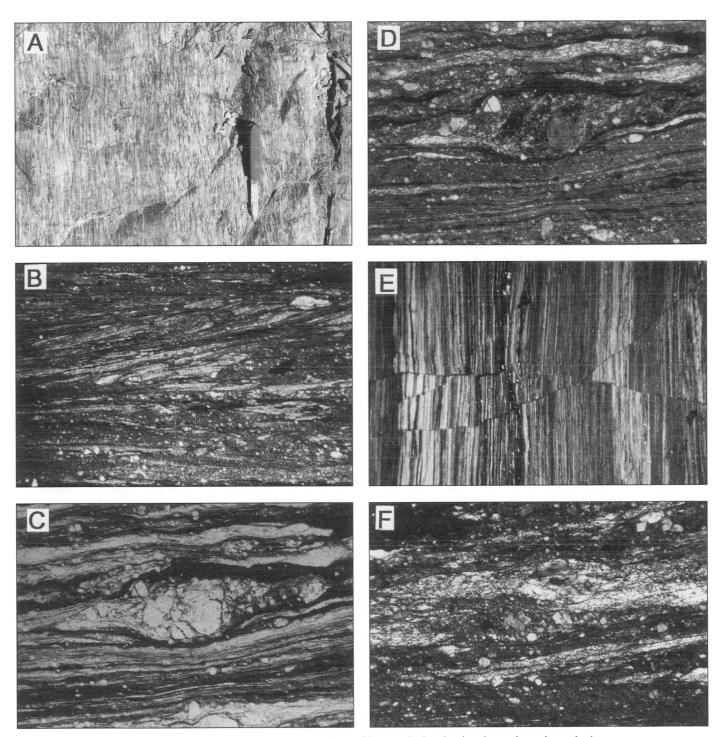

Figure 13. Stage 2 mylonite and ultramylonite. A: Photograph showing interlayered streaky mylonite and (at base of knife) ultramylonite. Knife is 15.5 cm long. B–F: Photomicrographs of mylonite and ultramylonite. Width of fields = 8.5 mm. B: S-C mylonite. Crossed polarizers. C, D: Large feldspar porphyroclast showing brittle internal fracturing. c = plane polarized, d = crossed polarizers. E: Ultramylonite with layering cut by stage 3 conjugate microfaults. Uncrossed polarizers. F: Band of angular cataclasite within the mylonite.

	Deblois pluton (this study)		Fredericton belt (Ludman, 1998)
Stage 4	Sinistral shearing produces faults oriented 340°-350°		Fractures (no consistent offset sense) oriented 340°-350°
Stage 3	Dextral shearing produces faults oriented 290°-310° (fine-grained cataclasite)		Fractures (no consistent offset sense) oriented 290°-310°
Stage 2	Dextral shearing produces brittle 040°-060° faults (fine-grained cataclasite; mylonite and ultramylonite)		Dextral shearing produces brittle 040°-060° faults (fine-grained cataclasite and coarse fault breccia)
	Strain-free interval		Strain-free interval
Stage 1	Recurrent shearing on 020° faults and foliation surfaces 020° dextral shearing produces foliation	Episodic dike intrusion / Episodic quartz veining and Felsite dikes	Recurrent activity on 020° faults Recurrent activity on 020° faults 020° dextral shearing produces bed-parallel faults

Figure 14. Comparison of Kellyland fault zone shearing in the Deblois pluton and metasedimentary rocks of the Fredericton belt.

(e.g., Hadizadeh et al., 1991). Neither explanation satisfactorily explains the observed stage 1 features, suggesting mylonitization at cool, shallow-crustal conditions by processes not yet fully understood or, alternatively, ultracataclasis.

Questions also remain concerning the precise relationship between stages 1 and 2; although stage 1 fabrics are found throughout the Fredericton belt, they are observed in the Deblois granite only in the stage 2 Kellyland fault zone. Thus, whereas the evidence presented here shows that the two were separate events, this relationship suggests that stages 1 and 2 at Wabassus Mountain were both related to the Kellyland fault zone and that stage 1 fabrics in the Fredericton metasedimentary rocks had a similar association with the other Norumbega high strain zones. In the larger picture, stages 1 and 2 were simply stages in the development of the northeast-trending Norumbega fault system. Stage 1 at Wabassus Mountain may represent part of an S-C fabric associated with the earliest faulting in the Kellyland fault zone, but stage 2 activity, at different temperatures and/or strain rate, has obliterated the initially associated S surfaces. In addition, the extent to which the current relationships reflect late Paleozoic reactivation of the Kellyland fault zone (Ludman et al., 1998) is not yet fully understood.

CONCLUSIONS

Epizonal granite at Wabassus Mountain records a complex four-stage deformation history where it is cut by the Kellyland fault zone, the southernmost high-strain zone in the Norumbega fault system in eastern Maine. Initial deformation took place near the brittle-ductile transition for the granite, but later shearing was accomplished by almost entirely brittle processes; the change was probably related to progressive cooling and unroofing of the pluton. Fluids appear to have played at most a very minor role in shearing of the granite. The multiple faulting history described here is compatible with evolution within the regional Norumbega fault system dextral strike-slip system, and indicates that the

Norumbega fault system extends far beyond the limited area shown on the state geologic map (Osberg et al., 1985).

The two earliest stages of shearing at Wabassus Mountain are equivalent to Kellyland fault zone events in metasedimentary rocks at its type locality, and evidence for these events is widespread throughout the Norumbega fault system in the Fredericton belt. The supracrustal segment of the Norumbega fault system thus evolved through a series of sporadic faulting episodes in a dextral shear couple that rotated from an initial north-northeast orientation to a more easterly attitude with time.

The evolution of deeper crustal segments of the Norumbega fault system was comparably complex, but differs in several important details. Uniform fabric orientations and ductile mechanisms along the Norumbega fault system in southwestern Maine contrast sharply with the multiple fault generations and orientations characteristic of the epizonal segment. More continuous displacement is inferred for the deeper levels (West and Hubbard, 1997; West, this volume), in contrast to the sporadic activity described here and by Ludman (1998). Strain is now well characterized at both levels but shows significant differences. First, most fault mechanisms reported from the deeper segment are ductile (West, 1993; Swanson, 1992), rather than the combination of ductile and brittle processes observed in eastern Maine. Strain partitioning is also different. The entire 30–40 km width of the Norumbega fault system in southwestern Maine is characterized by somewhat variable but generally high ductile strain levels. The shallow segment, however, consists largely of regions of low brittle strain, with the exception of the three high-strain zones identified here.

ACKNOWLEDGMENTS

The research reported here was made possible by financial support from several City University of New York Public Staff Congress-Board of Higher Education grants and by National Science Foundation grant EAR-9218833. We are also grateful

Bob Marvinney and Spike Berry of the Maine Geological Survey for their continued logistical support. Ideas expressed here about the Norumbega system have been shaped by discussions and field trips with several fellow Norumbega researchers to whom we wish to extend our thanks: Wang Chunzeng, John Costain, Bill Doll, Peter Gromet, Art Hussey, Mary Hubbard, Tomas Liogys, Dave Stewart, Mark Swanson, Jan Tullis, Terry Tullis, John Walsh, and Dave West. Special thanks to Spike Berry and Jerry Magloughlin for their comments on an earlier draft that significantly improved this paper.

REFERENCES CITED

Ayuso, R. A., 1984, Field relations, crystallization, and petrology of reversely zoned granitic plutons in the Bottle Lake complex, Maine: U.S. Geological Survey Professional Paper 1320, 58 p.

dePaor, D., and Simpson, C., 1993, New directions in structural geology: U.S. Geological Survey Short Course Notes, 128 p.

Guidotti, C. V., 1985, Regional metamorphic zones in Maine, *in* Osberg, P. H., Husey, A. M., II, and Boone, G. M., Bedrock geological map of Maine: Augusta, Maine Geological Survey, scale 1:500,000.

Hadizadeh, J., Babaie, H. A., and Babaei, A., 1991, Development of interlaced mylonites, cataclasites, and breccias: Example from the Towaliga fault, south-central Appalachians: Journal of Structural Geology, v. 13, p. 63–70.

Higgins, K., 1992, The Norumbega fault zone, Great Pond, Maine [M.A. thesis]: Orono, University of Maine, 94 p.

Hirth, G., and Tullis, J., 1992, Dislocation creep regimes in quartz aggregates: Journal of Structural Geology, v. 14, p. 145–159.

Hubbard, M., West, D. P., Jr., Ludman, A., Guidotti, C. V., and Lux, D., 1995, The Norumbega fault zone, Maine: Mid- to shallow level crustal section within a transcurrent fault zone: Atlantic Geology, v. 31, p. 109–116.

Hussey, A. M., II, Bothner, W. A., and Thompson, J. A., 1986, Geological comparisons across the Norumbega fault zone, southwestern Maine, *in* Newberg, D. W., ed., Guidebook to field trips in southwestern Maine: New England Intercollegiate Geological Conference Guidebook, v. 78, p. 164–183.

Larrabee, D. M., 1964, Reconnaissance bedrock geology of the Wabassus Lake quadrangle, Washington County, Maine: U.S. Geological Survey Mineral Investigation Field Studies Map MF 282, scale 1:62,500.

Larrabee, D. M., Spencer, C. W., and Swift, D. J. P., 1965, Bedrock geology of the Grand Lake area, Aroostook, Hancock, Penobscot, and Washington counties, Maine: U.S. Geological Survey Bulletin 1202-E, 38 p.

Ludman, A., 1991, The Fredericton Trough and Norumbega fault zone in eastern Maine, *in* Ludman, A., ed., Geology of the Coastal Lithotectonic Block and neighboring terranes, eastern Maine and southern New Brunswick: New England Intercollegiate Geological Conference Guidebook, v. 83, p. 186–208.

Ludman, A., 1995, Strain partitioning, timing, and amount of offset in the Norumbega fault zone, eastern Maine: Geological Society of America Abstracts with Programs, v. 27, p. 65.

Ludman, A., 1998, Evolution of a transcurrent fault zone in shallow crustal metasedimentary rocks: The Norumbega fault zone, eastern Maine: Journal of Structural Geology, v. 20, p. 93–107.

Ludman, A., and West, D. P., Jr., 1996, "Cool" shallow-crustal generation of mylonite: Examples from the Norumbega fault zone, Maine: Geological Society of America Abstracts with Programs, v. 28, no. 3, p. 77.

Ludman, A., Bromble, S., and DeMartinis, J., 1989, Multiple thermal metamorphism in the contact aureole of the Pocomoonshine gabbro-diorite, southeastern Maine, *in* Tucker, R. D., and Marvinney, R. G., eds., Studies in Maine geology, Volume 4: Petrology: Augusta, Maine Geological Survey, p. 1–12.

Ludman, A., Hopeck, J., and Brock, P. C., 1993, Nature of the Acadian orogeny in eastern Maine, *in* Roy, D. C., and Skehan, J. W., eds., The Acadian orogeny: Recent studies in New England, Maritime Canada, and the autochthonous foreland: Geological Society of America Special Paper 275, p. 67–84.

McLeod, M. J., Johnson, S. C., and Ruitenberg, A. A., 1994, Geological map of southwestern New Brunswick: New Brunswick Department of Natural Resources and Energy Map NR-5, scale 1:250,000.

Osberg, P. H., Hussey, A. M., II, and Boone, G. M., 1985, Bedrock geologic map of Maine: Augusta, Maine Geological Survey, scale 1:500,000.

Passchier, C. W., and Trouw, R. A. J., 1996, Microtectonics: Berlin, Springer-Verlag, 289 p.

Rast, N., and Lutes, G. G., 1979, The metamorphic aureole of the Pokiok–Skiff Lake granite, southern New Brunswick, *in* Current research, Part A: Geological Survey of Canada Paper 79-1A, p. 267–271.

Swanson, M. T., 1992, Late Acadian–Alleghenian transpressional deformation: Evidence from asymmetric boudinage in the Casco Bay area, coastal Maine: Journal of Structural Geology, v. 14, p. 323–341.

Swanson, M. T., 1995, Distributed ductile dextral shear strain throughout the Casco Bay area, *in* Hussey, A. M., III, and Johnston, R. A., eds., Guidebook to field trips in southern Maine and adjacent New Hampshire: New England Intercollegiate Geological Field Conference Guidebook, v. 87, p. 1–14.

Tullis, J. T., Snoke, A. W., and Todd, V. R., 1982, Significance of petrogenesis of mylonitic rocks: Geology, v. 10, p. 227–230.

West, D. P., Jr., 1993, Nature, timing, and extent of dextral shear deformation in south-central Maine [Ph.D. thesis]: University of Maine, Orono, 228 p.

West, D. P., Jr., 1995, The Norumbega fault zone in south-central Maine: A trip through 80 million years of dextral shear deformation, *in* Hussey, A. M., II, and Johnston, R. A., eds., Guidebook to field trips in Southern Maine and adjacent New Hampshire: New England Intercollegiate Geological Field Conference Guidebook, v. 87, p. 125–144.

West, D. P., Jr., and Lux, D. R., 1993, Dating mylonitic deformation by the ^{40}Ar-^{39}Ar method: An example from the Norumbega fault zone, Maine: Earth and Planetary Science Letters, v. 120, p. 221–237.

West, D. P., Jr., and Hubbard, M. S., 1997, Progressive localization of deformation during exhumation of a major strike-slip shear zone: Norumbega fault zone, south-central Maine, USA: Tectonophysics, v. 273, p. 185–202.

Wones, D. R., and Ayuso, R. A., 1993, Geologic map of the Lucerne granite, Hancock and Penobscot counties, Maine: U.S. Geological Survey Miscellaneous Investigations Map I-2360, scale 1:62,500.

MANUSCRIPT ACCEPTED BY THE SOCIETY JUNE 9, 1998

Printed in U.S.A.

Geological Society of America
Special Paper 331
1999

Norumbega connections: Casco Bay, Maine, to Massachusetts?

Wallace A. Bothner
Department of Earth Sciences, University of New Hampshire, Durham, New Hampshire 03824
Arthur M. Hussey, II
Department of Geology, Bowdoin College, Brunswick, Maine 04011

ABSTRACT

The Norumbega fault zone has been traced from southern New Brunswick to Merrymeeting Bay in south-central Maine. In south-central Maine the zone contains a complex record of narrow dextral high-strain shear zones set in a 20–40-km-wide zone of weaker dextral strain. Numerous brittle faults showing normal and reverse dip-slip and left-lateral strike-slip motion are also in this area. Age assignments for the various types of movement in the Norumbega fault zone in the Casco Bay–Merrymeeting Bay area range from middle and late Paleozoic to Mesozoic. The broad zone of weaker dextral shear is of Middle to Late Devonian age and coincident with the latest stage of high-grade metamorphism late in the Acadian orogeny. High-strain zones are of probable Permian age followed by brittle faults of Mesozoic age.

In the Casco Bay area, the Norumbega fault zone widens, and narrow high-strain zones, represented by the Flying Point, South Harpswell, and Broad Cove faults, and the Macworth phyllonite splay out as curvilinear strands trending south and southwest toward large granitic to intermediate plutons of Devonian to Carboniferous age (Biddeford, Webhannet, Lyman and Exeter). The plutons are on strike and mostly older than the Norumbega fault zone high-strain segments, but show neither significant shear fabric nor mappable contact offsets. Several high-strain zones have been recognized in New Hampshire. The Portsmouth and Great Commons faults are along and within the Rye (mylonite) complex, and the Nannie Island and Calef faults are within the Merrimack Group. Outcrop evidence for connecting these faults in southeastern New Hampshire with those of the Casco Bay area is sparse; potential connections are constrained to corridors between plutons and to offshore areas.

Possible onshore correlations include projections of the Broad Cove and Flying Point faults to the Nannie Island and Calef fault zones of southeastern New Hampshire via a corridor between the Biddeford and Lyman plutons, and west of the Webhannet pluton. Additional strain of the Norumbega fault zone may be more broadly distributed through phyllonitic rocks of the Macworth and Eliot Formations of the Merrimack Group, and the mylonites of the Rye complex in New Hampshire. Offshore, curvilinear structural trends indicated by regional aeromagnetic anomalies suggest a connection between rocks of the Casco Bay sequence and the Rye complex, and thus potentially the South Harpswell and Portsmouth faults. Farther offshore, parallel curvilinear aeromagnetic anomalies are interpreted to correspond to rocks of the Fredericton trough and sequences to the east and to the belt of Coastal Maine plutons. The anomaly patterns are sigmoidal, consistent with rock sequences deformed within a large dextral shear zone, the boundaries of which are interpreted to be Norumbega

Bothner, W. A., and Hussey, A. M., II, 1999, Norumbega connections: Casco Bay, Maine to Massachusetts?, *in* Ludman, A., and West, D. P., Jr., eds., Norumbega Fault System of the Northern Appalachians: Boulder, Colorado, Geological Society of America Special Paper 331.

fault zone high strain zones and the offshore extension of the Clinton–Newbury–Bloody Bluff fault system of Massachusetts. Such a connection with the Gulf of Maine fault zone suggests possible transfer of regional dextral strain between the Norumbega fault zone and the faults of central and southern New England during Alleghanian transpression.

INTRODUCTION

The Norumbega fault zone extends more or less continuously from southern New Brunswick to the northern part of Casco Bay in the Freeport-Brunswick area (Fig. 1). In the south-central Maine segment of this fault zone (Liberty to Freeport-Brunswick area), the Norumbega fault zone is a 20–25-km-wide zone of older distributive ductile shear within which are several narrow high-strain zones as wide as 1 km (Hubbard et al., 1995; Pankiwskyj, 1996; West and Lux, 1993; West, 1993, 1995). They parallel the main strike and are characterized by mylonite, ultramylonite, and, locally, pseudotachylite. These high-strain zones include the Sandhill Corner, Hill 806, and Sunnyside faults (Pankiwskyj, 1976, 1996; Bickel, 1976). In the Casco Bay region, the Norumbega fault zone is a broader area of older distributive dextral shear, but still retains several narrow high-strain zones that diverge to the south. These high-strain zones include the Flying Point, South Harpswell, and Broad Cove faults, and the Macworth phyllonite (Hussey, 1985, 1988; Swanson, 1992). These appear to be splays of the Sandhill Corner fault in the Liberty area (Pankiwskyj, 1976) which is on strike with the Flying Point fault (Fig. 2). Within and to the east of the Norumbega fault zone in the Casco Bay–Boothbay Harbor area (Fig. 1), several brittle faults of inferred younger ages exhibit high-angle dip-slip and sinistral strike-slip motion. From southeastern New Hampshire through eastern Massachusetts, similar but discontinuous ductile and brittle faults are recognized. However, connection of the New Hampshire faults with those of Casco Bay, and thence with the Norumbega fault zone, is difficult. Few faults have been mapped in the metasedimentary sequences in the area from Biddeford to the Maine–New Hampshire border because of the lack of outcrops and mid-Paleozoic plutons that are older than Norumbega-related high-strain faults show essentially no offsets of contacts and, internally, little or no shear fabric. In addition, major strands of the Norumbega fault zone trend out to sea. The purpose of this chapter is to examine the lithologic, structural, geophysical, and temporal evidence for the extension of the high-strain segments of the Norumbega fault zone from the Casco Bay area to southeastern New Hampshire and eastern Massachusetts.

MAJOR LITHOTECTONIC SEQUENCES IN THE NORUMBEGA FAULT ZONE

In southwestern Maine, southeastern New Hampshire, and eastern Massachusetts major lithotectonic sequences are cut or bounded by faults, including probable splays of the Norumbega fault zone (Fig. 2). These include the Late Ordovician(?) to Early Silurian Fredericton trough sequence, the Ordovician Casco Bay sequence, the Falmouth-Brunswick sequence of Ordovician(?) age, the Merrimack Group of Ordovician(?) to Early Silurian age, the Central Maine sequence of Late Ordovician through Early Devonian age, the Rye complex of unknown, but presumed Ordovician or older age, and other rocks east of the Sennebec Pond fault (the St. Croix, Rockport, and Coastal Maine volcanic sequences; Osberg et al., 1995). A review of the general lithic and structural characteristics of these rock sequences is provided to examine correlation possibilities and problems along and across strike throughout the study area.

The Fredericton trough sequence is represented by the Bucksport and Appleton Ridge Formations. In this study area only the Bucksport Formation is traceable from its type area to the coast at Boothbay Harbor. It is present in a 100-km-long belt interrupted only by the Mt. Waldo granite pluton just southwest of Bucksport. The sequence consists typically of interbedded feldspathic metawacke and calc-silicate granofels, with minor rusty-weathering sulfidic muscovite-biotite schist. The northwestern boundary of this belt with the Casco Bay sequence is an inferred folded thrust (Osberg et al., 1985, 1995).

The Casco Bay sequence is a heterogeneous package of metavolcanic and metasedimentary rocks occupying a 170-km-long belt from just north of Saco northeastward to the Liberty area of south-central Maine (Hussey, 1988; Hussey and Marvinney, 1998; Pankiwskyj, 1996). The basal unit consists of metamorphosed felsic to intermediate volcanic rocks with minor amphibolite, calc-silicate granofels and gneiss, marble, and sulfidic granofels and schist (Cushing Formation). Above this is a sequence of thin-bedded feldspathic metawackes and metapelites (Cape Elizabeth Formation), followed by mafic to intermediate metavolcanic strata, locally with bedded felsic metavolcanics and volcanogenic metasedimentary rocks (Spring Point Formation). Above these volcanic strata are, successively, a thin distinctive unit of black graphitic nonbedded phyllonite (Diamond Island Formation) and sulfidic and nonsulfidic metapelites and metalimestone (Scarboro, Spurwink, and Jewell Formations). A unit of calcareous metawacke (Macworth Formation), formally interpreted by Katz (1917) to be the top of the Casco Bay sequence, is now assigned to the Merrimack Group (Hussey et al., 1993). The Passagassawakeag gneiss in the Liberty area is correlated with the Cape Elizabeth Formation (Berry and Osberg, 1989).

The Cape Elizabeth through Jewell Formations are considered by most (Hussey, 1985, 1988; Berry and Osberg, 1989) to be a conformable sequence. The relationship of these rocks to the underlying Cushing Formation is less-well known. Hussey (1985, 1988) suggested an unconformable relation between the Cushing

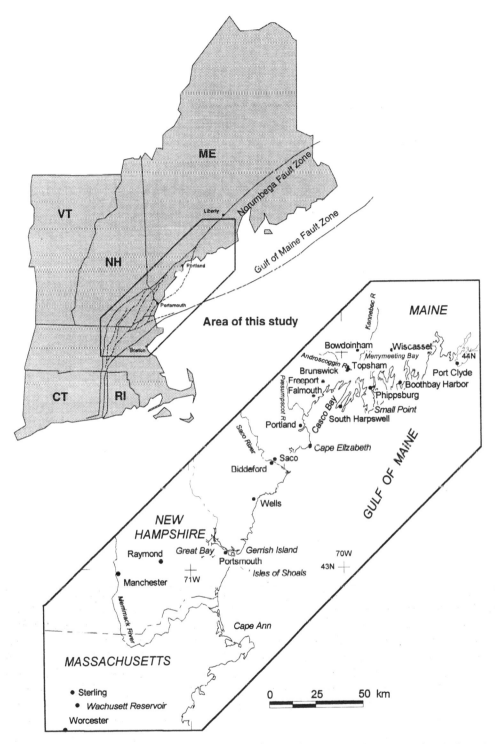

Figure 1. Index map showing geographic localities referred to in text. Inset shows area of study, boundaries and major faults of coastal New England, and the Gulf of Maine fault zone.

and the Cape Elizabeth Formation. An alternative hypothesis that the base of the Cape Elizabeth Formation represents the sole of a klippe was advanced by Osberg et al. (1995). If correct, this premetamorphic fault separating the Cape Elizabeth and Bucksport Formations predates the Norumbega fault zone and therefore does not bear on the question at hand.

The Falmouth-Brunswick sequence consists of two dominant map units, the Mount Ararat and the Nehumkeag Pond Formations (Hussey, 1988; Hussey and Marvinney, 1998). The Mount Ararat Formation consists of thin alternations of feld-

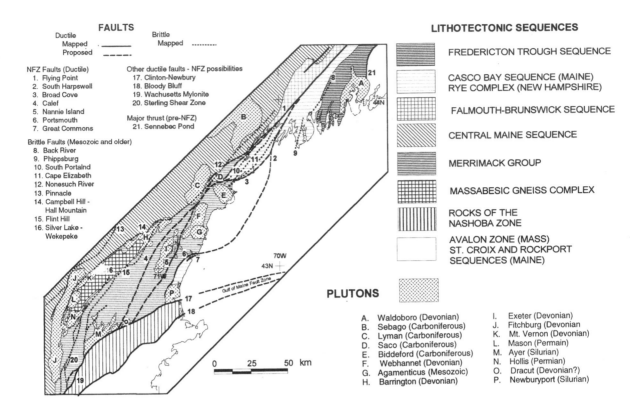

Figure 2. Generalized geologic map of the study area showing major faults, plutons, and lithotectonic sequences affected by the Norumbega fault zone (NFZ). Solid and dashed lines depict ductile faults considered part of the NFZ; dotted lines trace younger brittle faults that may or may not be directly tied to the NFZ.

spathic granofels and amphibolite interpreted to be alternating felsic and mafic metavolcanic ash beds, respectively (Hussey and Marvinney, 1998). The Nehumkeag Pond Formation is a more heterogeneous assemblage of feldspathic metavolcanic rocks and volcanogenic metasedimentary rocks, with minor rusty and non-rusty graphitic metapelite, amphibolite, and impure marble.

The Merrimack Group, as originally defined by Katz (1917), consists of the Kittery, Eliot, and Berwick Formations. The Kittery Formation is a variably thin- to thick-bedded sequence of feldspathic and calcareous, ankeritic metaturbidites with well-preserved graded bedding, cross-bedding, and small-scale channel cut and fill structures. The Eliot Formation is a thinly layered sequence of calcareous and ankeritic feldspathic metasiltstone and metashale (not notably aluminous because it lacks typical aluminous minerals at higher grades of metamorphism). Graded bedding, cross-bedding, and other characteristics of turbidites are rare. Along the western edge of the outcrop belt of the Eliot Formation in New Hampshire, Katz (1917) noted graphitic and muscovitic phyllite which was later separated as the Calef Member of the Eliot Formation (Freedman, 1950). The Berwick Formation consists of interlayered feldspathic metawacke and calc-silicate granofels. Minor thin zones of rusty weathering mica

schist are common within the Berwick Formation. An important aluminous silvery muscovitic metapelite mapped as the Gonic Formation in southwestern Maine and as the Gove Member of Berwick Formation in southeastern New Hampshire contains abundant porphyroblasts of garnet, and staurolite or sillimanite at appropriate metamorphic grade. Parts of the Berwick Formation west of the Gove Member in New Hampshire are characterized by zones of sillimanite-rich, but muscovite-poor, schist inter-bedded with the feldspathic metawacke.

The Central Maine sequence of Late Ordovician(?) to Early Devonian age is a thick sequence of calcareous, feldspathic, and sulfidic metaturbidites and is the only sequence discussed in this chapter that contains fossils (although there are none in this study area). Most of the Central Maine sequence in Figure 2 north and east of Biddeford was mapped previously as the Vassalboro Forma-tion. The name Vassalboro Formation has now been abandoned in the type area, and much of it has been reassigned to the Hutchins Corner Formation (Osberg, 1988). In the area of Figure 2, Hussey and Marvinney (1998) included in the Central Maine sequence cal-careous feldspathic metawacke containing sporadic interbeds of calc-silicate granofels (Hutchins Corner Formation); feldspathic subaluminous schist and gneiss with minor sillimanite, garnet, and sporadic thin beds of coticule (Richmond Corner Formation); and a rusty graphitic metapelite at the base (Torrey Hill Formation). The Richmond Corner and Torrey Hill Formations were originally included in the Falmouth-Brunswick sequence (Hussey, 1988), but have been reassigned on the basis of sedimentological conformity to the Central Maine sequence (Hussey and Marvinney, 1998).

In southwestern Maine and southeastern New Hampshire, Eusden et al. (1987) and Eusden and Lyons (1993) included in the Central Maine sequence variably bedded pelitic and psammitic gneiss, schist, and granofels (Rangeley Formation), well-bedded pelitic schist and quartzite (Perry Mountain Formation), sulfidic, rusty-weathering, occasionally graphitic schist (Smalls Falls Formation), metawacke containing thin interbeds of calc-silicate granofels (Madrid Formation), and thin, often rhythmically bedded metapelite and metasiltstone (Littleton Formation).

The Rye complex crops out in the southwestern tip of Maine at Gerrish Island and along the coast of New Hampshire. It is a heterogeneous assemblage of blastomylonites representing migmatized and nonmigmatized feldspathic metawacke, calcareous metawacke, and metapelite cut at shallow angles by metaigneous granitic rocks. All of these rocks share variable shear fabrics. Minor discontinuously mappable units within the complex include amphibolite, marble, and rusty weathering sulfidic graphitic phyllonite. Two prominent high strain zones are identified by ~50-m-wide bands of ultramylonite, often containing stringers of pseudotachylite (Hussey, 1980; Carrigan, 1984; Swanson, 1988). One is within the Portsmouth fault zone near the contact with the Kittery Formation, and the other is identified as the Great Commons fault within the complex (Carrigan, 1984).

REGIONAL CORRELATIONS: POSSIBILITIES AND PROBLEMS

In the absence of fossil control, possible correlations of lithotectonic sequences in southern Maine and New Hampshire are made on the basis of lithic similarity, metamorphic grade, degree of deformation, and relative age relationships. Radiometric attempts to fix age of protolith and/or of age of intrusive, metamorphic, and deformational events and geophysical anomaly characteristics are incorporated while recognizing that each approach is subject to varying interpretations and has limits of resolution. Even long-noted lithologic similarity between several fault-bounded lithostratigraphic packages sparks lively debate (e.g., Merrimack and Central Maine sequences, Bothner et al., 1984). The following section reviews possible correlations that are pertinent to this discussion of the Norumbega fault zone in southern Maine and New Hampshire. Figure 2 groups those lithostratigraphic sequences to illustrate their relationships to the faults of the Norumbega fault zone.

Rye-Cape Elizabeth correlation

The Rye and Cape Elizabeth Formations are lithically similar in broad respects. Aside from the extensive mylonitization of the Rye Formation, both formations consist dominantly of metapelite and feldspathic metawacke, contain minor units of amphibolite and calc-silicate rocks, and have similar styles of migmatization at high grades of metamorphism. On the Isles of Shoals 8 km east of Portsmouth, New Hampshire, less-intensely sheared metasedimentary rocks of the Rye Formation (Fowler Billings, 1959) are strikingly similar to the high-grade migmatized Cape Elizabeth Formation in the Phippsburg–Boothbay Harbor area, Maine.

Correlation by lithic similarity of the Cape Elizabeth Formation and the Rye complex is further supported by radiometric determinations. Deformed metadiorite crops out on New Castle Island, east of Portsmouth, New Hampshire, and on the Isles of Shoals. Samples from the latter give a 472 ± 10 Ma Rb/Sr whole-rock date (Olszewski et al., 1984; H. E. Gaudette, 1996, written commun.) that provides a minimum age for the Rye complex. Further attempts to constrain the age of the Rye using $^{40}Ar/^{39}Ar$ methods (West et al., 1993) yielded highly variable, unreliable ages, perhaps reflecting mobility of Ar during high strain events.

The Cape Elizabeth Formation, if in sequence, is believed to be slightly older than the overlying Spring Point Formation from which volcanic zircons yielded a U/Pb age of 469 ± 3 Ma (Osberg et al., 1995). On the basis of the presence of dated crosscutting rocks (Appledore diorite) and dated units related stratigraphically or structurally, Ordovician ages are allowable for both the Rye and Cape Elizabeth Formations.

Hepburn et al. (1995) noted the strong similarity of the Nashoba Formation, exposed between the Clinton-Newbury and Bloody Bluff faults of central and eastern Massachusetts, and parts of the Casco Bay sequence (the Cushing, Cape Elizabeth, and Passagassawakeag Formations) of coastal Maine. Castle (1965) described the Boxford Formation, now included as a member of the Nashoba Formation (Zen, 1983), as a probable correlative of the Rye Formation in New Hampshire. Both the Boxford and the Nashoba Formations crop out on the south side of the Clinton-Newbury fault which, if correlation with the Rye is correct, would imply dextral offset on this fault. Such a correlation is permissible on both lithologic and geophysical grounds.

Merrimack Group–Casco Bay relationships

The Eliot Formation (the middle unit of the Merrimack Group) and the Cape Elizabeth Formation of the Casco Bay sequence were originally correlated by Katz (1917). Recent and ongoing reexamination (Hussey and Bothner, 1993) affirms that certain low grade calcareous and ankeritic phyllites between Saco and South Portland, originally included by Katz (1917) in the Cape Elizabeth Formation, correlate with the Eliot Formation. However, these rocks are now separated from the Cape Elizabeth Formation, which is pelitic rather than calcareous and clearly in sequence with higher and lower units of the Casco Bay Group. Similar carbonate-rich phyllonite of the Macworth Formation occupying an area bounded by the Flying Point and an unnamed fault (between Portland and Freeport) is also correlated with the Eliot Formation (Hussey et al., 1993).

Chlorite-grade rocks east of the Broad Cove fault in the town of

Cape Elizabeth, originally mapped as part of Cape Elizabeth Formation (Katz, 1917), are now correlated with the Kittery Formation on the basis of similarity of composition (calcareous rather than pelitic metawacke), bedding thickness, and primary sedimentary structures such as graded bedding, cross bedding, and minor channel cuts and fills (Berry and Osberg, 1989; Hussey et al. 1993; Hussey and Bothner, 1995). These rocks are thus considered to be part of the Merrimack Group, and not the Cape Elizabeth Formation.

The reassignment of these low-grade rocks to the Merrimack Group leaves the relationship between the Merrimack Group and Casco Bay sequence unresolved. They are now interpreted to be separated everywhere by faults, the details of which remain unclear.

Merrimack–Central Maine correlations

The lithic similarity of the Berwick Formation of the Merrimack Group with the Hutchins Corner Formation (originally the Vassalboro Formation) was noted by Billings (1956). Both formations consist of metamorphosed feldspathic wackes with variable amounts of interbedded calc-silicate granofels and thin zones of rusty-weathering sulfidic quartzo-feldspathic muscovite-biotite schist. Bothner et al. (1984), on the basis of an Early Ordovician determination for the crosscutting Exeter pluton (473 ± 37 Ma Rb-Sr whole rock, Gaudette et al., 1984), interpreted the Berwick Formation to be as old as late Precambrian. This would have precluded its correlation with Upper Ordovician(?)–Silurian units of the Central Maine sequence. Precise U/Pb zircon age determinations (Bothner et al., 1993; Aleinikoff et al., 1995; Hussey et al., 1993) have shown that the Exeter is Devonian rather than Early Ordovician and that the Berwick Formation may be Silurian, allowing the correlation of parts of the Merrimack Group and Central Maine sequences, as Billings originally envisioned.

Merrimack Group–Fredericton trough correlations

Rocks of the Bucksport Formation in the Boothbay Harbor area are very similar to the rocks of the Merrimack Group, particularly the Berwick Formation, in that both consist dominantly of feldspathic biotite ± hornblende metawacke with prominent thin to medium beds of calc-silicate granofels and thin intervals of sulfidic schist. Correlation of those units also would suggest a connection between the Fredericton trough sequence and the Hutchins Corner Formation of the Central Maine sequence (Berry and Osberg, 1989), following the reasoning given here, and lend credence to Bradley's (1983) earlier suggestion of a tie between the two at a broader regional scale.

MAJOR FAULTS OF SOUTHWESTERN MAINE AND SOUTHEASTERN NEW HAMPSHIRE

Major faults recognized in the Casco Bay area include the following named faults (Fig. 2): Flying Point, Cape Elizabeth, South Portland, South Harpswell, Nonesuch River, Phippsburg,

Back River, and Broad Cove (Hussey, 1988; Hussey and Marvinney, 1998). Of these, the Flying Point, Broad Cove, and South Harpswell faults are here considered the high-strain segments of the Norumbega fault zone in the Casco Bay area (and are shown as solid lines in Fig. 2). In addition, the Macworth Formation shows such extensive shearing as to suggest that it is a distributive zone of ductile high strain. We refer to this as the Macworth phyllonite zone. The other named faults, and numerous minor faults, show more brittle behavior (dotted traces in Fig. 2) and are interpreted to be Mesozoic normal faults (Hussey, 1988; West et al., 1993).

The ductile shear zones within the Merrimack Group and the Rye complex (solid or dashed traces on Fig. 2) are important for this discussion. These include the Calef and Nannie Island faults, both significant phyllonites, and the Portsmouth and Great Commons faults that bound and lie within the Rye complex, respectively, and are characterized by early ductile and later brittle fabrics.

Previous interpretations have traced the Nonesuch River fault into the Campbell Hill–Hall Mountain fault on the northwest side of the Massabesic Gneiss complex in New Hampshire, where they have been considered the continuation of the Norumbega fault (Lyons et al., 1982; West et al., 1993; Osberg et al., 1985; Wintsch et al., 1992). Another family of brittle faults, similar to those in the Casco Bay area, is on the southeast side of the Massabesic Gneiss complex, largely in the Merrimack Group. Robinson (1989) and Eusden (1988) reported minor ductile shear in both the Campbell Hill–Hall Mountain and the Flint Hill faults at their northeastern ends in New Hampshire. The Flint Hill and Silver Lake faults are the most prominent and significant of these and continue south into Massachusetts as the Wekepeke fault (Robinson, 1979). They share a parallel relationship with the Nonesuch–Campbell Hill–Hall Mountain fault, but not a direct connection. These faults are shown dotted in Figure 2.

Maine faults

The Flying Point fault (Fig. 2) separates high-grade gneisses of the Falmouth-Brunswick sequence from low-grade, extensively sheared rocks of the Macworth Formation. It was mapped by Hussey (1988) and Swanson (1992) in the Falmouth to Topsham area, and by Newberg (1984) in the Richmond to Gardiner area. It is on strike with and may trace into the Sandhill Corner fault mapped by Pankiwskyj (1976, 1996), West (1995), and Bickel (1976) in the Liberty area. The Sandhill Corner fault is characterized by mylonite and ultramylonite and is interpreted to be one of the principal ductile high-strain zones of the Norumbega fault zone in south-central Maine (West, 1995). Control on the location of the Flying Point fault south of Portland is uncertain because of paucity of outcrop, but it has been extended south, bounding higher grade rocks of the Falmouth-Brunswick and Central Maine sequences on the west from lower grade rocks of the Merrimack and Casco Bay sequences on the east (Hussey, 1985).

Detailed studies of strain geometry and history of the Flying Point fault, carried out by Swanson (1992) and West et al. (1993), indicate two contrasting types of movement at different times along it. Swanson (1992) discussed strain indicators that characterize the Flying Point fault as a right-lateral ductile high strain zone ~1 km wide. This zone involves high-grade gneisses of the Falmouth-Brunswick and Casco Bay sequences, as well as low-grade phyllonites of the Macworth Formation, and occurs toward the western edge of a 40-km-wide zone of more broadly distributed ductile shear that encompasses essentially the entire Casco Bay and Falmouth-Brunswick belts in the northern Casco Bay area.

West et al. (1993) showed that $^{40}Ar/^{39}Ar$ cooling ages of hornblendes from the broad lower strain zone in the Casco Bay sequence indicate that metamorphism of these rocks occurred during Middle Devonian time. The high-strain movement along the Flying Point fault is thus Acadian, or slightly younger. West and Lux (1993) inferred a ca. ~290 Ma age from $^{40}Ar/^{39}Ar$ analysis of recrystallized muscovite from a single sample of mylonite of the Sandhill Corner fault; they interpret the date to be the time of mylonitic deformation along the Sandhill Corner fault. If the link between the Flying Point and Sandhill Corner faults should be confirmed by future mapping, a Permian age for ductile dextral shear along the Flying Point fault would be indicated.

West et al. (1993) discussed contrasts in the cooling history (based on $^{40}Ar/^{39}Ar$ ages of hornblende, biotite, and muscovite) of the rocks on the northwest versus the southeast side of the Flying Point fault in the Merrymeeting Bay area. Here, dip-slip northwest-side-up displacement of about 4 km occurred during Mesozoic time and is responsible for juxtaposition of the high-grade Falmouth-Brunswick sequence against the lower grade Macworth Formation.

The South Harpswell fault may be the principal splay of the Norumbega fault zone in the Casco Bay area, diverging from the Flying Point fault in the northern Merrymeeting Bay area. The actual fault zone is not exposed but is inferred on the basis of extensive right-lateral strain indicators in rocks exposed along the western shore of Harpswell Neck and particularly in the high-strain zone at Barnes Island, South Harpswell (Swanson et al., 1986; Swanson, 1992). The amount of right-lateral slip along this fault is limited to 3 to 5 km at most, as suggested by the distribution of units of the upper Casco Bay sequence and members of the Cushing Formation in the middle to northern part of Casco Bay (Hussey, 1971a, 1971b).

The Broad Cove fault (Hussey, 1985) separates Casco Bay sequence rocks from Merrimack Group rocks in the Two Lights area of Cape Elizabeth. Detailed studies by Swanson (1992) indicate that rocks on both sides of the fault preserve kinematic indicators of extensive dextral shear (sheath folds in quartz veins, shear bands, rotated quartz veins); however, ultramylonite, characteristic of Norumbega high strain zones to the north, has not been observed from rocks adjacent to the Broad Cove fault. Furthermore, no evidence that the fault might be a thrust fault or high-angle dip-slip fault has been observed. We interpret the Broad Cove fault to be a splay of the South Harpswell fault,

diverging from it in the middle of Casco Bay. We suggest that the southern end of the Casco Bay sequence is bounded by segments of the Broad Cove fault offset by the later brittle normal faults of the Casco Bay area (Fig. 2). The southwestern extension or termination of the Broad Cove fault has not been defined. No shear indicators have been observed in the Biddeford pluton, thus restricting any extension of the Broad Cove fault to the metasedimentary corridor between the southern edge of the Saco pluton and the northern edge of the Biddeford pluton, an area where outcrops are sparse. It probably merges with the Flying Point fault in the area between the Biddeford and Lyman plutons.

Other named faults in the Casco Bay area (South Portland, Cape Elizabeth, Back River, Phippsburg, and Nonesuch River faults) and minor unnamed faults seen in outcrop exhibit breccia, silicification, gouge, and slickensides, indicative of higher crustal-level, brittle faulting. The ages of these faults are not well constrained, but most likely are younger than either the narrow high-strain and broad gentler strain faulting, and may be as young as middle Mesozoic. Most minor brittle faults show high-angle dip-slip–oriented slickensides in outcrop. Two of the named faults, the Back River and Cape Elizabeth, involve apparent left-lateral offset in excess of 1 km. These brittle high-angle dip-slip or left-lateral strike-slip faults reflect later movement, probably not related genetically to the dextral ductile shearing that more typically characterize the Norumbega fault zone.

New Hampshire faults

The most important ductile structure in New Hampshire is the Rye complex. It is juxtaposed against the Merrimack Group along the Portsmouth fault zone, which is a 100–300-m-wide, north- and northeast-trending, northwest-dipping fault zone that is mapped from southeastern coastal New Hampshire to Gerrish Island, Kittery, Maine, where it projects ~N70E offshore. Both ductile and later brittle fault fabrics characterize this fault zone and were described in detail by Swanson and Carrigan (1984) and Hussey and Bothner (1993, 1995). Ductile fabrics are represented by mylonitic textures that range from protomylonite to ultramylonite, the latter ~50 m wide, which have dominant right-slip shear sense. Subsequent brittle faulting indicates that last motion was dip slip, northwest side down.

The Great Commons fault zone (Carrigan, 1984) and its extension east into the Fort Foster brittle zone (Swanson, 1988, 1995) of southwestern Maine represent a significant ~50-m-wide internal break within the Rye complex. Like the Portsmouth fault zone, this zone is identified by both early ductile and later brittle fault fabrics. It separates less migmatized lithologies of the Rye complex on the southeast from more migmatized lithologies on the northwest (Carrigan, 1984; Welch, 1993). Rocks on both sides of this fault are variably mylonitized. Boeckeler (1994), following Peterman and Day (1989), obtained Rb/Sr whole-rock ages of 277 ± 16 Ma and 270 ± 32 Ma from pseudotachylite from metapelitic and amphibolitic ultramylonite (Boeckeler, 1996, personal commun.), respectively, in the Fort Foster brittle zone

(Great Commons fault). These dates provide a best estimate for "last" motion within this mylonite zone and their ranges include the age of the recrystallized muscovite (ca. 290 Ma ^{40}Ar/^{39}Ar) reported from the Sandhill Corner fault of the Norumbega fault zone in central Maine (West and Lux, 1993).

Two other high-strain zones in southeastern New Hampshire are represented by the Calef and Nannie Island phyllonites. They are both poorly exposed narrow (<200 m) shear zones involving rocks most like the Eliot and Macworth Formations (Fargo and Bothner, 1995). Within the Nannie Island zone phyllitic layers are dismembered and commonly display foliation ("phyllite") fish with dominant dextral shear. More competent light brown calcareous metasiltstone, typical of the Eliot Formation, is strongly laminated. Layers are isoclinally folded, primary sedimentary structures are rarely preserved, and limbs are strongly attenuated or completely lost—only the hinges remain lying parallel to mylonitic (phyllonitic) foliation. The Calef phyllonite is carbonaceous and has fewer metasiltstone laminations. Although we have not been able to confirm a direct connection, the projected northeast traces of the Calef and Nannie Island shear zones pass between the major plutons of southeastern New Hampshire and southwestern Maine toward a southerly projection of the Norumbega fault zone.

The Campbell Hill–Hall Mountain, Pinnacle, Flint Hill, and Silver Lake faults are the principle brittle faults in southeastern New Hampshire (Lyons et al., 1997). Like those in Maine, they are marked by discontinuous silicified zones and topographic lineaments. They truncate major structures, offset metamorphic isograds, and cut Devonian plutons; dip-slip, dextral, and sinistral strike-slip motion have been reported for some of them (Eichhorn, 1990; Robinson, 1989; Hussey and Newburg, 1978). The Pinnacle and Campbell Hill–Hall Mountain faults are on the northwestern side of the Massabesic Gneiss complex. The latter, approximately bounding the Massabesic Gneiss complex, traces into the Nonesuch River fault in Maine. The Flint Hill and Silver Lake faults are on the east side of the Massabesic Gneiss complex and are traceable from nearly the Maine–New Hampshire border to Massachusetts, where they join the Beaver Brook–Wekepeke fault system that continues south to Worcester, Massachusetts, and the Clinton–Newbury fault system. A 160 Ma zircon fission-track date from a White Mountains series dike crosscutting the Campbell Hill–Hall Mountain fault places an upper bound on the age of brittle fault movement (Aleinikoff, 1978). Robinson (1989) suggested that there was late Paleozoic through middle Mesozoic movement on the Flint Hill in the area of Raymond, New Hampshire, on the basis of fracture pattern analysis. As much as 2 km of dip-slip motion, east side down, has been suggested from petrologic data along the Flint Hill fault (Allard et al., 1997) which confirms an earlier estimate by Lyons et al. (1982) for the Silver Lake fault.

In addition to the Wekepeke fault in central Massachusetts, Goldstein (1994) recognized a 15-km-wide zone of ductile shear called the Sterling shear zone that is approximately bisected by the Wekepeke fault, and a narrower high-strain zone called the Wachusett mylonite zone that is cut by the Clinton Newbury fault. The Sterling shear zone is largely within the southern continuation of the Merrimack Group (the Paxton Group and Oakdale and Worcester Formations in Massachusetts; Pease, 1989) and the faults contained therein.

NORUMBEGA "CONNECTION"—ONSHORE AND/OR OFF?

How are the ductile faults of the Norumbega fault zone (South Harpswell, Broad Cove, Flying Point, and Macworth phyllonite zone) expressed south of Casco Bay? What fault(s) in southeastern New Hampshire and northeastern Massachusetts have the appropriate character and timing to be in the Norumbega fault zone? The following factors make fault continuity studies difficult: (1) widespread Pleistocene deposits (Thompson and Borns, 1985); (2) the presence of Devonian (Webhannet) and Early Carboniferous (Biddeford) plutons in the critical area between Biddeford, Maine, and the Maine–New Hampshire border; and (3) the offshore region from Casco Bay to the Massachusetts coast at Cape Ann. Three distinct possibilities, however, meet the criteria of character and timing and thus warrant serious consideration. Two of these possibilities are hypothesized to be onshore and a third, offshore.

First, the Calef and Nannie Island shear zones can be individually projected from New Hampshire north to possible connections with the Flying Point and Broad Cove faults and south toward the Clinton–Newbury fault. The traces project between Paleozoic plutons. To the north, the Calef and Nannie Island zones occupy the metasedimentary corridor between the Webhannet and Biddeford on the southeast and the Lyman pluton on the northwest (C, E, and F, Fig. 2). To the south they can be projected between the Ayer and Dracut plutons (M and O, Fig. 2). Only the Carboniferous (307 ± 20 Rb/Sr, Gaudette et al., 1982) Saco pluton (D, Fig. 2) is strongly sheared and extensively altered (Marvinney et al., 1995). It is located where we interpret the connection of the Flying Point–Broad Cove and Calef–Nannie Island faults. An appealing aspect of this hypothesis is that individual strands miss all but one Paleozoic pluton (or these plutons acted as shear deflectors during the transpressional evolution of the Norumbega fault zone). The remaining difficulty is the lack of ground truth in tracing the New Hampshire shear zones into the faults of Casco Bay, Maine, and into Massachusetts.

Second, the higher strain may be distributed within the strongly sheared Macworth and Eliot Formations, both as wide as 4 km. In the Casco Bay and Great Bay areas, parts to most of these units are so thoroughly sheared as to warrant a lithotectonic as well as lithostratigraphic interpretation. In this hypothesis, the Norumbega fault zone becomes intraformational as it traces to the south and shares some of the same features of the ~6-km-wide Sterling shear zone described by Goldstein (1994) in central Massachusetts. This speculation also needs further evidence.

Third, an offshore connection between the South Harpswell fault and the Portsmouth and/or Clinton–Newbury–Bloody Bluff faults is suggested by their offshore trends and the geophysical expressions of the lithologies involved. Aeromagnetic and gravity maps have been used to interpret present subsurface structural arrangements as well as to test plate tectonic reconstructions (e.g., Hoffman, 1987; Chandler and Southwick, 1990). Of the many "local" examples, the gravity (Haworth et al., 1980) and aeromagnetic (Zeitz et al., 1980a) compilations have provided important springboards for tectonic analysis of the Appalachian orogen (Harwood and Zeitz, 1977; Zeitz et al., 1980b). For coastal New England and the Gulf of Maine (Brooks and Bothner, 1989; Brooks, 1990), the compilation of Macnab et al. (1990) provides the most complete digital aeromagnetic data coverage.

Figure 3 is a colored aeromagnetic map, contoured at 25–100 nT, of the central New England coast and the westernmost part of the Gulf of Maine at 42°–45°N and 68°–72°W taken from the open-file map of Macnab et al. (1990). The most prominent aeromagnetic signatures of rock packages and their boundaries pertinent to this discussion are designated in the figure. They are the following.

1. A steep aeromagnetic gradient is associated with the boundary between rocks of the Nashoba zone and Merrimack Group and its offshore continuation as the Gulf of Maine fault zone (Hutchinson et al., 1988; Kane et al., 1972).

2. A strong aeromagnetic linear anomaly tracks rocks mapped as the Cape Elizabeth Formation, including the Passagassawakeag gneiss (hence the cep anomaly), from northeast of Merrymeeting Bay south along Harpswell Neck and offshore with decreasing amplitude.

3. An irregular anomaly field is punctuated by circular aeromagnetic highs west of the cep anomaly and includes a number of closed, high-frequency anomalies that correspond to mapped intrusive complexes of the Mesozoic White Mountain plutonic–volcanic suite (w) in all lithotectonic sequences.

Three other regions with strong aeromagnetic signatures are within the map area. These include: (1) northeast-trending positive anomalies tracking the plutonic and volcanic rocks of the Ordovician Bronson Hill (bh) magmatic arc (Bothner et al., 1986) and a broad negative field with strong circular magnetic highs (w) in the northwestern third of the map; (2) the broad area of magnetic (and gravity) highs and lows that are underlain by abundant middle Paleozoic felsic and mafic plutons (cm) of eastern coastal Maine; and (3) the anomalies associated with the Ordovician Cape Ann intrusives (ca) and, offshore, the Cashes Ledge plutonic complex (cl, 42.7°N and 69°W, Hermes et al., 1978). The aeromagnetic low immediately north of Cape Ann corresponds to the Silurian Newbury volcanics (sv, Shride, 1976); a similar negative anomaly associated with correlative rocks occurs in the Penobscot Bay area just west of the Coastal Maine pluton magnetic high (Brookins et al., 1973).

The splays of the Norumbega fault zone must be within the area bounded by the offshore continuation of the cep, the discontinuous linear aeromagnetic high that includes the Massabesic Gneiss complex (m) in New Hampshire, and the anomalies associated with the rocks bounded by the Clinton-Newbury and Bloody Bluff faults and their offshore extensions within the Gulf of Maine fault zone (Fig. 3). Within this area the Massabesic Gneiss produces a strong positive anomaly probably because this migmatite complex contains abundant magnetite euhedra in several localities. The gneiss is also intruded at its northeastern end by magnetite rich rocks of the Mt. Pawtuckaway complex, a member of the Mesozoic White Mountain plutonic-volcanic suite, which superimpose its own strong aeromagnetic signature. At this scale there is little obvious aeromagnetic signature associated with the trace of the Nonesuch River and Campbell Hill Hall Mountain fault traces. At larger scale, however, Bothner et al. (1988) reported that the pyrrhotite-bearing Smalls Falls Formation, one of the few magnetic metasedimentary units in the Central Maine sequence (e.g., Phillips, 1990), is truncated against the Campbell Hill–Hall Mountain fault on the west side of the Massabesic Gneiss. On the east side of the Massabesic and within the Merrimack Group are several linear anomalies. The westernmost of these tracks the Calef (c) phyllonite, another corresponds directly with the Early Devonian Exeter diorite (e), another approximately traces the Nannie Island fault (n), and one is bounded by the Portsmouth fault (PF) and the Rye complex (Rye anomaly, ra). The latter anomaly is clearly traceable offshore.

Perhaps the most striking of these features is the curvilinear aeromagnetic anomaly that tracks the Cape Elizabeth Formation (cep). Onshore, northeast of Casco Bay where it trends northeast, the anomaly closely follows the boundary between the Casco Bay sequence and the Falmouth-Brunswick sequence. At Merrymeeting Bay, the anomaly departs from the boundary between the two sequences and turns southerly tracking amphibolites and coticule-bearing units within the Cape Elizabeth Formation east of Phippsburg and continues offshore. The anomaly maintains its linear character, but with decreasing amplitude due to increasing water depth, and curves increasingly westward to parallel a series of linear magnetic anomalies continuous with the anomaly associated with the Coastal Maine plutons (cm). They all merge with the magnetic anomalies in the Gulf of Maine fault zone. The cep anomaly is the more western of this group of linear anomalies and parallels the seaward extension of the Rye anomaly (ra) and extends toward the Rye complex. As such, it provides some support for a correlation of the Cape Elizabeth Formation and Rye complex, from which we speculate that the high strain character of the Rye complex may be related to high-strain segments of the Norumbega fault zone in south-central Maine.

The Portsmouth fault zone is mapped just north of and is parallel to the Rye anomaly. The onshore segment of the South Harpswell fault is mapped west of and is parallel to the Cape Elizabeth–Passagassawakeag anomaly. We infer that these two faults connect offshore approximately parallel to the curvilinear anomalies offshore. The traces of the Flying Point and Broad Cove faults are not represented aeromagnetically within an area dominated by the effects of Paleozoic and Mesozoic plutons.

The cep anomaly bounds the western of two additional aeromagnetic anomaly fields, both having a general sigmoidal shape. Immediately west of the cep is a zone characterized by magnetic

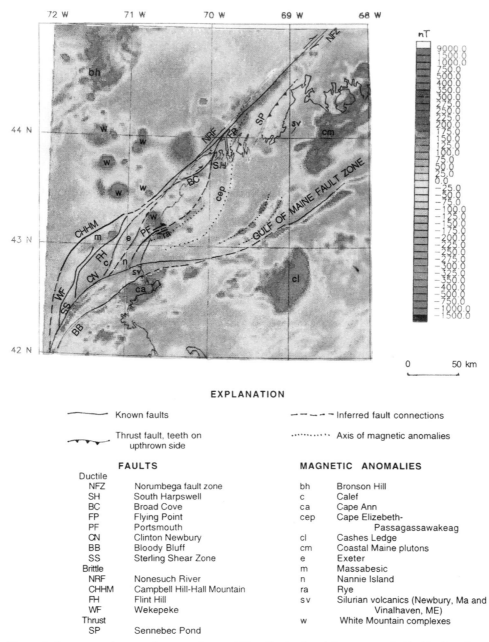

Figure 3. Aeromagnetic anomaly map of central New England and the western Gulf of Maine (from Macnab et al., 1990). Interpreted color aeromagnetic map shows the close association of linear aeromagnetic anomalies and traces of major and inferred faults of the Norumbega and Gulf of Maine fault zones; contour interval varies from 25 to 1000 nT. Abbreviations keyed to explanation and text.

lows (the offshore part of this region, however, has poorer coverage that may account for the rather abrupt east-west anomaly boundary where the Sennebec Pond fault (SP) projects offshore; McNab et al., 1990), followed by a zone dominated by magnetic highs associated onshore with the Coastal Maine plutons (cm). The first zone includes rocks of the Fredericton trough (Bucksport Formation) and sequences to the east (St. Croix and Rockport sequences of Osberg et al., 1995), the older Sennebec Pond fault (SP), a westerly directed pre-Norumbega thrust that separates them, and the minima associated with the Silurian volcanic

rocks in Maine (and their correlatives in Massachusetts). The second includes the Coastal Maine volcanic sequence (Osberg et al., 1995) and the bimodal intrusive suites (cm).

The sigmoidal shape of these combined anomalies is consistent with belts of rocks of appropriate magnetic susceptibility caught between and rotated within a larger dextral strike-slip system (a general shape likened to the sigma grains commonly found in mylonites). In spite of the large difference in scale, these shapes bear a remarkable similarity to a reverse image of the sinistral Najd shear system in Arabia and Egypt discussed by Sultan et al.

RECEIVED AUG 3 1999

(1988), which is reproduced here for comparison with a gray-scale shaded relief map (contoured at 50 nT) of the Gulf of Maine (Fig. 4). By that analogy, we suggest that the Norumbega and Gulf of Maine fault zones are related in space, and thus also in time, by a transfer zone that accommodated variable Alleghanian (and older) strain within several regions identified above. An additional important implication is that the Clinton-Newbury and/or Bloody Bluff fault zones, via the Gulf of Maine fault zone, are genetically related to the Norumbega fault zone, whether or not they are physically linked (Gates et al., 1986; Goldstein, 1989).

Swanson (1992) suggested the presence of a restraining bend near Merrymeeting Bay that he interpreted to be responsible for north-trending folds and related thrust components on later faults. By our interpretation, if there is a restraining bend in the Norumbega system, it more likely occurs offshore along the cep and ra than onshore. In addition, most of the area from Casco Bay to southern New Hampshire appears to be characterized by a complex system of releasing bends that may have predisposed the area to regional tension. In this zone normal faulting represented by several named brittle faults may have been triggered by early

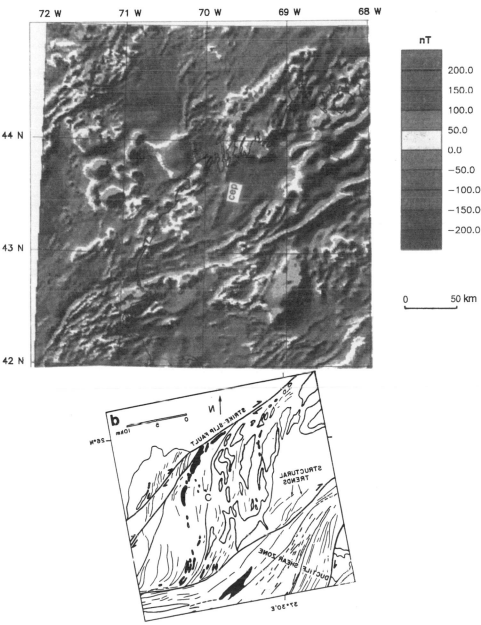

Figure 4. Shaded gray scale relief aeromagnetic map, contour interval 200 nT, of the study area (from Macnab et al., 1990) and a comparative reverse image of the Najd shear system of Egypt and Arabia (Sultan et al., 1988). Maps arranged such that the Cape Elizabeth–Passagassawakeag anomaly (cep) is parallel with C in the reverse image. Scale between the two maps differs by a factor of ~6.

Mesozoic rifting accompanying the opening of the middle section of the Atlantic Ocean.

CONCLUSIONS

The Flying Point, Broad Cove, and South Harpswell faults in the Casco Bay area and the Calef and Nannie Island faults in southeastern New Hampshire share similar character, sense of motion, and probable timing to be included in the Norumbega fault zone. As splays, we speculate that they represent possible onstrike continuations of the Norumbega fault zone southwest to New Hampshire and Massachusetts. In addition, some of the high strain of the Norumbega system may be more broadly distributed within the highly strained Macworth and Eliot Formations, perhaps as far south as the Sterling shear zone of Goldstein (1994) and the Clinton-Newbury fault.

The aeromagnetic expression of well-defined lithic sequences in this study area, the shapes of those anomaly fields, and the gradients marking their boundaries provide strong evidence for continuity of rock sequence and structure between the Norumbega fault zone and the Gulf of Maine fault zone. The tightest control is indicated by the offshore continuation of the Cape Elizabeth–Passagassawaukeg anomaly that is interpreted to link rocks of the Casco Bay sequence and the Rye complex and, by inference, the offshore projections of the South Harpswell and Portsmouth faults that bound them. To the east and farther offshore, the sigmoidal shapes of anomaly fields are interpreted to reflect dextrally sheared rock sequences within a transfer zone between the Norumbega fault zone and the Gulf of Maine fault zone (including the Clinton-Newbury and Bloody Bluff faults onshore). Such a transfer might also account for some of the difficulties in establishing unequivocal onshore connections of the Norumbega fault zone south of Casco Bay. In spite of a long history of documented fault movement in the Norumbega fault zone and the Clinton–Newbury–Bloody Bluff and related faults in southern New England, the current disposition of anomaly-causing rock sequences between the two fault zones in this study area most likely reflects Alleghanian transpression, the last significant orogenic event to affect New England.

ACKNOWLEDGMENTS

Our review of potential connectors from well-established faults of the Norumbega fault zone through the largely covered coastal lowlands and "flooded" near-continental shelf to the Clinton–Newbury Bloody Bluff and their seaward continuation as the Gulf of Maine fault zone has benefited substantially by the careful and thorough reviews of H. N (Spike) Berry, IV, of the Maine Geological Survey, and David B. Stewart of the U.S. Geological Survey. Nikki Delude was very helpful in preparing digital map figures. Hussey gratefully acknowledges the support of the Maine Geological Survey for field work in southwestern Maine. We thank all of the above, and the editors of this volume, Allan Ludman and David West.

REFERENCES CITED

Aleinikoff, J. N., 1978, Structure, petrology, and U-Th-Pb geochronology in the Milford (15') quadrangle, New Hampshire [Ph.D. thesis]: Hanover, New Hampshire, Dartmouth College, 247 p.

Aleinikoff, J. N., Walter, M., and Fanning, C. M., 1995, U-Pb ages of zircon, monazite, and sphene from rocks of the Massabesic Gneiss complex and Berwick Formation, New Hampshire and Massachusetts: Geological Society of America Abstracts with Programs, v. 27, no. 1, p. 26.

Allard, S. T., Laird, J., and Bothner, W. A., 1997, A comparison of metamorphic grade east and west of the Flint Hill Fault, Raymond, NH: Geological Society of America Abstracts with Programs, v. 29, no. 1, p. 26.

Berry, H. N., IV, and Osberg, P. H., 1989, A stratigraphic synthesis of eastern Maine and western New Brunswick, in Tucker, R. D., and Marvinney, R. G., eds., Studies in Maine geology, Volume 2: Structure and stratigraphy: Augusta, Maine Geological Survey, p. 1–32.

Bickel, C. E., 1976, Stratigraphy of the Belfast quadrangle, Maine, in Page, L. R., ed., Contributions to the stratigraphy of New England: Geological Society of America Memoir 148, p. 179–216.

Billings, M. P., 1956, The Geology of New Hampshire, Part 2, Bedrock geology: Concord, New Hampshire State Planning and Development Commission, 203 p.

Boeckeler, A. J., 1994, Isotopic ages of pseudotachylite veins from coastal New Hampshire and SW Maine: Evidence for post-Acadian strike-slip motion: Geological Society of America Abstracts with Programs, v. 26, no. 3, p. 7.

Bothner, W. A., Boudette, E. L., Fagan, T. J., Gaudette, H. E., Laird, J., and Olszewski, W. J., 1984, Geologic framework of the Massabesic Anticlinorium and the Merrimack Trough, southeastern New Hampshire, in Hanson, L. S., ed., Geology of the Coastal Lowlands, Boston, Mass., to Kennebunk, Maine: New England Intercollegiate Geological Conference Guidebook, v. 76, p. 186–206.

Bothner, W. A., Jahrling, C. E., and Kucks, R. P., 1986, Bouguer gravity and aeromagnetic maps of the wildernesses and roadless areas of the White Mountains National Forest, Coos, Carroll, and Grafton Counties, New Hampshire: U.S. Geological Survey Miscellaneous Publications 1594-D, scale 1:125000.

Bothner, W. A., Brooks, J. A., and Eusden, J. D., 1988, Geology and geophysics of the Massabesic, Merrimack, and Rye "zones" in central coastal New England: Geological Society of America Abstracts with Programs, v. 20, no. 1, p. 8.

Bothner, W. A., Gaudette, H. E., Fargo, T. G., Bowring, S. A., and Isachsen, C. E., 1993, Zircon and sphene U/Pb age of the Exeter Pluton: Constraints on the Merrimack Group and part of the Avalon composite terrane: Geological Society of America Abstracts with Programs, v. 25, no. 2, p. A-485.

Bradley, D. C., 1983, Tectonics of the Acadian orogeny in New England and adjacent Canada: Journal of Geology, v. 91, p. 381–400.

Brookins, D. G., Berdan, J. M., and Stewart, D. B., 1973, Isotopic and paleontological evidence for correlating three volcanic sequences in the Maine coastal volcanic belt: Geological Society of America Bulletin, v. 84, p. 1619–1628.

Brooks, J. A., 1990, The petrogenesis of the Agamenticus Complex and late Paleozoic and Mesozoic tectonics in New England [Ph.D. thesis]: Durham, University of New Hampshire, 317 p.

Brooks, J. A., and Bothner, W. A., 1989, Late(?) Alleghanian dextral transpression and terrane accretion within coastal New England and western Gulf of Maine as interpreted from regional aeromagnetic and gravity maps: Eos (Transactions, American Geophysical Union), v. 70, p. 462.

Carrigan, J. A., 1984, Geology of the Rye Formation, New Castle Island and adjacent parts of Portsmouth Harbor, New Hampshire [M.S. thesis]: Durham, University of New Hampshire, 128 p.

Castle, R. O., 1965, Gneissic rocks in the South Groveland quadrangle, Essex County, Massachusetts: U.S. Geological Survey Professional Paper 525-C, p. C81–C86.

Chandler, V. W., and Southwick, D. L., 1990, Aeromagnetic Minnesota: Eos (Transactions, American Geophysical Union), v. 71, p. 1.

Eichhorn, R. J., 1990, A geophysical investigation of the Nonesuch River fault, southeastern New Hampshire and southwestern Maine [M.S. thesis]: Durham, University of New Hampshire, 74 p.

Eusden, J. D., 1988, Stratigraphy, structure, and metamorphism across the "Dorsal Zone," central New Hampshire, *in* Bothner, W. A., ed., Guidebook for field trips in southwestern New Hampshire, southeastern Vermont, and north-central Massachusetts, New England Intercollegiate Geological Conference Guidebook, v. 80, p. 40–59.

Eusden, J. D., and Lyons, J. B., 1993, The sequence of Acadian deformations in central New Hampshire, *in* Roy, D. C., and Skehan, J. W., eds., The Acadian orogeny: Recent studies in New England, Maritime Canada, and the autochthonous foreland: Geological Society of America Special Paper 275, p. 51–66.

Eusden, J. D., Bothner, W. A., and Hussey, A. M., II, 1987, The Kearsarge–Central Maine synclinorium of southeastern New Hampshire and southwestern Maine: Stratigraphic and structural relations of an inverted section: American Journal of Science, v. 287, p. 242–264.

Fargo, T. R., and Bothner, W. A., 1995, Polydeformation in the Merrimack Group, southeastern New Hampshire and southwestern Maine, *in* Hussey, A. M., II, and Johnston, R. A., eds., Guidebook to field trips in southern Maine and adjacent New Hampshire: New England Intercollegiate Geological Conference Guidebook, v. 87, p. 15–28.

Fowler-Billings, K., 1959, Geology of the Isles of Shoals, New Hampshire and Maine: Concord, New Hampshire State Planning and Development Commission, 51 p.

Freedman, J., 1950, Stratigraphy and structure of the Mt. Pawtuckaway quadrangle, southeastern New Hampshire: Geological Society of America Bulletin, v. 61, p. 449–492.

Gates, A. E., Simpson, C., and Glover, L., 1986, Appalachian Carboniferous dextral strike-slip faults: An example from Brookneal, Virginia: Tectonics, v. 5, p. 119–133.

Gaudette, H. E., Kovach, A., and Hussey, A. M., II, 1982, Ages of some intrusive rocks of southwestern Maine: Canadian Journal of Earth Sciences, v. 19, p. 1350–1357.

Gaudette, H. E., Bothner, W. A., Laird, J., Olszewski, W. J., and Cheatham, M. M., 1984, Late Precambrian/early Paleozoic deformation and metamorphism in southeastern New Hampshire—Confirmation of an exotic terrane: Geological Society of America Abstracts with Programs, v. 16, p. 516.

Goldstein, A. G., 1989, Tectonic significance of multiple motions on terrane-bounding faults in the northern Appalachians: Geological Society of America Bulletin, v. 101, p. 927–938.

Goldstein, A. G., 1994, A shear zone origin for Alleghanian (Permian) multiple deformation in eastern Massachusetts: Tectonics, v. 13, p. 52–77.

Harwood, D. S., and Zietz, I., 1977, Geologic interpretation of an aeromagnetic map of southern New England: U.S. Geological Survey Geophysical Investigations Map GP-906, 11 p.

Haworth, R. T., Daniels, D. L., Williams, H., and Zietz, I., 1980, Bouguer gravity anomaly map of the Appalachian orogen: Memorial University of Newfoundland, Map No. 3, scale 1:1,000,000, Map No. 3a, scale 1:2,000,000.

Hepburn, J. C., Dunning, G. R., and Hon, R., 1995, Geochronology and regional tectonic implications of Silurian Deformation in the Nashoba Terrane, southeastern New England, USA, *in* Hibbard, J. P., van Staal, C. R., and Cawood, P. A., eds., Current perspectives in the Appalachian-Caledonian orogen: Geological Association of Canada Special Paper 41, p. 349–366.

Hermes, O. D., Ballard, R. D., and Banks, P. O., 1978, Upper Ordovician peralkalic granites from the Gulf of Maine: Geological Society of America Bulletin, v. 89, p. 1761–1774.

Hoffman, P. F., 1987, Continental transform tectonics: Great Slave Lake shear zone (ca. 1.9 Ga), northwest Canada: Geology, v. 15, p. 785–788.

Hubbard, M. S., West, D. P., Jr., Ludman, A., Guidotti, C. V., and Lux, D. R., 1995, The Norumbega fault zone, Maine: A mid- to shallow-level crustal section within a transcurrent shear zone: Atlantic Geology, v. 31, p. 109–116.

Hussey, A. M., II, 1971a, Geologic map and cross-sections of the Orrs Island 7.5′ map and adjacent area: Maine Geologic Survey Map GM-2, scale 1:24,000, 18 p.

Hussey, A. M., II, 1971b, Geologic map of the Portland 15′ quadrangle, Maine: Maine Geological Survey Map GM-1, scale 1:62,500, 19 p.

Hussey, A. M., II, 1980, The Rye Formation of Gerrish Island, Kittery, Maine: A reinterpretation: The Maine Geologist, v. 7, no. 2, p. 2–3.

Hussey, A. M., II, 1985, The bedrock geology of the Bath and Portland 2 degree sheets, Maine: Maine Geological Survey Open File Report no. 85 87, 2 maps, 82 p.

Hussey, A. M., II, 1988, Lithotectonic stratigraphy, deformation, plutonism, and metamorphism, greater Casco Bay region, southwestern Maine, *in* Tucker, R. D., and Marvinney, F. G., eds., Studies in Maine geology, Volume 1: Structure and stratigraphy: Augusta, Maine Geological Survey, p. 17–34.

Hussey, A. M., II, and Bothner, W. A., 1993, Geology of the coastal lithotectonic belt, SW Maine and SE New Hampshire, *in* Cheney, J. T., and Hepburn, J. C., eds., Field trip guidebook for the northeastern United States: Amherst, University of Massachusetts, Department of Geology and Geography Contribution no. 67, p. K1–K19.

Hussey, A. M., II, and Bothner, W. A., 1995, Geology of the coastal lithotectonic belt, SW Maine and SE New Hampshire, *in* Hussey, A. M., II, and Johnston, R. A., eds., Guidebook to field trips in southern Maine and adjacent New Hampshire, New England Intercollegiate Geological Conference Guidebook, v. 87, p. 211–228.

Hussey, A. M., II, and Marvinney, R. G., 1998, Geology of the Bath 1:100,000 map sheet: Augusta, Maine Geological Survey (in press).

Hussey, A. M., II, and Newberg, D. W., 1978, Major faulting in the Merrimack synclinorium between Hollis, New Hampshire, and Biddeford, Maine: Geological Society of America Abstracts with Programs, v. 10, p. 48.

Hussey, A. M., II, Aleinikoff, J., and Marvinney, R. G., 1993, Reinterpretation of age and correlations between tectonostratigraphic units, southwestern Maine: Geological Society of America Abstracts with Programs, v. 25, no. 2, p. 25.

Hutchinson, D. R., Klitgord, K. D., Lee, M. W., and Trehu, A. M., 1988, U.S. Geological Survey deep seismic reflection profile across the Gulf of Maine: Geological Society of America Bulletin, v. 100, p. 172–184.

Kane, M. F., Yellin, M. J., Bell, K. G., and Zietz, I., 1972, Gravity and magnetic evidence of lithology and structure in the Gulf of Maine region: U.S. Geological Survey Professional Paper 726-B, 22 p.

Katz, F. J., 1917, Stratigraphy of southwestern Maine and southeastern New Hampshire: U.S. Geological Survey Professional Paper 108-I, p. 165–177.

Lyons, J. B., Aleinikoff, J. N., and Boudette, E. L., 1982, The Avalonian and Gander zones in central eastern New England, *in* St. Julien, P., and Beland, J., eds., Major structural zones and faults of the Northern Appalachians: Geological Association of Canada Special Paper 24, p. 43–66.

Lyons, J. B., Bothner, W. A., Moench, R. H., and Thompson, J. B., Jr., 1997, Bedrock geologic map of New Hampshire: U.S. Geological Survey State Map Series, scales 1:250,000 and 1:500,000.

Macnab, R., Shih, K.-G., Bothner, W. A., Brooks, J. A., Delorey, C., and Klitgord, K. D., 1990, Magnetic data over Gulf of Maine and adjacent land areas: Preparation of a data base for a 1:500,000 magnetic anomaly map: Geological Survey of Canada Open-File 2295, 19 p.

Marvinney, R. G., Hussey, A. M., II, and Starer, A. L., 1995, Bedrock geology of the lower Saco River area and its potential relationship to arsenic in ground water, *in* Hussey, A. M., II, and Johnston, R. A., eds., Guidebook to field trips in southern Maine and adjacent New Hampshire: New England Intercollegiate Geological Conference Guidebook, v. 87, p. 243–258.

Newberg, D. W., 1984, Bedrock geology of the Gardiner 15′ quadrangle, Maine: Maine Geological Survey Open-File Report no. 84-8, scale 1:62,500.

Olszewski, W. J., Gaudette, H. E., Bothner, W. A., Laird, J., and Cheatham, M. W., 1984, The Precambrian (?) rocks of southeastern New Hampshire, a forgotten land: Geological Society of America Abstracts with Programs, v. 16, p. 54.

Osberg, P. H., 1988, Geologic relations within the shale-wacke sequence in south central Maine, *in* Tucker, R. D., and Marvinney, R. G., eds., Studies in Maine geology, Volume 1: Structure and stratigraphy: Augusta, Maine

Geological Survey, p. 51–73.

Osberg, P. H., Hussey, A. M., II, and Boone, G. M., 1985, Bedrock geologic map of Maine: Augusta, Maine Geological Survey, scale 1:500,000.

Osberg, P. H., Tucker, R. D., and Berry, H. N., IV, 1995, Is the Acadian suture lost?, *in* Hussey, A. M., II, and Johnston, R. A., eds., Guidebook to field trips in southern Maine and adjacent New Hampshire: New England Intercollegiate Geological Conference Guidebook, v. 87, p. 145–172.

Pankiwskyj, K. A., 1976, Preliminary report on the geology of the Liberty 15′ quadrangle and adjoining parts of the Burnham, Brooks, Belfast, and Vassalboro quadrangles in south-central Maine: Maine Geological Survey Open File No. 76-29, scale 1:62,500.

Pankiwskyj, K. A., 1996, Structure and stratigraphy across the Hackmatack Pond fault, Kennebeck and Waldo Counties, Maine: Maine Geological Survey Open File No. 96-2, 2 maps, 15 p..

Pease, M. H., Jr., 1989, Correlation of the Oakdale Formation and Paxton Group of central Massachusetts with strata in northeastern Connecticut: U.S. Geological Survey Bulletin 1796, 26 p.

Peterman, Z. E., and Day, W., 1989, Early Proterozoic activity on Archean faults in the western Superior province—Evidence from pseudotachylite: Geology, v. 17, p. 1089–1092.

Phillips, J. D., 1990, Integration of potential-field and digital geologic data for two North American geoscience traverses: Journal of Geological Education, v. 38, p. 330–338.

Robinson, G. R., 1979, Bedrock geology of the Nashua River area, Massachusetts–New Hampshire [Ph.D. thesis]: Cambridge, Massachusetts, Harvard University, 172 p.

Robinson, J. C., 1989, A brittle fracture analysis of the Flint Hill Fault Zone, southeastern New Hampshire [M.S. thesis]: Amherst, University of Massachusetts, 91 p.

Shride, A. F., 1976, Stratigraphy and correlation of the Newbury volcanic complex, northeastern Massachusetts, *in* Page, L. R., ed., Contributions to the stratigraphy of New England: Geological Society of America Memoir 148, p. 147–177.

Sultan, M., Arvidson, R. E., Duncan, I. J., Stern, R. J., and El Kaliouby, B., 1988, Extension of the Najd shear system from Saudi Arabia to the central eastern desert of Egypt based on integrated field and Landsat observations: Tectonics, v. 7, p. 1291–1306.

Swanson, M. T., 1988, Pseudotachylite-bearing strike-slip duplex structures in the Fort Foster brittle zone, southern Maine: Journal of Structural Geology, v. 10, p. 813–828.

Swanson, M. T., 1992, Late Acadian–Alleghanian transpressional deformation: Evidence from asymmetric boudinage in the Casco Bay area, coastal Maine: Journal of Structural Geology, v. 14, p. 323–341.

Swanson, M. T., 1995, Detailed structure of brittle strike-slip faults in coastal Maine exposures, *in* Hussey, A. M., II, and Johnston, R. A., eds., Guidebook to field trips in southern Maine and adjacent New Hampshire: New England Intercollegiate Geological Conference Guidebook, v. 87, Maine, p. 291–302.

Swanson, M. T., and Carrigan, J. A., 1984, Ductile and brittle structures within the Rye Formation of coastal Maine and New Hampshire, *in* Hansen, L. S., ed., Geology of the Coastal Lowlands, Boston to Kennebunkport, Maine: New England Intercollegiate Geological Conference Guidebook, v. 76, p. 165–185.

Swanson, M. T., Pollock, S. G., and Hussey, A. M., II, 1986, The structural and stratigraphic development of the Casco Bay Group at Harpswell Neck, Maine, *in* Newberg, D. W., ed., Guidebook for field trips in southwestern Maine, New England Intercollegiate Geological Conference Guidebook v. 78, p. 350–370.

Thompson, W., and Borns, H., 1985, Surficial geologic map of Maine: Augusta, Maine Geological Survey, scale 1:500,000.

Welch, P., 1993, Petrology and fabric analysis across the Great Commons fault zone (GCFZ) within the Rye Formation, New Castle, New Hampshire: Geological Society of America Abstracts with Programs, v. 25, no. 6, p. A-265.

West, D. P., Jr., 1993, The eastern limit of Acadian high-grade metamorphism in northern New England: Implications for the location of the "Acadian suture": Geological Society of America Abstracts with Programs, v. 25, no. 2, p. 89.

West, D. P., Jr., 1995, The Norumbega fault zone in south-central Maine: A trip through 80 million years of dextral shear deformation, *in* Hussey, A. M., II, and Johnston, R. A., eds., Guidebook to field trips in southern Maine and adjacent New Hampshire: New England Intercollegiate Geological Conference Guidebook, v. 87, p. 125–143.

West, D. P., Jr., and Lux, D. R., 1993, Dating mylonitic deformation by the ^{40}AR-^{39}Ar method: An example from the Norumbega fault zone, Maine: Earth and Planetary Science Letters, v. 120, p. 221–237.

West, D. P., Jr., Lux, D. R., and Hussey, A. M., II, 1993, Contrasting thermal histories across the Flying Point fault, southwestern Maine: Evidence for Mesozoic displacement: Geological Society of America Bulletin, v. 105, p. 1478–1490.

Wintsch, R. P., Sutter, J. F., Kunk, M. J., Aleinikoff, J. N., and Dorais, M. J., 1992, Contrasting P-T-t paths: Thermochronologic evidence for a late Paleozoic final assemblage of the Avalon Composite Terrane in the New England Appalachians: Tectonics, v. 11, p. 672–689.

Zeitz, I., Haworth, R. T., Williams, H., and Daniels, D. L., 1980a, Magnetic anomaly map of the Appalachian orogen: Memorial University of Newfoundland, Map No. 2, scale 1:1,00,000, Map No. 2a, scale 1:2,000,000.

Zeitz, I., Gilbert, F. P., and Kirby, J. R., 1980b, Aeromagnetic map of Connecticut, Massachusetts, New Hampshire, Rhode Island, and part of New York: U.S. Geological Survey Geophysical Investigations Map GP-928, scale 1,000,000.

Zen, E-an, ed., 1983, Bedrock geologic map of Massachusetts: U.S. Geological Survey, scale 1:250,000, 3 sheets.

MANUSCRIPT ACCEPTED BY THE SOCIETY JUNE 9, 1998

Geological Society of America
Special Paper 331
1999

Possible correlations of the Norumbega fault system with faults in southeastern New England

Arthur Goldstein
Department of Geology, Colgate University, Hamilton, New York 13346
J. Christopher Hepburn
Department of Geology and Geophysics, Boston College, Chestnut Hill, Massachusetts 02167

ABSTRACT

The Norumbega fault system in coastal Maine has been shown to be a transcurrent fault of great extent that underwent dextral displacements in both mid-Paleozoic and late Paleozoic time. The fault can be convincingly traced southwestward from New Brunswick, where it is referred to as the Fredricton fault, to the region of Casco Bay, Maine, but its continuation beyond that point remains a matter of speculation. Various workers have claimed that the Norumbega fault system continues southwestward as either the Campbell Hill–Nonesuch River faults in southeastern New Hampshire, the Clinton Newbury fault in eastern Massachusetts, or the Bloody Bluff fault in eastern Massachusetts. We examine the criteria necessary to show that any two faults were either continuous or related and apply those criteria to the faults noted here. We find that the Bloody Bluff fault and the Norumbega fault system were active as dextral transcurrent faults in the mid-Paleozoic and thus may be either related or direct continuations of each other. However, no late Paleozoic activity occurred on Bloody Bluff fault, although its southern portion was reactivated as a normal fault at that time. We propose that the late Paleozoic Norumbega fault system turns southward in the Casco Bay region and remains offshore with a northerly strike. We speculate that it merges with the Fundy fault in the Gulf of Maine and underwent Pennsylvanian sinistral displacements, allowing the opening of the Narragansett basin, and dextral displacements in the latest Pennsylvanian and Permian causing closure, deformation, and metamorphism of the Narragansett basin. This deformation could also be related to widespread ductile deformation of crystalline basement surrounding the basin, local crustal thickening and northwest-directed extension evidenced by widespread low-angle and high-angle normal faults.

INTRODUCTION

The role of faults in the assembly and tectonics of mountain belts is a topic that has received considerable attention. Whereas we realize that faults are responsible for terrane accretion and dispersion and that they serve to thin and thicken the crust, identifying the tectonic significance of specific faults in any mountain belt remains one of the more difficult tasks in tectonics. The problems lie in determining the timing, direction, sense, and amount of fault displacement. Once formed, faults are commonly reactivated numerous times, making tectonic interpretations even more difficult. An example is the Norumbega fault, a very long transcurrent fault in eastern Maine and New Brunswick. The fault was initially described by Stewart and Wones (1974) and Wones (1978) and it has since been recognized as being more than 400 km in length. Displacements on various parts of the fault have been described as dextral transcurrent (e.g., Hubbard et al., 1995), sinistral transcurrent (Kent

Goldstein, A., and Hepburn, J. C., 1999, Possible correlations of the Norumbega fault system with faults in southeastern New England, *in* Ludman, A., and West, D. P., Jr., eds., Norumbega Fault System of the Northern Appalachians: Boulder, Colorado, Geological Society of America Special Paper 331.

and Opdyke, 1978), reverse (Osberg et al., 1985), and normal (West et al., 1993), and some workers believe that the fault marks a terrane boundary. Papers in this volume make significant contributions toward resolving many of those disagreements. In particular, Ludman and West (this volume) make a distinction between the Norumbega fault zone and the Norumbega fault system. In southern Maine, the zone is a narrow, ~200-m-wide zone of dextral displacement active ca. 290 Ma (Late Pennsylvanian–Early Permian) embedded in a much wider (~30 km) fault system that underwent ductile dextral shear ca. 380 Ma (Middle Devonian). Because the two are essentially coincident, and to avoid confusion, in this chapter we consider the two features to represent two episodes of dextral displacement on a single feature, which we will refer to as the Norumbega fault system. The southern continuation of the system is largely unknown. The fault zone can be traced convincingly to the area of Casco Bay, Maine (West, 1995), but there is considerable disagreement about which, if any, of the large faults in southeastern New England represents the southern continuation of the Norumbega fault system, despite the realization that a fault of such great length must continue along strike or end in some recognizable cross structure. The purpose of this chapter is to discuss what is currently known of the displacement history of faults in southeastern New England and to compare these histories to what is currently known about the Norumbega fault system. We hope that this discussion of the timing and kinematics of faulting in eastern Massachusetts will not only provide the framework within which to discuss southern continuations of the Norumbega fault system, but will also provide additional data for a more complete understanding of the tectonics of southeastern New England, especially during the late Paleozoic Alleghanian orogeny.

CRITERIA FOR CORRELATING AND RELATING FAULTS

There are two related topics to consider when attempting to either correlate or relate faults. One concerns direct correlation of fault strands, whereas the other concerns determining if separate faults moved at approximately the same time under the same stress state. In order for faults that cannot be mapped as direct continuations of each other to be considered the same structure or related in some way, several criteria must be met. First, and perhaps most significant, the faults must be shown to have been active at the same time. Determining timing of fault activity with sufficient precision to do this is not always possible. New methods of dating fault motion (e.g., West and Lux, 1993) have been applied with considerable success to the Norumbega fault system, but many other faults in the northern Appalachians have much less-well constrained histories. In addition to timing, the faults must have comparable kinematics. That is, the direction and sense of motion must be the same for both faults. Furthermore, the thermal regime of faulting must be comparable within one area. Fault activity at elevated temperatures results in wide zones of mylonitization, whereas shallow crustal faulting produces cataclasites and slickensides. We would not expect to find synchronous cataclastic or brittle faulting and high-temperature mylonitization occurring in the same area at the same time, although a single feature might display both high- and low-temperature phenomena along strike. The amounts of displacement on the faults must be of similar magnitude; this is perhaps most difficult to determine. For example, if one fault can be shown to have only a few kilometers of total offset and the other is known to accommodate tens or even hundreds of kilometers of displacement, it would be difficult to consider the two as coincident, although timing and kinematics might suggest that they were related.

Relating faults to each other is a much less specific task, although distinct criteria must also be met. Knowing that certain faults were active at the same time would be the best way to establish a relationship, but such data are rarely available. Thus, geometric criteria will be very useful in attempting to establish a relationship between faults. Large faults, such as the Norumbega fault system, commonly have many smaller faults associated with them. Some of these may be geometrically similar, such as small-displacement dextral faults parallel to a large dextral fault. However, large strike-slip faults rarely remain strictly straight over their entire length, and bends in the fault can produce associated faults with orientations and senses of displacement very dissimilar to the main fault. For example, strike-slip faults with either releasing or confining bends may be associated with normal or thrust (reverse) faults, respectively. For this to be shown, the geometry of the strike-slip fault must be appropriate for the thrust or normal faults. That is, given the sense of strike-slip displacement and the change in orientation of the fault, releasing bends must be associated with normal faults and confining bends associated with thrust (reverse) faults. A simple comparison of directions of displacement between the main fault and possibly related, small displacement faults, as marked by slickenlines or mylonitic lineations, may not reveal the relationship because transpressional and transtensional settings may give rise to a variety of oblique-slip faults. Our ability to determine all these various criteria is imperfect, making the task of finding the southern continuation of the Norumbega fault system a difficult one. Nevertheless, we summarize what is known about many of the larger faults in southeastern New England and constrain the southern continuation of the Norumbega fault system as best as possible with the available data (Table 1).

NORUMBEGA FAULT SYSTEM

The Norumbega fault system is a steeply dipping, northeast-striking (N30–60°E) fault that has a polyphase history of motion (Hubbard et al., 1995; West and Lux, 1993; West, 1995). The system in southern Maine (Casco Bay) is marked by a wide (~30 km) zone of steep foliation and heterogeneous mylonitization as well as a narrow (~1 km) zone of steep foliation and

TABLE 1. SUMMARY OF FAULT ORIENTATIONS AND MOTION HISTORIES FOR SOUTHEASTERN NEW ENGLAND

	NFZ	LCF*	HHF	WF	CNF	BBF	SSZ	FPF (etc.)
Strike Dip	NE 90°	~N 0-50°W	~E-W 30-50°N	Domical	NE ~70°NW	NE 80-90°NW	NE ~40°NW	NE Variable but steep
Mesozoic	Normal					Normal		Normal
Permian	Dextral	Normal in direction 300°-330° Movement continues during unroofing and cooling Possible early thrusting			Normal		Late normal Early Sinistral	
Pennsylvanian								
Mississippian	Normal?							
Devonian	Dextral	Possible early motion: xenoliths of mylonite in Preston Gabbro (424 Ma)				Late dextral Early sinistral		
Silurian								
Ordovician								
Cambrian								
Precambrian						?		

Note: See text for sources of information and details. NFZ = Norumbega Fault System; LCF = Lake Char Fault; HHF = Honey Hill Fault; WF = Wekepeke Fault; CNF = Clinton-Newbury Fault; BBF = Bloody Bluff Fault; SSZ = Sterling Shear Zone; FPF = Flying Point Fault.

intense mylonitization (West and Lux, 1993; West, 1995). Farther northeast, the zone of mylonitization narrows and the fault zone is ~5 km wide and characterized by brittle features (Hubbard et al., 1995). Brittle faults related to the Norumbega fault system occur in a zone at least 40 km wide (Ludman, this volume). Within the wide zone of mylonitization, abundant asymmetric fabrics indicate dextral shear, and $^{40}Ar/^{39}Ar$ data show that these rocks cooled below ~320 °C by the Early Carboniferous (320–360 Ma; West, 1995; West and Lux, 1993). Considering that many of the asymmetric fabrics must have formed at temperatures above ~320 °C, West (1995) and West and Lux (1993) concluded that dextral shearing must have occurred before Early Carboniferous time. Because $^{40}Ar/^{39}Ar$ data also show that the last amphibolite facies metamorphism in this area occurred between 368 and 381 Ma (Middle Devonian), West and Lux (1993) concluded that high-temperature dextral shearing occurred during and perhaps before that time. Thus, these data suggest a Late Silurian–Middle Devonian age for distributed dextral motion on the Norumbega fault system. Ludman et al. (this volume) have also described Devonian (ca. 380 Ma) dextral shear in northeastern Maine. In contrast, detailed $^{40}Ar/^{39}Ar$ analyses show that the narrow zone of intense shear-

ing was active ca. 290 Ma (Late Carboniferous–Early Permian; Ludman et al., this volume; West and Lux, 1993). One can conclude, therefore, that at least two episodes of motion occurred on the Norumbega fault system, one during the middle Paleozoic (Silurian-Devonian) and one during the late Paleozoic (Late Pennsylvanian–Permian), and that both periods of motion were characterized by dextral displacement. West et al. (1993) and Doll et al. (1996) suggested an additional episode of Mesozoic or even post-Mesozoic dip-slip reactivation of the Norumbega fault system. Furthermore, Ludman et al. (this volume) and West (this volume) both infer a period of Carboniferous activity on the Norumbega fault system from the presence of terrestrial basins in Maine and New Brunswick, which they believe formed in associated with releasing bends along the Norumbega fault system.

FAULTS IN EASTERN MASSACHUSETTS AND CONNECTICUT

A number of major faults have been recognized in southeastern New England and were described by Castle et al. (1976), Dixon and Lundgren (1968), Skehan (1968), Goldstein (1982,

1989, 1994), Goldsmith (1991), Wintsch (1979), and others. Major faults composing this system include the Honey Hill fault, Lake Chargoggagoggmanchauggauggagoggchaubunagungamaugg fault (Lake Char fault), Willimantic fault, Clinton-Newbury fault, and Bloody Bluff fault (Figs. 1 and 2). The Honey Hill, Lake Char, and Willimantic faults in Connecticut comprise a single surface separating late Precambrian gneisses and quartzites from early Paleozoic(?) metasedimentary and metavolcanic rocks. The surface is complexly convoluted and dips shallowly to moderately to the north, west, and northwest, except along the southern and eastern margins of the Willimantic dome, where dips are to the south and east.. Along most of its length, this surface is marked by a wide zone of mylonitization with prominent mineral elongation lineations that trend N30°–60°W. Abundant kinematic indicators in these mylonites record a sense of motion that is top-down-to-the-northwest, most conveniently thought of as low-angle normal displacement (Goldstein, 1989). Largely on the basis of isotopic data, Wintsch et al. (1992), Wintsch and Sutter (1985), and Getty and Gromet (1992a, 1992b) suggested that prior to normal motion this fault system moved in thrust mode. Rare thrust-sense microscopic kinematic indicators suggest that this may be the case. It is significant that the fact that nearly all thrust-sense kinematic indicators have been overprinted by normal-sense indicators shows that the crustal extension along the Honey Hill–Lake Char–Willimantic faults was not trivial. No one has proposed dextral displacement on any of these faults; therefore, they are poor candidates for a southward continuation of the Norumbega fault system, although they may have been active at the same time and be located in a releasing and/or confining bend setting.

The lineations and kinematic indicators associated with normal displacement on the Lake Char–Honey Hill–Willimantic faults consist of ductilely deformed feldspars and quartz, indicating fault activity at high temperatures (upper greenschist–lower amphibolite facies; Goldstein, 1989). Brittlely deformed feldspars also occur with ductilely deformed quartz (indicating fault activity at moderate temperatures, lower and middle greenschist facies) as well as with brittlely deformed quartz (indicating fault activity at low temperatures, below ~200 °C) show that crustal extension and normal faulting continued during a period of cooling (Goldstein, 1989). Varieties of isotopic data show that southeastern New England was unroofed and cooled during the latest Paleozoic, the time during which these normal faults were active (Goldstein, 1989; Wintsch et al., 1992; Getty and Gromet, 1992a, 1992b). Thus, these faults represent a low-angle detachment surface separating basement and cover that was active during a period of unroofing and cooling. In this respect, they are similar to low-angle normal faults associated with metamorphic core complexes. Dixon (1982) described xenoliths of mylonite in the Preston Gabbro, a 424 ± 5 Ma intrusion at the intersection of the Lake Char and Honey Hill faults in southeastern Connecticut. These xenoliths suggest that the faults may have moved prior to the late Paleozoic, but it is difficult to impossible to constrain the nature of this early activity.

The Clinton-Newbury fault in Massachusetts (Figs. 1 and 2) is closely related to the Honey Hill, Lake Char, and Willimantic faults (Goldstein, 1989, 1994). The northwest-dipping normal Clinton-Newbury fault brings the moderately metamorphosed and deformed metasedimentary and igneous rocks of the Merrimack trough (hanging wall, northwest side) into contact with highly metamorphosed and deformed rocks of the Nashoba terrane (footwall, southeast side). The fault has been shown to be late Paleozoic in age (Goldstein, 1994) and no evidence of earlier motions has yet been found. It is interesting that the Clinton-Newbury fault cuts a wide mylonite zone that is identical in geometry and kinematics to the Lake Char fault. Goldstein (1994) named this the Wachusett mylonite zone and speculated that it represents the northward continuation of the Lake Char fault. If this is so, it suggests that late-stage, low-temperature normal motion occurred along the Honey Hill–Lake Char–Willimantic faults in southern Massachusetts and Connecticut, whereas in central Massachusetts the late-stage extension occurred on the new, higher angle Clinton-Newbury fault. The Clinton-Newbury fault has a distinctly different direction of motion from that of the other low-angle mylonite zones. Lineations in mylonites associated with the Clinton-Newbury fault trend nearly due west rather than northwest, as in the Honey Hill–Lake Char–Willimantic–Wachusett mylonite zone (Goldstein, 1994).

The Bloody Bluff fault (Figs. 1 and 2) forms the steeply northwest-dipping eastern boundary of the Nashoba zone in eastern Massachusetts, where it comes in contact with late Precambrian igneous and metamorphic rocks of the Boston Avalon zone (Goldsmith, 1991). The fault was first described by Cupels (1961) and has been referred to at times as the Burlington fault system (Castle et al., 1976). Two features are commonly associated with this fault: a wide zone of mylonitization that is for the most part in the rocks of the Boston Avalon zone (southeastern side; footwall) and a sharp break along the contact between the two terranes. Nelson (1976) observed that the mylonites of the footwall are intruded by the Peabody granite (365–395 Ma; Zartman, 1977) and Goldstein (1989) suggested that motion on the Bloody Bluff fault mylonites could be constrained as having occurred between 430 and 365 Ma. Although some uncertainties remain about timing of displacements that gave rise to Bloody Bluff fault mylonites (see following), it remains convincing that much of this deformation must be considered Middle Silurian–Middle Devonian. There is good evidence for at least three separate periods of motion along the Bloody Bluff fault (sinistral, dextral, and normal). Within the mylonites in the footwall, foliation is nearly vertical, lineations plunge gently toward the northeast, and kinematic indicators show that displacement associated with these fabrics was both sinistral and dextral. Goldstein (1989) described sinistral displacement and new, oriented thin sections of Bloody Bluff fault mylonite show an even more pronounced dextral overprint on the earlier sinistral fabrics. Regionally, this two-stage Silurian-Devonian transcurrent displacement history is in accord with other work in the northern Appalachians. Both Dube et al.

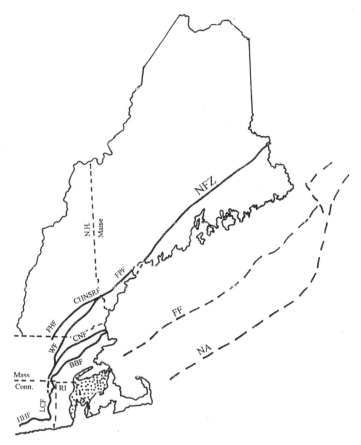

Figure 1. Map showing the Norumbega fault system (NFS) and other faults that are candidates for its southern continuation. FPF—Flying Point fault; CHNSRF—Campbell Hill–Nonesuch River fault; FHF—Flint Hill fault; WF—Wekepeke fault; CNF—Clinton-Newbury fault; BBF—Bloody Bluff fault; LCF—Lake Char fault; HHF—Honey Hill fault; PN—Putnam-Nashoba terrane; NA—Nauset anomaly; FF—Fundy Fault.

reflective of normal motion during the Permian. Thus, the Bloody Bluff fault is best described as a fault accommodating mid-Paleozoic sinistral and dextral displacements with a late Paleozoic normal overprint along its southern portion and Mesozoic normal overprinting in some segments.

Rast et al. (1993) and Rast and Skehan (1995) argued that some of the mylonites associated with the Bloody Bluff fault are Proterozoic in age, rather than Middle Paleozoic. They described sinistral and dextral kinematic indicators in several distinct shear zones as well as in the major body of Bloody Bluff fault mylonites. Much of their evidence for the age of fault activity is based on intrusive relationships, and it is prudent at this time to suggest that some of the mylonitization associated with the Bloody Bluff fault may be late Precambrian. Other observations suggest, however, that mid-Paleozoic was also a time of transcurrent fault activity in eastern Massachusetts. Both sinistral and dextral shear zones have been identified in rocks of the Nashoba terrane. Hepburn et al. (1995) showed that rocks of this terrane are Late Cambrian to Early Silurian and their metamorphism and deformation are constrained to be mid-Paleozoic. Thus, although some mylonitization in eastern Massachusetts may record Precambrian activity, middle Paleozoic sinistral and dextral displacements seem assured.

OTHER FAULTS IN SOUTHEASTERN NEW ENGLAND

The faults we have discussed are well known and reasonably well characterized, although opinions vary about their displacement history and tectonic significance. Other major structures in this part of the northern Appalachians have been proposed but are less-well documented. Goldstein (1994) suggested that a wide, late Paleozoic, transcurrent ductile shear zone (the Sterling shear zone) is in rocks of the Merrimack trough just west of the Clinton-Newbury fault near Clinton, Massachusetts. This suggestion was based on an abrupt strain gradient across which late Paleozoic cleavages and retrograde metamorphism disappear and across which orientations of bedding and foliation change abruptly. Goldstein (1994) proposed that this strain gradient marks a shear-zone boundary and that the Sterling shear zone must have undergone sinistral displacement early in the Alleghanian orogeny. Following sinistral motion on the shear zone, all other late Paleozoic fault displacements accommodated normal slip. O'Hara and Gromet (1985) described a fault, the Hope Valley shear zone, which they believe is within the composite Avalon terrane of southeastern New England and juxtaposes two distinct late Precambrian terranes. They described this feature as having dextral displacement during the Alleghanian orogeny. The existence of the Hope Valley shear zone has been questioned by some workers (e.g., Goldstein, 1986) and, as with the Sterling shear zone, it must remain a matter for additional work. The Ponkapoag fault forms the southern side of the Norfolk basin (the northern appendage of the Narragansett basin, Zen et al., 1983) where it separates Pennsylvanian sedimentary rocks from the Protero-

(1996) and O'Brien et al. (1993) described Late Silurian–Early Devonian sinistral followed by dextral displacement histories for faults in Newfoundland. More commonly, only a single episode of transcurrent displacement can be identified, such as the prominent dextral displacement recognized for the Norumbega fault system or the sinistral displacement described for the northeastern Gander zone in Newfoundland by Hanmer (1981) or other mid-Paleozoic faults in the Caledonides (Powell and Phillips, 1985; Harland, 1985; Steltenpohl and Bartley, 1988).

In some areas near the Bloody Bluff fault there are chlorite streaks that plunge downdip on foliation planes (Goldstein, 1989). The most common occurrence of these dip-slip lineations is in association with a small Mesozoic basin near Middleton, Massachusetts (Kaye, 1983), and it is most likely that they reflect Mesozoic normal reactivation of the Bloody Bluff fault. It may be that other displacements occurred along the fault between Middle Devonian and Mesozoic time. This is most easily determined along the southern Bloody Bluff fault, where the fault fabrics are identical to those along the Honey Hill–Lake Char–Willimantic–Wachuset mylonite zone and are

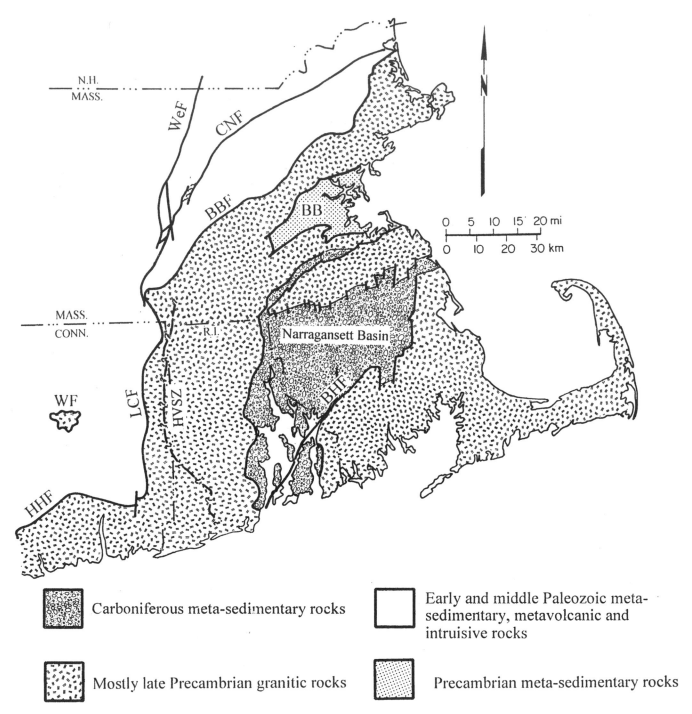

Figure 2. Generalized geologic map of southeastern New England showing locations of faults mentioned in text. Map modified from Zen et al. (1983), Hermes et al. (1994) and Rogers (1985). WeF—Wekepeke Fault ; HVSZ—Hope Valley Shear Zone; BHF—Beverhead Fault; PF—Portsmouth Fault; other abbreviations as in Figure 1.

zoic Z Dedham Granite (Fig. 2). East of the Norfolk basin, the Pennsylvanian rocks are cut out along the fault. There it separates the Quincy Granite and Cambrian Braintree Formation from the Dedham Granite or is entirely within the Dedham Granite near the coast (Goldsmith, 1991). Not much is known about movements on the Ponkapoag fault. It is now a steep

fault, but it is inferred to have been rotated into its present attitude after originating as a northward-directed, southeasterly dipping thrust (Billings, 1976; Skehan, 1983; Goldsmith, 1991). However, Billings (1982) also proposed normal movement along the Ponkapoag fault. Numerous other map-scale faults exist in southeastern New England but none are of sufficient magnitude or sufficiently well documented to be considered as continuations of the Norumbega fault.

FAULTS IN THE GULF OF MAINE

Major fault zones have been identified offshore in the northwestern Gulf of Maine on the basis of geophysics (e.g., Ballard and Uchupi, 1975; Hutchinson et al., 1988; Klitgord et al., 1988; Keen et al., 1991). One of the most prominent is the Fundy fault, which extends southwestward from the northern margin of the Bay of Fundy, parallel to and roughly 100 km east of the Norumbega fault system (Fig. 1). This fault forms the southeastern margin of the Gulf of Maine fault zone (Hutchinson et al., 1988), a distinctive zone 30–50-km-wide of strong linear magnetic anomalies and southeasterly dipping crustal seismic reflectors that have been interpreted as a series of stacked fault zones. Current interpretations (Keen et al., 1991; Hutchinson et al., 1988) suggest that the Fundy fault, and others in the Gulf of Maine fault zone, originated as Carboniferous to late Paleozoic Alleghanian thrust faults near the limit of strong Variscan-Alleghanian deformation (the Variscan front of Rast and Grant, 1973; Rast, 1983). Many of these faults, including the Fundy fault, were subsequently reactivated by Mesozoic extension (Keen et al., 1991; Hutchinson et al., 1988). Basement samples of peralkalic granite collected from the zone of linear anomalies associated with the Gulf of Maine fault zone and from just southeast of the Fundy fault are Ordovician to Silurian in age (Hermes et al., 1978). They indicate that the bedrock of this area can be correlated with the Avalonian composite terrane of southeastern New England (Hermes et al., 1978; Hutchinson et al., 1988).

The Gulf of Maine fault zone comes on land in the Avalon terranes of eastern coastal Maine and southern New Brunswick (Keen et al., 1991; Hutchinson et al., 1988) and also likely comes onshore in eastern Massachusetts, but exact correlations are debated. The northwestern side of the Gulf of Maine fault zone, corresponding to the Variscan front, has been interpreted to be either along the Clinton-Newbury fault (Thompson et al., 1993) or the Bloody Bluff fault (Hutchinson et al., 1988). Hutchinson et al. (1988) indicated that on the basis of magnetic anomaly trends, the Fundy fault (the southeast boundary of the Gulf of Maine fault zone) projects ashore either near the Bloody Bluff fault north of Cape Ann or near the Ponkapoag fault south of the Boston basin (Fig. 2). However, they also indicated that the magnetic anomalies associated with the Gulf of Maine fault zone pinch out toward the Bloody Bluff fault zone and appear to merge with the anomalies associated with the Ponkapoag fault. Because of this and the fact that basement samples from the Gulf of Maine fault zone are correlated with rocks of the Avalon composite terrane, and not the Nashoba terrane, Hutchinson et al. (1988) indicated that it is more likely that the Fundy fault projects ashore at or near the Ponkapoag fault. This interpretation was shared by Thompson et al. (1993).

The relationship between the Gulf of Maine fault zone and the Fundy fault to the Norumbega fault system is unclear. The problems in attempting to trace the Norumbega fault system offshore include the difficulty in relating mapped faults on land to geophysical data offshore. The fault system is vertical to northwest dipping. The Gulf of Maine fault zone and Fundy fault are interpreted as dipping moderately to the southeast, on the basis of seismic reflections. However, reflection seismology will not image steep structures well, leaving open the possibility of more steeply dipping structures in the Gulf of Maine. The straight trace of the Fundy fault and its parallelism with the Norumbega fault system suggest that it is more likely a steep structure that underwent strike-slip displacements. Brooks and Bothner (1989) indicated evidence for this in offset magnetic anomalies in the western Gulf of Maine which they attributed to strike-slip motion during Alleghanian dextral transpression.

A prominent magnetic anomaly, the Nauset anomaly, extends through eastern Cape Cod, continues northeast across the Gulf of Maine, and into the Bay of Fundy (Fig. 1; Hutchinson et al., 1988). This anomaly has been suggested to be at or near the Avalon-Meguma boundary (Keen et al., 1991) and thus would be the southeasternmost limit of any continuation of the Norumbega fault system into southeastern New England.

SOUTHWARD CONTINUATIONS OF THE NORUMBEGA FAULT SYSTEM

Following Lyons et al. (1982), several workers have suggested that the Norumbega fault system continues southwest to the Maine–New Hampshire border and from there into northeastern Massachusetts. This is indicated on the bedrock geologic map of Maine (Osberg et al., 1985) and is shown in West et al. (1993), Hussey and Bothner (1993, 1995), Swanson (1995), and others. As shown in Figure 1, if the Norumbega fault system continues southwestward as the Flying Point–Campbell Hill–Nonesuch River fault (Hussey, 1985) from Maine into New Hampshire, it most likely connects with the Flint Hill, Silver Lake, Pinnacle, and Hall Mountain faults bounding the Massabesic gneiss belt and, farther southward, the Wekepeke fault in eastern Massachusetts (Lyons et al., 1982). Such a continuation seems unlikely given the apparent small magnitude of offset on these faults in New Hampshire and Massachusetts and the lack of any wide zone of ductile shear along them. As we noted, the southern portion of the Norumbega fault in Maine, near Casco Bay, is characterized by a wide zone of steep mylonitic foliation, subhorizontal lineations, and dextral kinematic indicators (Fig. 3). No corresponding zone of widespread ductile deformation has been reported along the faults noted herein that might represent the southward continuation of the Norumbega fault. At least one of these faults, the Flying Point fault, has been shown to have undergone ~4 km of dip-slip displacement (northwest-side up) in post-Paleozoic time (West et al., 1993). Another of these faults, the Wekepeke fault, has been described as a small feature that accommodated minor Permian displacements associated with normal displacement on the Clinton-Newbury fault (Goldstein, 1994). Lyons et al. (1982) showed the Nonesuch River fault, in southern Maine and south-

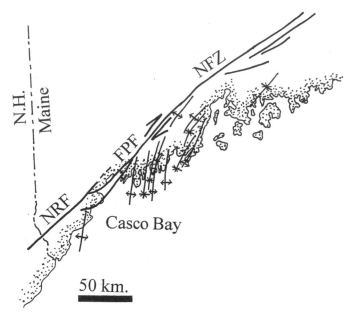

Figure 3. Oblique folds in the area of Casco Bay, Maine, believed by Swanson (1995) to be related to a confining bend in the Norumbega fault system. Map modified from Swanson (1995). NRF—Nonesuch River Fault; NFZ—Norumbega Fault Zone; FPF—Flying Point Fault.

eastern New Hampshire, crossing several mid-Paleozoic plutons (326 and 398 Ma) without displacing their borders, making it difficult for there to be any large-magnitude late Paleozoic dextral displacement. Furthermore, they noted that 330 Ma plutons in southern Maine are not appreciably offset by the Nonesuch River fault (Lyons et al., 1982). Thus, we can find no evidence (given the currently available data) suggesting that any of the faults in southeastern New Hampshire represents the southwestward continuation of the Norumbega fault.

However, steep mylonitic fabrics with subhorizontal lineations and dextral shear-sense indicators have been observed along coastal exposures in southern Maine and New Hampshire (the Portsmouth fault; Hussey and Bothner, 1995; Bothner and Hussey, this volume) and along the Bloody Bluff fault in northeastern Massachusetts. Although the Portsmouth fault has not been intensively studied, it is most likely not a direct continuation of the Norumbega fault system (Goldsmith, 1991). For such a connection to exist, the system would have to turn sharply so as to be offshore in Casco Bay yet connect with the Portsmouth fault in coastal New Hampshire. Similarly, we do not yet know when the Portsmouth fault was active. However, the Bloody Bluff fault was active as a dextral transcurrent fault in the middle Paleozoic, and we suggest that the Bloody Bluff fault represents the best possible southern continuation of the Norumbega fault system in middle Paleozoic time (Fig. 4A). It is likely that much of the eastern side of the northern Appalachians was in a dextral transcurrent tectonic environment during the middle Paleozoic (Acadian) orogeny and many structures, including the Norumbega fault system, Bloody Bluff fault, and Portsmouth fault–Rye mylonites may all reflect this. Thus, it is also conceivable that the Bloody

Bluff fault and the Norumbega fault system are not direct continuations of each other and represent different faults active at the same time under the same stress conditions. Although we do not believe that the Portsmouth fault is a direct continuation of the Norumbega fault system, it is conceivable that it was also active as a dextral transcurrent fault in middle Paleozoic time.

Correlating the Norumbega fault system and Bloody Bluff fault (Fig. 4A) requires that the system turn southward in the Casco Bay region. Such a geometry is supported by the magnetic field anomalies in this area. Bothner and Hussey (this volume) show a prominent northeast-trending anomaly in this area which they term the "cep anomaly" and they also hypothesize a major Norumbega fault system strand along it. Furthermore, Lyons et al. (1982) showed faults apparently related to the Norumbega fault system turning abruptly southward in the Casco Bay area. Klitgord et al. (1988) also showed several south-trending faults that extend into Casco Bay that may be related to similarly oriented faults shown on the Maine geological map (Osberg et al., 1985). Ballard and Uchupi (1975) indicated that the strikes of Mesozoic faults, which are likely reactivated Paleozoic faults, turn from southwesterly to more southerly in the same area. Thus, there seems to be ample evidence to suggest a southward bend in the Norumbega fault system in the Casco Bay area (see also Bothner and Hussey, this volume). Such a bend in a dextral strike-slip fault would produce local horizontal compression, which could account for the oblique folds (Fig. 3) and inferred positive flower structure in the Casco Bay area, as described by Swanson (1993, 1995).

Identifying possible Norumbega fault system connections for late Paleozoic activity is more difficult than for middle Paleozoic activity. The only large faults in southeastern New England that have documented late Paleozoic activity are normal faults (Honey Hill–Lake Char–Clinton-Newbury faults) or are of modest displacement (e.g., Beaverhead fault; Mosher, 1983). However, there is a late Paleozoic feature in southeastern New England that does require large-magnitude faulting, although the faults have not been identified. The Narragansett basin of Rhode Island and southeastern Massachusetts (Fig. 2) most likely formed as a pull-apart basin along a releasing bend in a transcurrent fault, and is filled with Pennsylvanian clastic sedimentary rocks (Mosher, 1983). These Pennsylvanian rocks were intensely deformed and metamorphosed during the latest Pennsylvanian and Permian and record some of the best evidence for the Alleghanian orogeny in New England. Mosher (1983) suggested that the Narragansett basin opened along a releasing bend in a northeast-striking sinistral transcurrent fault system. Here, we propose that the Norumbega fault system was part of that sinistral fault system. Evidence for sinistral displacement on the system or related faults is not great, but there are enough data to support this hypothesis. In addition to Mosher's (1983) requirement for northeast sinistral displacements in opening the Narragansett basin, Hamidzada and Hermes (1984) noted normal-sense ductile shear zones in Rhode Island with the correct timing and orientation to be related to northeast-striking

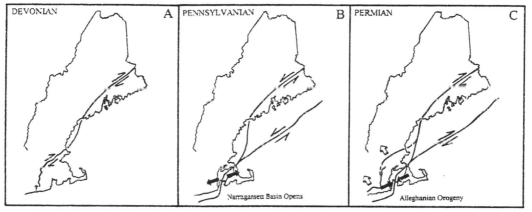

Figure 4. Hypothetical trace of the Norumbega fault system (NFS) in offshore New England at various times. A: NFS is continuous with Bloody Bluff fault during Acadian orogeny. B: Hypothesized sinistral faults which account for Pennsylvanian opening of the Narranagnseet basin. C: Dextral offset on the NFS and FF during the Late Pennsylvanian and Permian accounts for deformation of Narragansett basin. Open arrows show motion of hanging wall of Honey Hill–Clinton-Newbury–Lake Char faults, shown in map, and solid arrows indicate direction of shortening resulting from fault displacement in confining bend.

sinistral displacement. Bothner and Hussey (this volume) note that sinistral strike-slip faults are present to the east of the Norumbega fault system in the Casco Bay–Boothbay Harbor area and A. Ludman (1997, personal commun.) noted rare occurrences of sinistral kinematic indicators in the Norumbega fault system in northeastern Maine. Webb (1963) cited strong evidence for Pennsylvanian sinistral displacement on the Harvey-Hopewell fault in New Brunswick and Goldstein (1994) discussed "early Alleghanian" sinistral displacements on a wide ductile shear zone in eastern Massachusetts west of the Clinton-Newbury fault. Thus, although there is little direct evidence for sinistral offset on the Norumbega fault system, it appears that sinistral displacements occurred in the eastern regions of the northern Appalachians in Pennsylvanian time. It is likely that the major Pennsylvanian sinistral displacement occurred on the Fundy fault with only small-magnitude sinistral displacement on the Norumbega fault system, considering the rarity with which sinistral indicators have been found in the system.

As noted here, the Fundy fault can be traced offshore to near the Massachusetts coast, but which fault is its onshore extension is a matter of some speculation. Hutchinson et al. (1988) suggested that the Ponkapoag fault is the onshore expression of the Fundy fault, but we propose that the onshore expression of the Fundy fault is just south of the Ponkapoag fault buried beneath the Narragansett basin. If this is the case, then sinistral displacement on the Fundy fault coupled with a releasing bend also buried beneath the Narragansett basin could account for opening of the basin in the Pennsylvanian (Fig. 4B). Subsequent deformation of the Narragansett basin could be related to dextral offset on the Fundy fault, coupled with dextral offset on the Norumbega fault system. Considering that we have some difficulty locating any faults in southeastern New England that undewent dextral displacement in latest Pennsylvanian and Permian time, it is reasonable to believe that the

southward bend in the Norumbega fault system near Casco Bay was utilized for late Paleozoic as well as Devonian offset. However, unlike Devonian displacement, there is no evidence for latest Paleozoic dextral displacement on the Bloody Bluff fault. Thus, we suggest that the Norumbega fault system merged with the Fundy fault at this time and the offset on both was combined. This can explain the deformation of Narragansett basin sedimentary rocks, the deformation of the crystalline basement adjacent to it and the normal displacement on the Honey Hill–Lake Char–Willimantic–Wachusett mylonite zone and Clinton-Newbury fault (Fig. 4C). The same bend in the Fundy fault that allowed opening of the Narragansett basin in Pennsylvanian time would have caused east-northeast shortening of the basin during dextral displacement in latest Pennsylvanian and Permian time. This shortening could also have caused widespread ductile deformation of the crystalline basement of the Avalon terrane of southeastern New England. This horizontal shortening would have thickened the crust and might have provided the origin for the contemporaneous normal motion on faults described by Goldstein (1994, 1989, 1982) and Getty and Gromet (1992a, 1992b). It is interesting that the direction of the motion of the hanging walls of those faults was to the northwest (Goldstein, 1989, 1994), essentially perpendicular to the shortening direction one would expect for shortening along the Narragansett basin confining bend (Fig. 4C). This provides a possible explanation for contemporaneous shortening and extension. Extension driven by tectonic stresses would not be expected to occur parallel to the principal shortening direction, but would more likely occur perpendicular to it. Whereas such a scenario is speculative, it provides the best explanation for many aspects of the geology of southeastern New England as well as explaining where the Norumbega fault system is southwest of Casco Bay, Maine.

Thus, our conclusions are that the Bloody Bluff fault represents the best possible southward continuation of the

Norumbega fault system in Devonian time and other faults, especially the Portsmouth fault, may also have been active at this time. However, the geometry of fault associations changed in later Paleozoic time. We speculate that the Norumbega fault system and the Fundy fault both underwent sinistral displacement in Pennsylvanian time before displacement changed to dextral in latest Pennsylvanian and Permian time. During both those displacement episodes, the Norumbega fault system merged with the Fundy fault and their displacement was combined to result in first opening and then closure of the Narragansett basin. Closure of the basin along a confining bend could also account for widespread ductile deformation of the crystalline basement in southeastern New England as well as contemporaneous extension in higher structural levels as evidenced by low-angle normal faults. The Norumbega fault system thus may have southern extensions in southeastern New England, but these exist through a complex relationship, first in a releasing bend and then in a confining bend, rather than as a single large transcurrent fault zone such as exists in eastern Maine.

ACKNOWLEDGMENTS

We have benefited from discussions with colleagues too numerous to list. The paper was greatly improved by thoughtful, constructive reviews by Allan Ludman, Dan Murray, and Pat Brock.

REFERENCES CITED

Ballard, R. D., and Uchupi, E., 1975, Triassic rift structure in the Gulf of Maine: American Association of Petroleum Geologists Bulletin, v. 59, p. 1041–1072.

Billings, M. P., 1976, Bedrock geology of the Boston basin, *in* Cameron, B., ed., Geology of southeastern New England: A guidebook for field trips to the Boston area and vicinity, New England Intercollegiate Geological Conference Guidebook, v. 68, p. 28–45.

Billings, M. P., 1982, Ordovician cauldron subsidence of the Blue Hills Complex, eastern Massachusetts: Geological Society of America Bulletin, v. 93, p. 909–920.

Brooks, J. A., and Bothner, W. A., 1989, Late (?) Alleghanian dextral transpression and terrane accretion within coastal New England and western Gulf of Maine as interpreted from regional aeromagnetic and gravity maps: Eos (Transactions, American Geophysical Union), v. 70, p. 462.

Castle, R. O., Dixon, H. R., Grew, E. S., Griscom, A., and Zeitz, I., 1976, Structural dislocations in eastern Massachusetts: U.S. Geological Survey Bulletin 1410, 39 p.

Cuppels, N. P., 1961, Post-Carboniferous deformation of metamorphic and igneous rocks near the northern boundary fault, Boston basin, Massachusetts: U.S. Geological Survey Professional Paper 424-D, p. D46–D48.

Dixon, H. R., 1982, Multistage deformation of the Preston Gabbro, eastern Connecticut, *in* Josten, R., and Quarrier, S., eds., Guidebook for field trips in Connecticut and south-central Massachusetts: Connecticut Geological and Natural History Survey Guidebook 5, p. 453–463.

Dixon, H. R., and Lundgren, L., 1968, The structure of eastern Connecticut, *in* Zen, E-an, White, Hadley, and Thompson, eds., Studies in Appalachian geology, northern and maritime: New York, Wiley Interscience, p. 219–229.

Doll, W. E., Domoracki, W. J., Costain, J. K., Coruh, C., Ludman, A., and Hopeck, J. T., 1996, Seismic reflection evidence for the evolution of a transcurrent fault system: The Norumbega fault system, Maine: Geology, v. 24, p. 251–254.

Dubé, B., Dunning, G. R., Lauzière, K., and Roddick, J. C., 1996, New insights into the Appalachian orogen from geology and geochronology along the Cape Ray fault zone, southwest Newfoundland: Geological Society of America Bulletin, v. 108, p. 101–116.

Getty, S. R., and Gromet, L. P., 1992a, Evidence for extension at the Willimantic Dome, Connecticut: Implications for the late Paleozoic tectonic evolution of the New England Appalachians: American Journal of Science, v. 292, p. 398–420.

Getty, S. R., and Gromet, L. P., 1992b, Geochronological constraints on the ductile deformation, crustal extension and doming about a basement-cover contact, New England Appalachians: American Journal of Science, v. 292, p. 359–397.

Goldsmith, R., 1991, Structural and metamorphic history of eastern Massachusetts, *in* Hatch, N. L., ed., The bedrock geology of Massachusetts: U.S. Geological Survey Professional Paper 1366, p. H1–H63.

Goldstein, A. G., 1982, Geometry and kinematics of ductile faulting in a portion of the Lake Char mylonite zone, Massachusetts and Connecticut: American Journal of Science, v. 282, p. 1378–1405.

Goldstein, A. G., 1986, Two distinct late Precambrian (Avalonian) terranes in southeastern New England and their late Paleozoic juxtaposition: Comment: American Journal of Science, v. 286, p. 659–663.

Goldstein, A. G., 1989, Tectonic significance of multiple motions on terrane-bounding faults in the northern Appalachians: Geological Society of America Bulletin, v. 101, p. 927–938.

Goldstein, A. G., 1994, A shear zone origin for Alleghanian (Permian) multiple deformation in eastern Massachusetts: Tectonics, v. 13, p. 62–77.

Hamidzada, N. A., and Hermes, O. D., 1984, Ductile shear zones in north-central Rhode Island and their bearing on Devonian plutonism and basin formation: Geological Society of America Abstracts with Programs, v. 16, p. 22.

Hanmer, S., 1981, Tectonic significance of the northeastern Gander zone, Newfoundland: An Acadian ductile shear zone: Canadian Journal of Earth Sciences, v. 18, p. 120–135.

Harland, W. B., 1985, Caledonide Svalbard, *in* Gee, D., and Sturt, B., eds., The Caledonide orogen—Scandinavia and related areas: New York, John Wiley and Sons, p. 999–1016.

Hepburn, J. C., Dunning, G. R., and Hon, R., 1995, Geochronology and regional tectonic implications of Silurian deformation in the Nashoba terrane, southeastern New England, USA, *in* Hibbard, J. P., van Staal, C. R., and Cawood, P. A., eds., Current perspectives in the Appalachian-Caledonian orogen: Geological Association of Canada Special Paper 41, p. 349–366.

Hermes, O. D., Ballard, R. D., and Banks, P. O., 1978, Upper Ordovician peralkalic granites from the Gulf of Maine: Geological Society of America Bulletin, v. 89, p. 1761–1774.

Hermes, O. D., Gromet, L. P., and Murray, D. P., 1994, Bedrock geologic map of Rhode Island: Office of the Rhode Island State Geologist, scale 1:100,000.

Hubbard, M., West, D., Ludman, A., Guidotti, C., and Lux, D. R., 1995, The Norumbega fault system, Maine: A mid- to shallow-level crustal section within a transcurrent shear zone: Atlantic Geology, v. 31, p. 109–116.

Hussey, A. M., II, 1985, The bedrock geology of the Bath and Portland 2 degree map sheets, Maine: Maine Geological Survey, Open-File Report no. 85-87, 80 p.

Hussey, A. M., II, and Bothner, W. A., 1993, Geology of the Coastal Lithotectonic belt—SE Maine and SE New Hampshire, *in* Cheney, J. T., and Hepburn, J. C., eds., Field trip guidebook for the northeastern United States: Amherst, University of Massachusetts, Department of Geology and Geography contribution no. 67, p. K1–K19.

Hussey, A. M., II, and Bothner, W. A., 1995, Geology of the Coastal Lithotectonic belt SW Maine and SE New Hampshire, *in* Hussey, A. M., II, and Johnston, R. A., eds., Guidebook to field trips in southern Maine and adjacent New Hampshire: New England Intercollegiate Geological Conference Guidebook, v. 87, p. 211–228.

Hutchinson, D. R., Klitgord, K. D., Lee, M. W., and Trehu, A. M., 1988, U.S. Geological Survey deep seismic reflection profile across the Gulf of Maine: Geological Society of America Bulletin, v. 100, p. 172–184.

Kaye, C., 1983, Discovery of a Late Triassic basin north of Boston and some implications as to the post-Paleozoic tectonics in northeastern Massachusetts: American Journal of Science, v. 283, p. 1060–1079.

Keen, C. E., Kay, W. A., Keppie, D., Marillier, F., Pe Piper, G., and Waldron, J. W. F., 1991, Deep seismic reflection data from the Bay of Fundy and Gulf of Maine: Tectonic implications for the northern Appalachians: Canadian Journal of Earth Sciences, v. 28, p. 1096–1111.

Kent, D. V., and Opdyke, N. D., 1978, Paleomagnetism of the Devonian Catskill red beds: Evidence for motion of the coastal New England–Canadian Maritime region relative to cratonic North America: Journal of Geophysical Research, v. 83, p. 4441–4450.

Klitgord, K. D., Hutchinson, D. R., and Schouten, H., 1988, U.S. Atlantic continental margin: Structural and tectonic framework, *in* Sheridan, R. E., and Grow, J. A., eds., The Atlantic continental margin, U.S.: Boulder, Colorado, Geological Society of America, Geology of North America, v. I-2, p. 19–55.

Lyons, J. B., Boudette, E. L., and Aleinikoff, J. N., 1982, The Avalonian and Gander zones in central eastern New England, *in* St. Julien, P., and Beland, J., eds., Major structural zones and faults of the Northern Appalachians: Geological Association of Canada Special Paper 24, p. 43–66.

Mosher, S., 1983, Kinematic history of the Narragansett basin, Massachusetts and Rhode Island: Constraints on late Paleozoic plate reconstructions: Tectonics, v. 2, p. 327–344.

Nelson, A. E., 1976, Structural elements and deformational history of rocks in eastern Massachusetts: Geological Society of America Bulletin, v. 87, p. 1377–1383.

O'Brien, B. H., O'Brien, S. J., Dunning, G. R., and Tucker, R. D., 1993, Episodic reactivation of a late Precambrian mylonite zone on the Gondwana margin of the Appalachians, southern Newfoundland: Tectonics, v. 12, p. 1043–1055.

O'Hara, K., and Gromet, L. P., 1985, Two distinct late Precambrian (Avalonian) terranes in southeastern New England and their late Paleozoic juxtaposition: American Journal of Science, v. 285, p. 673–709.

Osberg, P. H., Hussey, A. M., II, and Boone, G. M., 1985, Bedrock geologic map of Maine: Augusta, Maine Geological Survey, scale 1:500,000.

Powell, D., and Phillips, W. E. A., 1985, Time and deformation in the Caledonide orogen of Britain and Ireland, *in* Harris, A. L., ed., The nature and timing of orogenic activity in the Caledonian rocks of the British Isles: London, Blackwell Scientific, p. 17–39.

Rast, N., 1983, The northern Appalachian traverses in the maritimes of Canada, *in* Rast, N., and Delany, F. M., eds., Profiles of orogenic belts: American Geophysical Union Geodynamics Series, v. 10, p. 243–274.

Rast, N., and Grant, R., 1973, Transatlantic correlation of the Variscan Appalachian orogeny: American Journal of Science, v. 273, p. 572–579.

Rast, N., and Skehan, J. W., 1995, Avalonian (Pan-African) mylonitic deformation west of Boston, USA: Journal of Geodynamics, v. 19, p. 289–302.

Rast, N., Skehan, J. W., and Grimes, S. W., 1993, Highlights of Proterozoic geology of Boston, *in* Cheney, J. T., and Hepburn, J. C., eds., Field trip guidebook for the northeastern United States: Amherst, University of Massachusetts, Department of Geology and Geography Contribution No. 67, p. S1–S16.

Rogers, J., 1984, Bedrock geologic map of Connecticut: Connecticut Geological and Natural History Survey and U.S. Geological Survey, scale 1:125,000.

Skehan, J. W., 1968, Fracture tectonics of southeastern New England as illustrated by the Wachusett-Marlborough tunnel, east-central Massachusetts, *in* Zen, E-An, W. S. White, J. B. Hadley, and J. B. Thompson, eds., Studies in Appalachian geology, northern and Maritime: New York, Wiley Interscience, p. 281–290.

Skehan, J. W., 1983, Geological profiles through the Avalonian terrain of southeastern Massachusetts, Rhode Island, and eastern Connecticut, U.S.A., *in* Rast, N., and Delany, F. M., eds., Profiles of orogenic belts: American Geophysical Union Geodynamics Series, v. 10, p. 275–300.

Steltenpohl, M. G., and Bartley, J. M., 1988, Cross folds and back folds in the Ofoten Tysfjord area, north Norway, and their significance for Caledonian tectonics: Geological Society of America Bulletin, v. 100, p. 140–151.

Stewart, D. B., and Wones, D. R., 1974, Bedrock geology of northern Penobscot Bay area, *in* Osberg, P. H., ed., New England Intercollegiate Geological Conference guidebook for field trips in east central and north central Maine: New England Intercollegiate Geological Conference Guidebook, v. 66, p. 223–239.

Swanson, M. T., 1993, Stretching lineations, shear zone kinematics and dextral transpression along the Flying Point/Norumbega fault system, Casco Bay, Maine: Geological Society of America Abstracts with Programs, v. 25, no. 1, p. 83.

Swanson, M. T., 1995, Distributed ductile dextral shear strain throughout the Casco Bay area, *in* Hussey, A. M., II, and Johnston, R. A., eds., Guidebook to field trips in southern Maine and adjacent New Hampshire: New England Intercollegiate Geological Conference Guidebook, v. 87, p. 1–13.

Thompson, J. B., Jr., Bothner, W. A., Robinson, P., and Klitgord, K. D., 1993, E-1, Adirondacks to Georges Bank: Geological Society of America, Centennial Continent/Ocean Transect TRA-E-1, 2 plates, 55 p.

Webb, G. W., 1963, Occurrence and exploration significance of strike-slip faults in southern New Brunswick, Canada: American Association of Petroleum Geologists Bulletin, v. 47, p. 1904–1927.

West, D. P., 1995, The Norumbega fault system in south-central Maine: A trip through 80 million years of dextral shear deformation, *in* Hussey, A. M., II, and Johnston, R. A., eds., Guidebook to field trips in southern Maine and adjacent New Hampshire: New England Intercollegiate Geological Conference Guidebook, v. 87, p. 125–143.

West, D. P., and Lux, D. R., 1993, Dating mylonitic deformation by the Ar/Ar method: An example from the Norumbega fault system, Maine: Earth and Planetary Science Letters, v. 120, p. 221–237.

West, D. P., Lux, D. R., and Hussey, A. M., II, 1993, Contrasting thermal histories across the Flying Point fault, southwestern Maine: Evidence for Mesozoic displacement: Geological Society of America Bulletin, v. 105, p. 1478–1490.

Wintsch, R. P., 1979, The Willimantic fault: A ductile fault in eastern Connecticut: American Journal of Science, v. 279, p. 367–393.

Wintsch, R. P., and Sutter, J. F., 1985, A tectonic model for the late Paleozoic of southeastern New England: Journal of Geology, v. 94, p. 459–472.

Wintsch, R. P., Sutter, J. F., Kunk, M. J., Alcinikoff, J. N., and Dorais, M. J., 1992, Contrasting P-T-t paths: Thermochronologic evidence for a late Paleozoic final assembly of the Avalon composite terrane in the New England Appalachians: Tectonics, v. 11, p. 672–689.

Wones, D. R., 1978, Norumbega fault system, Maine: U.S. Geological Survey Summary of Technical Reports VIII, National Hazards Reduction Program, p. 108–111.

Zartman, R. E., 1977, Geochronology of some alkaline rock provinces in eastern and central United States: Annual Reviews of Earth and Planetary Sciences, v. 5, p. 257–286.

Zen, E-an, Goldsmith, R., Ratcliffe, N. M., Robinson, P, and Stanley, R. S., compilers, 1983, Bedrock geologic map of Massachusetts: Reston, Virginia, U.S. Geological Survey, 3 sheets, scale 1:250,000.

MANUSCRIPT ACCEPTED BY THE SOCIETY JUNE 9, 1998

Geological Society of America
Special Paper 331
1999

Dextral transpression at the Casco Bay restraining bend, Norumbega fault zone, coastal Maine

Mark T. Swanson
Department of Geosciences, University of Southern Maine, Gorham, Maine 04038

ABSTRACT

The southwestern end of the Norumbega fault zone forms a 14° restraining bend in a prominent orogen-parallel dextral strike-slip system within the northern Appalachians. Late Paleozoic transpression at the Casco Bay restraining bend was controlled by the geometry of dextral strike-slip faults within an otherwise regional transtensional dextral strike-slip system. Regional shearing within this system may have begun in the Early Devonian and persisted until the latest Paleozoic with late high strain localization and syntectonic to post-tectonic granitic intrusion. Deformation related to this restraining bend involved distributed dextral shear strain and crustal shortening in a complex zone, ~30 km wide, referred to as the Casco Bay shear zone system. Regional upright F2 folds in this area are oblique to subparallel to the fault trace and developed strong hinge-parallel elongation. This is reflected in initially orthogonal boudin partings and veins within upright fold limbs. As these F2 folds were tightened and reoriented toward the fault trace, the limbs developed pervasive dextral shear fabrics and asymmetric kinematic indicators. Higher ductile shear strains were accommodated along lithologic contacts and within less-competent units. The cross-section geometry of the Casco Bay shear zones is interpreted as a positive flower structure that cored a transpressional zone of shortening, thickening, and dextral shear accompanied by strain-localized syntectonic intrusion. Oblique-slip lineations in a number of zones suggest vertical components to dextral shear including an early phase of dextral overthrusting to the northwest and a later phase of dextral oblique extension, down to the southeast, along the main Flying Point fault zone. Late structures including small normal faults, normal kink-bands to several meters in width, chevron folds, and crenulations with horizontal axial planes suggest late vertical shortening of the transpressional uplift.

INTRODUCTION

The bedrock geologic map of Maine (Osberg et al., 1985) shows the Norumbega fault zone (Fig. 1) dominating the coastal and near-coastal geology, and controlling the overall pattern of deformation, intrusion, and metamorphism. This regional pattern of deformation is most intense in the Casco Bay area, where numerous mapped Norumbega system fault splays coincide with high-grade metamorphism and tight upright folding (Fig. 2). This chapter makes the link between this major strike-slip fault zone and the history of regional deformation as part of a generalized pattern of dextral transpression throughout the northern Appalachians. The results of this research have significant implications for the interpreted displacement history of the Norumbega fault system (sense and magnitude of displacement, ductile vs. brittle mode, relative timing), the correlation of stratigraphic units throughout the area (that must reflect the orogen-parallel displacements and strain-related fabrics), and the deformation history (which may involve orthogonal shortening, oblique convergence, regional extension, dextral transpression) of a major part of the northern Appalachians.

Swanson, M. T., 1999, Dextral transpression at the Casco Bay restraining bend, Norumbega fault zone, coastal Maine, *in* Ludman, A., and West, D. P., Jr., eds., Norumbega Fault System of the Northern Appalachians: Boulder, Colorado, Geological Society of America Special Paper 331.

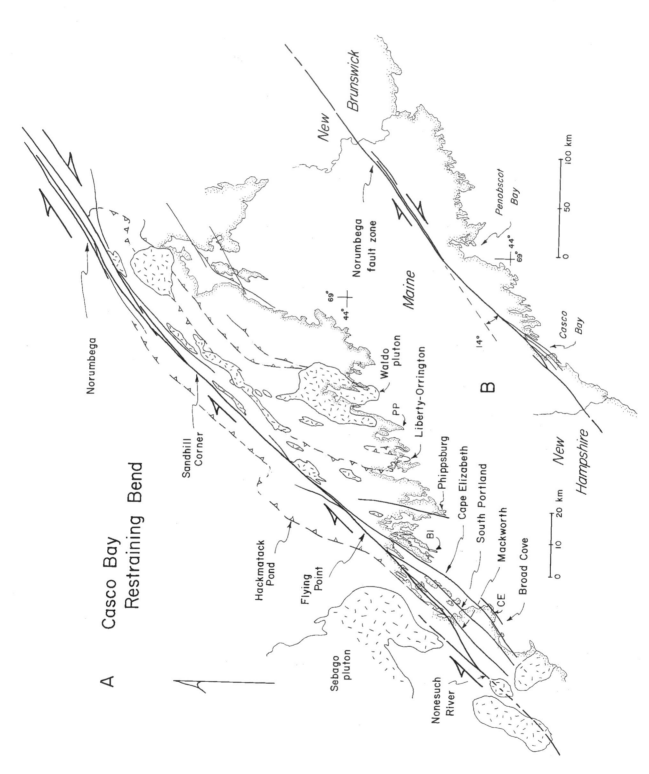

Figure 1. Regional structural setting for dextral transpression. A: Restraining-bend segment of the Norumbega fault zone showing principal fault zones in the Casco Bay shear-zone system (Broad Cove, Mackworth, South Portland, Cape Elizabeth, and Phippsburg fault zones), older flanking thrusts (Hackmatack Pond and Liberty-Orrington), and selected intrusions (after Osberg et al., 1985; Hussey, 1988; Hussey and Bothner, 1995). Pemaquid Point (PP), Bailey Island (BI), and Cape Elizabeth (CE) refer to geographic localities mentioned in the text. B: Inset map shows the Norumbega fault system and the position of the restraining bend in the Casco Bay area.

Previous work

Extensive geologic mapping in the Casco Bay area (summarized by Hussey, 1985, 1988) has established the overall characteristics of the complexly deformed metavolcanic and metasedimentary rocks of the Casco Bay Group. Early deformation consisted of major northeast-trending F1 recumbent folds (Hussey, 1985, 1988) most likely related to convergence during the early stages of the Acadian orogeny (Bradley, 1983; Osberg et al., 1989). The major deformation of these lithologies and earlier structures, however, resulted in major upright to slightly overturned F2 fold structures (Hussey, 1985). In the Casco Bay area, these F2 folds are open to isoclinal with north- to northeast-trending fold axes (Fig. 2) of gentle to moderate plunges to both the northeast and southwest. These F2 folds are thought to be Acadian (Hussey, 1985), contemporaneous with the early stages of intrusion of Late Devonian syntectonic granitic plutons and prior to the latest Paleozoic post-tectonic intrusives. Mafic dikes have been sporadically intruded throughout the area (Swanson, 1992a) marking the transition to Mesozoic rifting.

Norumbega fault system. A synthesis by Hubbard et al. (1995) characterized the Norumbega fault zone as a major transcurrent shear zone of late Paleozoic age, parallel to the northern Appalachian orogen. This dextral strike-slip fault system is variably exposed, from mid-crustal levels in the southwest with distributed ductile shear to shallow-crustal levels in the northeast with localized brittle fabrics. The Casco Bay area represents the deeper crustal exposures characterized by localized shearing as well as more distributed regional ductile strain accommodation.

As it extends into the Casco Bay area, the Norumbega fault zone (Pankiwskyj, 1978; Hussey, 1971; Newberg, 1981) develops several subparallel fault strands (Fig. 2A) as the Casco Bay shear-zone system (Swanson, 1995). Individual faults in the Casco Bay area include the South Portland, Cape Elizabeth, Broad Cove, and Flying Point fault zones and they serve as a linking structure to the Nonesuch River–Campbell Hill fault to the southwest (Eusden and Barreiro, 1988; Hussey and Newberg, 1978). Continuation of these faults to the southwest, however, is problematic, hampered by poor exposure.

The Norumbega fault zone has long been established as a dextral strike-slip structure (Stewart and Wones, 1974). However, displacements along faults in the more deeply exposed Casco Bay area have remained speculative, and have been inferred on the basis of lithologic and metamorphic correlations across the faults rather than direct kinematic structural evidence from exposed fault zones or adjacent lithologies. Many were simply mapped as "high-angle" faults (Hussey, 1988), marked by lithologic discontinuities, abundant white quartz boudins, and veins and minor slickenside surfaces with downdip striae. Hussey (1985, 1988) suggested that sinistral strike-slip motion occurred on the Cape Elizabeth and Flying Point faults on the basis of lithologic and isograd correlations. West et al. (1993) suggested significant dip-slip motion along the Flying Point fault on the basis of thermochronologic studies. Recent field studies, how-

ever, have revealed an abundance of unequivocal kinematic indicators for dominantly dextral strike-slip motions (Swanson, 1989, 1992b, 1993a, 1993b, 1995, and this volume) along these zones.

These recent field studies have also shown a distinctive pattern of regional strain accommodation associated with the shear-zone system. Upright isoclinal folds with well-developed, subhorizontal, hinge-parallel lineations and dextral kinematic indicators suggest a history of regional strike-slip shearing. This pattern of regional strain is interpreted as transpressional in nature and can be shown to be related to the overall geometry of the Norumbega fault zone and its continuation southwest into the Casco Bay area (Swanson, 1992b, 1993a, 1993b).

CASCO BAY RESTRAINING BEND

Restraining bend geometry

The southwest end of the Norumbega fault zone (Figs. 1 and 2A) continues toward the Nonesuch River fault of Hussey and Newberg (1978) through a series of fault splays and structural complications in the Casco Bay area. The trend of this fault system shows a distinct change in orientation from N56E along the Norumbega fault to N42E along the southwestern section through the Casco Bay area (Osberg et al., 1985). This change in orientation creates a 14° restraining bend (Fig. 1B) that begins just southwest of Bangor and continues for ~150 km through the Casco Bay area. It is this restraining bend that appears to control the pattern of regional deformation. The orientations of shear-related lineations in conjunction with asymmetric kinematic indicators help to reveal the sequence of deformation associated with this restraining bend.

Casco Bay shear zone system

The relatively simple trace of the northeast section of the Norumbega fault zone develops a splay-fault pattern localized in the Casco Bay area (Figs. 1 and 2A). F2 folds adjacent to the main fault are nearly parallel to the trace of the fault and are laced with localized zones of high shear as the Casco Bay shear-zone system (Swanson, 1995). The fault zones include the main Flying Point fault zone, the Mackworth or John's Point fault zone of the inner Casco Bay, and the South Portland, Cape Elizabeth, and Broad Cove fault zones as they are exposed in the Cape Elizabeth peninsula. Fault traces were delineated by lithologic mapping (Hussey, 1985) and were considered discrete high-angle fault structures that were exclusively postmetamorphic and associated with retrograde chloritization. Field studies (Swanson, 1993a, 1993b, 1995) have shown that these fault zones have an extensive history of ductile dextral shearing in kilometer-wide high-strain zones marked by the development of fine-grained mylonitic gneisses, phacoidal schists, and phyllonites. These high-strain zones typically developed a strong lineation parallel to the shear direction, numerous sheath folds, as well as an abundance of distinctive kinematic indicators (Swanson, this volume).

These relatively narrow shear zones are distributed within a wider zone (~30 km) of regional ductile shear (Fig. 2A) and referred to as the Casco Bay shear-zone system (Swanson, 1995).

Initially oblique, upright, F2 fold system

Upright F2 fold structures (Figs. 2B and 3A) as described by Hussey (1985, 1988) and Osberg et al. (1985) for the Casco Bay and nearby coastal areas are in an oblique orientation relative to the Norumbega fault system, particularly in the area around the Casco Bay restraining bend. These folds are tight to isoclinal, plunge gently to moderately northeast and southwest, and are associated with the development of strong hinge-parallel lineation. The mapped traces of these folds show a change in orientation from northerly trends oblique to the dominant fault trace to more northeasterly trends as they approach the main fault zone along the inner Casco Bay and northeast along the main fault zone (Kaszuba and Simpson, 1989). The overall oblique orientation of these folds and their apparent rotation toward the fault trace reflect regional dextral shearing along the Norumbega fault system (Swanson, 1993a, and this volume). Similar oblique fold systems on a smaller scale were described by Bürgmann (1991) along the San Andreas fault zone.

Syntectonic igneous and hydrothermal activity

Minor granitic intrusion and quartz veining within the highly sheared rocks of the Casco Bay area is best characterized as syntectonic. Both pegmatite intrusions and quartz veins show varied orientations relative to the sheared foliations that depend on the age of emplacement within the shear zones. The intrusives are peraluminous granitic pegmatites containing biotite, tourmaline, and garnet (Tomascak and Francis, 1995). The quartz veins also contain calcite, ankerite, chlorite, or actinolite. The latest undeformed intrusions and veins are found perpendicular to the local lineation direction. Older, deformed intrusions and veins are found at lower angles, as slightly discordant boudin strings within the flow layering. The cores of the larger granitic boudins retain their coarse grain size, suggesting resistance to shear. Minor mafic intrusions, possibly syntectonic, are also evident along inner Casco Bay as large, 10 m mafic amphibolitic boudins within rocks of the northwestern side of the fault zone. Core zones within some of these boudins also show remnant coarse igneous textures. Dates of various suites of pegmatite intrusions range from 380 Ma (Rb/Sr, reported by Hussey, 1988) to 270 Ma (U-Pb, Tomascak and Francis, 1995), implying ~100 m.y. of igneous activity that corresponds to the timing of regional and localized shear along the major fault zones (West, 1995).

Kinematic indicators

The asymmetric structures indicating shear are superimposed on the upright layering in tight F2 folds (Fig. 3B). These include asymmetric boudinage, shear-band fabrics, crenulation cleavages, asymmetric folds, kinks, and minor faults (discussed in more detail in Swanson, this volume).

Foliations and/or lineations. Flow foliations in these rocks are steeply to moderately dipping dominantly to the southeast. Mylonitic textures indicating high shear strain vary from coarsely heteroclastic with asymmetric porphyroclasts to fine-grained homoclastic with straight, planar flow layering (classification after Hanmer, 1987). Pegmatite intrusion and quartz veining during shear has resulted in deformed and disaggregated textures within the surviving lithologies. Stretching lineations (Fig. 3, C and D) are developed throughout the study area, parallel to local F2 fold hinges. Lineations are defined by alignment of elongate minerals such as hornblende, anthophyllite, and actinolite, and elongation of mineral aggregates of quartz, biotite, muscovite, tourmaline, and garnet, as well as stretched volcanic clasts.

Reoriented boudin partings, planar quartz veins, and pegmatite intrusions. Subhorizontal extension develops initially symmetric boudinage of foliations and competent layers. This boudinage is expressed as high-angle fractures that dilate in response to continued extension. This created millimeter- to centimeter-scale partings and larger quartz-filled veins that form the ends of individual blocks in segmented layering. Continued extension and dilation of these partings result in blocky bone-shaped and fishmouth geometries for gap mineralization formed between boudin ends (Swanson, 1992b). Larger quartz veins and granitic pegmatite intrusions to tens of meters in length are also formed in response to the elongation. Undeformed partings, veins, and intrusions are consistently orthogonal to the local lineation, whereas older deformed ones show progressive clockwise rotation and elongation due to shear. Veins and intrusions are reoriented to lower angles with respect to the foliation and are now preserved as oblique strings of quartz and pegmatite boudins. Younger veins and intrusions consistently crosscut older deformed and reoriented veins and intrusions. Equal-area plots can be used to define shear sense, shear direction, and kinematic rotation axes for ductile shear (Swanson, 1992b, and this volume). In all cases, the analysis verifies the overall dextral shear sense and the L2 lineation as the shear direction.

Other kinematic indicators. Dextral shear bands (Swanson, 1992b, 1995) are common and form asymmetric boudinage where they crosscut foliation, competent layers, or older veins and intrusions. Minor asymmetric folds with steeply plunging

---

Figure 2. Structural elements in the Casco Bay area. A: Casco Bay shear-zone system where the main Flying Point fault zone (FP) splays out into several lesser shear zones exposed throughout the Casco Bay area (after Osberg et al., 1985; Hussey and Bothner, 1995); geographic localities are in italics; faults include the Flying Point (FP), Nonesuch River (NR), Phippsburg (PB), Broad Cove (BC), Cape Elizabeth (CE), Spring Point (SP), and Mackworth (MK). B: Related F2 folds are dominated by hinge-parallel elongation and limb shear that becomes more intense from east to west with progressive clockwise rotation of obliquely oriented folds to nearly parallel with the main Flying Point fault zone; dashed lines are faults; solid lines indicate fold forms; major anticlinal and synclinal axes are as indicated.

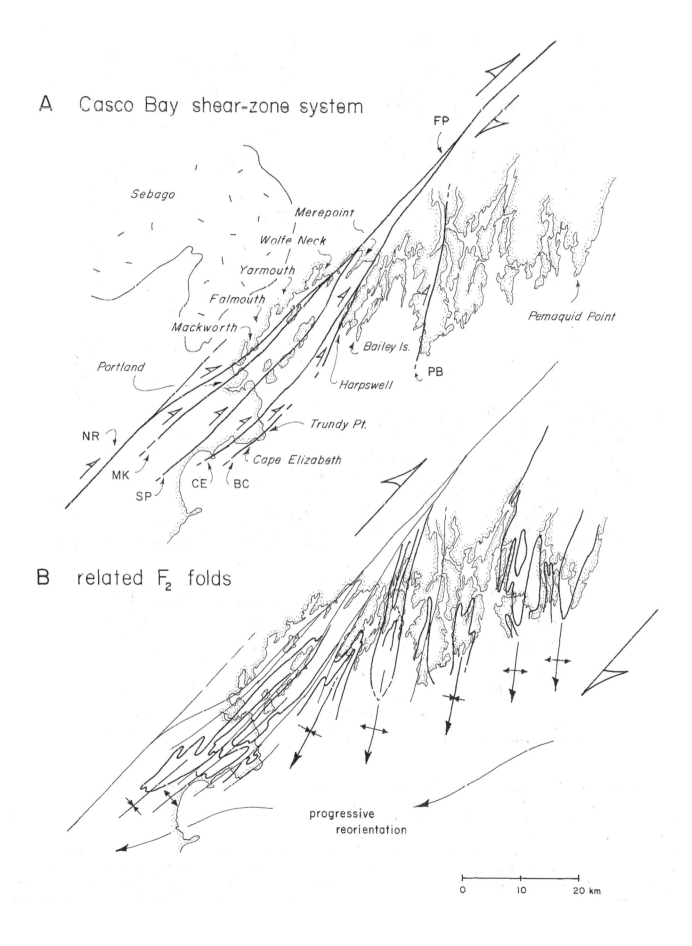

A Casco Bay shear-zone system

Sebago

Merepoint

Wolfe Neck

Yarmouth

Falmouth

Mackworth

Portland

FP

Pemaquid Point

Bailey Is.

PB

Harpswell

Trundy Pt.

Cape Elizabeth

NR

MK

SP

CE

BC

B related F₂ folds

progressive
reorientation

0   10   20 km

Figure 3. Upright F2 folds, hinge-parallel elongation, boudinage, and dextral shear shown from east to west with progressively higher levels of shear strain (see Figs. 1A and 2A for locations). A: Upright isoclinal fold in the Bucksport Formation at Pemaquid Point representative of distal areas to the main fault zone. Flanking limbs display gently plunging hinge-parallel lineations. Scale bar represents ~0.5 m. B: Asymmetric boudinage of amphibolite layer at Bailey Island closer to the main fault exhibits more than 1 m of separation and distortion of boudin ends by layer-parallel dextral shear. C: Horizontal stretching lineations within the Cushing Formation at Simpson Point define the shear direction in areas of higher dextral shear strain proximal to the main fault zone. Note the vertical quartz veins as boudin partings perpendicular to the lineation in response to stretching during shear. Other areas of this exposure show quartz partings (foliation boudinage) in various degrees of clockwise rotation due to modification by simple shear (see data in Fig. 6C). Pencil is 14 cm long. D: Plunging lineations in highly sheared Cushing Formation at Sow Island (inner Casco Bay) within the main Flying Point fault zone. Southeast-dipping flow foliations with southwest-plunging lineations during dextral shear indicate an extensional component to shear along this main zone. Pencil is 14 cm long.

axes are also present and some have been modified to lineation-parallel sheath folds. Late sinistral strike-slip kink bands from a few millimeters to more than 30 m in width are prominent locally within the study area where they functioned as antithetic Reidel shears (R' shears) during late dextral shearing. Normal-slip kink bands and horizontal chevron folds and crenulations also indicate a vertical maximum compressive stress direction late in the deformation history.

Thermochronology and deformation

For the northeastern end of the restraining segment, $^{40}Ar/^{39}Ar$ thermochronologic studies (West and Lux, 1993) have recorded regional muscovite cooling ages of ca. 340–360 Ma, suggesting a Late Devonian age for distributed shear. Finer grained recrystallized micas from the high-strain mylonite zone along the fault date the end of mylonitization as about 290 Ma. Rb/Sr ages for syntectonic pegmatites in the Falmouth area reported by Hussey (1988) are 385 Ma for concordant (deformed?) veins and 375 Ma for discordant (but still deformed?) veins. More recent U-Pb determinations reported by Tomascak and Francis (1995) and Tomascak and Solar (1996) have shown much younger ages of ca. 274–269 Ma for syntectonic to post-tectonic pegmatites in the Topsham area to the northeast.

Studies across the Flying Point fault (West et al., 1993) along the southwest end of the restraining segment show age discordance across the fault with younger hornblende of 290–270 Ma. for the Falmouth-Brunswick sequence on the northwest side of the fault. The Saco-Harpswell sequence southeast of the Flying Point fault shows older hornblende ages of 355–324 Ma. The younger high-temperature hornblende ages in the Falmouth-Brunswick sequence northwest of the Flying Point fault were interpreted (West et al., 1989) to reflect a late Paleozoic thermal event, but the relationship to regional deformation at that time was unclear. The rocks northwest of the Flying Point fault show evidence for strong internal shearing as a phase of oblique dextral thrusting and might be linked to this suggested thermal event. Hansen (1989) found similar thermochronologic relationships in parts of the Teslin suture zone in the Canadian Rockies and theorized that because of thrusting, the hanging-wall rocks cooled quickly, while the footwall rocks were tectonically buried and insulated from any conductive heat loss and only cooled during later exposure by uplift and erosion. Likewise, rocks to the northwest of the Casco Bay area, buried by oblique dextral thrusting (360–320 Ma) during regional shearing, may have cooled rapidly during extensional shearing along the Flying Point fault zone that ended by ca. 290–270 Ma. In summary, the deformation described in this chapter appears to have evolved from an Early Devonian transition to regional ductile dextral shear with oblique F2 folding, distributed regional strain accommodation, metamorphism, and granitic intrusion that persisted through latest Devonian into Carboniferous time. Localized shearing in high-strain mylonite zones continued until the Early Permian.

Structural history of the Casco Bay region

Dextral shear indicators are widespread throughout the Casco Bay area and L2 lineations are generally described as shallowly plunging. Shearing was localized along upright (initially oblique) F2 fold limbs that have rotated into the trend of the fault. Rotation of folds led to a late strain localization at the main Flying Point fault zone and the rest of the Casco Bay shear-zone system. Detailed structural patterns, however, vary. Lineation plunges range from strike slip to dip slip (Fig. 3, C and D) with abrupt transitions in plunge directions into the main fault zone. The higher strain rocks of the inner Casco Bay area (proximal to the main Flying Point fault zone) represent the end product of shearing and the latest stages in strain evolution for this area. Lower strain rocks farther to the east (distal to the fault zone) are interpreted to represent an early deformational style dominated by oblique folding. The rotation of folds into the shear zone leads

to a progressive structural development to the higher strains of the inner Casco Bay area. The proposed structural sequence is illustrated in Figure 4.

Oblique fold formation and rotation. Eastern sections of the oblique F2 fold system outside of the immediate Casco Bay area, are exposed from Bailey Island to Pemaquid Point, to 30 km from the restraining fault segment (Fig. 2B). These outlying or distal areas show broader F2 folds that are less deformed and less reoriented than areas adjacent to the fault. At Pemaquid Point, for example, prominent upright F2 folds within the Bucksport Formation (Fig. 3A) display well-developed, gently plunging, hinge-parallel L2 lineations. Steeply dipping foliations and compositional layering within the Bucksport Formation are oriented at ~N18E, indicating fold reorientation to ~24° to the trace of the fault. These are some of the same regional F2 folds that can be traced along strike to the north-northeast (Fig. 2B) and become progressively reoriented and attenuated along the fault zone (Kazsuba and Simpson, 1989; Osberg et al., 1985).

At Pemaquid Point localized granitic melts intruded parallel and perpendicular to the foliation and/or lineation fabric. Layer-parallel injections to 2–3 m in width show prominent pinch-and-swell type symmetric boudinage. Orthogonal injections of melt show effects of shortening as seen in thin ptygmatic quartz veins and buckled granitic dikes. This suggests a dominance of layer-normal shortening rather than layer-parallel shear. Where reorientation is recorded it is counterclockwise, indicating sinistral shear rather than dextral (Fig. 5). Some areas show only slightly asymmetric geometries with minimal counterclockwise rotation of the orthogonal veins, dikes, and boudin partition mineralization (Fig. 5B); others show moderate rotation (Fig. 5D). Such a sinistral or antithetic shear phase is expected in the early stages of fold reorientation under regional dextral shear (Fig. 4A) along with fold flattening and hinge-parallel elongation. This early stage was modeled experimentally by Richard et al. (1991). To accommodate reorientation during shear, oblique folds must slip antithetically relative to one another during rotation. Early antithetic shears were found to become inactive as reorientation progressed and then to reactivate with the overall shear sense. The reoriented folds at Pemaquid Point had not reached this transition in shear sense and record only the early phases of fold rotation.

Exposures at Bailey Island, ~20 km closer to the restraining bend, have undergone greater clockwise reorientation. Compositional layering is oriented ~N26E, indicating rotations to within 16° to the trace of the main fault. This is consistent with elongations of boudined amphibolite layers in these exposures, which have been estimated at ~220% (Swanson, 1994; Jamison, 1991). Dextral shear along fold limbs would be expected to begin at ~15° of fold rotation, as shown by modeling studies of Richard et al. (1991), and is expressed here as the moderate clockwise reorientation of quartz-filled boudin partings. Farther to the west along the coast through the islands and peninsulas of the middle and outer Casco Bay area, F2 folds become more reoriented until they are subparallel to the main fault zone (Fig. 2B). Foliations and compositional layering are typically subvertical and strike

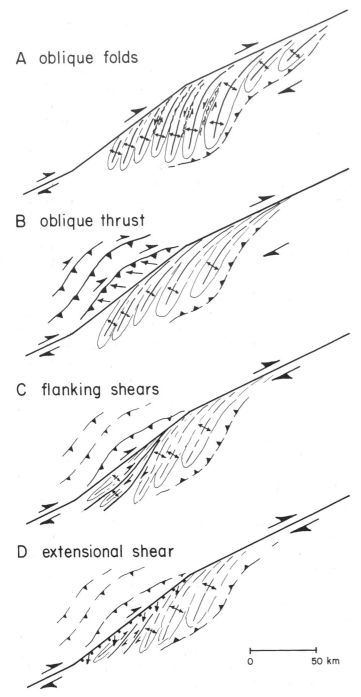

Figure 4. Structural sequence for restraining-bend deformation in the Casco Bay area. A: Oblique fold formation on southeast side of restraining bend with clockwise reorientation to lower angles during shear along the fault; rotation accommodated by antithetic slip along upright limbs. B: West-directed oblique dextral thrusting with east-plunging lineations along southeast-dipping foliations. C: Flanking dextral shear-zone system along sheared limbs of earlier folds; note that faults serve as mechanism to bypass the restraining bend and that the fault-bounded fold packets become aligned parallel to the fault trace. D: Dextral shear with southwest-plunging lineations on southeast-dipping layers suggesting oblique extensional shear.

~N36–48E, essentially parallel to the main fault trace at N42E. These layers have been isoclinally folded with a well-developed hinge-parallel lineation that varies in plunge from subhorizontal to moderate to the southwest (Fig. 6, B and C). The steeply dipping layers record a strong component of dextral shear, as expressed by a range of asymmetric boudin features (Fig. 5, A and C), minor folds, and fabrics (Swanson, this volume). Measurements of reoriented veins and boudin partings from localities such as Ft. Williams on Cape Elizabeth, Cliff and adjacent islands, and Simpson's Point (Fig. 6C), for example, document the clockwise rotation due to layer-parallel dextral shear. Reorientation of initially lineation-orthogonal planar features has been moderate to extreme, attesting to the relatively high shear strains recorded in these rocks.

Northwest dextral thrusting. Northwest of the main Flying Point shear zone, the rocks of the inner Casco Bay shoreline of Falmouth, Yarmouth, and Freeport and out along Wolfe's Neck exhibit foliations and compositional layers that dip moderately to the southeast with prominent east-plunging lineations (Figs. 6B and 7A). This foliation and/or lineation geometry in conjunction with dextral shear indicators indicates a phase of dextral overthrusting to the northwest (Fig. 4B). This lineation pattern adjacent to the fault zone on the northwest side persists for at least 40 km along the restraining segment to the northeast into the Brunswick-Topsham area and at least 25 km to the northwest away from the fault into the Sebago area. Solar (1996) in studies ~100 km to the northwest found similar dextral overthrust fabrics within steeply dipping flow layers, and suggested a relationship to Norumbega shearing and this restraining bend. The Falmouth-Brunswick sequence on the northwest side of the fault is dominated by syntectonic pegmatite intrusions, described by Hussey (1971) as a "zone of migmatization." Many of these initially orthogonal intrusions have undergone reorientation and accompanying boudinage. Data distributions in equal-area plots illustrate the progressive rotation of these orthogonal intrusions about rotation axes perpendicular to the lineations (Fig. 6A). Dextral kinematic indicators in exposures parallel to this lineation and perpendicular to foliation show that shearing within this northwest flanking block was oblique slip as dextral overthrusting to the northwest parallel to the lineation. The previously mapped Hackmatack Pond fault zone (Hussey, 1985, 1988) as a folded premetamorphic thrust may be exposed here due to this younger oblique dextral thrusting concentrated as a broad elongate zone that flanks the entire 150 km length of this restraining bend (Osberg et al., 1985).

The dominant dextral oblique thrust fabrics along the northwest side of the restraining Flying Point segment (Fig. 4B) suggest a phase of localized uplift related to this transpression. Evidence for structural thickening and associated uplift can be found in the younger hornblende ages for the northwest side of the fault (West et al., 1989), which suggests burial by oblique thrusting. Additional support for localized uplift in the Casco Bay area is provided by the pattern of current indicators in the late Paleozoic (310–280 Ma) basins to the northeast. Gibling et al.

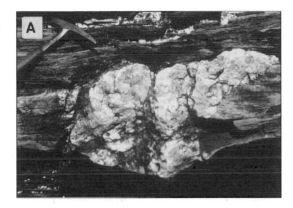

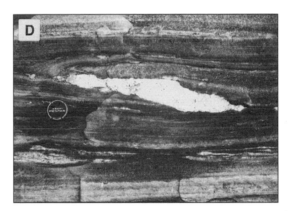

Figure 5. Comparison of kinematic indicators for the proximal Casco Bay area (dextral) and distal Pemaquid Point area (sinistral or antithetic). A: Competent-layer boudinage along quartzite layer with distortion of quartz partition by clockwise rotation during dextral shear (Harpswell). Hammer is 28 cm long. B: Competent-layer boudinage of quartzite layer with distortion of quartz partition by counterclockwise rotation during sinistral shear (Pemaquid Point). Hammer handle is 15 cm long. C: Isolated quartz lens produced by clockwise rotation and elongation during dextral shear of veins initially perpendicular to flow layering (Harpswell). D: Isolated quartz boudin produced by counterclockwise rotation and elongation during sinistral shear of veins initially perpendicular to flow layering (Pemaquid Point). Lens cap for scale is 5.4 cm in diameter.

(1992) interpreted a northeasterly, fault-parallel transport of sediment from a source to the southwest, possibly localized transpressional uplift in the Casco Bay area.

To the southeast, closer to the main Flying Point fault zone along the inner Casco Bay exposures, highly sheared pegmatite-intruded exposures are dominated by coarse heteroclastic mylonite textures as the coarse granitic material was disaggregated by shear flow. In addition, large amphibolite boudins, tens of meters in width, are within the sheared rocks. The shear foliation and amphibolite pods within this inner zone bend or anastomose into the flow fabric of the main Flying Point fault zone with a distinct transition in plunge directions (Fig. 7A) (discussed in more detail in the following).

Formation of flanking shears. Localization of the shear strain component within oblique folds on the southeast side of the main fault zone was initiated during fold reorientation and probably continued during the dextral overthrusting stage described above. This localization led to the development of a set of flanking shear zones (Figs. 2A and 4C) along severely reoriented fold limbs represented by the Casco Bay shear-zone system. Initial shearing may have been localized within tight synclinal axes, as suggested by the modeling studies of Richard et al. (1991). In the Casco Bay area these synclinal axes would localize shear due to the relative incompetence of the schistose metasedimentary units of the upper Casco Bay stratigraphy. The lower, thicker, metavolcanic units, however, were more competent, so that anticlinal cores would have been more resistant to shear. This is much the pattern in the Casco Bay area, where core zones appear to contain a higher constrictional strain component with prominent fold hinge-parallel elongation. Flanking limb areas show extreme dextral shear concentrated in more schistose units, as can be seen in the Broad Cove, Cape Elizabeth, and South Portland faults of Cape Elizabeth in the southwestern section of the bay area. The development of this flanking shear system served as an effective bypass mechanism to move crustal slivers past the obstruction to shear created by the restraining bend and the dextral oblique thrust fabrics of the northwest side of the fault.

Extensional dextral shearing. Lineations within the southeast-dipping foliation planes of the inner Casco Bay change from east-plunging on the northwest side of the Flying Point fault zone (Fig. 6A) to southwest-plunging (Fig. 6B) within the highly strained core of the shear zone just to the southeast. Within the 4–5-km-wide Flying Point fault zone lineation trends are uniform; there are moderate plunges to the southwest (Figs. 6 and 7C) in foliations that consistently dip to the southeast. Such a geometry with dextral shear indicators suggests an extensional component to this phase of dextral strike-slip (Fig. 4D). Map relations (Fig. 7) show foliations that anastamose into this high-strain zone, suggesting that later strain is localized along this main shear zone. The highly deformed Mackworth Formation (Fig. 7) is also interpreted to have been intensely sheared, dragged, and attenuated by dextral shear at this boundary as well as being reactivated in normal slip and late vertical shortening (discussed in more detail in the following). This particular lithology within the shear zone shows complex lineation patterns within the stretched and sheared layer-parallel quartz sheets throughout the formation (Fig. 8A). Lineations show the typical southwest plunge for this shear zone but with considerable variability from strike slip to dip slip. The dip-slip lineations are associated with overthrust kinematic indicators, such as shear bands as at Mackworth Island. However, these same quartz sheets are cut by high-angle R′ shears that indicate late normal slip, perhaps synchronous with this phase of extensional shear.

This high-strain zone is also conspicuously barren of any discordant pegmatite intrusions or quartz veins, in contrast to the pegmatite-injected rocks just to the northwest. Strains were likely sufficient for complete transposition and extensive grain-size reduction to produce finely layered "granofels" (after Hussey, 1985) or "straight planar gneisses" (Nadeau and Hanmer, 1992), as in Grenville rocks. These fine and uniformly layered quartzo-feldspathic rocks of the inner Casco Bay area are interpreted as products of high shear strains.

High shear strains along this shear zone with prominent southwest-plunging lineations (Fig. 7C) suggest that this extensional dextral shear phase (Fig. 4D) was a significant part of the restraining bend deformation. A normal dip-slip or extensional component to this late strain localization marks the end of the uplift-building stage of deformation due to oblique dextral thrusting. Initial oblique thrusting gave way to oblique extension along the main Flying Point shear-zone boundary to accommodate collapse of the topographic uplift.

Late subvertical shortening. An additional phase in the deformation is suggested by a range of outcrop-scale structures (Figs. 8 and 9) that includes normal dip-slip kink bands to several meters in width, often in conjugate pairs; high-angle striated normal faults; minor crenulation lineations; and locally, centimeter-scale chevron folds with horizontal axial planes. Such structures require subvertical shortening directions to initiate folding or kinking of steeply dipping foliations. The kink bands

are best seen within the phyllites of the Mackworth Formation as a reactivated sliver within the Maine Flying Point fault zone (Fig. 9, A and B). Structural data on kink-band orientations (Fig. 8B) indicates conjugate sets of northwest- and southeast-dipping kink bands with subhorizontal rotation axes. These orientations suggest a late phase of vertical shortening. This late phase must be linked closely to the waning stages of regional dextral shear, as evidenced by crosscutting relations on Mackworth Island. Here sinistral R′ strike-slip kink bands and shears as dextral shear indicators can be seen to crosscut the sets of conjugate normal kink bands.

The growth of a localized transpressional uplift by upright folding and northwestward thrusting may have been responsible for initiating this phase of vertical shortening. Similar structures have been described by deRoo and van Stal (1994) as flat belts of horizontal schistosity and minor open recumbent folds in northern New Brunswick. This flat-lying S3 schistosity is attributed to vertical compression following crustal thickening during Silurian convergence. Aerdan (1994), likewise, interpreted horizontal crenulation cleavage in the Lys-Cailleouas massif in the Pyrenees as due to collapse of the thickened orogen. The kink bands in the Casco Bay area are also similar to the larger scale kink bands and folds reported by Cunningham et al. (1996) and attributed to extensional movements on the Tsaagan Cholo shear zone associated with transpressional deformation in central Asia.

Cross-sectional model

Given the dextral strike-slip nature of the deformation and the restraining-bend geometry of the Casco Bay area (Fig. 10A), a likely cross-section configuration consists of a downward-converging array of oblique-slip and strike-slip fault zones that creates a positive "palm tree" flower structure and an associated transpressional uplift (Fig. 10B). The oblique block

Figure 6. Equal-area stereograms of structural data from the inner Casco Bay area including: left—poles to foliation (open circles), trace of average foliation, and L2 lineations (dots), and right—poles to pegmatite intrusions and quartz veins. The trend from planar to deformed intrusions and veins, as indicated, clocks the path of pole reorientation during deformation represented as a great circle (dashed) about a kinematic rotation axis (hexagon) for dextral shear. Data are from the three structural domains depicted in Figures 7 and 10C. A: Oblique thrusting on northwest side of main fault zone (Wolf Neck and inner Casco Bay shoreline) with east-plunging L2 lineations within southeast-dipping foliations (left); poles to syntectonic pegmatite intrusions (right) show clockwise rotation from initially orthogonal orientations (perpendicular to L2 lineations) to stretched and boudinaged veins nearly parallel to flow layering. B: Main extensional shear zone (Flying Point and adjacent islands) with southwest-plunging lineations in southeast-dipping foliations (left); poles to quartz veins and boudin partings (right) show clockwise rotation from initially orthogonal orientations (perpendicular to L2 lineations) to stretched and boudinaged veins nearly parallel to the flow layering. C: Flanking horizontal F2/L2 shear zones on the southeast side (Simpsons Point and adjacent islands) with subhorizontal lineations in southeast-dipping foliations (left); poles to quartz veins and boudin partings (right) also show clockwise rotation.

A northwest oblique thrust zone

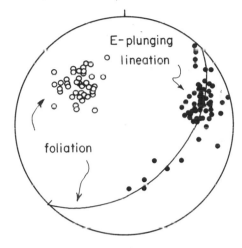

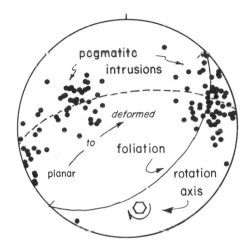

B main extensional shear zone

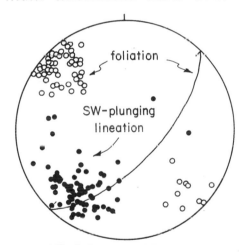

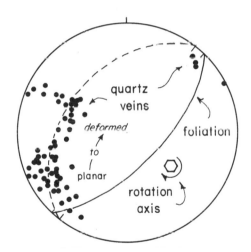

C southeast subhorizontal shear zone

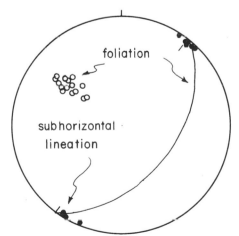

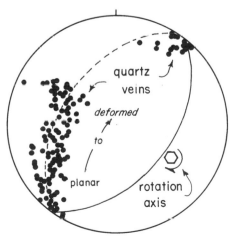

diagram illustrated in Figure 10C shows the variation in lineation trends that occurs across the main Flying Point fault zone. Here, the main extensional shear zone separates the dextral oblique thrust fabrics of the northwest side of the fault from the oblique folds and strike-slip shear zones of the southeast side of the fault.

The existing H-H''' cross section from Maine's bedrock geologic map (Osberg et al., 1985) cuts across the Flying Point fault zone and the heart of the Casco Bay shear-zone system (Fig. 11A). The cross section shows several of the mapped fault traces with dip-slip as well as sinistral strike-slip motion. Fault strands are shown to project downward, but as separate unrelated structures. Considering the expected positive flower structure for transpressional strike-slip fault zones, this cross section is redrawn using the same constraints from surface geology (Fig. 11B). The mapped fault traces are depicted as dextral strike-slip surfaces with their appropriate dip-slip components. The Flying Point fault zone with its extensional component separates the profile into the oblique dextral thrust area to the northwest and the outboard oblique fold and intervening sinistral-dextral shear-zone system to the southeast. The projection of these faults at depth is shown as a downward-converging flower structure typical of transpressional strike-slip fault zones. This cross section view also allows the depiction of the expected uplift and crustal thickening characteristics of transpressional deformation (Norris et al., 1990) and the present-day erosion level. Uplift and crustal thickening driven by shortening within the restraining bend produced the oblique fold terrain depicted as a broad uplifted plateau. Lower crustal thickening is depicted as a keel-type structure similar to an interpretation for the Great Glen fault zone (McBride, 1995) based on the seismic signature.

DISCUSSION

Displacement estimates

The lack of crosscut preexisting markers along the Norumbega fault is problematic for an accurate determination of displacement across the shear system. Early estimates from offset plutons (Wones and Stewart, 1976) gave only 35 km of displacement with considerable ductile shear likely before intrusion. In the Casco Bay area the rotation of secondary quartz veins and planar pegmatite intrusions introduced during deformation can be used to estimate minimum shear strain for these exposures, assuming a simple shear model for the deformation and an initial orthogonal orientation for veins and intrusions. Minimum shear strain can be determined using the strain equations of Ramsay and Graham (1970), such as reported by Strayer et al. (1989) for reoriented mafic dikes in mylonite zones, and for reoriented quartz-filled boudin partings in Casco Bay (Swanson, 1992b). Reoriented quartz veins in the Two Lights exposures of Cape Elizabeth (just outside of the Casco Bay shear-zone system), for example, with rotation of initially orthogonal veins to angles of ~15° relative to the shear direction suggest minimum gamma

shear strains of ~5 (Swanson, 1992b). Higher shear strains and lower angles necessitate a different technique.

Recent work (Swanson, 1994) has explored techniques for estimating shear strains from elongation measurements for reoriented boudin strings by a surface-area restoration technique (also used by Lacassin et al., 1993) using photo mosaics and detailed field diagrams. Elongation estimates for quartz boudin strings within the higher strain zones of the inner Casco Bay were found to range from 410% to 2360% (Swanson, 1994). These measurements and calculations show that minimum gamma-shear strain values for these rocks vary from 4–5 for the oblique fold terrains in the Cape Elizabeth and Bailey Island areas to 10–25 for some of the higher strain units along the Flying Point fault zone of the inner Casco Bay area.

However, these methods may overestimate the shear strains if there is a component of shortening across the shear zone. The effect of such layer-normal flattening components during shear deformation may be difficult to assess, but plays a role in transpression. The influence of pure shear on minimum shear-strain calculations was considered by Lacassin et al. (1993), for example, and was shown to have little influence on high shear-strain estimates as long as the pure shear component was relatively small. Until the role of pure shear in this Casco Bay deformation can be more closely addressed, these strain values must be viewed with caution, as order of magnitude estimates only.

With this in mind, these minimum shear-strain estimates, when distributed over the 35+ km outcrop width for the Casco Bay shear-zone system, show that regional right-lateral displacements in the 100–150 km range are not unlikely (Swanson, 1992b, 1994). Similarly, in the shallow northeastern section of the Norumbega fault, Ludman (1998) estimated ~125 km of displacement from offset lithologic contacts based on detailed mapping. Displacement estimates across other faults within the generally late Paleozoic system are also of similar orders of magnitude. These include ~65 km for the Lubec–Belle Isle fault (Webb, 1969), ~200 km for the southern New Brunswick fault zones (Webb, 1969), and ~360 km across the entire northern Appalachian system (Gates, 1987). Malo and Béland (1989) reported an additional ~155 km of dextral displacement for outlying faults to the northwest in the Gaspé peninsula. These estimates for regional dextral shear are certainly significant and must be incorporated into any structural and/or tectonic modeling for this part of the northern Appalachians.

Regional model for the northern Appalachians

Localized transpression at this restraining bend is part of a generally dextral transpressive regime associated with the northern Appalachians (Kirkwood and Malo, 1993; Dostal et al., 1993; Malo and Béland, 1989) attributed to oblique convergence (Keppie, 1989; Stockmal et al., 1987, 1990), and culminated in the formation of an orogen-parallel strike-slip fault system. The complex late Paleozoic fault system (Bradley, 1982; Webb, 1969) in New England and the Maritimes consists of a prominent north-

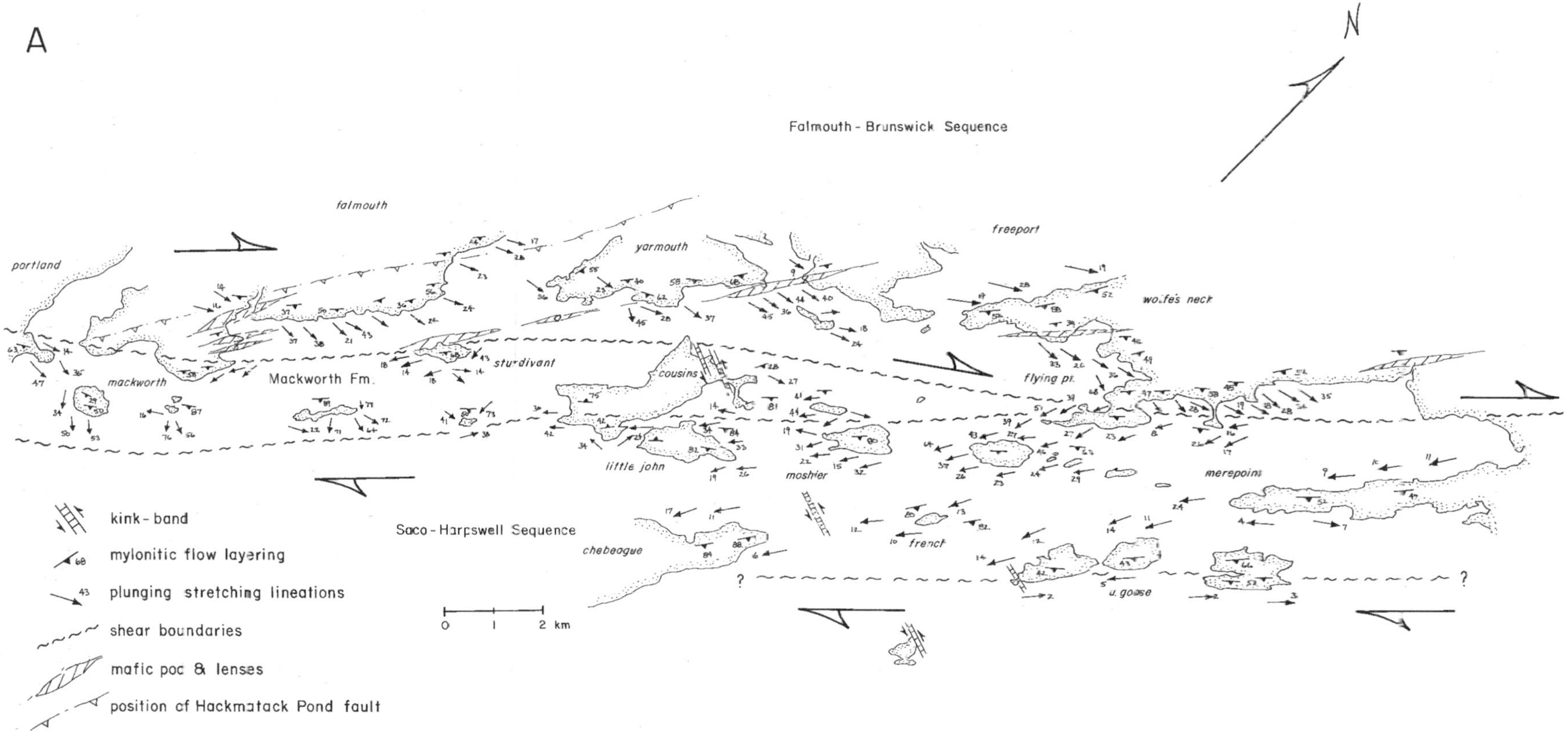

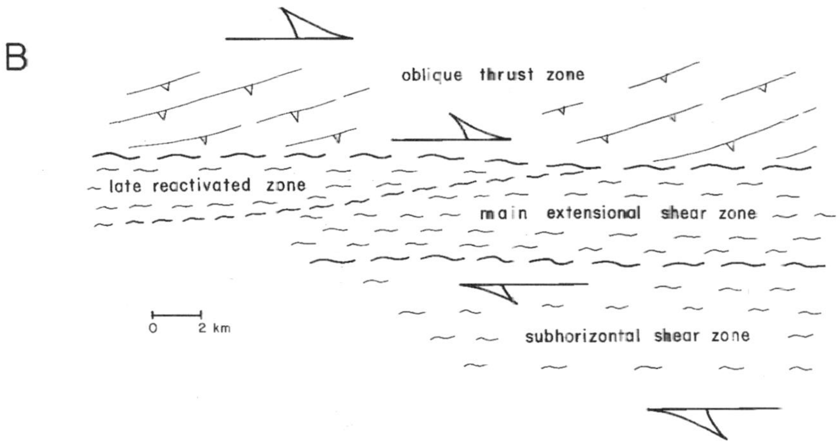

Figure 7. Structure of the highly sheared inner Casco Bay area along the Flying Point fault zone showing the reversal of plunge directions for stretching lineations that mark the shear direction in southeast-dipping flow layers. A: The trace of the Flying Point fault (Hussey, 1988) was mapped as the boundary between the Falmouth-Brunswick and Saco-Harpswell sequences of the Casco Bay Group metasedimentary rocks, but it also marks the transition from east-plunging lineations on the northwest side of the trace as a zone of west-directed oblique thrusting; to southwest-plunging lineations on the southeast side of the trace as a 4-km-wide extensional dextral shear zone, down to the southeast. Subhorizontal lineations and dextral shear dominate farther to the southeast in the horizontal F2/L2 shear zone. The Mackworth Formation within the main fault zone occurs as a distinctive phyllitic lithotectonic unit attenuated along the fault zone. Variably plunging lineations within this unit suggest complex vertical components to the dextral shear deformation as a late reactivated zone. Note the late antithetic kinkbands that cut across this inner bay area. B: Simplified structure map showing interpretations of structural zones on either side of the main extensional dextral shear zone, including the oblique thrust zone to the northwest, the subhorizontal shear zones to the southeast, and a complex late reactivated zone localized within the Mackworth phyllites where smeared and attenuated along the outer Flying Point boundary.

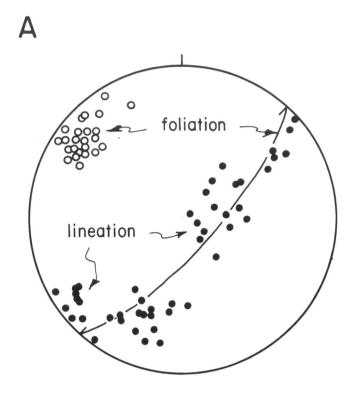

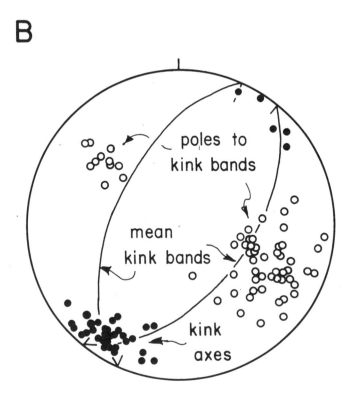

Figure 8. Structural data from the reactivated Mackworth Formation within the Flying Point fault zone. A: Poles to L2 lineations within southeast-dipping foliation planes show a wide array of plunge directions that vary from strike slip to dip slip. B: Poles to conjugate normal kink-band boundaries with dominantly subhorizontal rotation axes suggesting late vertical shortening.

east-trending dextral shear system and, in New Brunswick and Nova Scotia, an east-west–trending dextral system along the Cobequid-Chedabucto fault (Keppie, 1989; Nance, 1987). Convergence in the central and coastal Maine areas was well underway by the Early to Middle Devonian (Osberg et al., 1995). Strain partitioning due to an oblique component (Fig. 12A) would have set up the formation of orogen-parallel thrusts and fold systems as well as intervening zones of orogen-parallel dextral shear, which in several places evolved into major strike-slip fault zones. The regional northeast-trending fault array developed from a right-stepping en echelon fault system that extended from the Norumbega and Lubec–Belle Isle faults of Maine and New Brunswick, across to the Hollow and Aspy faults of Nova Scotia, and the Green Bay and Long Range fault zones of Newfoundland (Bradley, 1982). This right-stepping geometry is the result of orogen-parallel shear across the southern edge of the St. Lawrence promontory, as outlined by Stockmal et al. (1990). This imposed right-stepping geometry was likely controlled by preexisting structural discontinuities and set up several extensional stepovers or offset zones that served as broad and more localized zones of crustal extension, subsidence, and sedimentation, particularly during the Carboniferous, as illustrated by Bradley (1982) and Stockmal et al. (1990).

In coastal New Brunswick, the Lubec–Belle Isle fault zone steps across to the northwest to the Norumbega fault zone in coastal Maine. This geometry creates a large releasing offset or stepover zone, 75 km in width (Fig. 12, A and B), that may be responsible for the generation and localization of intrusions of the coastal Maine magmatic province (Hogan and Sinha, 1989). The origin of these coastal Maine plutons has been attributed to formation in just such an extensional environment, on the basis of detailed geochemical characteristics (Hogan and Sinha, 1989) such as Fe-enrichment trends and the high alumina-alkali-calcic compositions associated with the bimodal plutonism. The offset geometry and displacement transfer may also have shielded most of these intrusions from the effects of transpression that are more prominent to the southwest in the Casco Bay area.

The restraining bend in the Casco Bay area (Fig. 12B), in contrast to the regional releasing offset fault pattern, may be locally controlled by preexisting structures within the crust that helped to site the initial zones of orogen-parallel shear and defined the bend geometry. Dextral strike-slip motion along the fault system drove localized transpressional deformation with its oblique folds and flanking shear-zone system along the restraining segment of the fault zone southwest through the Casco Bay area.

Localized transpression along coastal New Brunswick at this time, as described by Nance (1987), is attributed to the westward encroachment of the Meguma terrain (Fig. 12C) along the east-west–trending Cobequid-Chedabucto fault zone. This westward convergence is thought to drive oblique thrusting along the offshore Fundy zone (Keppie, 1989), and led to the development of localized transpression (Nance, 1987) along coastal New Brunswick. Regional studies in New

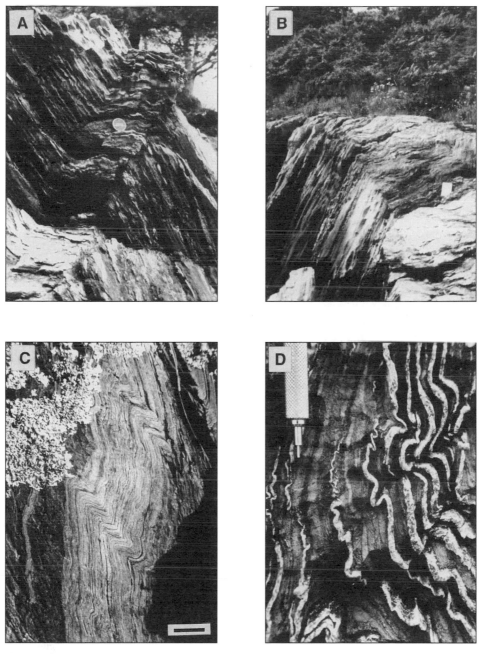

Figure 9. Outcrop structures in cross section attributed to a late phase of vertical compression related to transpressional uplift. A: Northwest-dipping, normal-slip kink band in sheared phyllites at Mackworth Island, inner Casco Bay. Lens cap is 5.4 cm in diameter. B: Large 2-m-wide kink band (northwest-dipping) in sheared steeply southeast dipping phyllites of Sturdivant Island, inner Casco Bay (field book for scale is 12 cm wide). C: Small-scale, northwest-dipping asymmetric folds indicating normal slip in Cape Elizabeth, southeast of the main shear zone (scale bar represents 2 cm). D: Opposing vergence in small-scale folds with horizontal axes in quartz layers on the southeast flank of the Cape Elizabeth fault zone indicating vertical shortening. Pencil barrel is 0.8 cm in width.

Brunswick (Nance, 1987; Leger and Williams, 1986; Park et al., 1994) recognize an early phase of ductile dextral shear with a distinct transition to westward convergence at ca. 320–310 Ma. This corresponds to the beginning of a significant Pennsylvanian displacement along the Cobequid-Chedabucto fault zone (Nance, 1987) and the development of localized transpression with oblique folds, thrusts, and syntectonic sedimentation, that ended ca. 290 Ma. Keppie and Dallmeyer (1987) also reported $^{39}Ar/^{40}Ar$ ages for micas in shear-related fabrics along the Cobequid-Chedabucto fault zone that ranged to 270 Ma. Coastal New Brunswick deformation appears synchronous with restraining-bend deformation in the Casco Bay area, where shearing in the high-strain zone was over by ca. 290 Ma. (West and Lux, 1993). The westward encroachment of the Meguma terrane on the orogenic fabrics in coastal Maine from ca. 320 to 290 Ma would have driven the entire Norumbega system into a renewed and intensified phase of dextral shear with localized transpression in the Casco Bay area. Localized uplift in the Casco Bay area as a result of this transpression may have provided the sediment source for orogen-parallel transport to the developing pull-apart basins in the Maritimes (Gibling et al., 1992).

CONCLUSIONS

Regional dextral shearing and accompanying upright folding, granitic intrusion, and metamorphism in coastal Maine can be linked to a restraining-bend geometry along the Norumbega fault system in the Casco Bay area. The oblique F2 folding and shear-zone deformation combine to form a positive flower structure related to transpressive dextral strike-slip deformation. Localized structural thickening due to oblique convergence, upright folding, and dextral overthrusting to the northwest were responsible for lower crustal melting and widespread syntectonic granitic intrusion. Late-stage extensional shearing may be related to vertical shortening of the localized transpressional uplift. Regional strain accommodation associated with this transpressive shearing appears to be widely distributed throughout southeastern Maine and points out the importance of dextral shear and transpression in the late accretionary history of this and other parts of the northern Appalachians.

ACKNOWLEDGMENTS

Field work for this project was initially undertaken during sabbatical leave from the University of Southern Maine (USM) during the fall 1990 semester. Continued field work was funded by the National Science Foundation's Crustal Structure and Tectonics Program (grant EAR-9104575) for 1991–1992. I thank Arthur Hussey of Bowdoin College for his long history of geologic quadrangle mapping in this area without which this project would not have been possible; Nathan Hamilton of the USM Department of Geography and Anthropology for the use of their Boston Whaler for field work on the many islands in Casco Bay; and Dave West, Alex Gates, and Laurel Goodwin for helpful suggestions on improving the manuscript.

REFERENCES CITED

Aerden, D. G. A. M., 1994, Kinematics of orogenic collapse in the Variscan Pyrenees deduced from microstructures in porphyroblastic rocks from the Lys-Caillaouas massif: Tectonophysics, v. 238, p. 139–160.
Bradley, D. C., 1982, Subsidence in late Paleozoic basins in the Northern Appalachians: Tectonics, v. 1, p. 107–123.
Bradley, D. C., 1983, Tectonics of the Acadian orogeny in New England and adjacent Canada: Journal of Geology, v. 91, p. 381–400.
Bürgmann, R., 1991, Transpression along the southern San Andreas fault, Durmid Hill, California: Tectonics, v. 10, p. 1152–1163.
Cunningham, W. D., Windley, B. F., Dorjnamjaa, D., Badamgarov, G., and Saandaar, M., 1996, A structural transect across the Mongolian western Altai: Active transpressional mountain building in central Asia: Tectonics, v. 15, p. 142–156.
deRoo, J. A., and van Staal, C. R., 1994, Transpression and extensional collapse: Steep belts and flat belts in the Appalachian central mobile belt, northern New Brunswick, Canada: Geological Society of America Bulletin, v. 106, p. 541–552.
Dostal, J., Laurent, R., and Keppie, J. D., 1993, Late Silurian–Early Devonian rifting during dextral transpression in the southern Gaspé Peninsula (Quebec): Petrogenesis of volcanic rocks: Canadian Journal of Earth Sciences, v. 30, p. 2283–2294.
Eusden, J. D., Jr., and Barreiro, B., 1988, The timing of peak high grade metamorphism in central eastern New England: Maritime Sediments and Atlantic Geology, v. 24, p. 241–255.
Gates, A. E., 1987, Transpressional dome formation in the southwest Virginia Piedmont: American Journal of Science, v. 287, p. 927–949.
Gibling, M. R., Calder, J. H., Ryan, R., van de Poll, H. W., and Yeo, G. M., 1992, Late Carboniferous and Early Permian drainage patterns in Atlantic Canada: Canadian Journal of Earth Sciences, v. 29, p. 338–352.
Hanmer, S., 1987, Textural map units in quartz-feldspathic mylonitic rocks: Canadian Journal of Earth Sciences, v. 24, p. 2065–2073.
Hansen, V. L., 1989, Structural and kinematic evolution of the Teslin suture zone, Yukon: Record of an ancient transpressional margin: Journal of Structural Geology, v. 7, p. 37–44.
Hogan, J. P., and Sinha, A. K., 1989, Compositional variation of plutonism in the coastal Maine magmatic province: Mode of origin and tectonic setting, *in* Tucker, R. D., and Marvinney, R. G., eds., Studies in Maine geology, Volume 4: Igneous and metamorphic geology: Augusta, Maine Geological Survey, p. 1–34.
Hubbard, M. S., West, D. P., Jr., Ludman, A., Guidotti, C. V., and Lux, D. R., 1995, The Norumbega fault zone, Maine: A mid- to shallow-level crustal section within a transcurrent shear zone: Atlantic Geology, v. 31, p. 109–116.
Hussey, A. M., II, 1971, Geologic map of the Portland 15′ quadrangle, Maine: Maine Geological Survey Map GM-1, p. 1–19.
Hussey, A. M., II, 1985, Geology of the Bath and Portland 1°×2° sheets: Maine Geological Survey Open-file Report 85-87, p. 1–82.
Hussey, A. M., II, 1988, Lithotectonic stratigraphy, deformation, plutonism and metamorphism, greater Casco Bay region, southwestern Maine, *in* Tucker R. D., and Marvinney, R. G., eds., Studies in Maine Geology, Volume 1: Structure and stratigraphy: Augusta, Maine Geological Survey, p. 17–34.
Hussey, A. M., II, and Bothner, W. A., 1995, Geology of the coastal lithotectonic belt, SW Maine and SE New Hampshire, *in* Hussey, A. M., II, and Johnston, R. A., eds., Guidebook to fieldtrips in southern Maine and adjacent New Hampshire: New England Intercollegiate Geologic Conference Guidebook, v. 87, p. 211–228.
Hussey, A. M., II, and Newberg, D. W., 1978, Major faulting in the Merrimack Synclinorium between Hollis, New Hampshire and Biddeford, Maine: Geological Society of America Abstracts with Programs, v. 10, p. 48.
Jamison, W. R., 1991, Kinematics of compressional fold development in convergent wrench zones: Tectonophysics, v. 190, p. 209–232.
Kaszuba, J. P., and Simpson, C., 1989, Polyphase deformation in the Penobscot Bay area, coastal Maine, *in* Tucker, R. D., and Marvinney, R. G., eds., Studies in Maine geology, Volume 2: Structure and stratigraphy: Augusta, Maine Geological Survey, p. 145–161.
Keppie, J. D., 1989, Northern Appalachian terranes and their accretionary history, *in* Dallmeyer, R. D., ed., Terranes in Circum-Atlantic Paleozoic orogens: Geological Society of America Special Paper 230, p. 159–192.
Keppie, J. D., and Dallmeyer, R. D., 1987, Dating transcurrent terrane accretion: An example from the Meguma and Avalon composite terranes in the

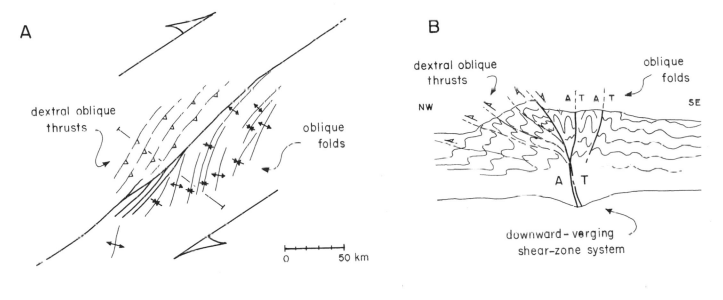

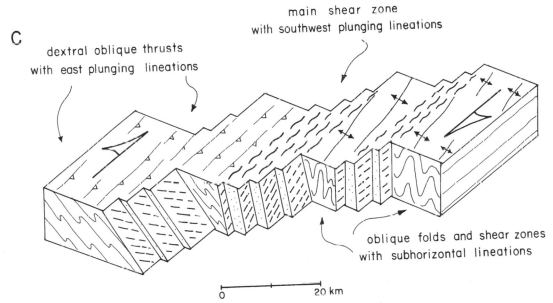

Figure 10. Regional structure and interpreted geometry of the Casco Bay restraining bend. A: Regional structure about the restraining-bend segment and Casco Bay shear-zone system showing oblique F2 fold systems on the southeast side (from Osberg et al., 1985) and the dextral oblique thrust fabric on the northwest side. B: Interpreted positive flower structure showing the thrust and extensional components to the dextral shearing. A is away, T is toward. C: Oblique block diagram to show the change in plunge directions for L2 lineations within the three structural domains of the inner Casco Bay exposures depicted in Figure 7.

Northern Appalachians: Tectonics, v. 6, p. 831–847.

Kirkwood, D., and Malo, M., 1993, Across-strike geometry of the Grand Pabos fault zone: Evidence for Devonian dextral transpression in the Quebec Appalachians: Canadian Journal of Earth Sciences, v. 30, p. 1363–1373.

Lacassin, R., Leloup, P. H., and Tapponnier, P., 1993, Bounds on strain in large Tertiary shear zones of SE Asia from boudinage restoration: Journal of Structural Geology, v. 15, p. 677–692.

Leger, A., and Williams, P. F., 1986, Transcurrent faulting history of southern New Brunswick, *in* Current research, Part B: Geological Survey of Canada Paper 86-1B, p. 111–120.

Ludman, A., 1998, Evolution of a transcurrent fault system in shallow crustal metasedimentary rocks: The Norumbega fault zone, eastern Maine: Journal of Structural Geology, v. 20, p. 93–107.

Malo, M., and Béland, J., 1989, Acadian strike-slip tectonics in the Gaspé region, Quebec Appalachians: Canadian Journal of Earth Sciences, v. 26, p. 1764–1777.

McBride, J. H., 1995, Does the Great Glen fault really disrupt Moho and upper mantle structure?: Tectonics, v. 14, p. 422–434.

Nadeau, L., and Hanmer, S., 1992, Deep-crustal break-back stacking and slow exhumation of the continental footwall beneath a thrusted marginal basin, Grenville orogen, Canada: Tectonophysics, v. 210, p. 215–233.

Nance, R. D., 1987, Dextral transpression and Late Carboniferous sedimentation in

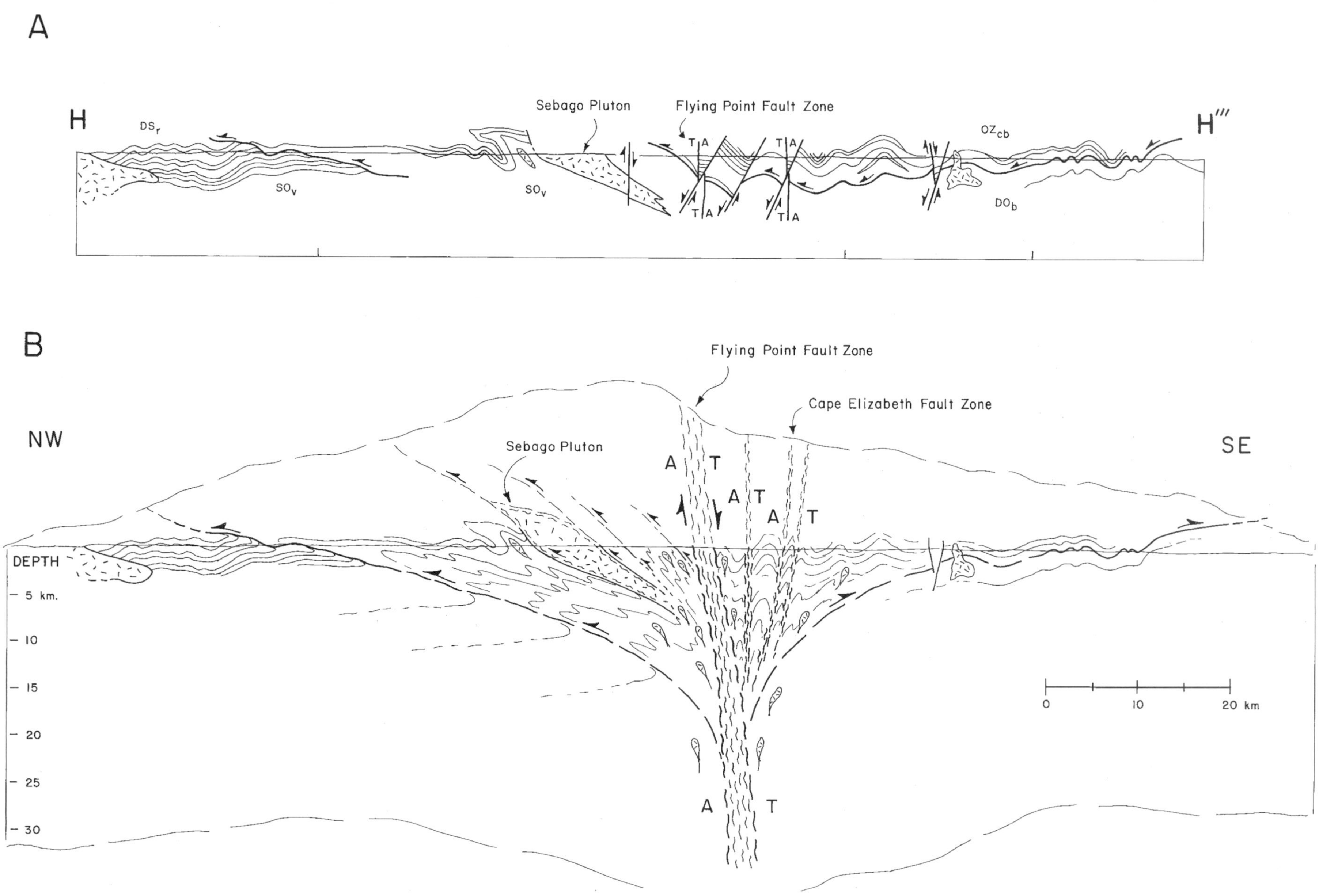

Figure 11. Reinterpreted cross section through the Norumbega fault system. A: Original H-H''' cross section across the Casco Bay area (from Osberg et al., 1985). B: Reinterpreted cross section using the same surface constraints showing the Casco Bay shear-zone system as a transpressional flower structure, with an outlying oblique fold system to the southeast- and west-directed oblique thrusting along the northwest side. Scale as indicated for both A and B. A indicates motion away from viewer, T indicates motion toward the viewer. Ds_r = Rangeley Formation, So_v = Vassalboro Formation, Oz_{cb} = Casco Bay metasedimentary rocks, and Do_b = Bucksport Formation.

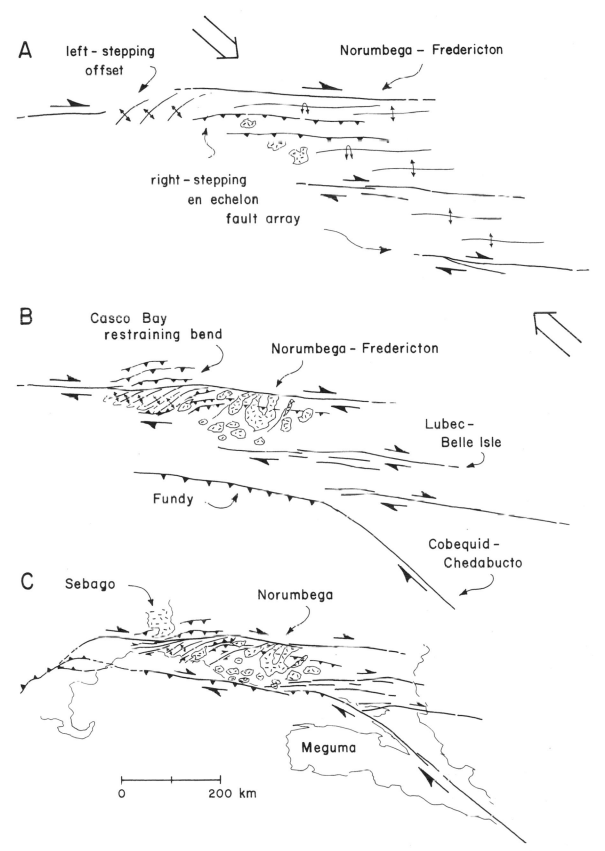

Figure 12. Regional model for development of the Norumbega fault system and transpression in the Casco Bay area. A: Middle to Late Devonian— oblique convergence with strain partitioning into orogen-parallel folds and/or thrusts and intervening dextral shear zones. Note the left-stepping off-set and localized oblique folds in the Casco Bay area in an otherwise right-stepping system that extends through Maine and New Brunswick. B: Late Devonian to Early Carboniferous—continued oblique convergence with strain localization along major shear zones and the development of the Casco Bay restraining bend. C: Late Carboniferous to Early Permian—dextral transpression during final emplacement of Meguma. Convergence along the east-west–trending Cobequid-Chedabucto fault zone led to local transpression in coastal New Brunswick, which in turn continued trans-pression in the Casco Bay area with west-directed oblique dextral thrusting and late extensional shear along the main fault zone.

the Fundy Coastal Zone of southern New Brunswick, *in* Beaumont, C., and Tankard, A. J., eds., Sedimentary basins and basin-forming mechanisms: Canadian Society of Petroleum Geologists Memoir 12, p. 363–377.

Newberg, D. W., 1981, Bedrock geology and structure of the Gardiner 15′ quadrangle, southwestern Maine, *in* New England Seismotectonic Study, Activities in Maine during Fiscal Year 1981: Augusta, Maine Geological Survey, p. 57–66.

Norris, R. J., Koons, P. O., and Cooper, A. F., 1990, The obliquely-convergent plate boundary in the South Island of New Zealand: Implications for ancient collision zones: Journal of Structural Geology, v. 12, p. 715–725.

Osberg, P. H., Hussey, A. M., II, and Boone, G. M., 1985, Bedrock geologic map of Maine: Augusta, Maine Geological Survey, scale 1:500,000.

Osberg, P. H., Tull, J. F., Robinson, P., Hon, R., and Butler, J. R., 1989, The Acadian orogeny, *in* Hatcher, R. D., Jr., Thomas, W. A., and Viele, G. W., eds., The Appalachian-Ouachita orogen in the United States: Boulder, Colorado, Geological Society of America, Geology of North America, v. F-2, p. 179–232.

Osberg, P. H., Tucker, R. D., and Berry, H. N., 1995, Is the Acadian suture lost?, *in* Hussey, A. M., II, and Johnston, R. A., eds., Guidebook to field trips in southern Maine and adjacent New Hampshire: New England Intercollegiate Geologic Conference Guidebook, v. 87, p. 145–171.

Pankiwskyj, K. A., 1978, Bedrock geology of the Coopers Mills–Liberty area: Guidebook for field trips 3 and 4: Augusta, Maine Geological Society, p. 5–8.

Park, A. F., Williams, P. F., Ralser, S., and Léger, A., 1994, Geometry and kinematics of a major crustal shear zone segment within the Appalachians of southern New Brunswick: Canadian Journal of Earth Sciences, v. 31, p. 1523–1535.

Ramsay, J. G., and Graham, R. H., 1970, Strain variations in shear belts: Canadian Journal of Earth Sciences, v. 7, p. 786–813.

Richard, P., Mocquet, B., and Cobbold, P. R., 1991, Experiments on simultaneous faulting and folding above a basement wrench fault: Tectonophysics, v. 188, p. 133–141.

Solar, G. S., 1996, Relationship between ductile deformation and granite magma transfer: Tumbledown Mountain area, west central Maine, *in* VanBaalen, M. R., ed., Guidebook to field trips in northern New Hampshire and adjacent regions of Maine and Vermont: New England Intercollegiate Geologic Conference Guidebook, v. 88, p. 341–362.

Stewart, D. B., and Wones, D. R., 1974, Bedrock geology of northern Penobscot Bay area, *in* Osberg, P. H., ed., Geology of east-central and north-central Maine: New England Intercollegiate Geologic Conference, v. 66, p. 223–239.

Stockmal, G. S., Colman-Sadd, S. P., Keen, C. E., O'Brien, S. J., and Quinlan, G., 1987, Collision along an irregular margin: A regional plate tectonic interpretation of the Canadian Appalachians: Canadian Journal of Earth Sciences, v. 24, p. 1098–1107.

Stockmal, G. S., Colman-Sadd, S. P., Keen, C. E., Marillier, F., O'Brien, S. J., and Quinlan, G. M., 1990, Deep seismic structure and plate tectonic evolution of the Canadian Appalachians: Tectonics, v. 9, p. 45–62.

Strayer, L. M., IV, Hyndman, D. W., Sears, J. W., and Myers, P. E., 1989, Direction and shear sense during suturing of the Seven Devils–Wallowa terrane against North America in western Idaho: Geology, v. 17, p. 1025–1028.

Swanson, M. T., 1989, Mesoscale Acadian deformation mechanisms during regional horizontal F2 hinge-parallel extension and distributed dextral strike-slip simple shear strain, Casco Bay, Maine: Geological Society of America Abstracts with Programs, v. 21, no. 6, p. 66.

Swanson, M. T., 1992a, Structural sequence and tectonic significance of Mesozoic dikes in southern coastal Maine, *in* Puffer, J. H., and Raglund, P. C., eds., Eastern North American Mesozoic magmatism: Geological Society of America, Special Paper 268, p. 37–62.

Swanson, M. T., 1992b, Late Acadian–Alleghenian transpressional deformation: Evidence from asymmetric boudinage in the Casco Bay area, coastal Maine: Journal of Structural Geology, v. 14, p. 323–341.

Swanson, M. T., 1993a, The Casco Bay restraining bend on the Norumbega Fault Zone: A model for regional deformation in coastal Maine: Geological Society of America Abstracts with Programs, v. 25, no. 6, p. 478.

Swanson, M. T., 1993b, Stretching lineations, shear zone kinematics and dextral transpression along the Flying Point/Norumbega Fault Zone, Casco Bay, Maine: Geological Society of America Abstracts with Programs, v. 25, no. 2, p. 82.

Swanson, M. T., 1994, Minimum dextral shear strain estimates in the Casco Bay area of coastal Maine from vein reorientation and elongation: Geological Society of America Abstracts with Programs, v. 26, no. 3, p. 75.

Swanson, M. T., 1995, Distributed ductile dextral shear strain throughout the Casco Bay area, *in* Hussey, A. M., II, and Johnston, R. A., eds., Guidebook to fieldtrips in southern Maine and adjacent New Hampshire: New England Intercollegiate Geologic Conference Guidebook, v. 87, p. 1–13.

Tomascak, P. B., and Francis, C., 1995, Geochemistry and petrology of Permian pegmatites and granite in the Topsham-Brunswick area, *in* Hussey, A. M., II, and Johnston, R. A., eds., Guidebook to field trips in southern Maine and adjacent New Hampshire: New England Intercollegiate Geologic Conference Guidebook, v. 87, p. 279–288.

Tomascak, P. B., and Solar, G. S., 1996, Norumbega fault zone, Maine: A wide ductile shear zone?: Geological Society of America Abstracts with Programs, v. 28, no. 3, p. 105.

Webb, G. W., 1969, Paleozoic wrench faults in the Canadian Appalachians, *in* Kay, M., ed., North Atlantic geology and continental drift: American Association of Petroleum Geologists Memoir 12, p. 754–786.

West, D. P., Jr., 1995, The Norumbega fault zone in south-central Maine: A trip through 80 million years of dextral shear deformation, *in* Hussey, A. M., II, and Johnston, R. A., eds., Guidebook to field trips in southern Maine and adjacent New Hampshire: New England Intercollegiate Geologic Conference Guidebook, v. 87, p. 125–143.

West, D. P., Jr., and Lux, D. R., 1993, Dating mylonitic deformation by the ^{40}Ar-^{39}Ar method: An example from the Norumbega fault zone, Maine: Earth and Planetary Science Letters, v. 120, p. 221–237.

West, D. P., Jr., Lux, D. R., and Hussey, A. M., II, 1989, ^{40}Ar/^{39}Ar hornblende ages from southwestern Maine: Evidence for late Paleozoic metamorphism: Maritime Sediments and Atlantic Geology, v. 24, p. 225–239.

West, D. P., Jr., Lux, D. R., and Hussey, A. M., II, 1993, Contrasting thermal histories across the Flying Point fault, southwestern Maine: Evidence for Mesozoic displacement: Geological Society of America Bulletin, v. 105, p. 1478–1490.

Wones, D. R., and Stewart, D. B., 1976, Middle Paleozoic regional right-lateral strike-slip faults in central coastal Maine: Geological Society of America Abstracts with Programs, v. 8, p. 304.

MANUSCRIPT ACCEPTED BY THE SOCIETY JUNE 9, 1998

Geological Society of America
Special Paper 331
1999

Significance of the Norumbega fault zone in southwestern Maine: Clues from the geochemistry of granitic rocks

Paul B. Tomascak,* Eirik J. Krogstad,† and Richard J. Walker
*Isotope Geochemistry Laboratory, Department of Geology, University of Maryland at College Park,
College Park, Maryland 20742-4211*

ABSTRACT

Mineralogically distinct leucogranite bodies in the Topsham-Brunswick area of coastal southwestern Maine have principally Permian crystallization ages, and similar initial Nd (ε_{Nd} [278 Ma] = –5.2 to –3.7) and Pb isotope compositions ($^{206}Pb/^{204}Pb$ = 18.40–18.46; $^{207}Pb/^{204}Pb$ = 15.61–15.66; $^{208}Pb/^{204}Pb$ = 38.19–38.41), indicating their derivation from similar source materials. However, the major and trace element contrast between these rocks does not favor their relation through simple fractionation processes. The sources of the leucogranites are distinct from the sources of fine-grained biotite granites farther east in Phippsburg (ε_{Nd} [278 Ma] = –2.4 to –1.6) and from country-rock migmatites (–2.9 to +0.8). The leucogranites have initial Pb isotopic compositions that overlap those of abundant evolved granitic pegmatites in Topsham.

The biotite granite in Phippsburg may be derived completely from material with relatively juvenile Nd isotope signatures, comparable to Avalon-like basement or to the Topsham-Brunswick area migmatites. The Topsham-Brunswick leucogranite Nd isotope data require input from more evolved sources than the rocks they intrude. A Central Maine belt source component is not favored, due to regional tectonic relations. The leucogranite isotope data are best explained through derivation from non-North American sources. These sources display a degree of Nd isotope distinction from typical Avalonian basement. Juxtaposition across the Norumbega fault zone of granites derived from isotopically distinct basement sources may indicate that this structure is at some crustal level a fundamental division between different exotic basement terranes.

INTRODUCTION

As more detailed studies of the geology of the eastern North American margin are conducted, more refined plate tectonic reconstructions are made possible. With clearer chemical and isotopic definition of basement blocks, we are able to more precisely differentiate between terranes accreted to North American during the Paleozoic closure of the Iapetus ocean. Whereas recent

advances have been made in the use of Nd isotopes to identify crustal basement terranes in Maritime Canada (Barr and Hegner, 1992; Whalen et al., 1994, 1996a, 1996b; Kerr et al., 1995) and, to a lesser extent, in more inland parts of New England (Lathrop et al., 1996; Pressley et al., 1996; Samson and Tremblay, 1996; Tomascak et al., 1996b), there are few appropriate data for an extensive section of New England, including coastal Maine.

Among the radiogenic isotope systems, Nd and Pb have the potential to provide important information about the nature and age of sources of magmatic rocks. The Sm-Nd isotope systematics of granitic rocks are ordinarily much more resistant to postcrystallization disturbance than O and Sr isotopes. The Sm-Nd

*Present addresses: Tomascak, Lamont-Doherty Earth Observatory of Columbia University, Route 9W, Palisades, NY 10964; Krogstad, Dansk Lithosfærcenter, Øster Voldgade 10, 1350 København K, Denmark.

Tomascak, P. B., Krogstad, E. J., and Walker, R. J., 1999, Significance of the Norumbega fault zone in southwestern Maine: Clues from the geochemistry of granitic rocks, *in* Ludman, A., and West, D. P., Jr., eds., Norumbega Fault System of the Northern Appalachians: Boulder, Colorado, Geological Society of America Special Paper 331.

system is useful for placing broad age constraints on source rocks, as well as for inferring details about magmatic processes involving trace rare earth element (REE) rich minerals. Common Pb isotopic compositions of granites reflect the isotopic character of source rocks and can constrain the ages of sources as well as their time-integrated U-Th-Pb histories. The combination of whole-rock and K-feldspar Pb isotopic compositions can yield further information about magma sources and the extent and timing of U/Pb and Th/U changes in a magmatic system.

The purpose of this work is to characterize the crust in southwestern Maine with isotope and elemental data from granites and metamorphic country rocks in the Topsham-Brunswick area. The use of granites as probes of the hidden portions of the crust is now firmly established (Michard-Vitrac et al., 1980; Frost and O'Nions, 1985; Krogstad and Walker, 1996). This area provides a particularly good starting point for such a study because the timing of granitic magmatism relative to regional high-temperature deformation has been precisely constrained (West et al., 1993; Tomascak et al., 1996a). Furthermore, a data set for Pb isotopes in northern Appalachian granites (Ayuso, 1986; Ayuso et al., 1988; Ayuso and Bevier, 1991), facilitates regional comparisons. The area presents an opportunity to examine magmatic rocks juxtaposed by the Norumbega fault zone, and to use these rocks as probes to examine if the fault zone juxtaposes basement terranes. Given the interpretations of the large-scale significance of this structure (Andrew et al., 1983; Zen, 1983; Ludman et al., 1993; West et al., 1993, Nance and Murphy, 1994), it seems appropriate to study the Norumbega fault zone in the Topsham-Brunswick area, where the level of exposure is deeper than elsewhere in Maine.

GEOLOGIC CONTEXT

The granitic rocks of the Topsham-Brunswick area intrude amphibolite facies rocks of the Coastal lithotectonic belt in Maine (Hussey, 1988; Fig. 1A). Leucogranites and granitic pegmatites in this area are separated from biotite granites ~15 km east in the Phippsburg area by the Flying Point and Cape Elizabeth faults, structures associated with the regionally extensive Norumbega fault zone. In the Topsham-Brunswick area, the Flying Point fault is a relatively wide ductile zone of late Paleozoic dextral shear deformation (Swanson, 1992, 1993; Tomascak and Solar, 1996). West et al. (1993), on the basis of thermochronological discontinuity, suggested that the Flying Point fault was reactivated in post-Paleozoic time as a normal fault with west-side-up displacement. Brunswick is also ~15 km east of the eastern margin of the Sebago batholith (293 ± 2 Ma, U-Pb monazite; Tomascak et al., 1996a), which is in the Central Maine belt. The Hackmatack Pond boundary separates the Central Maine belt and Falmouth-Brunswick sequence and appears as a west-dipping reflector on regional seismic profiles (Stewart et al., 1986). This boundary has been described as either a thrust fault (Pankiwskyj, 1976) or a stratigraphic unconformity (Osberg, 1988).

The bedrock exposed in the Topsham-Brunswick area is the Falmouth-Brunswick sequence, comprising polymetamorphic

quartzofeldspathic to semipelitic gneisses (migmatites) and minor associated amphibolite and calc-silicate. These rocks were interpreted by Hussey (1988) as metamorphosed lavas and volcanogenic sediments, largely on the basis of along-strike correlation with rocks of lower metamorphic grade. However, unambiguous evidence of a particular protolith in these ductilely deformed rocks is lacking. The absence of widespread aluminous lithologies in the Falmouth-Brunswick sequence hinders quantitative petrology. The conditions of metamorphism, estimated from more aluminous schists and gneisses farther east, were at least 550 °C and 230–330 MPa (Lang and Dunn, 1990), perhaps significantly greater in both pressure and temperature. The age of the Falmouth-Brunswick sequence in the Topsham-Brunswick area is unknown; however, Osberg et al. (1995) gave an age of 460 ± 2 Ma (mean U-Pb zircon $^{207}Pb^*/^{206}Pb^*$) for correlative rocks 60 km northeast.

Proximal to this area, metasedimentary rocks of the Central Maine belt are represented by the Hutchins Corner Formation, composed primarily of semipelitic schists that reached temperatures of 550–600 °C and pressures of 300–380 MPa during peak metamorphism (Osberg, 1988). Granitic rocks east of the Flying Point fault intrude the Casco Bay Group, which consists largely of pelitic schists, and which attained >590 °C and 280–330 MPa (Lang and Dunn, 1990). Using the U-Pb method on zircon of presumed igneous origin, Hussey et al. (1993) suggested that the basal part of the Casco Bay Group is 471 ± 3 Ma.

In the Topsham-Brunswick area, the Falmouth-Brunswick sequence is largely migmatitic. In this study two migmatite types are distinguished: regular migmatites and schlieric granites. The former comprise rocks ranging from stromatic migmatites, which display prominent tripartite structure, to equigranular gneisses with minor leucosome. These rocks have pervasive planar and linear fabrics. The schlieric granites are rocks with granitic-bulk mineral modes, highly inequigranular textures, and biotite-rich schlieren. The schlieric granites also have well-developed mineral elongation fabrics, but, in contrast to the regular migmatites, are dominated by leucosome.

At least some of the migmatitic rocks were likely generated prior to the generation of the granites. Three lines of evidence support this assertion. (1) The Rb-Sr data of Brookins and Hussey (1978), suggest ages for several of the pods and sills of schlieric granite in the range of 385–375 Ma. (2) In places where the two rock types occur together, granite cuts across the fabric of migmatite. (3) The migmatitic rocks are deformed, whereas the granites and pegmatites are not. Deformation at high temperature under ductile conditions is suggested by the occurrence of pervasively linear features, including lenticular quartz and rounded and stretched feldspar. There is no definitive evidence, however, to verify that the Middle Devonian Rb-Sr ages of Brookins and Hussey are undisturbed or that they are representative of all of the migmatitic rocks in the area.

The leucogranites in the Topsham-Brunswick area comprise both widespread two-mica leucogranite (278 ± 1.5 Ma mean $^{207}Pb^*/^{235}U$ monazite; Tomascak et al., 1996a) and spatially confined biotite leucogranite. Biotite granite in Phippsburg (Devo-

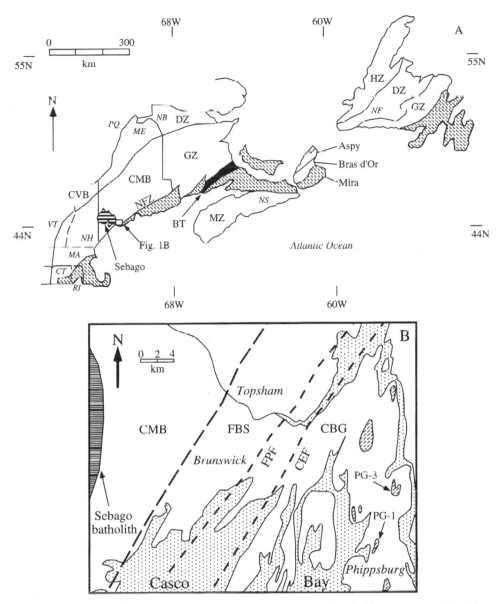

Figure 1. Regional geological relations. A: Terranes in the northern Appalachian orogen (modified from Wintsch et al., 1992; Kerr et al., 1995). Political boundaries are dashed and state or province abbreviations are italicized. Geological abbreviations: BT = Brookville terrane; CMB = Central Maine belt; CVB = Connecticut Valley belt; DZ = Dunnage zone; GZ = Gander zone; HZ = Humber zone; MZ = Meguma zone. Patterned region is the Avalon composite terrane. The Norumbega fault zone (NFZ) is shown intersecting the detail map in coastal Maine, adjacent to the Sebago batholith (striped). B: Generalized geology of the Topsham-Brunswick area. Local constituents of the Norumbega fault zone include the Flying Point fault (FPF) and Cape Elizabeth fault (CEF) (short dashed lines). Granites examined in Topsham and Brunswick come from sub-map-scale outcrops within the Falmouth-Brunswick sequence (FBS samples). The eastern margin of the Sebago batholith is shown on the western edge of the map, within the Central Maine belt. Biotite granite in Phippsburg come from bodies marked PG-1 and PG-3 which intrude the Casco Bay Group (CBG). Detailed sample localities are given in Tomascak (1995).

nian; Hussey, 1998) intruded the Casco Bay Group and formed elongate bodies. The intervening Norumbega fault zone complicates interpretations of relative juxtaposition of the different granitic rocks. If the estimates of West et al. (1993) of 4 km of normal displacement on this system during the Mesozoic are accurate, then granites on the eastern side of the Norumbega fault zone which were contemporaneous (or syngenetic) with the granites in the Topsham-Brunswick area may not be exposed currently.

Numerous granitic pegmatites crop out in the town of Topsham, many of which are large enough to have been economic sources of feldspar (Shainin, 1948). The pegmatites commonly exhibit well-defined internal mineralogical and textural zoning, although accessory minerals other than garnet, beryl, and columbite are rare in all but the minority of dikes. At Standpipe Hill (Fig. 1) pegmatites appear adjacent to, or in contact with, biotite leucogranite. This is the only location where granite and pegmatite crop out proximally. The pegmatites have U-Pb monazite ages that overlap in the range of 275–268 Ma (Tomascak et al., 1996a)

ANALYTICAL PROCEDURES

Major and trace element analyses were performed with a Philips PW-2400 XRF spectrometer at the University of Vienna (analyses provided by C. Dingeldey) and a Jobin-Yvon JY70 ICP atomic emission spectrometer at the Department of Terrestrial Magnetism, Carnegie Institution of Washington. Estimated uncertainty for major element concentrations is ±3% and ±6% for the trace elements (±10% for Ba). Analytical details were discussed in Tomascak et al. (1996b). REE analyses were made by isotope dilution using a mixed REE tracer. Samples were digested by flux fusion and the REE were coprecipitated with Fe-oxyhydroxides by titration to neutral pH with NH_4OH. The REE were purified and separated with two stages of cation-exchange chromatography (HCl and 2-methyllactic acid). Considering the REE abundances of the samples and the sample sizes (~0.2 g), no blank correction was warranted. Concentrations of the REE are reproducible to <±2.4% (2σ), based on repeated analyses of the U.S. Geological Survey (USGS) standard BCR-1. REE concentrations shown graphically are normalized to chondritic values (Masuda et al., 1973; multiplied by 1.2).

Rb in some samples was measured on powders digested in concentrated HF without exchange chromatography. Based on measurements of the USGS standard G-2, this method is precise to <1.5%. Whole-rock powders for Pb isotope analysis were digested at 220 °C for 48 hours in a mixture of concentrated HF and HNO_3 in capped Teflon vials. K-feldspars were leached and prepared as described in Tomascak et al. (1996b). Detailed analytical procedures are given in Tomascak (1995).

All isotope ratio measurements were carried out at the Isotope Geochemistry Laboratory, Department of Geology, University of Maryland at College Park, using Bobcat I, a National Bureau of Standards (NBS)-design 68° sector, 12″ radius of curvature, single-collector mass spectrometer, and Bobcat II, a VG Sector 54 mass spectrometer with 7 in-line Faraday collectors. Bobcat II isotope ratio measurements for Pb were made in static multicollector mode and Nd was measured with a dynamic peak-switching routine. Analyses of NBS Pb standard SRM-982 (n = 77) yielded the following average ratios: $^{206}Pb/^{204}Pb$ = 36.664% ± 0.1%; $^{208}Pb/^{206}Pb$ = 0.99756% ± 0.1%; $^{207}Pb/^{206}Pb$ = 0.46645% ± 0.06%. The data require a fractionation correction of 0.12% ± 0.01% amu^{-1}. Analyses of the LaJolla Nd standard (n = 21) yielded a mean $^{143}Nd/^{144}Nd$ of 0.511849 ± 0.000013. This translates to an uncertainty of ±0.35 ε unit. Nd isotope ratios were normalized to $^{146}Nd/^{144}Nd$ = 0.72190. Nd isotope compositions [$\varepsilon_{Nd} = (^{143}Nd/^{144}Nd_{sample} / {}^{143}Nd/^{144}Nd_{CHUR}) - 1) \times 10^4$] dis-

cussed in the text are calculated for 278 Ma, and use the measured ($^{147}Sm/^{144}Nd$) sample (Jacobsen and Wasserburg, 1980).

GEOCHEMICAL DATA

Major and trace element data for rocks in the Topsham-Brunswick area are given in Table 1. Pb isotope data are given in Tables 2 and 3, and Nd isotope data are given in Table 4.

Major and trace elements

The Topsham-Brunswick leucogranites are weakly peraluminous (or metaluminous, in the case of SHG-2). They are low in phosphorous (≤ 0.07 wt%), and contain only small modal proportions of apatite. Major element compositions of the Topsham-Brunswick two-mica leucogranites overlap those of the biotite leucogranites, except that the latter have lower degrees of alumina saturation (Fig. 2). The one Phippsburg biotite granite analyzed is richer in CaO and Na_2O and poorer in SiO_2 than the Topsham-Brunswick leucogranites. The leucogranites have a similarly limited range in SiO_2 and Mg# as the schlieric granites (Fig. 2). In addition, the leucogranites have K_2O/Na_2O equivalent to the schlieric granites, but higher that the regular migmatites. The regular migmatites are richer in Fe_2O_3 (total), MgO, and TiO_2 than the schlieric granites and leucogranites, as would be predicted by the leucocratic nature of the latter relative to the regular migmatites. The number of migmatite samples with elemental data is sufficiently small, however, that detailed assessment of their relative bulk chemical compositions cannot be made.

The leucogranites have a limited range in concentrations of Rb, Ba, and Sr (Fig. 3). The two-mica leucogranites have lower concentrations of Zr than the biotite leucogranites. The Ba concentration and Sr/Rb of the one Phippsburg biotite granite that was analyzed are considerably higher than the Topsham-Brunswick leucogranites. The leucogranites share major and trace element similarities with leucogranites from a variety of tectonic environments (e.g., Karakorum, Pakistan, Debon et al., 1987; southern Brittany: Strong and Hanmer, 1981; French Massif Central, Williamson et al., 1996). The different migmatite types do not display systematic differences in large ion lithophile (Rb, Sr, Ba) or high field strength elements (Zr, Nb).

The two-mica leucogranites are characterized by variable light REE concentrations, pronounced negative Eu anomalies, and similar heavy REE concentrations (Fig. 4A). The samples range from having $^{147}Sm/^{144}Nd$ nearly like that of average crust (~0.12) to having significant negative kinking at Nd. The leucogranites have consistent Eu/Eu* (0.21–0.36) and, except for the pattern of BG-3, Gd_N/Yb_N (2.6–5.7). The biotite leucogranites have kinked (or depleted and kinked) light REE patterns and have Y concentrations much higher than the other granites and migmatites (>120 ppm). Assuming that Y is a representative proxy for the heavy REE, the biotite leucogranites have very high concentrations of the heavy REEs. In contrast,

TABLE 1. WHOLE-ROCK MAJOR AND TRACE ELEMENT CONTENTS FOR SAMPLES FROM THE TOPSHAM-BRUNSWICK AREA

Sample Type*	BG-2 2m	BG-3 2m	BG-6 2m	BG-12 2m	SHG-2 bma	SHG-4 bma	PHP-1 bt	PHP-3 bt	BG-8 sg	BG-11 sg	BG-6M rm	TX-1 rm	HX-1 rm
(wt %)													
SiO_2	75.9	74.5	73.4	74.3	73.9	74.1	n.d.	70.8	72.9	75.9	73.7	n.d.	69.1
TiO_2	0.12	0.09	0.20	0.11	0.18	0.07	n.d.	0.40	0.20	0.14	0.32	n.d.	0.44
Al_2O_3	13.4	13.8	13.8	13.8	13.5	14.6	n.d.	15.5	13.8	13.1	13.1	n.d.	15.1
$(Fe_2O_3)_t$	0.94	0.79	1.42	0.69	1.53	0.73	n.d.	1.82	1.05	1.37	2.64	n.d.	3.88
MnO	0.03	0.03	0.02	0.02	0.07	0.03	n.d.	0.04	0.03	0.06	0.06	n.d.	0.11
MgO	0.20	0.14	0.31	0.33	0.32	0.11	n.d.	0.63	0.51	0.64	1.12	n.d.	0.65
CaO	0.76	0.79	0.80	0.87	1.19	1.07	n.d.	1.81	1.44	1.07	0.81	n.d.	1.75
Na_2O	3.62	3.65	3.05	2.26	3.83	3.92	n.d.	4.29	2.73	2.86	3.02	n.d.	4.89
K_2O	4.56	5.24	6.06	6.59	4.98	5.36	n.d.	3.83	6.57	5.62	4.71	n.d.	3.48
P_2O_5	0.05	0.05	0.06	0.07	0.04	0.05	n.d.	0.13	0.19	0.03	0.05	n.d.	n.d.
L.O.I.	0.55	0.50	0.31	0.43	0.27	0.38	n.d.	0.77	0.36	0.57	0.46	n.d.	0.50
Total	100.15	99.58	99.43	99.47	99.81	100.4	n.d.	99.89	99.78	101.33	99.99	n.d.	99.90
(ppm)													
Rb	220[†]	218[†]	231	224[†]	180[†]	185	82.1[†]	87.6[†]	138	n.d.	153	n.d.	75
Sr	n.d.	33	73	85	47	42	n.d.	555	313	135	79	n.d.	133
Ba	230	134	315	346	228	120	n.d.	970	601	1030	836	n.d.	n.d.
Zn	n.d.	37	52	21	47	18	n.d.	72	29	61	92	n.d.	72
Y	n.d.	24	19	18	129	193	n.d.	7	19	29	66	n.d.	20
Zr	n.d.	45	140	117	211	313	n.d.	238	137	284	370	n.d.	152
Nb	n.d.	18	11	5	15	7	n.d.	n.d.	8	n.d.	12	n.d.	n.d.
Ce	69.9	37.8	112	80.3	59.8	19.5	77.9	98.1	77.2	136	59.4	49.3	42.3
Nd	27.0	12.8	49.9	30.8	24.9	9.97	30.3	36.1	32.2	61.9	31.7	21.0	19.2
Sm	6.33	3.43	10.9	6.60	6.90	5.00	4.39	4.86	7.87	1.11	8.70	3.77	3.90
Eu	0.413	0.395	0.710	0.578	0.611	0.540	1.06	1.08	1.10	1.84	1.10	1.03	0.980
Gd	5.45	3.28	7.22	5.38	11.0	n.d.	2.79	2.61	7.45	7.89	n.d.	n.d.	3.53
Dy	4.40	3.61	4.19	3.38	19.7	n.d.	2.12	1.17	4.18	4.40	n.d.	3.08	3.19
Er	2.09	2.05	1.42	1.30	15.2	n.d.	1.13	0.480	1.34	3.33	n.d.	2.01	2.08
Yb	1.68	1.84	1.01	1.07	12.6	n.d.	0.946	0.427	0.728	4.38	n.d.	2.16	2.13
A/CNK	1.09	1.05	1.06	1.11	0.97	1.03	n.d.	1.07	0.97	1.03	1.14	n.d.	1.01
Mg#	32	28	32	51	32	25	n.d.	43	52	51	48	n.d.	27
K/Rb	172	200	218	244	230	240	n.d.	363	395	n.d.	256	n.d.	385
Eu/Eu*	0.21	0.36	0.23	0.29	0.22	n.d.	0.87	0.85	0.44	0.58	n.d.	n.d.	0.80
Ce_N/Yb_N	11	5.3	28	19	1.2	n.d.	21	59	27	7.9	n.d.	5.8	5.2
Gd_N/Yb_N	2.6	1.4	5.7	4.0	0.70	n.d.	2.4	4.9	8.2	1.4	n.d.	n.d.	1.3

*Sample types: 2m = two-mica leucogranite; bl = biotite leucogranite; bt = biotite granite; sg = schlieric granite; rm = regular migmatite.
$(Fe_2O_3)_t$ = total Fe as Fe_2O_3.
L.O.I. = loss on ignition.
A/CNK = molar $Al_2O_3/(Na_2O+K_2O+CaO)$.
Mg# = 100 x MgO/(MgO + FeO) (molar), where FeO $\approx$ 0.9 x total Fe.
Eu/Eu*, Ce_N/Yb_N, and Gd_N/Yb_N = chondrite normalized (Sm + Gd)/2, Ce/Yb, and Gd/Yb, respectively.
n.d. = not determined
[†]Rb determined by isotope dilution.

the Phippsburg biotite granites are characterized by steep REE patterns with negligible negative Eu anomalies (Eu/Eu* = 0.85–0.87; Gd_N/Yb_N = 2.3–5.0) (Fig. 4B). The migmatites have REE concentrations similar to those of the leucogranites; however, the shapes of the migmatite REE patterns are considerably more variable (Eu/Eu* = 0.31–0.58; Gd_N/Yb_N = 1.4–8.3) (Fig. 4C). Of the regular migmatites, two samples have REE distributions comparable to those of average shales (e.g., the North American shale composite of Gromet et al., 1984), but with slightly lower abundances.

Pb isotopes

Lead isotope data (Tables 2 and 3) reveal that the leached portions of the feldspars contain higher proportions of radiogenic Pb than the residues in almost all cases (except [207]Pb/[204]Pb and [208]Pb/[204]Pb in F-2). Leached K-feldspars from the leucogranites have a narrow range in Pb isotope composition that overlaps the value obtained for one sample of biotite granite from Phippsburg (Fig. 5, A and B). The migmatite K-feldspars show a similar range of [207]Pb/[204]Pb and [208]Pb/[204]Pb relative to the granites (Fig. 5, C and D).

TABLE 2. Pb ISOTOPIC COMPOSITIONS OF WHOLE ROCKS AND LEACHED ALKALI FELDSPARS FROM GRANITES AND MIGMATITES OF THE TOPSHAM-BRUNSWICK AREA

Sample	Type*	$\frac{^{206}Pb}{^{204}Pb}$	$\frac{^{207}Pb}{^{204}Pb}$	$\frac{^{208}Pb}{^{204}Pb}$	Model μ_f[†]	Model κ_f[§]
Two-mica leucogranites						
BG-1	KR	18.468	15.663	38.335		
BG-2	KR	18.404	15.614	38.275		
BG-3	KR	18.444	15.659	38.408		
BG-6	KR	18.417	15.617	38.320		
	WR	18.695	15.621	38.850	63	6.0
BG-12	KR	18.455	15.611	38.188		
	KL	18.497	15.649	38.329		
	WR	18.931	15.616	38.443	11	1.7
Biotite leucogranite						
SHG-2	KR	18.448	15.631	38.348		
	KL	18.555	15.720	38.561		
	WR	20.220	15.742	38.822	41	0.85
Schlieric granites						
BG-8	KR	18.340	15.614	38.143		
	WR	18.472	15.589	38.214	2.2	1.7
BG-9	KR	18.436	15.691	38.461		
BG-11	KR	18.275	15.609	38.086		
	WR	18.489	15.618	38.821	3.6	11
BG-3-1	KR	18.508	15.653	38.152		
BG-3-2	KR	18.486	15.635	38.210		
Regular migmatite						
BG-6M	KR	18.227	15.605	38.017		
Phippsburg biotite granite						
PG-3	KR	18.408	15.644	38.307		
	WR	18.524	15.636	38.517	1.9	5.8

*Sample types: KR = feldspar residue after HF decomposition; KL = feldspar leachate after ~ 50% decomposition in HF; WR = whole rock.
[†]Calculated final-stage $^{238}U/^{204}Pb$ for whole-rock–feldspar pair.
[§]Calculated final-stage $^{232}Th/^{238}U$ for whole-rock–feldspar pair.

TABLE 3. Pb ISOTOPIC COMPOSITIONS OF TOPSHAM PEGMATITE LEACHED ALKALI FELDSPARS

Sample	Type*	$\frac{^{206}Pb}{^{204}Pb}$	$\frac{^{207}Pb}{^{204}Pb}$	$\frac{^{208}Pb}{^{204}Pb}$
BC-1(1)	KR	18.494	15.641	38.257
BC-1(2)	KR	18.457	15.651	38.307
CQ-2	KR	18.522	15.659	38.339
	KL	18.525	15.671	38.369
BK-2	KR	18.420	15.646	38.230
F-2	KR	18.552	15.671	38.359
	KL	18.560	15.654	38.311
F-5	KR	19.080	15.693	38.387
F-9	KR	18.426	15.639	38.271
	KL	18.486	15.659	38.299
F-12A	KR	18.584	15.672	38.368
GC-7	KR	18.395	15.649	38.311
GC-9	KR	18.400	15.638	38.285
M-1	KR	18.444	15.657	38.310
P-1A	KR	18.382	15.658	38.339
P-1	KR	18.483	15.640	38.211
SQ-3A	KR	18.485	15.681	38.438
SQ-4	KR	18.474	15.655	38.339
MSH-1	KR	18.574	15.679	38.400
MSH-2	KR	18.461	15.657	38.343
MSH-3	KR	18.728	15.684	38.400
TU-3	KR	18.486	15.639	38.258
T-1A	KR	18.566	15.666	38.370
WL-1	KR	18.495	15.657	38.310

*Sample types as in Table 2. Individual pegmatite localities designated by different abbreviations; for reference with text, F = Fisher quarry; MSH = Main Standpipe Hill; details of localities are given in Tomascak, 1995.

Leached K-feldspars from the pegmatites have overlapping isotopic compositions of Pb (Fig. 6). This could indicate that the feldspars all crystallized from melts which were homogeneous with respect to Pb isotopes. Alternatively, the Pb isotope homogeneity could reflect postcrystallization homogenization of Pb isotopes, as by late-stage fluids (e.g., McCulloch and Woodhead, 1993). Because the feldspars were carefully hand-picked to avoid any visibly altered portions of grains, and considering the general lack of alteration of granites in the area, we favor the interpretation that the isotopic compositions are magmatic in origin.

Multiple alkali feldspars from the Main Standpipe Hill and Fisher quarry pegmatites display similar $^{207}Pb/^{204}Pb$ but are variable outside analytical uncertainty in $^{206}Pb/^{204}Pb$ (Fig. 6, C and D). This could reflect a lack of isotopic homogenization in the initial melt, or it could represent subsolidus alteration of initial systematics. For the Fisher quarry pegmatite, both perthite and cleavelandite (lamellar albite; F-12) were analyzed, and there is no systematic difference in Pb isotope composition between these minerals.

Cleavelandite has been implicated as a sink for postcrystallization remobilized Pb in pegmatites from Manitoba (Baadsgaard and Černý, 1993) and albite coexisting with K-feldspar may commonly have a higher proportion of radiogenic Pb (Housh and Bowring, 1991). That the Fisher quarry cleavelandite, which is part of the latest-crystallizing assemblage in the pegmatite, has the same Pb isotope composition as other feldspars is further evidence that Pb isotopes were not redistributed after crystallization.

Figure 7 shows Pb isotope data from pairs of coexisting K-feldspars and whole rocks. For all samples other than SHG-2, a biotite leucogranite, whole rocks exhibit $^{207}Pb/^{204}Pb$ which are no more radiogenic (within analytical uncertainty) than coexisting K-feldspars. Model final-stage μ_f (= $^{238}U/^{204}Pb$) and κ_f (= $^{232}Th/^{238}U$) values can be calculated in order to estimate the U/Th/Pb systematics of the rocks since crystallization. For these calculations, the use of 375 Ma rather than 278 Ma makes a difference of <0.5% in the Pb isotopic composition. The K-feldspar–whole-rock pairs of the two-mica leucogranites, biotite granite, and migmatites have μ_f values of 1.9 to 11, and κ_f values that range from 1.7 to 11. Biotite leucogranite sample SHG-2 is the one sample with significantly different model U/Pb and Th/U (μ_f = 41, k_f = 0.85).

TABLE 4. Sm-Nd ISOTOPE DATA FOR TOPSHAM-BRUNSWICK AREA
GRANITES AND MIGMATITES

Sample	Type*	$\frac{^{143}Nd}{^{144}Nd}$	$\frac{^{147}Sm}{^{144}Nd}$	$f_{Sm/Nd}$	ε_{Nd} (278 Ma)	T_{DM} (Ga)	T_{DM}[†] (Ga)
BG-2	2m	0.512317 (5)	0.1418	-0.279	-4.3	1.53	1.15
BG-3	2m	0.512308 (6)	0.1621	-0.176	-5.2	2.17	1.17
BG-6	2m	0.512313 (6)	0.1319	-0.329	-4.0	1.36	1.16
BG-12	2m	0.512256 (7)	0.1296	-0.341	-5.0	1.42	1.25
SHG-2	bl	0.512395 (7)	0.1675	-0.148	-3.7	2.14	1.06
SHG-2[§]	bl	0.512353 (5)	0.1615	-0.179	-4.3	2.01	1.10
SHG-4	bl	0.512623 (12)	0.3035	+0.543	-4.1	.......**	0.68
PG-1	bt	0.512315 (8)	0.0876	-0.555	-2.4	0.88	1.16
PG-3	bt	0.512344 (7)	0.0815	-0.586	-1.6	0.81	1.11
BG-8	sg	0.512418 (9)	0.1476	-0.250	-2.6	1.43	1.00
BG-11	sg	0.512518 (9)	0.1079	-0.451	+0.8	0.76	0.84
BG-6M	rm	0.512565 (6)	0.1660	-0.156	-0.3	1.51	0.77
HX-1	rm	0.512356 (6)	0.1230	-0.374	-2.9	1.15	1.09

*Sample types: 2m = two-mica leucogranite; bl = biotite leucogranite; bt = biotite granite; sg = schlieric granite; rm = regular migmatite.
[†]Model age calculated using $^{147}Sm/^{144}Nd = 0.12$.
[§]Replicate analysis.
**....... = model age not meaningful due to high Sm/Nd. Values of $f_{Sm/Nd}$ and ε_{Nd} are the chondrite normalized $^{147}Sm/^{144}Nd$ and $^{143}Nd/^{144}Nd$, respectively.

Nd isotopes

The Topsham-Brunswick area two-mica leucogranites have a relatively restricted range in $\varepsilon_{Nd}(278\ Ma)$ (-5.2 to -4.0), which overlaps that of the biotite leucogranites (-4.1 to -3.7). The biotite granites in Phippsburg have higher $\varepsilon_{Nd}(278\ Ma)$ than this range (-2.6 to -1.6). The Falmouth-Brunswick sequence migmatites, which host the Topsham-Brunswick leucogranites, have a range of $\varepsilon_{Nd}(278\ Ma)$, the lowest values of which do not overlap those of the leucogranites (schlieric granites = -2.6 to +0.8, regular migmatites = -2.9 to -0.3). There is no perceptible spatial pattern to the distribution of Nd isotopic compositions among the migmatites.

DISCUSSION

Petrogenesis of granites

Elemental and isotopic evidence. Peraluminous granites elsewhere in the northern Appalachians are interpreted as having a mixture of crustal and mantle source components (e.g., Clarke et al., 1988). There is little Nd isotopic evidence for a direct mantle connection to the Topsham-Brunswick leucogranites. Two-component mixing calculations indicate that the leucogranites cannot be mixtures of rocks like those of the Falmouth-Brunswick sequence and plausible mantle end members (from either mid-ocean ridge basalt or estimated subcontinental lithosphere sources; e.g., Pegram, 1990). Similarly, mixing between mantle components and rocks of the Central Maine belt require >50% mafic end member, which is not geologically reasonable.

Moreover, geologic evidence does not support significant mantle input into these magmas. No coeval mafic rocks (or siliceous rocks with more primitive bulk compositions, e.g., granodiorites and diorites) are exposed in the Topsham-Brunswick area. Although many of the leucogranites are rich in micaceous schlieren, none contain microdioritic enclaves that might be preserved from the interaction of siliceous and mafic melts (Didier et al., 1982; Petrík and Broska, 1994). Granites of similar bulk composition exposed in coastal eastern Maine similarly exhibit no field evidence for physical interaction with mantle melts (Hogan and Sinha, 1989).

Although the two-mica and biotite leucogranites share isotopic similarities, major and trace element evidence refutes a direct relationship between them through fractionation of a single parent melt. These rocks have overlapping Mg# (Fig. 2), which rules out a relation through fractionation of ferromagnesian minerals. The elevated heavy REE contents of the biotite leucogranites compared to the two-mica leucogranites are also difficult to explain by crystal fractionation.

The two-mica leucogranites do not display the light REE depletion that is common among leucogranites elsewhere (e.g., Vidal et al., 1982; Walker et al., 1986; Dostal and Chatterjee, 1995). The biotite leucogranites are variably light REE depleted and have high Sm/Nd ratios (Fig. 4). If this high Sm/Nd was the result of disequilibrium melting controlled by a light REE–enriched mineral (e.g., Nabelek and Glascock, 1995), then the $\varepsilon_{Nd}(t)$ (t = crystallization age) of these granites might not be an accurate reflection of the granite sources. Such disequilibrium has been demonstrated experimentally for Sr isotopes (Hammouda et al., 1996). Nevertheless, the degree of heavy REE

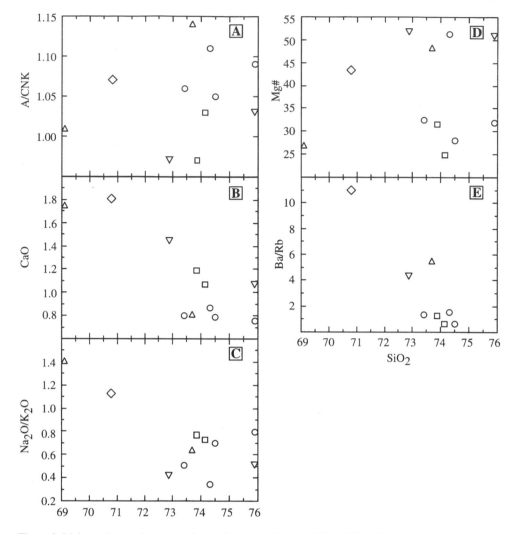

Figure 2. Major and trace element variation diagrams relative to SiO$_2$. Major elements in weight%, trace elements in ppm. A/CNK = (molar) Al$_2$O$_3$ / (Na$_2$O + K$_2$O + CaO); Mg# = 100 × MgO / (MgO + FeO) (molar). Circles = two-mica leucogranite; squares = biotite leucogranites; diamonds = biotite granites; inverted triangles = schlieric granites; triangles = regular migmatites.

enrichment in these granites makes such a mechanism of light REE depletion unlikely. If a mineral such as monazite was not able to equilibrate with melts in the biotite leucogranite sources, the bulk REE concentrations of the disequilibrium melts would be expected to be low, not just the light REE.

Another means of developing the kinked REE patterns of the biotite leucogranites is by the fractionation of minerals with very different light REE/heavy REE partitioning capacities. The biotite leucogranites carry conspicuous allanite, which is ordinarily strongly light REE enriched (e.g., Bea, 1996) and has high Th/U (von Blanckenburg, 1992). Removal of allanite from the biotite leucogranite melt (or retention of the mineral in source rocks) would efficiently reduce magmatic light REE contents. The resultant magma would also have reduced Th/U, a feature suggested by Pb isotope data (see following). The high Zr concentrations and

elevated heavy REE and Y contents of the biotite leucogranites may indicate that these rocks retain a component of restitic or xenocrystic zircon that is not present in the other leucogranites.

The major and trace element data for the biotite granites in Phippsburg are sufficient to highlight several petrogenetic features. The REE patterns of these granites are distinct from those of the Topsham-Brunswick leucogranites and bear closest similarity to some of the regular migmatites in terms of smoothness of patterns and lack of large negative Eu anomalies. The extreme steepness of these patterns (Ce$_N$/Yb$_N$ = 21–59), however, necessitates very efficient fractionation of light from heavy REE. Evidence that the biotite granites have a component of cumulate plagioclase is supported by the minor negative Eu anomaly and alkalic element contents (high K/Rb and Ba/Rb) relative to granites and migmatites.

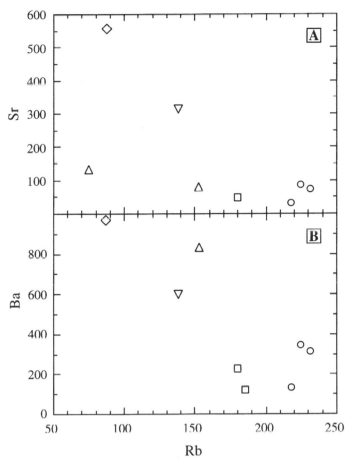

Figure 3. Comparison of alkali trace element concentrations (in ppm) in rocks of the Topsham-Brunswick area. Symbols as in Figure 2.

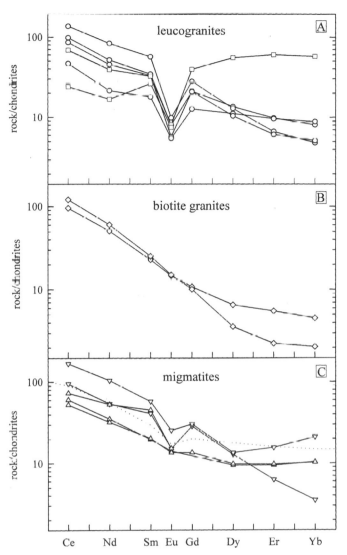

Figure 4. Chondrite-normalized rare earth element patterns from Topsham area samples. A: Topsham-Brunswick leucogranites (circles = two-mica, squares = biotite). B: Biotite granite from Phippsburg. C: Migmatites (inverted triangles = schlieric granites, triangles = regular migmatites, dashed pattern = North American shale composite of Gromet et al., 1984).

That the feldspar data are advanced relative to a $\mu = 8$, $\kappa = 4$ growth curve (Fig. 7) indicates that the sources of the magmas underwent coherent change in Th/Pb and U/Pb during their evolution. Judging from the $^{208}Pb/^{206}Pb$ relations of the feldspars, however, the sources of the granites were ordinary with respect to time-integrated Th/U. The feldspar–whole-rock relations suggest that the latest stage of Pb growth for most of the samples took place under low μ (<7), but somewhat variable κ conditions. The two-mica leucogranites are characterized by higher mean μ_f than the migmatites (8.7 vs. 2.9), yet the κ_f values of these rocks overlap completely. SHG-2, a biotite leucogranite, is the only sample with highly elevated μ_f; this sample also has a significantly lower κ_f than the other samples.

Comparison with the Sebago batholith. There are several major and trace element similarities between the granitic rocks in the Topsham-Brunswick area and granites that compose the Sebago batholith, the largest exposed granite pluton in New England (Fig. 1). The two-mica leucogranites show ranges in major elements and alkali trace elements similar to those of two-mica granites from schlieren-rich outcrops of Sebago granite (group 2 granites of Tomascak et al., 1996b). These granites also

have similar REE patterns, in terms of overall abundance range and slope (Ce$_N$/Yb$_N$ Sebago = 6.1–67, Topsham-Brunswick = 5.3–28; $^{147}Sm/^{144}Nd$ Sebago = 0.098–0.170, Topsham-Brunswick = 0.130–0.162).

The biotite granites in Phippsburg bear similarities to relatively isolated biotite granites in the northern part of the Sebago batholith. Both are depleted in SiO$_2$ and enriched in MgO, CaO, Sr, and Ba relative to the two-mica granites. The Sebago biotite granites are strongly light REE enriched, and the REE pattern of one of the samples has a slope and an Eu anomaly similar to those of the Phippsburg biotite granites (Ce$_N$/Yb$_N$ Sebago = 51, Phippsburg = 21–59; Eu/Eu* Sebago = 0.85–0.87, Phippsburg = 0.84).

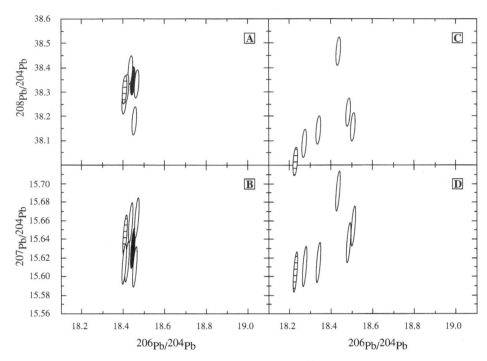

Figure 5. $^{208}Pb/^{204}Pb$ vs. $^{206}Pb/^{204}Pb$ and $^{207}Pb/^{204}Pb$ vs. $^{206}Pb/^{204}Pb$ plots of leached feldspar residue data. A, B: Data from two-mica leucogranites (open ellipses), biotite leucogranite (solid ellipse) and biotite granite from Phippsburg (striped ellipse). C, D: Data from migmatites (striped ellipse = leucosome of regular migmatite, open ellipses = schlieric granites). Ellipses are 2σ uncertainties given error correlation of 0.9.

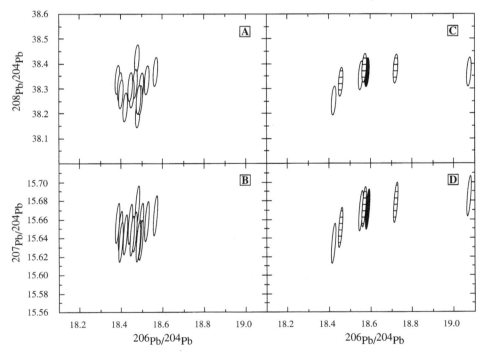

Figure 6. $^{208}Pb/^{204}Pb$ vs. $^{206}Pb/^{204}Pb$ and $^{207}Pb/^{204}Pb$ vs. $^{206}Pb/^{204}Pb$ plots with data from Topsham pegmatite leached feldspar residues. A, B: Isotopic compositions of feldspar from 10 Topsham pegmatites. C, D: Isotopic compositions of feldspar from the Fisher quarry (open ellipses = perthite, shaded ellipse = cleavelandite) and Main Standpipe Hill (striped ellipses) pegmatites. The isotopic variation within a single pegmatite can be greater than the variability among different pegmatites in Topsham.

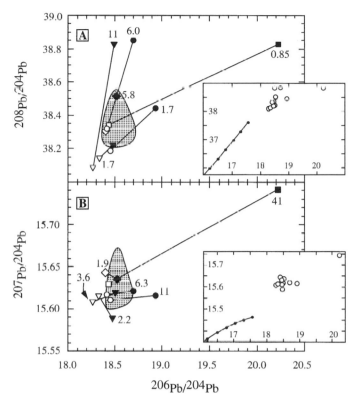

Figure 7. Pb isotope plots for K-feldspar–whole-rock pairs, with symbols as in Figures 2–4 (open symbols are K-feldspar residues, solid symbols are associated whole rocks) A: ^{208}Pb/^{204}Pb vs. ^{206}Pb/^{204}Pb. B: ^{207}Pb/^{204}Pb vs. ^{206}Pb/^{204}Pb. Tie lines connect coexisting samples; numbers next to tie lines indicate model κ_f and μ_f. Insets show the data relative to $\mu = 8$ and $\mu = 8$, $\kappa = 4$ growth curves (tic interval = 200 m.y.). For comparison, shaded fields represent leached K-feldspar data from the Sebago batholith (Tomascak et al., 1996b).

Petrogenesis of pegmatites

Variability in Pb isotopic compositions of the Topsham pegmatites is restricted. There is greater spread in the isotope composition of feldspars from different mineralogical zones of a single pegmatite than within the entire range of other individual dikes (Fig. 5). The overlap in both ^{207}Pb/^{204}Pb–^{206}Pb/^{204}Pb and ^{208}Pb/^{204}Pb–^{206}Pb/^{204}Pb and similar crystallization ages permit the interpretation that all of the pegmatites were derived from similar sources, however, Sm-Nd isotope mineral data suggest that the pegmatites have more complex origins (Tomascak et al., 1998).

The Pb isotopic compositions of pegmatite feldspars overlap broadly those from the granitic rocks in the area. The mean isotopic composition of leached feldspar from pegmatites is, however, slightly more radiogenic than the mean from leucogranite K-feldspars. This difference is not a feature common to linked granite-pegmatite systems elsewhere (e.g., Krogstad et al., 1993). The tendency toward higher Pb isotope ratios may reflect the incorporation of microscopic U-Th-rich inclusions in the pegmatite samples (Housh and Bowring, 1991). Nevertheless, the

general uniformity of the isotopic compositions from multiple granitic pegmatites argues against such an effect.

Constraints on sources

Pb isotopes. One fundamental constraint on the sources of the Topsham-Brunswick magmas is that the high ^{207}Pb/^{204}Pb ($\geq$ 15.60) relative to ^{206}Pb/^{204}Pb requires a source component which had high μ prior to about 2 Ga. This is a consequence of the shorter half life of ^{235}U compared to ^{238}U. Production of ^{207}Pb slowed by the end of the Archean, such that magmas generated in the Phanerozoic from $\mu = 8$ sources after 2 Ga cannot evolve to ^{207}Pb/^{204}Pb higher than about 15.55 for ^{206}Pb/^{204}Pb = 18.2, regardless of the complexity of the multistage history or the magnitude of U/Pb change over time.

The high ^{207}Pb/^{204}Pb at similar ^{206}Pb/^{204}Pb are similar to Avalon-like Pb sources (Ayuso and Bevier, 1991). The elevated ^{207}Pb/^{204}Pb signature is also seen in Silurian to Devonian plutons throughout the Central Maine belt in New Brunswick (i.e., Gander zone). On the basis of these and other isotope and geochemical data, Whalen et al. (1996b) interpreted the Silurian and Devonian granites of central New Brunswick to be derived from crust that bears similarities to that in the New Brunswick Avalon zone. This crust has internal complexity, however, which is not apparent in the Pb data. Thus, in spite of the sharp contrast between the initial Pb isotopic compositions of plutons derived from broadly North American (Laurentian) and non–North American (Avalon-like) sources, there appears to be little internal Pb isotopic distinction between the potentially discrete components that make up the Avalon composite terrane in the northern Appalachians.

The Pb isotopic compositions of feldspars from the Falmouth-Brunswick sequence migmatites span a wider range in ^{206}Pb/^{204}Pb, ^{207}Pb/^{204}Pb, and ^{208}Pb/^{204}Pb than the leucogranites, and isotopic composition does not appear to correlate with migmatite type (Fig. 5, C and D). The migmatite feldspar data provide a reasonable estimate of the Pb isotopic signature of the Falmouth-Brunswick sequence, an approach similar to that of Gariépy et al. (1985) for the estimation of host-rock Pb isotope signature. The range in ^{208}Pb/^{204}Pb of all the analyzed feldspars, given their ^{206}Pb/^{204}Pb, is inconsistent with models for lower crustal Pb isotopic evolution (Zartman and Doe, 1981). As the lower crust probably develops high time-integrated Th/U (Heier, 1973), rocks with old lower crustal sources should reflect this with elevated ^{208}Pb/^{204}Pb at given values of ^{206}Pb/^{204}Pb.

Nd isotopes. The overlap in ε_{Nd}(278 Ma) between the two-mica leucogranites and the biotite leucogranites permits the interpretation that they were derived from common sources. The biotite granites in Phippsburg were derived from higher ε_{Nd}(278 Ma) sources, or had a larger proportion of this type material in their source area. This indicates that the sources of the Phippsburg biotite granites are dominated by material added to the crust after ca. 1.2 Ga (Fig. 8).

In many areas, isotope similarities permit the interpretation that crustally derived granites are generated substantially from rocks which they intrude (e.g., Lathrop et al., 1994). Comparison of the Nd isotopic compositions of the leucogranites with those of their migmatitic country rocks suggests that the leucogranites cannot have been derived through in situ melting of the exposed rocks. Among the migmatites, the heterogeneity in ε_{Nd}(278 Ma) could be an expression of isotopically heterogeneous protoliths, although no such heterogeneity is demonstrated with Pb isotopes. A similar relationship was noted by Hogan and Sinha (1991) in their analysis of isotope data of Vidal et al. (1982) from Himalayan peraluminous leucogranite. As the Nd isotopic compositions of the different Falmouth-Brunswick sequence migmatite types overlap, the sources of the migmatites are plausibly the same.

The majority of crustal rocks from which granites are derived have a restricted range of $^{147}Sm/^{144}Nd$. Many granites, however, particularly leucogranites, have $^{147}Sm/^{144}Nd$ ratios that are much higher than this (e.g., Williamson et al., 1996); this is the case with the Topsham-Brunswick leucogranites. Depleted mantle model ages (T_{DM}) using the high measured $^{147}Sm/^{144}Nd$ will be erroneously old (e.g., Sevigny, 1993). Average crustal $^{147}Sm/^{144}Nd$ may better approximate that of the granite sources, and hence yield more meaningful ages of extraction of granite sources from the mantle. This assumes merely that the granites were derived from crust that was ordinary with respect to the distribution of the REEs, and that the sources did not undergo significant changes in Sm/Nd throughout their histories. Values of T_{DM} calculated in this fashion are between 1.3–0.7 Ga for all of the granites. The migmatites have overlapping T_{DM} (1.1–0.8 Ga) when $^{147}Sm/^{144}Nd = 0.12$ is used, although most of the migmatite model ages are younger than those of the granites. The lack of material with pre-Middle-Proterozoic T_{DM} suggests that, in spite of an apparent ancient Pb isotope source component, these rocks all have source materials with limited crustal residence times.

Models suggest that the solubility of zircon in peraluminous granitic melts, such as those that produced the Topsham-Brunswick two-mica leucogranites, is somewhat restricted (Watson and Harrison, 1983). Although peraluminous partial melts will likely reach zircon saturation rapidly, some zircon in the source will probably melt. Clastic sedimentary rocks (which dominate the sources of the leucogranites in this study) commonly carry zircon populations that reflect provenance age diversity. Considering this, zircons derived from rocks significantly older than the granite sources will contribute radiogenic Pb to the melt. Through this mechanism, the calculations of Hogan and Sinha (1991) indicate that low-temperature, peraluminous granitic melts derived from sources that contain inherited Archean zircons will contain some component of "excess" radiogenic Pb. If such a scenario applies to the Topsham-Brunswick leucogranites and their sources, this would explain the apparent antiquity of sources from the common Pb data, and the lack of legitimate old Nd model ages.

Comparisons along the Gander-Avalon margin. Given the isotopic and petrologic constraints, it is apparent that the Topsham-Brunswick leucogranites were derived principally, if not exclusively, from sources in the middle to lower crust. The sources (Fig. 8) bear greatest similarity to the sources of middle Paleozoic plutons in the Brookville terrane and the Gander zone of New Brunswick (Whalen et al., 1994, 1996b), rocks making up the Bras d'Or terrane in Cape Breton Island (Barr and Hegner, 1992), and granites along the Gander-Avalon boundary in southeastern Newfoundland (Fryer et al., 1992; Kerr et al., 1995) (total range in ε_{Nd}[278 Ma] = –5.4 to +0.7). These Nd isotopic compositions are from plutons that demonstrably lack significant chemical input of mantle material and show the least evidence for upper crustal contamination. The Brookville and Bras d'Or terranes form the western borders to regions populated by plutons with wholly Avalon-like Nd isotope signatures (ε_{Nd}[278 Ma] = –3 to ≥+3; Barr and Hegner, 1992; Kerr et al., 1995).

The Sm-Nd isotope data from the Topsham-Brunswick leucogranites need not characterize a singular source. For example, the data permit the leucogranites to be products of a mixture of juvenile Avalon-like crust and Central Maine belt metasedimentary rocks, characterized by ε_{Nd}[278 Ma] ≤–6 (Lathrop et al., 1996). This would require Central Maine belt supracrustal rocks to underlie the Coastal lithotectonic belt despite the interpreted west-dipping fault (Hackmatack Pond boundary) that separates the two domains (e.g., Stewart et al., 1986). Hence, the proportion of Central Maine belt material involved in the genesis of the Topsham-Brunswick leucogranites is likely minimal.

Comparison with Sebago batholith sources. The initial Nd isotopic compositions of group 2 Sebago granites (that make up the periphery of the batholith) and Topsham-Brunswick leucogranites overlap. Nevertheless, the difference in setting between the two areas makes a crucial difference in the interpretation of their sources. Tomascak et al. (1996b) interpreted Sebago group 2 two-mica granites to have formed through mixing and subsequent fractionation. Their model suggests that magmas derived from Avalon-like sources were contaminated by melts derived more or less in situ, from Central Maine belt sources. The Topsham-Brunswick leucogranites intrude rocks with Nd isotopic characteristics distinct from the rocks of the Central Maine belt. As described herein, unless Central Maine belt rocks underlie the Falmouth-Brunswick sequence, or the two are interleaved at depth, the Topsham-Brunswick granites must not have significant Central Maine belt source components.

Identification of distinct basement terranes. Among the most compelling questions related to this study is whether a basement block distinct from rocks currently exposed in, e.g., the Newfoundland Avalon zone, can be confirmed or invalidated. The broader range in ε_{Nd} of plutons intruding the Gander Zone may reflect, at least in part, Avalon-like sources that contain a component derived from more evolved crust. Whalen et al. (1994) linked the more evolved source component of Silurian and Devonian Gander zone granites and plutons in the Brookville terrane to the hitherto enigmatic "Central crustal block" (Keen et al., 1986; Marillier et al., 1989).

The Topsham-Brunswick leucogranites are juxtaposed to the west of the biotite granites of Phippsburg, which have distinctly higher ε_{Nd}. The sources of the biotite granites resemble more closely plutons from proper Avalon sources. Analogous juxtaposition of rocks with Nd isotope distinctions is demonstrated throughout Maritime Canada (e.g., Barr and Hegner, 1992; Whalen et al., 1994; Kerr et al., 1995).

The sources of uncontaminated Sebago two-mica granites (group 1) ε_{Nd}(278 Ma) are typical of Avalon-like sources (–3.3 to –1.7). This isotopic signature, dominated by juvenile material, persists farther inland in Maine, away from the Norumbega fault zone (e.g., portions of the Philips pluton, ε_{Nd} [278 Ma] = –1.6 to –1.4; Pressley et al., 1996). Plutons with Nd isotopic compositions as high and higher than this are seen in the Gander zone, although they do not predominate. If the apparent difference in the Nd isotope signature of granites intruding the Central Maine belt in southern and western Maine and those in the Gander zone farther to the northeast is not an imprint of crustal contamination (as seen in the group 2 Sebago granites), then it is possible that the basement to the Central Maine belt, from which late Paleozoic granites were derived, changes along strike. This change implies sources with exclusively Avalonian ε_{Nd} in southwest and those with variable Proterozoic components in the Canadian Maritimes.

The best evidence for a Central crustal block source component in the granites of southern Maine comes from the Topsham-Brunswick leucogranites. The spatial extent of this source region in southern Maine may be limited, however, as the Topsham-Brunswick region is confined on east and west by granites that carry more juvenile ε_{Nd} (i.e., Phippsburg and Sebago, respectively). There is also evidence among the granitic pegmatites in Topsham for more distinctively Avalon-like source components (ε_{Nd}[278 Ma] = –2.2 to –1.4; Tomascak et al., 1998).

The major limitation to the use of Sm-Nd isotopes to discriminate Central crustal block sources from proper Avalon sources is the degree of overlap between the ε_{Nd} these sources. Although values of ε_{Nd}(278 Ma) <–3 appear to be characteristic of Central crustal block sources and values >+0.7 are common among proper Avalon samples, the intervening range of about 4 ε units typifies both terranes. The lack of strong geochemical contrast between Avalonian and hypothetical Central crustal block sources does not permit conclusive constraints to be placed on the crustal architecture in southwestern Maine, and the northern Appalachians in general.

Regardless of the lack of a clear Nd isotope distinction between these potential basement terranes, given the geochemical contrasts between the Topsham-Brunswick and Phippsburg biotite granite sources, as well as other geological observations, it is apparent that the Norunbega fault zone is an important tectonic boundary in southern Maine. If the Topsham-Brunswick leucogranites and the Phippsburg biotite granites are derived from distinct basement terranes, it follows that the Norumbega fault zone is a suture (or at least a reactivated suture) between those terranes.

SUMMARY

The mineralogically and texturally diverse, principally Permian, granitic rocks exposed in the Topsham-Brunswick area of southwestern Maine have similar initial Nd and Pb isotope characteristics, permitting their derivation from similar source materials. However, the major and trace element contrast between these rocks does not favor their relation through simple fractionation processes. Their sources are distinct from the sources of biotite granites farther east in Phippsburg, as well as from the migmatitic rocks they intrude. In addition, in spite of chemical and isotopic similarities, the Topsham-Brunswick leucogranites are not related in time or source components to the adjacent Late Pennsylvanian Sebago batholith.

The biotite granite in Phippsburg can be derived completely from material with relatively juvenile Nd isotope signatures, comparable to Avalon-like basement or migmatites exposed in the Topsham-Brunswick area. The Nd isotope data from the Topsham-Brunswick leucogranites require input from more evolved sources than the rocks they intrude. This source component is satisfied by metasedimentary rocks of the Central Maine belt, although this is not favored for tectonic reasons. The Topsham-Brunswick leucogranite Nd data are also satisfied by derivation from an isotopically distinct basement block, as has been suggested in similarly juxtaposed regions in Maritime Canada (Central crustal block source). Juxtaposition across the Norumbega fault zone may indicate that this structure is at some crustal level a fundamental division between different non-North American basement terranes.

ACKNOWLEDGMENTS

We thank Arthur Hussey, David West and Gary Solar for many discussions. Reviews by Michael Brown, John Hogan and Joe Whalen, and the editorial comments of David West, allowed us to improve significantly on the original manuscript. The field and lab work received support from the Geological Society of America and Sigma Xi, in the form of student grants to PBT.

REFERENCES CITED

Andrew, A. S., Loiselle, M. C., and Wones, D. R., 1983, Granitic plutonism as an indicator of microplates in the Palaeozoic of central and eastern Maine: Earth and Planetary Science Letters, v. 66, p. 151–165.

Ayuso, R .A., 1986, Lead-isotopic evidence for distinct sources of granite and for distinct basements in the northern Appalachians, Maine: Geology, v. 14, p. 322–325.

Ayuso, R .A., and Bevier, M. L., 1991, Regional differences in Pb isotopic compositions of feldspars in plutonic rocks of the northern Appalachian mountains, U.S.A. and Canada: A geochemical method of terrane correlation: Tectonics, v. 10, p. 191–212.

Ayuso, R. A., Horan, M. F., and Criss, R. E., 1988, Pb and O isotope geochemistry of granitic plutons in northern Maine: American Journal of Science, v. 288-A, p. 421–460.

Baadsgaard, H., and Černý, P., 1993, Geochronological studies in the Winnipeg River pegmatite populations, southeastern Manitoba: Geological Association of Canada–Mineralogical Association of Canada Program with Abstracts, p. A5.

Barr, S. M., and Hegner, E., 1992, Nd isotopic compositions of felsic igneous rocks in Cape Breton Island, Nova Scotia: Canadian Journal of Earth Sciences, v. 29, p. 65–657.

Bea, F., 1996, Residence of REE, Y, Th and U in granites and crustal protoliths;

implications for the chemistry of crustal melts: Journal of Petrology, v. 37, p. 521–552.

Brookins, D. G., and Hussey, A. M., II, 1978, Rb-Sr ages for the Casco Bay Group and other rocks from the Portland–Orrs Island area, Maine: Geological Society of America Abstracts with Programs, v. 10, no. 2, p. 34.

Clarke, D. B., Halliday, A. N., and Hamilton, P J., 1988, Neodymium and strontium isotopic constraints on the origin of the peraluminous granitoids of the South Mountain batholith, Nova Scotia, Canada: Chemical Geology, v. 73, p. 15–24.

Debon, F., Le Fort, P., Dautel, D., Sonet, J., and Zimmermann, J. L., 1987, Granites of western Karakorum and northern Kohistan (Pakistan): A composite mid-Cretaceous to upper Cenozoic magmatism: Lithos, v. 20, p. 19–40.

Didier, J., Duthou, J. L., and Lameyre, J., 1982, Mantle and crustal granites: Genetic classification of orogenic granites and the nature of their enclaves: Journal of Volcanology and Geothermal Research, v. 14, p. 125–132.

Dostal, J., and Chatterjee, A. K., 1995, Origin of topaz-bearing and related peraluminous granites of the Late Devonian Davis Lake pluton, Nova Scotia, Canada: Crystal versus fluid fractionation: Chemical Geology, v. 123, p. 67–88.

Frost, C. D., and O'Nions, R. K., 1985, Caledonian magma genesis and crustal recycling: Journal of Petrology, v. 26, p. 515–544.

Fryer, B. J., Kerr, A., Jenner, G. A., and Longstaffe, F. J., 1992, Probing the crust with plutons: Regional isotope geochemistry of granitoid intrusions across insular Newfoundland: Newfoundland Geological Surveys Branch Report 90-1, p. 131–144.

Gariépy, C., Allègre, C J., and Xu, R. H., 1985, The Pb-isotope geochemistry of granitoids from the Himalaya-Tibet collision zone: Implications for crustal evolution: Earth and Planetary Science Letters, v. 74, p. 220–234.

Gromet, L. P., Dymek, R. F., Haskin, L. A., and Korotev, R. L., 1984, The "North American shale composite": Its compilation, major and trace element characteristics: Geochimica et Cosmochimica Acta, v. 48, p. 2469–2482.

Hammouda, T., Pichavant, M., and Chaussidon, M., 1996, Isotopic equilibration during partial melting: An experimental test of the behaviour of Sr: Earth and Planetary Science Letters, v. 144, p. 109–121.

Heier, K., 1973, Geochemistry of granulite facies rocks and problems of their origin: Royal Society of London, Philosophical Transactions ser A, v. 273, p. 429–442.

Hogan, J. P., and Sinha, A. K., 1989, Compositional variation of plutonism in the coastal Maine magmatic province: Mode of origin and tectonic setting, in Tucker, R. D., and Marvinney, R. G., eds., Studies in Maine geology, Volume 4: Augusta, Maine Geological Survey, p. 1–33.

Hogan, J. P., and Sinha, A. K., 1991, The effect of accessory minerals on the redistribution of lead isotopes during crustal anatexis: A model: Geochimica et Cosmochimica Acta, v. 55, p.335–348.

Housh, T., and Bowring, S. A., 1991, Lead isotopic heterogeneities within alkali feldspars: Implications for the determination of initial lead isotopic compositions: Geochimica et Cosmochimica Acta, v. 55, p. 2309–2316.

Hussey, A. M., II, 1988, Lithotectonic stratigraphy, deformation, plutonism, and metamorphism, greater Casco bay region, southwestern Maine, in Tucker, R. D., and Marvinney, R. G., eds., Studies in Maine geology, Volume 1: Augusta, Maine Geological Survey, p. 17–34.

Hussey, A. M., II, 1998, Geology of the Bath area: Augusta, Maine Geological Survey, scale 1:100,000 (in press).

Hussey, A. M., II, Aleinikoff, J. N., and Marvinney, R. G., 1993, Reinterpretation of age and correlation between tectonostratigraphic units, southwestern Maine: Geological Society of America Abstracts with Programs, v. 25, no. 2, p. 25.

Jacobsen, S. B., and Wasserburg, G. J., 1980, Sm-Nd isotopic evolution of chondrites: Earth and Planetary Science Letters, v. 50, p. 139–155.

Keen, C. E., Keen, M. J., Nichols, B., Reid, I., Stockmal, G. S., Colman-Sadd, S. P., O'Brien, S. J., Miller, H., Quinlan, G., Williams, H., and Wright, J. A., 1986, Deep seismic reflection profile across the northern Appalachians: Geology, v. 14, p. 141–145.

Kerr, A., Jenner, G. A., and Fryer, B. J., 1995, Sm-Nd isotope geochemistry of Precambrian to Paleozoic granitoid suites and the deep-crustal structure of

the southeast margin of the Newfoundland Appalachians: Canadian Journal of Earth Sciences, v. 32, p. 224–245.

Krogstad, E. J., and Walker, R. J., 1996, Heterogeneous sources for the Harney Peak granite, South Dakota: Nd isotopic evidence: Royal Society of Edinburgh Transactions, Earth Sciences, v. 87, p. 331–337.

Krogstad, E. J., Walker, R. J., Nabelek, P. I., and Russ-Nabelek, C., 1993, Lead isotopic evidence for mixed sources of Proterozoic granites and pegmatites, Black Hills, South Dakota, USA: Geochimica et Cosmochimica Acta, v. 57, p. 4677–4685.

Lang, H. M., and Dunn, G. R., 1990, Sequential porphyroblast growth during deformation in a low-pressure metamorphic terrain, Orrs Island–Harpswell Neck, Maine: Journal of Metamorphic Geology, v. 8, p. 199–216.

Lathrop, A. S., Blum, J. D., and Chamberlain, C. P., 1994, Isotopic evidence for closed-system anatexis at midcrustal levels: An example from the Acadian Appalachians of New England: Journal of Geophysical Research, v. 99, no. B5, p. 9453–9468.

Lathrop, A. S., Blum, J. D., and Chamberlain, C. P., 1996, Nd, Sr and O isotopic study of the petrogenesis of two syntectonic members of the New Hampshire Plutonic Series: Contributions to Mineralogy and Petrology, v. 124, p. 126–138.

Ludman, A., Hopeck, J. T., and Brock, P. C., 1993, Nature of the Acadian orogeny in eastern Maine, in Roy, D. C., and Skehan, J. W., eds., The Acadian orogeny: Recent studies in New England, Maritime Canada, and the autochthonous foreland: Geological Society of America Special Paper 275, p. 67–84.

Marillier, F., Keen, C. E., Stockmal, G. S., Quinlan, G., Williams, H., Colman-Sadd, S. P., and O'Brien, S. J., 1989, Crustal structure and surface zonation of the Canadian Appalachians: Implications of deep seismic reflection data: Canadian Journal of Earth Sciences, v. 26, p. 305–321.

Masuda, A., Nakamura, N., and Tanaka, T., 1973, Fine structures of mutually normalized rare-earth patterns of chondrites: Geochimica et Cosmochimica Acta, v. 37, p. 239–248.

McCulloch, M. T., and Woodhead, J. D., 1993, Lead isotopic evidence for deep crustal-scale fluid transport during granite petrogenesis: Geochimica et Cosmochimica Acta, v. 57, p. 659–674.

Michard-Vitrac, A., Albarède, F., Dupuis, C., and Taylor, H. P., 1980, The genesis of Variscan (Hercynian) plutonic rocks: Inferences from Sr, Pb and O studies on the Maladeta Igneous Complex, Central Pyrenees (Spain): Contributions to Mineralogy and Petrology, v. 72, p. 57–72.

Nabelek, P .I., and Glascock, M. D., 1995, Rare earth element-depleted leucogranites Black Hills, South Dakota: A consequence of disequilibrium melting of monazite-bearing schists: Journal of Petrology, v. 36, p. 1055–1071.

Nance, R. D., and Murphy, J. B., 1994, Contrasting basement isotopic signatures and the palinspastic restoration of peripheral orogens: Example from the Neoproterozoic Avalonian-Cadomian belt: Geology, v. 22, p. 617–620.

Osberg, P. H., 1988, Geologic relations within the shale-wacke sequence in south-central Maine, in Tucker, R. D., and Marvinney, R. G., eds., Studies in Maine geology, Volume 1: Augusta, Maine Geological Survey, p. 51–73.

Osberg, P. H., Tucker, R. D., and Berry, H. N., IV, 1995, Is the Acadian suture lost?, in Hussey, A. M., II, and Johnson, R. A., eds., Guidebook to field trips in southern Maine and adjacent New Hampshire: New England Intercollegiate Geological Conference Guidebook, v. 84, p. 145–171.

Pankiwskyj, K. A., 1976, Preliminary report on the geology of the Liberty 15' quadrangle and adjoining parts of the Burnham, Brooks, Belfast, and Vassalboro quadrangles in south-central Maine: Maine Geological Survey Open-File Report 76–29, 8 p.

Pegram, W. J., 1990, Development of continental lithospheric mantle as reflected in the chemistry of the Mesozoic Appalachian Tholeiites, U.S.A: Earth and Planetary Science Letters, v. 97, p. 316–331.

Petrík, I., and Broska, I., 1994, Petrology of two granite types from the Tribec Mountains, Western Carpathians: An example of allanite (+ magnetite) versus monazite dichotomy; Geological Journal, v. 29, p. 59–78.

Pressley, R. A., Brown, M., and Solar, G. S., 1996, Melt transfer through the middle crust—What do the granites tell us?: Geological Society of America Abstracts with Programs, v. 28, no. 7, p. A-496.

Samson, S. D., and Tremblay, A., 1996, Nd isotopic composition of volcanic rocks in the Ascot complex, Québec: Comparison with other Ordovician terranes: Geological Society of America Abstracts with Programs, v. 28, no. 3, p. 96.

Sevigny, J. H., 1993, Monazite controlled Sm/Nd fractionation in leucogranites: An ion microprobe study of garnet phenocrysts: Geochimica et Cosmochimica Acta, v. 57, p. 4095–4102.

Shainin, V. E., 1948, Economic geology of some pegmatites in Topsham, Maine: Geological Survey of Maine Bulletin 5, 32 p.

Stewart, D. B., Unger, J. D., Phillips, J. D., Goldsmith, R., Poole, W. H., Spencer, C. P., Green, A. G., Loiselle, M. C., and St. Julien, P., 1986, The Quebec–western Maine seismic reflection profile: Setting and first year results, *in* Barazangi, M., and Brown, L. D., eds., Reflection seismology: The continental crust: American Geophysical Union Geodynamics Series, v. 14, p.189–199.

Strong, D. F., and Hanmer, S. K., 1981, The leucogranites of southern Brittany: Origin by faulting, frictional heating, fluid flux and fractional melting: Canadian Mineralogist, v. 19, p. 163–176.

Swanson, M. T., 1992, Late Acadian–Alleghenian transpressional deformation: Evidence from asymmetric boudinage in the Casco Bay area, coastal Maine: Journal of Structural Geology, v. 14, p. 323–341.

Swanson, M. T., 1993, Stretching lineations, shear zone kinematics and dextral transpression along the Flying Point/Norumbega fault zone, Casco Bay, Maine: Geological Society of America Abstracts with Programs, v. 25, no. 2, p. 82.

Tomascak, P. B., 1995, The petrogenesis of granitic rocks in southwestern Maine: [Ph.D. thesis]: College Park, University of Maryland, 137 p.

Tomascak, P. B., and Solar, G. S., 1996, Norumbega fault zone, Maine: A wide ductile shear zone?: Geological Society of America Abstracts with Programs, v. 28, no. 3, p. 105.

Tomascak, P .B., Krogstad, E. J., and Walker, R. J., 1996a, U-Pb monazite geochronology of granitic rocks from Maine: Implications for late Paleozoic tectonics in the northern Appalachians: Journal of Geology, v. 104, p. 185–195.

Tomascak, P. B., Krogstad, E. J., and Walker, R. J., 1996b, Nature of the crust in Maine, USA: Evidence from the Sebago batholith: Contributions to Mineralogy and Petrology, v. 125, p. 45–59.

Tomascak, P. B., Krogstad, E. J., and Walker, R. J., 1998, Sm-Nd isotope systematics and the derivation of granitic pegmatites in southwestern Maine: Canadian Mineralogist, V. 36, p. 327–337.

Vidal, P., Cocherie, A., and Le Fort, P., 1982, Geochemical investigations of the origin of the Manaslu leucogranite (Himalaya, Nepal): Geochimica et Cosmochimica Acta, v. 46, p. 2279–2292.

von Blanckenburg, F., 1992, Combined high-precision chronometry and geochemical tracing using accessory minerals: Applied to the Central-Alpine Bergell intrusion (central Europe): Chemical Geology, v. 100, p. 19–40.

Walker, R. J., Hanson, G. N., Papike, J. J., and O'Neil, J. R., 1986, Nd, O and Sr isotope constraints on the origin of Precambrian rocks, southern Black Hills, South Dakota: Geochimica et Cosmochimica Acta, v. 50, p. 2833–2846.

Watson, E. B., and Harrison, T. M., 1983, Zircon saturation revisited: Temperature and composition effects in a variety of crustal magma types: Earth and Planetary Science Letters, v. 64, p. 295–304.

West, D. P., Jr., Lux, D. R., and Hussey, A. M., II, 1993, Contrasting thermal histories across the Flying Point fault, southwestern Maine: Evidence for Mesozoic displacement: Geological Society of America Bulletin, v. 105, p. 1478–1490.

Whalen, J. B., Jenner, G. A., Currie, K. L., Barr, S. M., Longstaffe, F. J., and Hegner, E., 1994, Geochemical and isotopic characteristics of granitoids of the Avalon Zone, southern New Brunswick: Possible evidence for repeated delamination events: Journal of Geology, v. 102, p. 269–282.

Whalen, J. B., Fyffe, L. R., Longstaffe, F. J., and Jenner, G. A., 1996a, The position and nature of the Gander-Avalon boundary, southern New Brunswick, based on geochemical and isotopic data from granitoid rocks: Canadian Journal of Earth Sciences, v. 33, p. 129–139.

Whalen, J. B., Jenner, G. A., Longstaffe, F. J., and Hegner, E., 1996b, Nature and evolution of the eastern margin of Iapetus: geochemical and isotopic constraints from Siluro-Devonian granitoid plutons in the New Brunswick Appalachian: Canadian Journal of Earth Sciences, v. 33, p. 140–155.

Williamson, B. J., Shaw, A., Downes, H., and Thirwall, M. F., 1996, Geochemical constraints on the genesis of Hercynian two-mica leucogranites from the Massif Central, France: Chemical Geology, v. 127, p. 25–42.

Wintsch, R. P., Sutter, J. F., Kunk, M. J., Aleinikoff, J. N., and Dorais, M. J., 1992, Contrasting P-T-t paths: Thermochronologic evidence for a late Paleozoic final assembly of the Avalon composite terrane in the New England Appalachians: Tectonics, v. 11, p. 672–689.

Zartman, R. A., and Doe, B. R., 1981, Plumbotectonics—the model: Tectonophysics, v. 75, p. 135–162.

Zen, E-an, 1983, Exotic terranes in the New England Appalachians—Limits, candidates, and ages: A speculative essay, *in* Hatcher, R. D., Williams, H., and Zietz, I., eds., Contributions to the tectonics and geophysics of mountain chains: Geological Society of America Memoir 158, p. 55–81.

MANUSCRIPT ACCEPTED BY THE SOCIETY JUNE 9, 1998

Geological Society of America
Special Paper 331
1999

Geochemical and metallogenic contrasts in Paleozoic granitic rocks of the northern New England Appalachians

Robert A. Ayuso

U.S. Geological Survey, National Center, MS 954, Reston, Virginia 20192

ABSTRACT

Paleozoic granitic rocks from the Brompton-Cameron terrane, Central Maine terrane, and peri-Gondwanan terranes in New England were investigated to contrast their geochemical and metallogenic features. Modal and major element compositions for 50 plutons (>900 determinations) generally lack diagnostic features or systematic gradients that uniquely distinguish terranes. Calc-alkalic series Ordovician-Devonian granites predominate in the Brompton-Cameron terrane as well as in Devonian granites from the Central Maine terrane and Silurian-Devonian granites from peri-Gondwanan terranes. No systematic major element differences exist among granitic rocks from different terranes. Trace element contents, however, point to groups showing subtle differences, broadly consistent with their distribution within known terrane subdivisions. For example, the highest contents of Sr (~200 to 800 ppm at SiO_2 = 65 wt%) are found in Brompton-Cameron plutons and the lowest (<350 ppm) are in peri-Gondwanan plutons; Central Maine terrane plutons are intermediate. Normal mid-ocean ridge basalt (N-MORB) normalized diagrams for Silurian and Devonian granites from all the terranes show deep Nb and Ta troughs. Deep negative Eu anomalies, generally flat rare earth element (REE) chondrite-normalized patterns, and high heavy REE (>10× chondrites) contents distinguish peri-Gondwanan granites (SiO_2 = 54–70 wt%) from Brompton-Cameron granites. Granites from the Central Maine terrane have moderate negative Eu anomalies and heavy REE contents intermediate between those of Brompton-Cameron and peri-Gondwanan granites. Ordovician and Devonian granites (SiO_2<70 wt%) in the Brompton-Cameron terrane indicate volcanic-arc affinities; the Devonian plutons also have late collisional and postcollisional affinities. Silurian granites in peri-Gondwanan terranes are related to volcanic-arc and within-plate tectonic settings, in contrast to Devonian granites, which occur in volcanic-arc, within-plate, and late collisional to postcollisional tectonic settings. Devonian granites from the Central Maine terrane also have strong affinities to volcanic-arc and within-plate tectonic settings.

The granitic rocks are associated with the following types of ore deposits: porphyry Cu-Mo; porphyry Mo(?); W-Mo stockworks, skarns, and greisens, and Sn veins; and U-Mo in veins, fractures, and shear zones. Granites associated with porphyry Cu-Mo mineralization in the Brompton-Cameron terrane are the most oxidized (Fe_2O_3/FeO ~0.6 to >10); granites hosting Sn occurrences in peri-Gondwanan terranes are the least oxidized (Fe_2O_3/FeO ~0.15 to 1) and those granites associated with W and Mo mineralization have intermediate values.

N-MORB normalized multielement diagrams and chondrite-normalized REE diagrams of representative, unaltered portions of Ordovician and Devonian granitic rocks

Ayuso, R. A., 1999, Geochemical and metallogenic contrasts in Paleozoic granitic rocks of the northern New England Appalachians, *in* Ludman, A., and West, D. P., Jr., eds., Norumbega Fault System of the Northern Appalachians: Boulder, Colorado, Geological Society of America Special Paper 331.

associated with Cu occurrences have small troughs for Sr and Ba, a wide range in REE abundances, and small or no negative Eu anomalies. In contrast, Silurian and Devonian granites associated with Mo (F-poor, calc-alkaline type) Sn, and W occurrences have deep troughs for Sr and Ba (and Ti), a wide range of abundances of REEs, and large negative Eu anomalies. Mo mineralization (and Sn) is widespread in New England: this means that mineralization is not geographically constrained and that it does not depend on chemical differences in the source region of the granites.

INTRODUCTION

A close genetic relation is thought to exist between mineral deposits and distinct types of granitic rocks (Strong, 1980), but the extent to which these relationships depend on original magmas, tectonic settings, paths of chemical evolution, or emplacement conditions remains problematic. This chapter examines the distribution and ratios of selected immobile siderophile elements and chalcophile trace elements from Ordovician through Devonian granitic rocks of New England in order to determine their salient metallogenic features (Fig. 1). Granitic rocks are commonly used to characterize separate source regions (Chappell et al., 1988). If common source terranes can be identified in the northern Appalachians, recent advances in understanding magmatic sources and ore-element ratios (Blevin and Chappell, 1992, 1995) and the geochemical aspects of these granites can be used to facilitate exploration for new ore deposits.

Several recent studies evaluated the potential for undiscovered mineral deposits in New England (Feiss and Slack, 1989; Slack, 1990; Slack et al., 1990; Moench, 1998) and in the Canadian Appalachians of Quebec (Gauthier et al., 1994). In addition, the potential of granitic rocks for hosting mineral deposits in New Brunswick, Canada, has been investigated using the distribution of known occurrences and mines as well as geochemical indices (Ruitenberg and Fyffe, 1982, 1992; Ruitenberg and McCutcheon, 1993; Whalen, 1993). As a result of such regional studies, a systematic investigation of the metallogeny of granitic rocks distributed among terranes in the New England Appalachians can now be made. This effort might provide better insights into the distribution of granite-associated mineral deposits and thus improve mineral resource assessments of the region; it will also help to determine whether regional differences exist between granite groups, and whether tectonostratigraphic boundaries exposed at the surface separate rocks having different metallogenic associations.

GEOLOGIC SETTING

The tectonic evolution and geology of the northern Appalachians was discussed by Rankin (1994a) and much of what follows is taken from his discussion (Fig. 1). Tectonic models attempting to establish a unified geologic framework explaining the origin of Paleozoic granitic plutonism in the New England Appalachians remain controversial, partly because of the intensity of superposed Paleozoic orogenic events that resulted in juxtaposition of unrelated crustal blocks and terranes

containing a great variety of plutonic rocks (e.g., Wones and Sinha, 1988; Osberg et al., 1989). In addition to this complex history (Stewart et al., 1995a, 1995b; van Staal, 1994; Ludman, 1986, 1991; Ludman et al., 1993), general neglect of granite metallogenic studies in New England has resulted from poor outcrop coverage because of widespread glacial debris, imperfectly preserved igneous systems because of deep erosion, and an incomplete geochemical database.

Terranes were accreted to the eastern margin of the North American craton (Laurentia) during Paleozoic orogenic events (Zen, 1983). The oldest rocks in the northern Appalachians are Grenville-type (Laurentian) rocks of the craton that underwent plutonism and metamorphism from 0.95 to 1.3 Ga and that include orthogneiss, paragneiss, anorthosite, metavolcanic rocks, and mafic rocks of Middle Proterozoic age.

The Brompton-Cameron and Central Maine terranes make up a composite island arc that had amalgamated as early as Late Cambrian, prior to its accretion to the Laurentian margin in the Ordovician (Taconian orogeny) (Boone and Boudette, 1989; Rankin, 1994a). Numerous granitic plutons are found in these terranes (Fig. 1). The Brompton-Cameron terrane consists of Cambrian to early Middle Ordovician sedimentary and volcanic rocks that were penetratively deformed and metamorphosed, and

Figure 1. Generalized maps for granitic rocks in this study. A: Distribution of granitic rocks (~52 plutons) (Wones and Sinha, 1988) and terrane subdivisions (Rankin, 1994a). Internal plutonic subdivisions are not shown; many granites are too small to be shown at this scale. Granites in the Brompton-Cameron terrane are black fields; Devonian granites in the Central Maine terrane are shaded fields; Mississippian and Pennsylvanian granites are light shaded fields; Silurian granites in peri-Gondwanan terranes (Merrimack-Harpswell, MH; Saint Croix, SC; and Ellsworth-Mascarene, EM) are black fields. The Norumbega fault and the Hackmatack Pond fault are depicted as the southern limit of the Central Maine terrane in Maine. Other symbols are as follows: Cu occurrences are crosses, Mo occurrences are circles, Sn occurrences are diamonds, W occurrences are squares, and U are inverted triangles. Localities mentioned in the text: 1, Willoughby granite; 2, Averill granodiorite in the Northeast Kingdom batholith (VT); 3, Skinner granodiorite; 4, Catheart Mountain (and Sally Mountain) granodiorite which intruded the Attean granodiorite in the Chain Lakes massif; 5, Priestly Lake granodiorite; 6, Deboullie syenite-granodiorite; 7, Sebago granite; 8, Mooselookmeguntic granodiorite; 9, Kathadin granite; 10, Whitney Cove granite; 11, Topsfield facies of the Bottle Lake Complex; 12, Lucerne granite; 13, Blue Hill granite; 14, Tunk Lake granodiorite; 15, Deblois granite; 16, Meddybemps granite; 17, Cadillac Mountain granite. Sources of data given in the text. B: granite mineralogy: h, hornblende (dark shade); b, biotite (medium shade); m, muscovite, light shade.

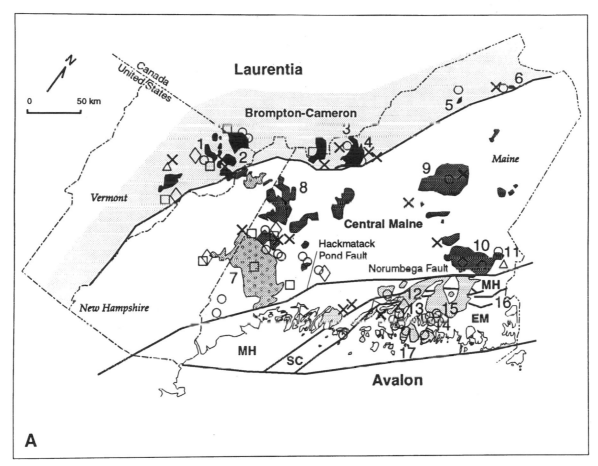

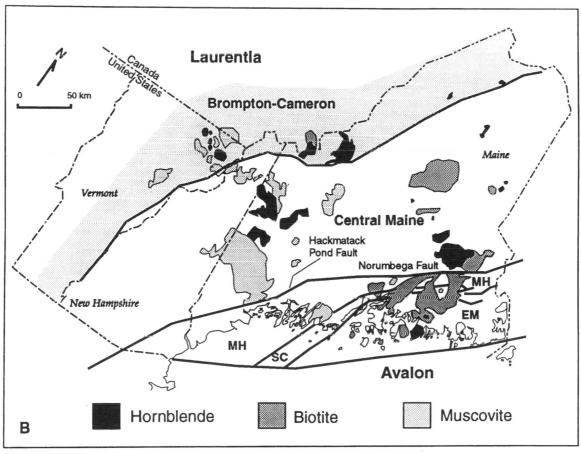

are thought to belong to the North American flank of Iapetus (Zen, 1989). Geologic (Zen, 1983), geophysical (Stewart, 1989; Stewart et al., 1993), and isotopic studies of granitic rocks indicate that the basement underlying the Brompton-Cameron terrane is Laurentian (Ayuso and Bevier, 1991; Arth and Ayuso, 1997; 1993, 1994). The Central Maine terrane consists of a different sequence of Cambrian and Ordovician rocks from those in the Brompton-Cameron terrane and may consist of several smaller blocks (e.g., Rankin, 1994a); the rocks also exhibit evidence for intense Acadian deformation and metamorphism, but contain a more distinct fauna than in the Brompton-Cameron terrane (Zen, 1989). Geologic observations (Zen, 1983) and isotopic studies indicate that basement underlying the Central Maine terrane is not Laurentian (Ayuso and Bevier, 1991).

Two proto-Gondwanan terranes (Fig. 1), St. Croix (Ludman, 1987) and Ellsworth-Mascarene, were first joined to one another by the Late Silurian (Salinian orogeny; van Staal, 1994; West et al., 1995; Stewart et al., 1995a, 1995b) and were then amalgamated to the Merrimack-Harpswell terrane. This peri-Gondwanan terrane collage (containing Cambrian fauna of the Atlantic province; Neuman et al., 1989) was subsequently accreted to Laurentia in the Devonian (Acadian orogeny) along the Hackmatack Pond fault (Pankiwskyj, 1996). The Avalon terrane (sensu stricto; Rankin, 1994a) is not exposed in the study area (Fig. 1) and was not amalgamated to the eastern United States in southern New England until the Alleghanian (Hercynian orogeny). Geologic (Zen, 1983; Stewart et al., 1995a, 1995b) and isotopic studies also indicate that basement rocks in these terranes are distinct from Laurentian rocks (Ayuso and Bevier, 1991).

Summary of age and petrographic features

The majority of the granitic rocks in this part of New England range from Ordovician to Mississippian and from deformed to massive, characteristic of Caledonian magmatism (e.g., Wones, 1980a, 1980b; Zartman, 1988; West et al., 1995; Stewart et al., 1995b; Moench et al., 1995). Although many granitic rocks have not been reliably dated, most are thought to be Silurian-Devonian, related to the Acadian orogeny; together with Mississippian-Alleghanian (Hercynian) granitic plutons, they occur in all terranes. Mesozoic plutons constitute the smallest fraction of plutonic rocks in the region studied and are known to be potential hosts of Au mineralization (Robinson, 1990)—they will not be discussed further in this chapter. The granitic rocks in this study do not show systematic age distributions among the terranes.

Granites (Streckeisen, 1974) predominate in northern New England, but locally granodiorite and tonalite are nearly as abundant (Wones and Sinha, 1988; Sinha, 1988). Modal compositions, however, lack systematic petrographic gradients or unique features that would distinguish the terranes on a regional basis. The majority of granitic rocks in the Brompton-Cameron terrane in this study belong to the New Hampshire plutonic suite (Devonian) and range from quartz gabbro and diorite to evolved two-mica leucogranite and rare syenite (e.g., Ayuso and Arth, 1992; Loferski

and Ayuso, 1995; Moench et al., 1995). Biotite-bearing (±hornblende) granodiorite to granite and muscovite-bearing biotite granodiorite to granite may be the most important rock types in this terrane (Fig. 1); titanite and magnetite are the major accessories.

A wide range of granitic rocks is found in the Central Maine terrane, from quartz gabbro and diorite to leucogranites (e.g., Scambos et al., 1986; Ayuso, 1984; Moench et al., 1995; Hon, 1980). Middle to Late Ordovician (Taconian) granitic rocks belonging to the calc-alkaline granite to tonalite Oliverian plutonic suite and Highlandcroft plutonic suite (Billings, 1956; Leo, 1991; Moench et al., 1995) are present along the western flank of the Central Maine terrane (Wones and Sinha, 1988). Devonian rocks predominate and consist mostly of sphene- and magnetite-bearing biotite- and two-mica–bearing granite and granodiorite. Hercynian batholiths (Aleinikoff et al., 1985) are prominent as large and dominantly peraluminous, pegmatite-rich bodies (Tomascak, 1995).

Granitic rocks in the peri-Gondwanan terranes vary from Ordovician to Mississippian (Osberg et al., 1985; Zartman and Hermes, 1987; Stewart et al., 1995a, 1995b; West et al., 1995). Significant Ordovician felsic plutonism, however, is absent in coastal Maine, in contrast to offshore Maine (Hermes and Banks, 1978) and coastal areas in Massachusetts and Rhode Island (Wones and Sinha, 1988). In coastal Maine, Silurian plutons are more common than previously thought (e.g., West et al., 1992, 1995; Stewart et al., 1995a, 1995b); many are bimodal and consist of gabbros and diorites associated with hornblende- and biotite-bearing granodiorites and granites (e.g., Hogan and Sinha, 1988; Stewart et al., 1988; Wiebe, 1993; Wiebe and Chapman, 1993; Ayuso and Arth, 1997). Silurian-Devonian felsic granites consist mostly of peraluminous two-mica granite and metaluminous biotite-bearing and hornblende-bearing granodiorite to granite but also include mildly alkaline to peralkaline granitic complexes that are especially abundant in peri-Gondwanan terranes (Hermes and Banks, 1978; Hogan and Sinha, 1988; Hermes and Murray, 1988; Wones and Sinha, 1988). Accessory minerals range from those typical of oxidized magmas (titanite and magnetite) to more reduced varieties (ilmenite).

DATA

The U.S. Geological Survey (USGS) has gathered an extensive database of chemical analyses on granitic rocks in the past decade; this information has been supplemented by data from university theses and from geochemical studies. We used a total of 968 analyses from ~50 plutons (the complete database will be released as a USGS Open-File Report as part of a regional mineral resource assessment project in progress). Of the analyses, ~40% are from granitic rocks containing SiO_2 <70 wt%. Virtually all of the analyses include major elements (Fe_2O_3 and FeO are included in most USGS data); a much smaller subset of this database also includes some trace and minor elements, as well as chalcophile and siderophile elements, and volatile components (e.g., water, S, CO_2, F, Cl). Various analytical methods have been used in the past decade at the USGS for major and trace element determinations, and for volatiles, including X-ray and wet chemistry determinations, inductively coupled plasma-mass spectrometry (ICP-MS), atomic absorption spectrophotometry, and instrumental neutron activation analysis (for a summary of techniques and detection limits, see Baedecker, 1987).

GEOCHEMISTRY

Classification of the granites

Loiselle and Ayuso (1980) applied the concept that granitic rocks image their source region (Chappell and White, 1974, 1992) in eastern and central Maine by contrasting petrographic and compositional features of granitic rocks on either side of the Norumbega fault zone (Fig. 1). This fault zone is the contact between the Central Maine terrane and the peri-Gondwanan terranes in eastern Maine. Granitic rocks in peri-Gondwanan rocks south of the fault zone were found to be somewhat more alkalic, and had slightly higher K_2O/Na_2O values and higher Rb and lower Sr contents than granitic rocks in the Central Maine terrane (Loiselle and Ayuso, 1980). However, systematic chemical gradients that would lead to a broad regional synthesis were not recognized. In contrast to batholiths from orogenic margins, e.g., the Peninsular Ranges batholith in California (Silver and Chappell, 1988), no gradients exist for Ba, Sr, Rb, Nb, and Th contents, and for ^{18}O, Sr, Nd, and Pb isotope values in the granitic rocks in this study.

A new and more complete summary of major element abundances reported here does not point unequivocally to discrete groups of granites characteristic of individual terranes (Table 1). In the interest of conciseness, the following discussion concentrates on variations between groups of granites instead of a detailed examination of chemical features within each pluton. For example, calc-alkalic series Ordovician-Devonian granites predominate in the Brompton-Cameron terrane (Peacock index: SiO_2 ~59 to 60 wt%). In the Devonian granites from the Central Maine terrane SiO_2 varies from ~57 to 60 wt%, and in Silurian-Devonian granites from peri-Gondwanan terranes SiO_2 varies from ~56 to 62 wt% (Fig. 2). On the basis of variations of total alkalic element abundances and silica, however, alkaline rocks are present in all terranes, although excess molar values of Al_2O_3 relative to $Na_2O + K_2O$ (Shand index) indicate that the rocks are metaluminous. These data show no systematic differences for values of K_2O, K_2O/Na_2O (mol) or K/Rb between the granitic rocks from the different terranes (Table 1).

Strongly peraluminous rocks (aluminum saturation index, A/CNK = molar $Al_2O_3/CaO + Na_2O + K_2O > 1.1$) account for no more than about one-half of the granites in this study; such granites are probably more abundant in the Brompton-Cameron terrane (Fig. 3). A/CNK values typically increase with increasing silica. Moreover, results indicate that a major portion of the granites are metaluminous to slightly peraluminous—thus, on the basis of Peacock indices, alkalic element contents, and A/CNK values, no unique groups, systematic distinctions, or gradients exist among granites from different terranes.

SiO_2 contents vary between ~48 to 77 wt% in all plutonic groups; in a few peri-Gondwanan composite Silurian plutons a narrow gap may exist at about 60%–65% SiO_2 (e.g., Stewart et al., 1988). Variations in total iron (as FeO_t) and in Fe_2O_3/FeO (wt%), the latter ratio proposed as an indicator of the oxidation state of the magmas, have been used to distinguish granitic rocks having different metallogenic attributes (e.g., Blevin and Chappell, 1995). The widest range (and highest values) is in the Brompton-Cameron terrane in granites associated with porphyry Cu-Mo deposits; such occurrences have Fe_2O_3/FeO ~0.6 to >10. The lowest range is in rocks hosting Sn occurrences in peri-Gondwanan terranes (Fe_2O_3/FeO ~0.15 to 1) (Fig. 4); intermediate values for Fe_2O_3/FeO are found in granites associated with W and Mo mineralization.

Trace elements

In contrast to the major elements, trace element contents of plutonic rocks point to chemical groups showing subtle differences that are consistent with their distribution within known terrane subdivisions. Normal-type mid-ocean ridge basalt (N-MORB) normalized multi-element diagrams (Pearce, 1983) of representative granitic rocks from each terrane are shown for comparison (Fig. 5). In order to minimize the effects of fractional crystallization the diagrams illustrate results for granitic rocks having SiO_2 = ~54–70 wt%; also, the diagrams include data for only the freshest and least altered samples.

Normalized diagrams show that the large ion lithophile mobile elements (Sr, K, Rb, and Ba) in all three terranes are enriched relative to N-MORB, with a peak for Rb and troughs for Sr and Ba in most rocks (Fig. 5A). However, the highest contents of Sr (~200 to 800 ppm at SiO_2 = 65 wt%) are found in the Brompton-Cameron granites and the lowest (<350 ppm) are in peri-Gondwanan granites; intermediate values are found in the Central Maine (Fig. 6A). Normalized diagrams show that immobile elements in all granites, Th and Ce, form peaks, and Ta, Nb, P, and Ti form troughs relative to N-MORB (Fig. 5). Sc, Cr, and Ni are depleted relative to MORB in virtually all the samples and show a wide range of abundances. In the Central Maine terrane, Sr, K, Rb, and Ba, as well as Ta, Nb, P, and Ti have patterns (but not abundances) (Fig. 5B) similar to those in the Brompton-Cameron terrane (Fig. 5A); Sc, Cr, and Ni are also significantly more depleted than in the Brompton Cameron terrane.

A wide range of multielement normalized patterns characterize Devonian and Silurian granitic rocks of peri-Gondwana (Fig. 5C), reflecting for the most part the wide petrographic variation of the Silurian composite plutons; as a group, however, peri-Gondwanan Silurian and Devonian granites retain general features found in the other granite groups, particularly the deep Nb and Ta troughs characteristic of rocks formed at orogenic margins (e.g., Pearce, 1996). An important distinguishing feature is that Nb and Ta troughs (Th >> Nb and Ta), as well as the Y and Yb troughs, are generally deeper in the plutonic rocks from the Brompton-Cameron terrane than in the Central Maine and peri-Gondwana ter-

TABLE 1. REPRESENTATIVE ANALYSES OF SAMPLES OF GRANITIC PLUTONS AND ASSOCIATED MAFIC ROCKS, NEW ENGLAND

(Page 1)

Sample	SM-90138	ATT-1	83-D-197	83-D-206	MH-102	83PL-215	ME-D-4	IP-NU-8
Pluton	Attean	Attean	Duboullie	Deboullie	Seven Ponds	Priestly Lake	Derby	Nulhegan
Terrane	Brompton-Cameron	Brompton-Cameron	Brompton-Cameron	Brompton Cameron	Brompton-Cameron	Brompton-Cameron	Brompton-Cameron	Brompton-Cameron
	Granodiorite	Granodiorite	Granodorite	Syenite	Granodiorite	Granodorite	Granodorite	Tonalite
Majors (wt.%)								
SiO_2	69.70	67.40	69.30	53.5	69.70	65.50	68.00	57.30
Al_2O_3	14.10	16.00	16.40	13.60	15.10	15.80	17.00	14.90
Fe_2O_3	1.66	2.54	0.96	2.62	0.81	1.45	0.40	1.13
FeO	2.70	n.d.	1.20	4.20	1.50	2.40	1.60	5.50
MgO	1.04	1.21	1.24	6.36	1.10	1.86	1.20	7.01
CaO	0.79	3.11	2.79	7.12	2.55	4.16	3.30	6.42
Na_2O	2.31	3.58	3.88	2.84	3.61	4.16	5.20	2.77
K_2O	4.84	3.88	3.62	4.85	3.50	2.37	2.20	2.16
TiO_2	0.26	0.33	0.41	1.19	0.38	0.65	0.34	1.14
P_2O_5	0.09	0.12	0.17	1.01	0.13	0.17	0.14	0.16
MnO	0.03	0.03	0.03	0.12	0.05	0.06	0.04	0.12
CO_2	0.04	0.01	0.03	0.06	0.01	0.24	0.02	0.04
S	0.46	0.06	0.01	0.02	0.03	0.01	0.01	n.d.
Cl	0.01	0.01	0.01	0.06	0.00	0.03	0.01	0.01
F	0.09	0.02	0.06	0.22	0.09	0.02	0.04	0.05
H_2O^+	1.30	0.90	0.38	0.93	0.54	0.68	0.48	0.60
H_2O^-	0.37	0.07	0.25	0.17	0.15	0.31	0.23	0.23
Subtotal	99.79	99.26	99.74	99.06	99.25	99.87	100.19	99.54
Less O	0.02	0.01	0.02	0.07	0.02	0.02	0.01	0.02
Total	99.8	99.3	99.7	99.0	99.2	99.9	100.2	99.5
Trace elements (ppm)								
Rb	173	84	139	178	146	112	68.7	86
Cs	2.23	0.46	1.65	2.35	2.74	2.39	2.82	5.70
Sr	236	584	547	1480	325	330	643	489
Ba	710	1380	948	2670	660	550	528	439
Pb	7.6	15	n.d.	n.d.	23	n.d.	n.d.	20
La	23.2	37.7	42	94	30.1	26.2	19.4	25.5
Ca	41.8	62.3	77	211	55.6	48	36	50.9
Nd	13.5	19.6	31	100	20.3	26	14.9	28
Sm	2.27	3.34	4.26	16.8	4.27	4.72	2.54	5.69
Eu	0.46	0.87	0.993	3.4	0.923	1.08	0.756	1.25
Tb	0.174	0.234	0.24	1.06	0.455	0.58	0.2	0.67
Tm	n.d.	n.d.	n.d.	n.d.	n.d.	0.29	0.06	0.29
Yb	0.42	0.61	0.73	2.09	1.14	1.86	0.39	1.87
Lu	0.062	0.086	0.111	0.26	0.164	0.283	0.054	0.27
Y	10	5	12	33	21	21	12	20
Zr	93	146	209	533	153	199	131	90
Hf	3.06	3.84	5.75	13.6	4.1	5.07	3.42	2.87
Nb	6.0	5.9	10.0	8.0	20.0	9.2	5.0	10.0
Ta	0.77	0.53	0.86	0.91	1.36	0.97	0.39	0.80
Th	12.48	10.43	18.60	20.50	11.57	11.20	3.65	6.20
U	2.68	1.58	1.92	2.45	2.00	1.60	1.03	2.19
Sc	3.99	4.39	4.38	19.20	5.45	9.36	3.74	19.80
Cr	130.0	11.3	28.3	246.0	24.0	31.5	17.7	266.0
Co	6.16	9.40	5.92	28.30	5.97	9.27	5.33	29.40
Ni	5	15	17	100	13	18	17	130
Cu	1836	2	35	68	n.d.	7	5	32
Zn	33.0	30.5	17.0	84.0	47.7	45.8	49.0	85.0
U	20	10	n.d.	23	41	26	40	36
Be	2.3	1.9	3.1	3.6	2.5	1.6	2.1	2.2
B	5.1	2.0	2.0	4.0	2.0	1.0	4.0	34.0

TABLE 1. REPRESENTATIVE ANALYSES OF SAMPLES OF GRANITIC PLUTONS AND ASSOCIATED MAFIC ROCKS, NEW ENGLAND
(Continued - Page 2)

Sample Pluton Terrane	SM-90138 Attean Brompton- Cameron Granodiorite	ATT-1 Attean Brompton- Cameron Granodiorite	83-D-197 Duboullie Brompton- Cameron Granodorite	83-D-206 Deboullie Brompton Cameron Syenite	MH-102 Seven Ponds Brompton- Cameron Granodiorite	83PL-215 Priestly Lake Brompton- Cameron Granodorite	ME-D-4 Derby Brompton- Cameron Granodorite	IP-NU-8 Nulhegan Brompton- Cameron Tonalite
Trace elements (ppm) - continued								
Sn	1.9	1.0	1.0	3.1	1.0	2.1	1.2	2.8
W	5.2	1.0	1.0	1.0	1.0	1.2	3.0	0.9
Mo	77.0	3.6	1.8	1.8	1.0	7.8	1.8	0.5
Sb	0.96	0.20	0.20	0.50	0.08	0.30	0.20	0.30
Ag	0.90	n.d.	n.d.	n.d.	n.d.	n.d.	n.d.	n.d.
Au (ppb)	0.01	n.d.	n.d.	n.d.	n.d.	n.d.	n.d.	n.d.
As	1.90	0.90	n.d.	n.d.	0.70	n.d.	n.d.	n.d.
Se	1.35	n.d.	n.d.	n.d.	n.d.	n.d.	n.d.	n.d.
A/CNK mol	1.35	1.02	1.00	0.59	1.05	0.93	1.00	0.80
$Fe_2O_3/FeO\%$	0.61	n.d.	0.80	0.67	0.61	0.60	0.25	0.21
FeO total	4.19	n.d.	2.06	6.74	2.23	3.70	1.96	6.52
K_2O/Na_2O mol	1.38	0.71	0.61	1.12	0.64	0.37	0.51	0.67
$CaO/Na_2O + K_2O$	0.11	0.42	0.37	0.93	0.36	0.64	0.45	1.30
Rb/Sr	0.7	0.1	0.3	0.1	0.4	0.3	0.1	0.2
K/Rb	0.023	0.038	0.022	0.023	0.020	0.018	0.027	0.021
F/Cl	8.0	2.0	6.0	3.7	22.5	0.7	4.0	5.0
U + Mo	79.7	5.1	3.7	4.3	3.0	9.4	2.8	2.7
Be + B + U + P	27.4	14.0	n.d.	31.0	45.6	28.7	46.2	72.3
F(Li + Rb/Sr + Ba)	18.0	1.0	n.d.	10.7	17.1	3.1	37.1	65.7
Cu/Mo	23.8	0.6	19.4	37.8	n.d.	0.9	2.8	61.5
Mo/W	14.8	3.5	1.8	1.8	1.0	6.5	0.6	0.6
Sn/W	0.4	1.0	1.0	3.1	1.0	1.8	0.4	3.1
Ca/Mo	0.5	17.8	42.8	117.2	55.6	6.2	20.0	97.9
Nb/Y	0.6	1.2	0.8	0.2	1.0	0.4	0.4	0.5
Comments	1	1	1	1	1	1	2	2

See text for analytical techniques and limits of detection; n.d. = not determined.
Sources of data: 1. this report; 2. from Ayuso and Arth, 1992; 3. from Ayuso and Wiebe, unpublished data; 4. from Stewart et al., 1988; 5. from Ayuso and Arth, 1997.

ranes (Fig. 5C). Thus, Yb contents exceed 1 ppm in most granitic rocks from the peri-Gondwana and Central Maine terranes; in contrast, Yb values are <1 (as low as 0.1 ppm) in most granites from Brompton-Cameron terrane. Ta values >2 ppm (as high as ~7 ppm) are found in many granitic rocks from peri-Gondwana and Central Maine. Moreover, high contents of Th and U (Th to ~60 ppm, and U ~20 ppm) are found in evolved peri-Gondwanan Devonian granites (Rb/Sr to ~20), and although similar values are also found in Devonian granitic rocks of the Brompton-Cameron terrane, those rocks are significantly less evolved (Rb/Sr <1) (Fig. 6C).

Rate earth element (REE) abundances and chondrite-normalized patterns (Fig. 7) illustrate the deeper negative Eu anomalies, generally flatter patterns, and somewhat higher heavy REE contents of peri-Gondwanan granitic rocks (SiO_2 = ~54–70 wt%) relative to those in Brompton-Cameron rocks (small to no negative Eu anomalies, steeper patterns, and contents of >10× chondrites for heavy REE) (Fig. 7A and C). Granites from

the Central Maine terrane have moderate negative Eu anomalies, and heavy REE contents intermediate between granitic rocks from Brompton-Cameron and peri-Gondwanan terranes (Fig. 7B). Results thus indicate that granitic rocks from the Brompton-Cameron terrane are distinct from those from peri-Gondwanan terranes, and that granitic rocks from the Central Maine terrane do not constitute a unique group. Another notable result is that although only a few Ordovician granites in the Brompton-Cameron terrane have SiO_2 <70 wt%, available data show that they also closely resemble the range of compositions found for the Devonian plutons. Similarly, no major chemical differences distinguish the Devonian from Silurian granites in peri-Gondwana.

Isotopic features

Major Pb isotopic differences exist between the granitic rocks that are consistent with terrane subdivisions (Ayuso, 1986;

TABLE 1. REPRESENTATIVE ANALYSES OF SAMPLES OF GRANITIC PLUTONS AND ASSOCIATED MAFIC ROCKS, NEW ENGLAND
(Continued - Page 3)

Sample	IP-NU-16	OS-ML-4	OS-ML-7	OQ-ML-20	PE-MK-5	P-62-43	P-61-23	SP-C-3
Pluton	Nulhegan	Mooselookmeguntic	Mooselookmeguntic	Mooselookmeguntic	Long Mountain	Pleasant Lake	Hunt Ridge	Bottle Lake
Terrane	Brompton-	Central	Central	Central	Central	Central	Central	Central
	Cameron	Maine	Maine	Maine	Maine	Maine	Maine	Maine
	Tonalite	Granodiorite	Granodiorite	Granodiorite	Granite	Granodiorite	Granodorite	Granite

Majors (wt.%)

SiO_2	65.10	62.80	54.80	69.90	70.00	65.90	61.30	69.50
Al_2O_3	15.40	17.80	18.60	15.30	14.90	15.80	18.80	15.30
Fe_2O_3	1.43	4.17	7.54	2.45	2.39	0.82	0.77	1.52
FeO	2.80	n.d.	n.d.	n.d.	n.d.	2.80	3.20	1.14
MgO	3.49	1.74	3.20	0.73	0.70	1.11	1.75	0.63
CaO	4.10	3.80	5.80	1.82	1.67	3.43	6.51	2.00
Na_2O	3.16	4.43	3.87	3.80	3.14	4.04	4.63	3.86
K_2O	3.23	3.51	2.47	3.89	4.76	4.38	1.38	4.84
TiO_2	0.77	0.56	1.42	0.36	0.35	0.62	0.70	0.44
P_2O_5	0.09	0.28	0.79	0.25	0.19	0.22	0.24	0.12
MnO	0.08	0.07	0.15	0.05	0.04	0.07	0.09	0.05
CO_2	0.03	0.01	0.01	0.01	0.02	0.01	0.11	0.15
S	n.d.	0.05	0.05	0.05	0.05	0.01	0.01	0.01
Cl	0.02	0.01	0.02	0.01	0.01	0.02	0.01	0.01
F	0.06	0.05	0.06	0.04	0.04	0.09	0.05	0.02
H_2O^+	0.94	0.70	1.46	0.84	0.98	0.01	0.04	0.42
H_2O^-	0.19	0.15	0.17	0.15	0.16	0.60	0.79	0.09
Subtotal	100.89	100.13	100.41	99.65	99.40	99.93	100.38	100.10
Less O	0.02	0.02	0.02	0.01	0.01	0.03	0.01	0.01
Total	100.9	100.1	100.4	99.6	99.4	99.9	100.4	100.1

Trace elements (ppm)

Rb	148	104	94	179	197	141	35	115
Cs	11.50	2.94	2.16	7.89	3.67	6.07	1.71	3.28
Sr	376	576	912	197	206	198	319	169
Ba	516	1030	745	501	770	347	221	640
Pb	20	63	24	26	30	28	22	17
La	30.2	89.9	52.6	38.7	55.8	38.3	18.6	45.3
Ca	55.3	152	101.5	71.2	105	85.6	39.6	87.2
Nd	32	42.4	41	24.8	37.9	37.8	20.9	30
Sm	4.53	5.4	6.88	4.82	7.2	8.62	5.71	5.96
Eu	0.95	0.985	1.62	0.819	1.051	1.16	1.52	1.24
Tb	0.48	0.63	0.56	0.62	0.97	1.28	0.92	0.79
Tm	0.23	n.d.	n.d.	n.d.	n.d.	n.d.	n.d.	n.d.
Yb	1.37	0.95	1.06	0.81	1.31	4.45	3.11	2.46
Lu	0.219	0.134	0.147	0.114	0.188	0.643	0.471	0.329
Y	20	8	15	17	24	44	33	29
Zr	161	274	127	178	192	435	434	229
Hf	4.9	6.25	3.66	5.07	5.33	12.39	12.1	6.2
Nb	11.0	10.0	16.0	12.0	17.0	10.0	10.0	13.0
Ta	0.92	0.65	1.16	2.13	1.22	1.61	1.03	1.18
Th	12.70	17.50	7.16	12.39	24.40	35.20	5.16	12.80
U	3.59	1.79	1.31	1.60	3.39	3.88	2.97	3.58
Sc	11.50	6.51	7.62	4.23	4.52	8.96	14.11	5.50
Cr	134.0	32.0	46.1	11.1	12.2	19.0	21.0	4.1
Co	15.70	8.29	19.70	3.88	3.50	10.00	15.00	4.16
Ni	69	13	17	6	6	7	10	2
Cu	25	2	7	2	2	7	15	5
Zn	58.0	74.0	118.0	64.2	49.3	51.7	62.1	40.3
U	60	33	81	120	27	36	27	24
Be	3.2	3.2	2.0	5.6	3.0	3.4	2.1	2.6
B	46.0	2.0	2.0	1.0	2.0	40.0	20.0	10.0

TABLE 1. REPRESENTATIVE ANALYSES OF SAMPLES OF GRANITIC PLUTONS AND ASSOCIATED MAFIC ROCKS, NEW ENGLAND
(Continued - Page 4)

Sample Pluton Terrane	IP-NU-16 Nulhegan Brompton- Cameron Tonalite	OS-ML-4 Mooselookmeguntic Central Maine Granodiorite	OS-ML-7 Mooselookmeguntic Central Maine Granodiorite	OQ-ML-20 Mooselookmeguntic Central Maine Granodiorite	PE-MK-5 Long Mountain Central Maine Granite	P-62-43 Pleasant Lake Central Maine Granodiorite	P-61-23 Hunt Ridge Central Maine Granodorite	SP-C-3 Bottle Lake Central Maine Granite
Trace elements (ppm) - continued								
Sn	3.1	3.0	3.6	6.5	1.7	7.2	3.7	2.0
W	0.8	2.0	2.0	2.0	2.0	2.0	0.5	1.0
Mo	0.4	1.0	1.0	1.0	1.0	1.0	1.0	1.0
Sb	0.35	0.30	0.30	0.20	0.22	0.90	0.39	0.27
Ag	n.d.	n.d.	n.d.	n.d.	n.d.	0.01	0.03	n.d.
Au (ppb)	n.d.	n.d.	n.d.	n.d.	n.d.	0.01	0.01	n.d.
As	n.d.	n.d.	n.d.	n.d.	n.d.	9.40	2.00	n.d.
Se	n.d.	n.d.	n.d.	n.d.	n.d.	n.d.	n.d.	n.d.
A/CNK mol	0.95	0.99	0.95	1.11	1.12	0.90	0.90	1.00
$Fe_2O_3/FeO\%$	0.51	n.d.	n.d.	n.d.	n.d.	0.29	0.24	1.33
FeO total	4.09	n.d.	n.d.	n.d.	n.d.	3.54	3.89	2.51
K_2O/Na_2O mol	n.d.	0.52	0.42	0.67	1.00	0.71	0.20	0.83
$CaO/Na_2O + K_2O$	0.64	0.21	0.33	0.13	0.15	0.15	0.16	0.23
Rb/Sr	0.4	0.2	0.1	0.9	1.0	0.7	0.1	0.7
K/Rb	0.018	0.028	0.022	0.018	0.020	0.026	0.033	0.035
F/Cl	3.0	5.0	3.0	4.0	4.0	5.3	8.3	2.0
U + Mo	4.0	2.8	2.3	2.6	4.4	4.9	4.0	4.6
Be + B + U + P	109.2	38.3	85.3	126.7	32.1	79.5	49.2	36.7
F(Li + Rb/Sr + Ba)	139.9	42.7	63.4	171.3	91.8	292.3	57.4	34.4
Cu/Mo	61.0	2.0	7.0	2.0	2.0	7.0	15.0	5.0
Mo/W	0.5	0.5	0.5	0.5	0.5	0.5	2.0	1.0
Sn/W	4.1	1.5	1.8	3.3	0.9	3.6	7.4	2.0
Ca/Mo	134.9	152.0	101.5	72.1	105.0	85.6	39.6	87.2
Nb/Y	0.6	1.3	1.1	0.7	0.7	0.2	0.3	0.4
Comments	2	1	1	1	1	1	1	1

See text for analytical techniques and limits of detection; n.d. = not determined.
Sources of data: 1. this report; 2. from Ayuso and Arth, 1992; 3. from Ayuso and Wiebe, unpublished data; 4. from Stewart et al., 1988; 5. from Ayuso and Arth, 1997.

Ayuso and Bevier, 1991; Tomascak, 1995). Mantle-like values found in the Brompton-Cameron terrane suggest generation from underplated or older mafic rocks in the Grenvillian basement. In contrast, results from granites in the peri-Gondwanan terranes suggest origins from various sources, including evolved crustal basements and from the mantle (e.g., Whalen, 1993; Ayuso and Arth, 1998). Thus, Pb isotopic results suggest broad agreement between isotopic groups and terrane boundaries.

Unlike Pb, Nd and Sr isotopic variations are subtle and unsystematic in northern New England (Arth and Ayuso, 1997; 1994), in contrast to neighboring New Brunswick and Quebec, where more systematic Nd (and Pb) isotopic differences have been documented among the terranes (Whalen, 1993; Whalen et al., 1994a, 1994b; Whalen et al. 1996a, 1996b). Oxygen isotopic variations of the granitic rocks have a wide range in every terrane, from ~7% to 14% (or from mantle-like to crustal-like values) (Andrew et al., 1983; Arth and Ayuso, 1997; Ayuso and

Arth, 1997)—thus, they cannot be used to uniquely group the plutons according to their terrane distribution.

GRANITE-ASSOCIATED DEPOSITS: Cu, Mo, Sn, W

Paleozoic plutons in Maine, New Hampshire, and Vermont are associated with <200 mineral occurrences (Slack, 1990; Moench et al., 1995; Ayuso, 1996). Figure 1 shows the distribution of selected Cu, Mo, Sn, W, and U occurrences that are likely to be related to nearby granitic rocks. The vast majority of these occurrences are minor showings and only a few have been explored in detail. Four major types of deposits (Cox and Singer, 1986) are associated with the granitic rocks: (1) porphyry Cu-Mo; (2) porphyry Mo(?); (3) W-Mo stockworks, skarns, and greisens, and Sn veins; and (4) U-Mo in veins, fractures, and shear zones. Short descriptions are hereby provided of representative occurrences and/or deposits in the context of the tectonic elements of the region.

TABLE 1. REPRESENTATIVE ANALYSES OF SAMPLES OF GRANITIC PLUTONS AND ASSOCIATED MAFIC ROCKS, NEW ENGLAND
(Continued - Page 5)

Sample	NL-B-3	NL-B-1	SL-D-17	LU-81-3	CG-85-5	CG-971	PP-85-1	S70-76
Pluton	Bottle Lake	Bottle Lake	Bottle Lake	Lucerne	Mt. Desert	Mt. Desert	Parks Pond	South Penobscot
Terrane	Central Maine Granite	Central Maine Granite	Central Maine Granite	Peri-Gondwana Granite	Peri-Gondwana Granodiorite	Peri-Gondwana Granodiorite	Peri-Gondwana Granodiorite	Peri-Gondwana Diorite
Majors (wt.%)								
SiO_2	68.70	65.90	68.90	65.30	70.30	69.50	58.10	56.40
Al_2O_3	14.60	15.70	15.00	13.30	13.70	14.00	12.30	16.60
Fe_2O_3	0.98	1.03	1.31	1.32	3.17	0.85	6.91	2.50
FeO	2.85	3.42	2.03	6.10	n.d.	2.70	n.d.	5.80
MgO	1.00	1.23	1.01	1.08	1.32	0.52	7.31	3.90
CaO	2.58	2.95	2.45	2.47	2.53	1.26	4.87	6.40
Na_2O	3.71	3.79	3.56	3.07	3.54	4.83	1.92	3.60
K_2O	4.09	4.28	3.98	3.33	3.96	3.15	5.31	1.30
TiO_2	0.62	0.74	0.61	1.01	0.40	0.51	1.14	1.40
P_2O_5	0.18	0.21	0.21	0.42	0.08	0.10	0.62	0.27
MnO	0.08	0.09	0.07	0.12	0.07	0.13	0.10	0.16
CO_2	0.01	0.01	0.01	0.04	0.01	0.20	0.01	0.02
S	0.03	0.01	0.02	0.02	0.01	0.01	0.01	n.d.
Cl	0.02	0.02	0.01	0.05	0.01	0.02	0.07	n.d.
F	0.06	0.04	0.04	0.68	0.04	0.12	0.15	n.d.
H_2O^+	0.50	0.58	0.50	1.50	0.67	1.20	0.71	1.40
H_2O^-	0.10	0.07	0.06	0.37	0.12	0.21	0.16	0.15
Subtotal	100.11	100.07	99.77	100.18	99.93	99.31	99.69	99.90
Less O	0.02	0.02	0.01	0.17	0.02	0.03	0.06	0.06
Total	100.1	100.1	99.8	100.0	99.9	99.3	99.6	99.8
Trace elements (ppm)								
Rb	140	119	173	465	149	106	248	72
Cs	2.56	2.98	6.61	44.40	4.14	0.78	14.23	2.14
Sr	212	233	306	62	118	128	614	298
Ba	495	658	615	187	399	620	1710	322
Pb	15	17	14	19	13	12	33	n.d.
La	64	44.1	50.5	110	23.1	58.5	57	24.2
Ca	124	98.3	90	223	58.8	106.7	122.8	54.1
Nd	49	44.3	34.6	95	15.8	43.4	54.1	31.5
Sm	10.18	10.14	7.12	21.8	5.61	11.67	12.4	7.83
Eu	1.369	1.55	1.349	0.79	0.79	1.91	2.45	1.75
Tb	1.26	1.44	0.83	3.26	1	1.89	1.37	1.17
Tm	n.d.	n.d.	n.d.	n.d.	n.d.	n.d.	n.d.	n.d.
Yb	4.35	4.44	1.64	8.23	4.07	7.95	2.44	3.59
Lu	0.635	0.617	0.252	1.07	0.606	1.11	0.34	0.56
Y	44	45	23	117	41	n.d.	25	43
Zr	341	340	209	408	138	530	255	243
Hf	10.05	10.7	5.78	12.3	4.41	22	8.1	6.23
Nb	16.0	19.0	15.0	51.0	14.0	21.0	16.0	16.0
Ta	1.77	1.55	2.56	3.92	1.50	1.56	1.64	0.81
Th	25.40	11.30	8.11	32.30	15.00	13.64	30.20	4.29
U	4.41	1.96	4.28	7.88	2.74	2.82	5.69	1.30
Sc	9.35	10.31	5.69	16.20	7.84	7.78	19.90	23.10
Cr	9.1	10.8	6.4	9.0	26.5	9.3	443.0	69.8
Co	7.01	8.16	5.69	n.d.	7.63	3.57	31.00	26.00
Ni	5	7	3	6	15	3.2	180	n.d.
Cu	5.4	5	5	n.d.	2	10	23	n.d.
Zn	57.2	62.7	53.7	177.0	39.1	80.0	75.8	91.0
U	31	33	53	670	10	8.2	26	n.d.
Be	3.1	2.5	5.6	7.1	2.2	5.1	4.3	n.d.
B	8.0	18.0	7.5	20.0	3.0	5.1	28.0	n.d.

TABLE 1. REPRESENTATIVE ANALYSES OF SAMPLES OF GRANITIC PLUTONS AND ASSOCIATED MAFIC ROCKS, NEW ENGLAND
(Continued - Page 6)

Sample	NL-B-3	NL-B-1	SL-D-17	LU-81-3	CG-85-5	CG-971	PP-85-1	S70-76
Pluton	Bottle Lake	Bottle Lake	Bottle Lake	Lucerne	Mt. Desert	Mt. Desert	Parks Pond	South Penobscot
Terrane	Central Maine	Central Maine	Central Maine	Peri Gondwana	Peri Gondwana	Peri Gondwana	Peri Gondwana	Peri Gondwana
	Granite	Granite	Granite	Granite	Granodiorite	Granodiorite	Granodiorite	Diorite
Trace elements (ppm) - continued								
Sn	2.0	4.0	5.0	15.0	3.2	3.0	5.9	n.d.
W	1.0	1.0	1.0	3.5	0.5	1.0	2.2	n.d.
Mo	1.0	4.4	1.0	4.5	1.0	1.0	1.0	n.d.
Sb	0.16	0.22	0.37	0.37	n.d.	0.30	0.97	n.d.
Ag	n.d.	n.d.	n.d.	0.02	n.d.	0.04	n.d.	n.d.
Au (ppb)	n.d.	n.d.	n.d.	0.01	0.00	n.d.	20.00	n.d.
As	n.d.	n.d.	n.d.	3.30	n.d.	0.94	6.50	n.d.
Se	n.d.	n.d.	n.d.	n.d.	n.d.	0.70	n.d.	n.d.
A/CNK mol	0.96	0.97	1.03	1.01	0.93	1.03	0.69	0.88
Fe_2O_3/FeO %	0.34	0.30	0.65	0.22	n.d.	0.31	n.d.	0.43
FeO total	3.73	4.35	3.21	7.29	n.d.	3.46	n.d.	8.05
K_2O/Na_2O mol	0.73	0.74	0.74	0.71	0.73	0.43	1.82	0.24
CaO/Na_2O + K_2O	0.33	0.37	0.32	0.39	0.34	0.16	0.67	1.31
Rb/Sr	0.7	0.5	0.6	7.5	1.3	0.8	0.4	0.2
K/Rb	0.024	0.030	0.019	0.006	0.022	0.025	0.018	0.015
F/Cl	3.0	2.0	4.0	15.1	3.1	7.5	2.3	n.d.
U + Mo	5.4	6.4	5.3	12.4	3.7	3.8	6.7	1.3
Be + B + U + P	42.2	53.6	66.2	697.3	15.2	18.4	58.6	0.1
F(Li + Rb/Sr + Ba)	145.1	68.2	98.2	30996.0	132.2	183.2	176.9	n.d.
Cu/Mo	5.4	5.0	5.0	n.d.	2.0	10.0	23.0	n.d.
Mo/W	1.0	4.4	1.0	1.3	2.0	1.0	0.5	n.d.
Sn/W	2.0	4.0	5.0	4.3	6.4	3.0	2.7	n.d.
Ca/Mo	124.0	22.3	90.0	49.6	58.8	106.7	122.8	n.d.
Nb/Y	0.4	0.4	0.7	0.4	0.3	n.d.	0.6	0.4
Comments	1	1	1	1	3	3	1	4

See text for analytical techniques and limits of detection; n.d. = not determined.
Sources of data: 1. this report; 2. from Ayuso and Arth, 1992; 3. from Ayuso and Wiebe, unpublished data; 4. from Stewart et al., 1988; 5. from Ayuso and Arth, 1997.

Selected mineral deposits and occurrences: Cu, Mo, Sn, W mineralization

Porphyry Cu-Mo. The majority of granitic rocks containing anomalously high Cu (to nearly 4000 ppm) are in the Brompton-Cameron terrane, related to volumetrically minor Ordovician granodiorites known to be associated with porphyry Cu-Mo–type deposits. Other Devonian granitic rocks from this terrane known to be barren, however, also contain relatively high Cu abundances (to ~150 ppm), in comparison to granitic rocks from the Central Maine and peri-Gondwanan terranes to (~90 ppm) (Table 1). These features attest to the potential for porphyry Cu-Mo deposits in the Brompton-Cameron terrane. The Ordovician Catheart Mountain granodiorite (Fig. 1) in the Brompton-Cameron terrane (Schmidt, 1974; Ayuso, 1988) is the largest porphyry Cu-Mo deposit in New England. Pyrite, chalcopyrite, and molybdenite occur in siliceous stockworks. A direct correlation between Cu

and Fe_2O_3/FeO (as well with K_2O/Na_2O values, and Rb enrichment) is indicated. Titanite and magnetite are found within the stock, in accordance with the idea that an oxidized source region is necessary for this type of deposit (e.g., Burnham and Ohmoto, 1980; Blevin and Chappell, 1992). Fluid inclusion data show that the mineralizing fluids were CO_2 rich (Foley and Ayuso, 1992), similar to those found in porphyry-Mo deposits associated with F-poor systems (Theodore and Menzie, 1984). The Catheart Mountain stock is one of several biotite-bearing (±hornblende) stocks in the region (Hollister et al., 1974; Hollister, 1978; Moench et al., 1995). Some of these stocks are associated with porphyry Cu-Au deposits and Cu-rich skarns in Quebec (Gauthier et al., 1994; Allcock, 1982; Whalen, 1993) and with Cu-Au deposits in New Brunswick (Ruitenberg and Fyffe, 1992). Pb-Cu-Zn veins and stream sediment geochemical anomalies for Cu, Mo, Pb, and Zn (Nowlan et al., 1990a, 1990b) also occur in the Chain Lakes massif. The Deboullie stock (Fig. 1A) in northern

Sample	S70-106	ORC-23	THSH-102	LI-WB-1	CG-85-4	CG-972	CG-973	CG-974
Pluton	South Penobscot	Wallamatogus	Spruce Head	Waldoboro	Mt. Desert	Mt. Desert	Mt. Desert	Mt. Desert
Terrane	Peri-Gondwana	Peri-Gondwana	Peri-Gondwana	Peri-Gondwana	Peri-Gondwana	Peri-Gondwana	Peri-Gondwana	Peri-Gondwana
	Granodiorite	Granodiorite	Granodiorite	Granodiorite	Diorite	Basalt	Gabbro	Gabbro
Majors (wt.%)								
SiO_2	61.00	62.70	65.00	65.80	49.30	46.20	46.60	47.40
Al_2O_3	16.10	18.80	16.80	16.20	15.70	18.00	18.00	19.20
Fe_2O_3	2.70	1.50	1.57	3.70	12.10	1.70	2.16	2.02
FeO	6.20	0.92	2.60	n.d.	n.d.	8.10	6.60	5.40
MgO	1.20	2.40	1.27	1.39	5.72	8.40	10.10	8.48
CaO	4.10	2.50	3.94	3.15	8.64	9.18	11.10	12.60
Na_2O	4.10	2.60	3.75	3.94	3.16	2.62	2.24	2.32
K_2O	1.08	4.00	2.84	3.29	1.10	0.58	0.13	0.20
TiO_2	1.10	1.20	0.56	0.77	2.07	1.10	0.96	0.94
P_2O_5	0.34	0.06	0.16	0.23	0.45	0.12	0.08	0.06
MnO	0.21	0.01	0.08	0.06	0.21	0.16	0.16	0.13
CO_2	0.04	0.04	0.01	0.18	0.01	0.02	0.08	0.19
S	n.d.	n.d.	0.07	<0.05	0.16	0.08	0.10	0.10
Cl	n.d.	n.d.	0.01	0.02	0.06	0.01	0.00	0.02
F	n.d.	0.04	0.05	0.07	0.06	0.06	0.01	0.02
H_2O^+	1.40	1.50	0.72	n.d.	1.40	3.30	1.20	0.98
H_2O^-	0.14	0.50	0.16	0.22	0.23	0.41	0.32	0.12
Subtotal	99.71	98.77	99.59	99.02	100.37	100.04	99.85	100.19
Less O	0.00	0.00	0.02	0.02	0.04	0.02	0.00	0.01
Total	99.7	98.8	99.6	99.0	100.3	100.0	99.8	100.2
Trace elements (ppm)								
Rb	100	138	94	94	44	25	10	10
Cs	3.88	11.00	4.63	2.25	1.51	1.44	2.17	0.70
Sr	244	n.d.	288	638	303	200	220	240
Ba	505	1854	1040	1050	216	78	<30	<30
Pb	n.d.	n.d.	11	17	30	3.6	2	2
La	32.2	62	30.1	82	18.6	8.45	3.19	2.01
Ca	79.6	125	79	160	44.7	20.1	9	5.9
Nd	45.3	64	25.1	58	25.3	12.4	6.2	4.4
Sm	12	11.4	5.67	11.1	7.36	3.61	2.31	1.84
Eu	3	1.87	1.55	1.77	2.2	1.1	0.888	0.785
Tb	1.89	1.34	0.76	0.993	1.21	0.68	0.54	0.414
Tm	n.d.	0.65	n.d.	n.d.	n.d.	n.d.	n.d.	n.d.
Yb	5.91	4.5	1.91	1.99	4.4	2.84	2.33	1.58
Lu	0.91	0.67	0.296	0.243	0.6	0.385	0.303	0.209
Y	67	n.d.	29	23	47	n.d.	n.d.	n.d.
Zr	239	185	207	368	193	114	69	42
Hf	6.56	4.5	5.8	9.19	4.82	2.51	1.58	1.21
Nb	22.0	n.d.	11.0	14.0	14.0	4.5	2.8	1.3
Ta	1.62	1.85	0.47	1.59	0.64	0.31	0.13	0.14
Th	10.60	21.30	6.65	18.00	1.95	2.27	0.28	0.19
U	4.44	13.0	0.89	1.72	1.00	0.63	<0.3	0.30
Sc	16.60	15.94	11.10	4.48	31.10	31.60	36.70	30.80
Cr	6.0	91.7	13.0	22.5	109.0	230.0	220.0	220.0
Co	8.90	0.70	7.00	7.49	37.90	44.70	47.50	38.40
Ni	n.d.	n.d.	6	9	51	130	210	170
Cu	n.d.	n.d.	2	2	34	55	53	48
Zn	118.0	76.0	62.0	59.7	122.0	71.0	43.2	41.0
U	n.d.	n.d.	54	59	12	57	6.7	5.1
Be	n.d.	n.d.	1.5	1.9	1.4	1.0	1.0	1.0
B	n.d.	n.d.	9.9	2.0	4.0	4.1	1.8	3.5

TABLE 1. REPRESENTATIVE ANALYSES OF SAMPLES OF GRANITIC PLUTONS AND ASSOCIATED MAFIC ROCKS, NEW ENGLAND
(Continued - Page 8)

Sample Pluton Terrane	S70-106 South Penobscot Peri- Gondwana Granodiorite	ORC-23 Wallamatogus Peri- Gondwana Granodiorite	THSH-102 Spruce Head Peri- Gondwana Granodiorite	LI-WB-1 Waldoboro Peri- Gondwana Granodiorite	CG-85-4 Mt. Desert Peri- Gondwana Diorite	CG-972 Mt. Desert Peri- Gondwana Basalt	CG-973 Mt. Desert Peri- Gondwana Gabbro	CG-974 Mt. Desert Peri- Gondwana Gabbro
Trace elements (ppm) - continued								
Sn	n.d.	n.d.	1.6	2.9	1.0	1.8	1.4	2.0
W	n.d.	n.d.	1.0	1.0	0.5	1.0	1.0	1.8
Mo	n.d.	n.d.	1.0	1.2	1.0	1.0	1.0	1.0
Sb	n.d.	0.40	0.20	0.20	0.80	0.10	0.08	0.20
Ag	n.d.	n.d.	n.d.	n.d.	n.d.	0.14	0.048	0.028
Au (ppb)	n.d.	n.d.	n.d.	n.d.	26	0.003	0.002	0.002
As	n.d.	n.d.	n.d.	1.10	2.7	0.78	0.5	0.5
Se	n.d.	n.d.	n.d.	n.d.	n.d.	1.6	0.7	0.7
A/CNK mol	1.06	1.43	1.02	1.03	0.71	0.83	0.75	0.71
Fe_2O_3/FeO%	0.44	1.63	0.60	n.d.	n.d.	0.21	0.33	0.37
FeO total	8.63	2.27	1.41	3.33	10.9	9.63	8.54	7.22
K_2O/Na_2O mol	1.73	1.01	0.50	0.55	0.23	0.15	0.04	0.06
$CaO/Na_2O + K_2O$	0.79	0.38	0.60	0.44	2.03	2.87	4.68	5.00
Rb/Sr	0.4	n.d.	0.3	0.1	0.1	0.1	0.0	0.0
K/Rb	0.009	0.024	0.025	0.029	0.021	0.019	0.011	0.017
F/Cl	n.d.	n.d.	5.0	3.5	0.9	5.3	3.3	1.0
U + Mo	4.4	13.0	1.9	2.9	2.0	1.6	n.d.	1.3
Be + B + U + P	0.1	0.0	65.5	63.0	17.6	62.2	9.5	9.6
F(Li + Rb/Sr + Ba)	n.d.	n.d.	55.7	63.4	60.4	185.8	n.d.	n.d.
Cu/Mo	n.d.	n.d.	2.0	1.7	34.0	55.0	53.0	48.0
Mo/W	n.d.	n.d.	1.0	1.2	2.0	1.0	1.0	0.6
Sn/W	n.d.	n.d.	1.6	2.9	2.0	1.8	1.4	1.1
Ca/Mo	n.d.	n.d.	79.0	133.3	44.7	20.1	9.0	5.9
Nb/Y	0.3	n.d.	0.4	0.6	0.3	n.d.	n.d.	n.d.
Comments	4	1	5	1	1	3	3	3

See text for analytical techniques and limits of detection; n.d. = not determined.
Sources of data: 1. this report; 2. from Ayuso and Arth, 1992; 3. from Ayuso and Wiebe, unpublished data; 4. from Stewart et al., 1988; 5. from Ayuso and Arth, 1997.

Maine is associated with porphyry Cu-Mo type mineralization, but in contrast to Catheart Mountain, the host rocks are Devonian and consist of titanite- and magnetite-bearing syenites (Boone, 1962; Loferski and Ayuso, 1995; Ayuso and Loferski, 1992).

Figure 4 illustrates variations in Fe_2O_3/FeO (wt%) of granites known to be associated with Cu in comparison with Mo, Sn, and W. Results corroborate the idea that granitic rocks associated with porphyry-Cu mineralization are oxidized (higher Fe_2O_3/FeO values) and found in host rocks having intermediate SiO_2 contents; those associated with tin mineralization are relatively reduced (lower Fe_2O_3/FeO values) and are the most felsic and evolved (Lehman, 1990). Tungsten- and molybdenum-mineralized granites—as well as those associated with somewhat anomalously high uranium contents—are intermediate in oxidation state between those with tin and copper, and range from intermediate to felsic, again in accordance to the proposed overall scheme of mineralization in granitic rocks (Blevin and Chappell, 1992).

Porphyry Mo, low-F. In the northern New England Appalachians this type of porphyry system is generally related to shallow intrusions that produced thin alteration zones flanking quartz stockworks (characteristically of low density), and concentrations of sulfides (molybdenite, pyrite, ± small amounts of chalcopyrite) primarily along joints and fractures. Although a few of the Mo occurrences in New England can be classified broadly as Climax type (White et al., 1981; Multschler et al., 1981), they are best described as belonging to the F-poor, calc-alkaline subtype resembling those from a late collisional to post-collisional tectonic setting (e.g., van Leeuwen et al., 1994) or from F-poor porphyry deposits (Carten et al., 1985). F-poor Mo deposits also occur in Canada (Ruitenberg and Fyffe, 1982, 1992; Ruitenberg and McCutcheon, 1993; Whalen, 1993) and Scotland (Plant et al., 1980). Granitic hosts in those deposits generally lack intrusive breccias and multiple ore shells, and commonly have higher contents of TiO_2 (0.3%–1%), equivalent

Sample	CG-975	CG-976	S70-58	S70-86	S67-175	S70-49	83-D-208	83-D-205
Pluton	Mt. Desert	Mt. Desert	South Penobscot	South Penobscot	South Penobscot	South Penobscot	Deboullie	Deboullie
Terrane	Peri-Gondwana	Peri-Gondwana	Peri-Gondwana	Peri-Gondwana	Peri-Gondwana	Peri-Gondwana	Brompton-Cameron	Brompton-Cameron
	Gabbro	Basalt	Gabbro	Diorite	Diorite	Diorite	Syenite	Syenite

Majors (wt.%)								
SiO_2	48.80	49.20	50.60	50.70	49.60	52.20	56.60	53.50
Al_2O_3	16.00	17.10	18.70	16.50	17.30	17.90	13.70	13.60
Fe_2O_3	2.00	2.50	1.50	2.60	1.80	1.90	1.46	2.82
FeO	8.10	6.30	5.80	8.30	7.50	8.80	4.40	4.20
MgO	7.33	7.55	7.30	4.60	6.90	4.80	5.33	6.36
CaO	8.51	11.00	8.70	8.00	8.20	7.60	5.45	7.12
Na_2O	3.09	2.73	3.60	3.60	2.50	2.90	2.96	2.84
K_2O	0.83	0.31	0.62	1.30	1.30	0.92	5.76	4.85
TiO_2	1.73	1.41	0.97	1.80	1.10	1.80	1.06	1.19
P_2O_5	0.23	0.12	0.16	0.29	0.17	0.36	0.88	1.01
MnO	0.22	0.16	0.16	0.27	0.22	0.29	0.09	0.12
CO_2	0.21	0.04	0.06	0.04	0.81	0.02	0.03	0.05
S	0.13	0.12	n.d.	n.d.	n.d.	n.d.	0.02	0.02
Cl	0.03	0.02	n.d.	n.d.	n.d.	n.d.	0.03	0.06
F	0.06	0.03	n.d.	n.d.	n.d.	n.d.	0.20	0.22
H_2O^+	2.40	1.30	1.80	1.30	1.90	1.80	0.96	0.93
H_2O^-	0.27	0.20	0.14	0.13	0.19	0.03	0.14	0.17
Subtotal	99.93	100.10	100.11	99.43	99.49	101.32	99.07	99.06
Less O	0.02	0.02	0.00	0.00	0.00	0.00	0.06	0.07
Total	99.9	100.1	100.1	99.4	99.5	101.3	99.0	99.0

Trace elements (ppm)								
Rb	33	11	39	70	88	37	240	178
Cs	1.02	1.43	3.91	3.49	4.75	2.25	3.84	2.35
Sr	240	215	372	248	303	338	1130	1480
Ba	162	<30	229	149	247	246	2070	2670
Pb	38	2	n.d.	n.d.	n.d.	n.d.	n.d.	n.d.
La	11.5	6.59	13.5	21.5	8.6	18.3	95	94
Ca	26.3	14.6	28.2	46	19.7	39.1	185	211
Nd	15.9	11.7	12.8	30	11.7	28	88	100
Sm	4.64	3.77	3.93	7.54	3.57	6.41	14	16.8
Eu	1.48	1.27	1.16	2.49	1.18	1.85	3.1	3.4
Tb	0.84	0.82	0.59	1.11	0.7	1.03	1.05	1.06
Tm	n.d.	n.d.	n.d.	n.d.	n.d.	n.d.	n.d.	n.d.
Yb	3.04	3.07	2.01	3.88	2.18	2.88	1.98	2.09
Lu	0.426	0.433	0.31	0.58	0.36	0.47	0.281	0.26
Y	n.d.	n.d.	22	45	21	39	30	33
Zr	154	118	109	148	80	135	466	533
Hf	3.41	2.62	2.49	3.89	2.11	3.43	16.9	13.6
Nb	8.0	2.2	9.0	11.0	6.0	11.0	15.0	8.0
Ta	0.51	0.30	0.31	0.60	0.34	0.70	1.44	0.91
Th	2.44	1.34	2.68	5.75	1.69	3.08	36.40	20.50
U	0.84	0.49	0.70	2.53	0.50	0.78	4.79	2.45
Sc	30.90	38.50	26.40	30.30	27.80	32.60	15.90	19.20
Cr	190.0	190.0	198.0	48.0	118.0	51.4	198.0	246.0
Co	40.70	42.10	34.70	30.20	35.40	26.30	21.70	28.30
Ni	100	100	n.d.	n.d.	n.d.	n.d.	90	100
Cu	47	73	n.d.	n.d.	n.d.	n.d.	81	68
Zn	104.0	53.0	67.0	107.0	77.0	116.0	68.0	84.0
U	19	13	n.d.	n.d.	n.d.	n.d.	24	23
Be	1.0	1.0	n.d.	n.d.	n.d.	n.d.	6.1	3.6
B	6.4	4.3	n.d.	n.d.	n.d.	n.d.	11.0	4.0

TABLE 1. REPRESENTATIVE ANALYSES OF SAMPLES OF GRANITIC PLUTONS AND ASSOCIATED MAFIC ROCKS, NEW ENGLAND
(Continued - Page 10)

Sample Pluton Terrane	CG-975 Mt. Desert Peri- Gondwana Gabbro	CG-976 Mt. Desert Peri- Gondwana Basalt	S70-58 South Penobscot Peri- Gondwana Gabbro	S70-86 South Penobscot Peri- Gondwana Diorite	S67-175 South Penobscot Peri- Gondwana Diorite	S70-49 South Penobscot Peri- Gondwana Diorite	83-D-208 Deboullie Brompton- Cameron Syenite	83-D-205 Deboullie Brompton- Cameron Syenite
Trace elements (ppm) - continued								
Sn	1.0	1.0	n.d.	n.d.	n.d.	n.d.	3.0	3.1
W	1.0	1.0	n.d.	n.d.	n.d.	n.d.	2.0	1.0
Mo	1.0	1.0	n.d.	n.d.	n.d.	n.d.	4.4	1.8
Sb	0.10	<0.08	n.d.	n.d.	n.d.	n.d.	0.64	0.50
Ag	0.062	0.17	n.d.	n.d.	n.d.	n.d.	n.d.	n.d.
Au (ppb)	0.002	0.002	n.d.	n.d.	n.d.	n.d.	n.d.	n.d.
As	1.32	1.27	n.d.	n.d.	n.d.	n.d.	n.d.	n.d.
Se	0.7	0.8	n.d.	n.d.	n.d.	n.d.	n.d.	n.d.
A/CNK mol	0.75	0.69	0.83	0.75	0.85	0.91	0.65	0.59
$Fe_2O_3/FeO\%$	0.25	0.40	0.26	0.31	0.24	0.22	0.33	0.67
FeO total	9.90	8.55	7.15	10.64	9.12	10.51	5.71	6.74
K_2O/Na_2O mol	0.18	0.07	0.11	0.24	0.34	0.21	1.28	1.12
$CaO/Na_2O + K_2O$	2.17	3.62	2.06	1.63	2.16	1.99	0.63	0.93
Rb/Sr	0.1	0.1	0.1	0.3	0.3	0.1	0.2	0.1
K/Rb	0.021	0.023	0.013	0.015	0.012	0.021	0.020	0.023
F/Cl	2.2	1.3	n.d.	n.d.	n.d.	n.d.	6.7	3.7
U + Mo	1.8	1.5	0.7	2.5	0.5	0.8	9.2	4.3
Be + B + U + P	26.5	18.4	0.1	0.1	0.1	0.2	41.5	31.0
F(Li + Rb/Sr + Ba)	75.0	n.d.	n.d.	n.d.	n.d.	n.d.	16.5	10.7
Cu/Mo	47.0	73.0	n.d.	n.d.	n.d.	n.d.	18.4	37.8
Mo/W	1.0	1.0	n.d.	n.d.	n.d.	n.d.	2.2	1.8
Sn/W	1.0	1.0	n.d.	n.d.	n.d.	n.d.	1.5	3.1
Ca/Mo	26.3	14.6	n.d.	n.d.	n.d.	n.d.	42.0	117.2
Nb/Y	n.d.	n.d.	0.4	0.2	0.3	0.3	0.5	0.2
Comments	3	3	4	4	4	4	1	1

See text for analytical techniques and limits of detection; n.d. = not determined.
Sources of data: 1. this report; 2. from Ayuso and Arth, 1992; 3. from Ayuso and Wiebe, unpublished data; 4. from Stewart et al., 1988; 5. from Ayuso and Arth, 1997.

Rb (100–155 ppm), F (to 0.07%), and Nb (<18 ppm), and somewhat lower Sr (to 415 ppm) and total alkalies (to ~7.3%) than in porphyry-Mo F-poor systems.

In the Brompton-Cameron terrane, hornblende + biotite– and biotite + muscovite–bearing plutons associated with Mo mineralization have no associated volcanic rocks. Mo mineralization is hosted by evolved portions of granitic stocks in quartz stockworks, concentrated in pegmatitic pods, or associated with aplitic dikes. Mo mineralization generally appears to be related to apical portions of the stocks and near contacts with country rocks. Porphyry Mo mineralization (molybdenite ± pyrite) occurs in the oxidized, hornblende- and biotite-bearing granodiorite of the Devonian Priestly Lake stock (Fig. 1A), where it is associated with porphyritic dikes (Ayuso and Shank, 1983). Alteration envelopes associated with the veins are thin. Similar types of porphyry Mo stockworks are found in Quebec, where they are associated with the Devonian Mont Ste-Cecile pluton (Gauthier et al., 1994).

Possible porphyry Cu-Mo and porphyry Mo-type deposits in the Central Maine (e.g., near the Katahdin granite) and peri-Gondwanan terranes have also been identified (Hollister, 1978, Hollister et al., 1974). However, very little is known regarding their size, regional alteration zones, and sulfide abundances; molybdenite also occurs in the Devonian Meddybemps granite, where it was mined early in the twentieth century. Moreover, molybdenite has been found in many other Devonian intrusions, including the alkaline Tunk Lake pluton, the Deblois pluton, and the Silurian Cadillac Mountain pluton (Fig. 1) (Schmidt, 1978).

Sn veins, W-Mo stockworks, skarns, greisens. The most evolved part of the Northeast Kingdom batholith in the Brompton-Cameron terrane (Fig. 1) is a two-mica, garnet-bearing leucogranite that intruded calc-silicate rocks (Ayuso and Arth, 1992; Arth and Ayuso, 1997); in Quebec, such leucogranites are associated with skarns and scheelite mineralization (Gauthier et al., 1994). In addition, small areas within the pluton contain sparse pyrite, cassiterite,

Sample	82-D-183	IP-EP-18L	IP-NU-13	IP-NU-11	ME-WC-4	ME-WC-2	ME-EP-5	S84GLSCM2
Pluton	Deboullie	Echo Pond	Nulhegan	Nulhegan	West Charleston	West Charleston	Echo Pond	Chandler Mtn.
Terrane	Brompton-Cameron	Brompton-Cameron	Brompton-Cameron	Brompton-Cameron	Brompton-Cameron	Brompton-Cameron	Brompton-Cameron	Brompton-Cameron
	Syenite	Gabbro	Diorite	Diorite	Gabbro	Gabbro	Diorite	Diorite

Majors (wt.%)								
SiO_2	57.80	53.70	57.40	60.50	47.70	50.10	52.50	56.90
Al_2O_3	14.20	9.50	14.80	15.00	16.40	11.40	12.80	16.80
Fe_2O_3	2.50	1.40	1.70	1.22	1.60	1.10	1.90	6.59
FeO	2.90	12.00	4.60	4.00	7.10	9.70	7.20	n.d.
MgO	4.40	13.50	6.79	5.87	9.20	13.80	10.20	4.15
CaO	4.80	4.00	5.53	6.02	9.80	7.40	8.40	6.85
Na_2O	3.80	1.00	3.01	3.22	3.10	1.40	2.80	4.66
K_2O	6.00	1.80	2.80	2.10	0.82	0.94	1.50	1.44
TiO_2	1.10	0.61	1.02	0.84	2.80	1.40	1.40	0.98
P_2O_5	0.58	0.11	0.15	0.14	0.37	0.42	0.28	0.28
MnO	0.10	0.27	0.11	0.10	0.12	0.19	0.18	0.06
CO_2	0.01	0.12	0.03	0.02	0.04	0.03	0.06	0.03
S	0.01	0.04	n.d.	n.d.	n.d.	0.28	0.15	0.06
Cl	0.05	0.01	0.03	0.01	0.01	0.01	0.01	0.06
F	0.21	0.12	0.07	0.06	0.09	0.06	0.04	0.04
H_2O^+	0.43	1.10	0.83	0.88	1.00	0.71	1.50	0.81
H_2O^-	0.05	0.21	0.50	0.12	0.29	0.35	0.25	0.19
Subtotal	98.94	99.49	99.37	100.10	100.44	99.29	101.15	99.90
Less O	0.07	0.03	0.03	0.02	0.02	0.02	0.01	0.03
Total	98.9	99.5	99.3	100.1	100.4	99.3	101.1	99.9

Trace elements (ppm)								
Rb	214	145	126	83	23	22	48	41
Cs	2.70	7.05	7.23	5.65	1.77	3.13	3.83	0.93
Sr	1085	148	531	561	547	330	392	1160
Ba	2110	170	720	496	139	108	128	637
Pb	n.d.	24	19	20	25	17	21	20
La	104	8.8	29.3	28.7	12	10.2	15	42.2
Ca	199	18.6	56	57.2	29	22.9	30	82.1
Nd	86	12	30	28	24	19	18	35.1
Sm	15.3	2.77	5.96	5.9	6.83	4.71	3.92	7.03
Eu	2.96	0.71	1.31	1.25	1.72	1.11	1.14	1.93
Tb	1.03	0.49	0.55	0.58	1.01	0.61	0.59	0.648
Tm	n.d.	0.32	0.25	0.15	0.38	0.28	0.36	
Yb	1.8	2.93	1.62	1.73	2.64	1.76	2.09	1.79
Lu	0.22	0.415	0.24	0.254	0.352	0.35	0.33	0.274
Y	29	24	19	20	25	17	21	19
Zr	783	82	109	135	80	77	129	168
Hf	19.6	2.65	2.94	4.31	2.06	1.71	3.22	4.43
Nb	24.9	4.8	12.0	9.0	12.0	7.4	10.0	9.1
Ta	1.49	0.98	0.88	0.63	0.73	0.53	0.77	0.55
Th	52.70	2.37	7.31	5.95	1.37	1.35	1.95	6.35
U	3.90	0.82	2.57	2.25	<0.6	0.59	1.20	1.49
Sc	13.20	29.60	16.50	16.00	53.50	31.80	30.50	16.60
Cr	159.0	176.0	308.0	254.0	43.4	138.0	549.0	85.0
Co	19.50	59.90	27.60	24.10	46.70	66.00	48.20	22.30
Ni	100	100	170	130	40	91	150	49
Cu	23	18	14	22	24	60	63	51
Zn	64.0	142.0	81.0	68.0	78.0	94.0	77.0	64.1
U	18	98	64	59	26	27	56	14
Be	5.6	6.6	2.7	2.6	1.3	0.9	1.2	2.0
B	8.5	2.8	31.0	36.0	4.0	8.0	4.3	6.0

TABLE 1. REPRESENTATIVE ANALYSES OF SAMPLES OF GRANITIC PLUTONS AND ASSOCIATED MAFIC ROCKS, NEW ENGLAND
(Continued - Page 12)

Sample Pluton Terrane	82-D-183 Deboullie Brompton- Cameron Syenite	IP-EP-18L Echo Pond Brompton- Cameron Gabbro	IP-NU-13 Nulhegan Brompton- Cameron Diorite	IP-NU-11 Nulhegan Brompton- Cameron Diorite	ME-WC-4 West Charleston Brompton- Cameron Gabbro	ME-WC-2 West Charleston Brompton- Cameron Gabbro	ME-EP-5 Echo Pond Brompton- Cameron Diorite	S84GLSCM2 Chandler Mtn. Brompton Cameron Diorite
Trace elements (ppm) - continued								
Sn	4.3	5.9	3.3	3.0	1.0	1.0	1.3	1.0
W	1.7	3.0	1.0	0.7	3.0	3.0	3.0	1.0
Mo	2.8	1.5	0.7	0.5	1.1	1.5	2.0	0.5
Sb	n.d.	0.50	0.31	0.20	0.60	0.50	0.50	0.23
Ag	n.d.	n.d.	n.d.	n.d.	n.d.	n.d.	n.d.	n.d.
Au (ppb)	n.d.	n.d.	n.d.	n.d.	n.d.	n.d.	n.d.	n.d.
As	n.d.	n.d.	n.d.	n.d.	n.d.	n.d.	n.d.	n.d.
Se	n.d.	n.d.	n.d.	n.d.	n.d.	n.d.	n.d.	n.d.
A/CNK mol	0.66	0.87	0.82	0.81	0.69	0.68	0.60	0.77
Fe_2O_3/FeO%	0.86	0.12	0.37	0.31	0.23	0.11	0.20	n.d.
FeO total	5.15	13.26	6.13	5.10	8.54	10.69	8.91	n.d.
K_2O/Na_2O mol	1.04	0.61	0.43	0.17	0.44	0.35	n.d.	0.20
$CaO/Na_2O + K_2O$	0.49	1.43	0.95	1.13	2.50	3.16	1.95	1.12
Rb/Sr	0.2	1.0	0.2	0.1	0.0	0.1	0.1	0.0
K/Rb	0.023	0.010	0.018	0.021	0.030	0.035	0.026	0.029
F/Cl	4.2	12.0	2.3	6.0	9.0	6.0	4.0	0.7
U + Mo	6.7	2.3	3.2	2.7	n.d.	2.1	3.2	2.0
Be + B + U + P	32.4	107.4	97.8	97.7	31.6	36.1	61.6	22.1
F(Li + Rb/Sr + Ba)	15.2	917.0	106.3	80.6	64.3	67.1	80.0	1.3
Cu/Mo	8.2	12.0	20.9	44.9	21.8	40.0	31.5	102.0
Mo/W	1.6	0.5	0.7	0.7	0.4	0.5	0.7	0.5
Sn/W	2.5	2.0	3.3	4.3	0.3	0.3	0.4	1.0
Ca/Mo	71.1	12.4	83.6	116.7	26.4	15.3	15.0	164.2
Nb/Y	0.9	0.2	0.6	0.5	0.5	0.4	0.5	0.5
Comments	1	2	2	2	2	2	2	1

See text for analytical techniques and limits of detection; n.d. = not determined.
Sources of data: 1. this report; 2. from Ayuso and Arth, 1992; 3. from Ayuso and Wiebe, unpublished data; 4. from Stewart et al., 1988; 5. from Ayuso and Arth, 1997.

and molybdenite. Stream sediment and heavy mineral concentrate data also point to additional Sn and W anomalies associated with the batholith (Nowlan et al., 1990c; Maurice, 1986).

Northwest-striking Sn (W) greisen veins are abundant in the southern part of the predominantly ilmenite- and biotite-bearing Devonian Lucerne granite (Fig. 1A), which intruded the peri-Gondwanan terranes in coastal Maine (Wones, 1980b; Wones and Ayuso, 1993). Rapakivi textures (Haapala, 1995) are common throughout the Lucerne granite and nearby Deblois batholith. Cassiterite, pyrite, arsenopyrite, and molybdenite(?) are widely scattered; alteration and metasomatic minerals (quartz, sericite, tourmaline, fluorite[?], epidote) and sulfides flank closely spaced fissures and/or fractures. As in other mineralized systems in the Appalachians (e.g., Ruitenberg and Fyffe, 1982, 1992; Kooiman, et al., 1986; Ruitenberg and McCutcheon, 1993; Whalen, et al., 1993; Whalen, 1996a), polymetallic (Sn, W, U, Mo) mineralization is related to specialized leucomonzogranites and leucogranites that have high contents of Li, Cs, F, Be, and Rb.

U-Mo veins, fractures, shear zones, contact zones. The Bottle Lake Complex (Fig. 1A) in the Central Maine terrane includes intensely fractured and, altered granitic rocks (Ayuso, 1984). Anomalously high abundances of U, Th, As, Mo, Sb, Bi, and W are found in stream sediments (Otton and Nowlan, 1980; Nowlan and Hessin, 1972; Post et al., 1967) derived from the biotite-bearing Topsfield facies in the complex. Sparse molybdenite, pyrite, and arsenopyrite are concentrated near shear zones. In addition, veins of Sb (Au base metal) and stockworks of W-Mo in New Brunswick (Seal et al., 1985; Whalen, 1993) are found in the vicinity of the Bottle Lake complex.

DISCUSSION

Genetic models attempting to systematically explain the origin of granitic rocks (e.g., Chappell and White, 1974; Pitcher, 1993; Clarke, 1992) have provided a framework for vigorous

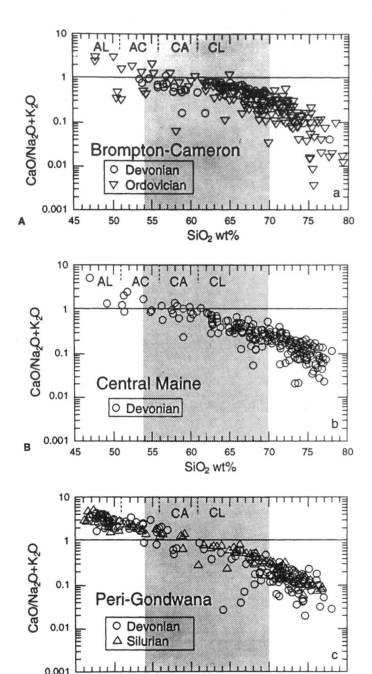

Figure 2. Plot of CaO/Na$_2$O + K$_2$O vs. SiO$_2$ (Peacock indices) for the plutonic rocks in this study. Abbreviations are as follows: AL, alkali series; AC, alkalic-calcic series; CA, calc-alkalic series; CL, calcic series. Database includes 326 samples from the (A) Brompton-Cameron terrane, 296 samples from the (B) Central Maine terrane, and 374 samples from the (C) peri-Gondwanan terranes. Shaded area represents the range in SiO$_2$ used for Figures 5, 7, and 10. Sources of data as summarized in the text.

debate regarding the metallogeny of granitic rocks (e.g., Westra and Keith, 1981; Sillitoe, 1986). The debate is focused on possible links between different ore-element associations and granite source material (i.e., composition, halogen content, oxidation state), contrasting tectonic settings (e.g., island continental arc, rift), and the relative importance of igneous processes operating during magma evolution (fractional crystallization, assimilation, mixing, fluid sources). The evolution of the host granitic rocks is a critical feature controlling the extent and type of mineralization (Lehman, 1990; Blevin and Chappell, 1992). In fact, species (e.g., H$_2$O, F, B, Be, P, Li) that lower magma viscosity and melting temperatures, and that promote magma generation and migration, are those typically found in source regions of magmatic rocks having economically important elements (Sn, W, U) (Strong, 1985).

In comparison to the western United States, relatively few types of granite-associated mineralization are known in New England. Also, the known occurrences are modest and appear to be restricted to a few major granitic batholiths. Nevertheless, many of the intrusions and shallow stocks have similar ages and compositions that closely resemble those in the Canadian Maritime provinces, Scottish Caledonides, and western Europe (Strong, 1980; Plant et al., 1980; Ruitenberg and Fyffe, 1992; Ruitenberg and McCutcheon, 1993; Whalen, 1993) known to contain economic concentrations of Cu, Sn, W, and U, among others.

Are the features summarized here characteristic of the source of mineralized magmas or are they process controlled? Average multielement N-MORB normalized patterns of the least-evolved portions (SiO$_2$ 54–70 wt%) of Ordovician and Devonian granitic rocks associated with Cu occurrences have small troughs for Sr and Ba, a wide range in REE abundances, and small or no negative Eu anomalies. In contrast, Silurian and Devonian granites associated with Mo, Sn, and W occurrences have deep troughs for Sr and Ba (and Ti), a wide range of abundances of REEs, and large negative Eu anomalies, particularly in rocks associated with Sn mineralization (Figs. 8 and 9). All of these features are consistent with the effects of volatile-enriched source rocks associated with Sn mineralization because the volatiles depress the solidus and permit extensive melting at lower temperatures (Strong, 1985). More important, volatile-rich conditions also allow for a longer cooling stage and thus promote extensive fractional crystallization, e.g., feldspar crystallization controlling the depletion of Sr, Ba, and Eu, as the magma intrudes to shallower depths where structural and hydrologic controls are more favorable for mineralization. Although Sn-W deposits are regarded by many as having an origin from melts obtained chiefly from reduced evolved felsic rocks in the crust (Lehmann, 1990), recent work suggests that much of the Sn mineralization in some areas previously linked to crustal rocks may instead be related to fractionated rocks originating from the mantle (e.g., Pollard et al., 1995). It seems feasible, however, that Sn-related mineralization cannot be genetically linked to a single source region but results from the fact that Sn mobilization and concentration depend on redox-controlled crystal-melt partition-

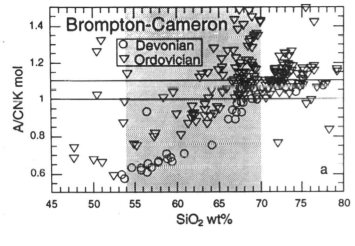

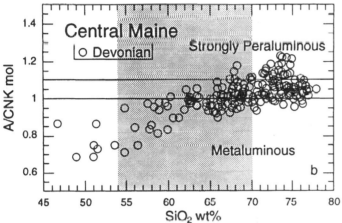

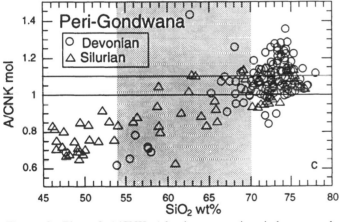

Figure 3. Plot of A/CNK (alumina saturation index = molar $Al_2O_3/CaO + Na_2O + K_2O$ vs. SiO_2 for plutonic rocks in this study.

ing and the S and Cl contents of granitic magmas (Blevin and Chappell, 1995).

In contrast to granitic rocks containing high Sn, REE patterns tend to be steep, and Eu anomalies are small or absent in intermediate and syenitic rocks associated with Cu and Mo as well as with W mineralization in the Brompton-Cameron terrane

(Fig. 9). The prevalent view is that porphyry Cu-Au and Cu-Mo deposits originated from oxidized magmas producing intermediate rocks which were ultimately derived from the mantle at orogenic margins, with contributions from pelagic sediments (Sillitoe, 1972)—others, however, think that the source of the metals is in the crust (Griffiths and Godwin, 1983) and that increases in Mo in porphyry Cu-Mo deposits point to the role of thickened crust as a source of metals as a result of contamination (Hollister, 1975).

The best-developed porphyry Cu-Mo deposit (Catheart Mountain) in New England is in the Brompton-Cameron terrane and formed during the Taconian orogeny. However, several Acadian porphyry Cu-Mo occurrences are thought to exist in the extension of the Brompton-Cameron terrane, in the Central Maine terrane, and the peri-Gondwanan terranes in New Brunswick and Quebec (Hollister, 1978; Ruitenberg and Fyffe, 1992; Whalen, 1993). This means that the distribution of porphyry Cu-Mo deposits is not unique, although the best known occurrences in New England are in the Brompton-Cameron terrane. Similarly, Mo mineralization of several types is known in all the terranes of New England (some containing anomalously high Cu) associated with Devonian or younger metaluminous to peraluminous, potassic, and silicic granites. Moreover, Devonian granites containing Sn occurrences are virtually all metaluminous to peraluminous and do not appear to be confined to a particular terrane; they do not seem to be related to peralkaline granites (rift related), which elsewhere are associated with major tin deposits. Granite-associated deposits formed during the Acadian orogeny in New England and Quebec are known to include hypothermal W-Mo deposits within contact-metamorphic aureoles, and Pb-Ag lodes surrounding the batholiths at a greater distance (Gauthier et al., 1994). Thus, although no systematic gradient or broad zonation of granite-associated deposit type can be identified in the orogen as a whole, there is evidence that the Acadian orogeny metallogenic province is zoned in the Quebec Appalachians, where mineral deposits generally young to the northwest (Gauthier et al., 1994). That individual crustal blocks exhibit no unique ore-element association attests to the complexity of the superposed tectonic events in the New England Appalachians, and in the following discussion a summary is given of the constraints on tectonic settings of the granitic rocks on the basis of trace element variations.

Discrimination diagrams for Yb and Ta (Fig. 10), and those involving Rb, Y, and Nb (Pearce et al., 1984) for Devonian granites (SiO_2 = 54–70 wt%) in the Brompton-Cameron terrane and for Silurian-Devonian granites from peri-Gondwanan terranes, show strong affinities with volcanic arc settings (VAG). In the Brompton-Cameron terrane the granitic rocks slightly overlap the syncollisional field (syn-Colg), which includes data for late collisional and postcollisional granites (Fig. 10A); in contrast, peri-Gondwanan granites overlap the fields for volcanic arc settings and within-plate settings (WPG) (Fig. 10C). Despite the fact that in both cases the results indicate transitional affinities evolving from those associated with volcanic arc granites, they point to

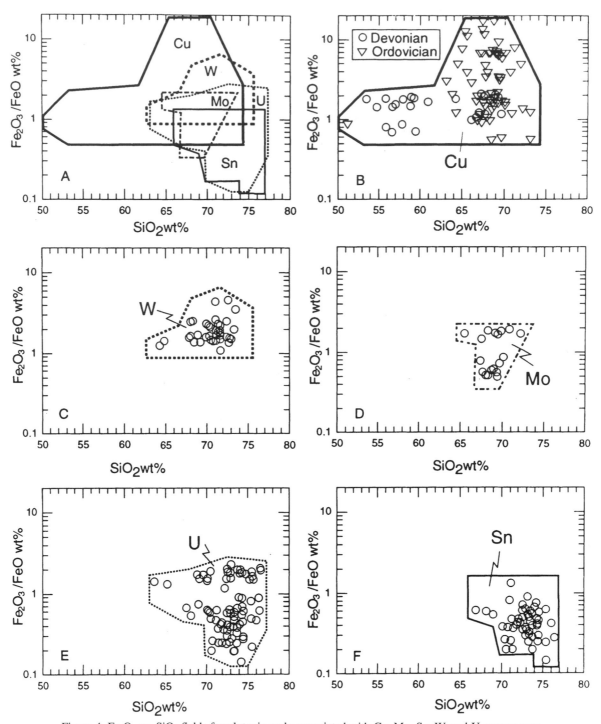

Figure 4. Fe$_2$O$_3$ vs. SiO$_2$ fields for plutonic rocks associated with Cu, Mo, Sn, W, and U occurrences. Summary plots for (A) Cu, Mo, Sn, W, and U; (B) for Cu; (C) for W; (D) for Mo; (E) for U; and (F) for Sn.

contrasting environments and different mixtures of protoliths in their source regions. Although progenitors derived from the mantle were involved in both volcanic arc settings, the crustal components were probably different—middle crust in the Brompton-Cameron terrane, instead of upper crust or perhaps an enhanced contribution of enriched subcontinental mantle in peri-Gondwanan terranes. Note, in addition, that in the Brompton-Cameron terrane, Ordovician granites are generally lower in Ta and Yb than the Devonian granites; in the peri-Gondwanan terranes, Silurian granites are lower in Ta (and thus plot dominantly as VAG in Fig. 10C) than Devonian granites (which overlap the VAG and WPG fields). This means that Devonian granites

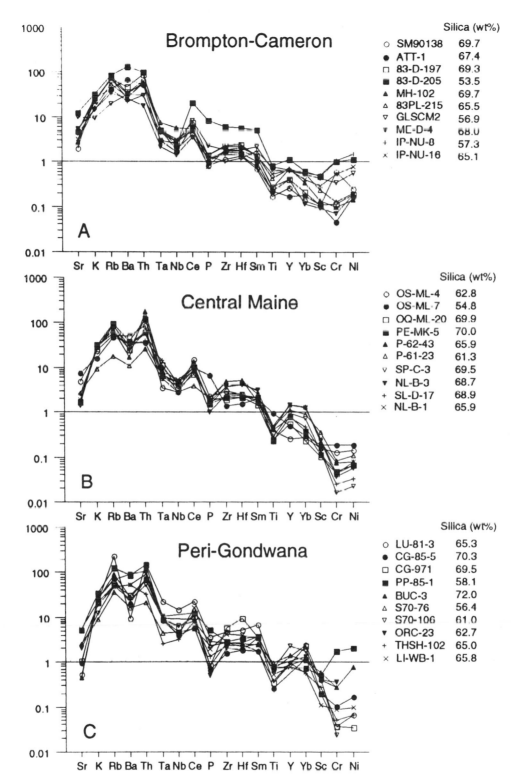

Figure 5. Normal mid-ocean ridge basalt–N-MORB normalized multielement diagrams (Pearce, 1983) for representative granitic rocks (SiO_2 = 54–70 wt%) illustrating the range in compositions in each terrane. A: Data for the Brompton-Cameron terrane: white circle, Ordovician Sally Mountain granodiorite (Maine); black circle, Attean granodiorite (Maine); and Devonian plutons: white square, Deboullie granodiorite (Maine); black square, Deboullie syenite (Maine); black triangle, Spider Lake granodiorite (Maine); white triangle, Priestly Lake granodiorite (Maine); inverted white triangle, Chandler Mountain granodiorite (Maine); inverted black triangle, Derby tonalite (Vermont); plus sign, x, Nulhegan tonalite (Vermont), B: Data for Devonian plutons from the Central Maine terrane: circles and white square, Mooselookmeguntic granodiorite (Maine); black square, Mississippian(?) Long Mountain granite (New Hampshire); black triangle, Pleasant Lake granodiorite (Maine); white triangle, Hunt Ridge granodiorite (Maine); inverted black triangle and x, Passadumkeag River granite (Maine); plus sign, Scraggly Lake granite (Maine); C:) Data for peri-Gondwanan terranes: white circle, Devonian Lucerne granite (Maine); black circle, white square, Silurian Cadillac Mountain granodiorite (Maine); black square, Devonian Parks Pond quartz monzonite (Maine); black triangle, Devonian Mt. Waldo granite (Maine); white triangles, Silurian South Penobscot granodiorite (Maine); black inverted triangles, Devonian Wallamatogous granite (Maine); plus sign, Silurian Spruce Head granodiorite (Maine); x, Devonian Waldoboro granodiorite (Maine).

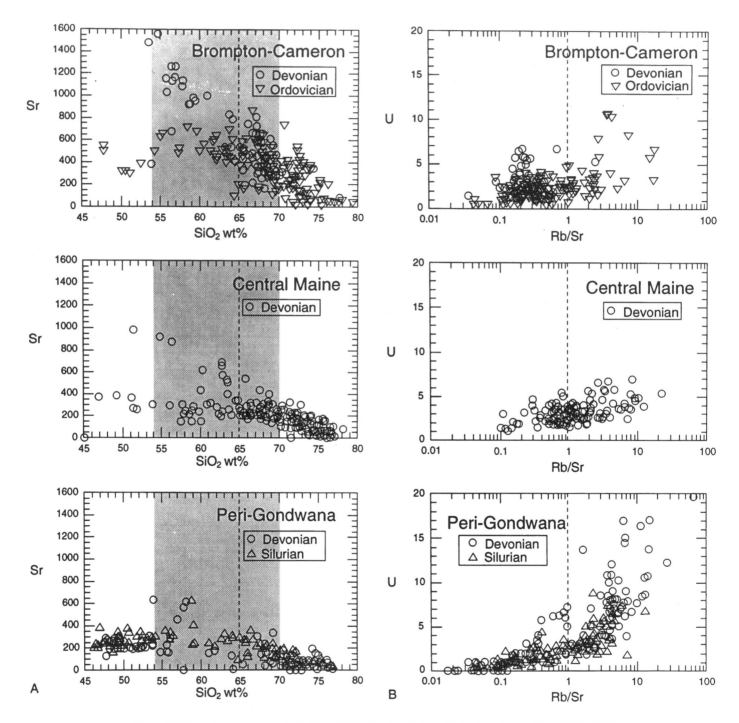

Figure 6 (this and opposite page). A: Sr vs. SiO$_2$ showing that the highest contents of Sr (~200 to 800 ppm at SiO$_2$ = 65 wt%) are in the Brompton-Cameron granitic rocks and the lowest (<350 ppm) in granitic rocks from peri-Gondwanan terranes. B: U vs. Rb/Sr. C: Th vs. Rb/Sr for plutonic rocks from the Brompton-Cameron, Central Maine, and peri-Gondwanan terranes. High contents of Th and U are found in evolved peri-Gondwanan Devonian granitic rocks (Rb/Sr to ~20). In the Devonian granitic rocks of the Brompton-Cameron terrane, high contents of Th and U are found in granitic rocks that are significantly less evolved (Rb/Sr <1) than in the peri-Gondwanan terranes. Shaded area represents the range in silica used for Figures 5, 7, and 10 (SiO$_2$ = 54–70 wt%).

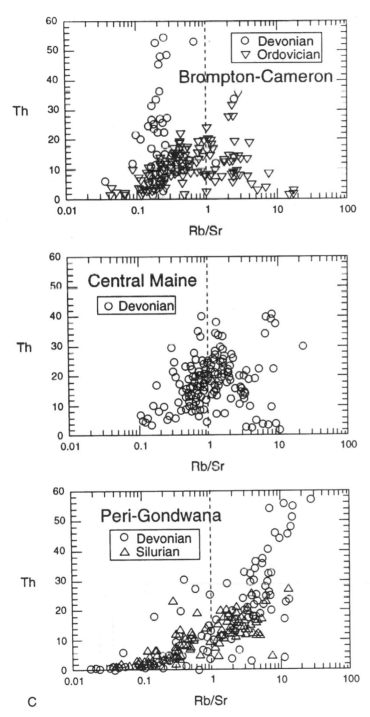

C

terrane (thought to represent the North American flank of Iapetus) and to the peri-Gondwanan terranes. Are the geochemical features characterizing granites from the intermediate Central Maine terrane distinct enough to represent a diagnostic source region? As summarized herein, granites from the Central Maine terrane have ranges of major and trace elements and isotope compositions that are almost invariably transitional between the granites from the Brompton-Cameron terrane and from peri-Gondwana. In the Central Maine terrane, the granites overlap the fields of volcanic arcs and within-plate settings for Ta and Yb and conceivably extend into the field of collisional granites (late collisional and postcollisional granites) (Fig. 10B). The granitic rocks thus exhibit transitional affinities, pointing to the contributions of diverse crustal sources into the magmas or to input from enriched mantle rocks beneath thickened continental lithosphere (Pearce et al., 1990).

Results for Devonian granites from the Central Maine and Brompton-Cameron terranes overlap greatly, and the most notable difference between them is the relative importance of within-plate settings, a feature that is virtually absent in the Brompton-Cameron terrane. That this feature is significant agrees with the interpretation of the regional Pb-isotope variations indicating that the granite source regions in these two terranes are different (Ayuso and Bevier, 1991). The intermediate nature of the isotopic data for the Central Maine terrane granites suggested a contribution of hybrid sources that combined features from both the Brompton-Cameron terrane and peri-Gondwanan terranes. This interpretation requires Laurentian affinities for the Brompton-Cameron terrane (Rankin, 1994a) and non-Laurentian or even peri-Gondwanan affinities for the Central Maine terrane. If this scenario is feasible, the Devonian granites from the Central Maine terrane would have been generated from sources that cannot be uniquely characterized.

That the Devonian granites of the Central Maine and peri-Gondwanan terranes overlap the field of within-plate granites means that the sources in these two terranes share at least some geochemical attributes (Fig. 10, B and C). Moreover, the relatively radiogenic Pb isotopic compositions (Ayuso and Bevier, 1991) and similarity of Nd isotopic compositions (Arth and Ayuso, 1993; Ayuso and Arth, 1998; Tomascak, 1995) imply that the source rocks were not sufficiently different to have produced geochemically distinct groups. Moreover, if, as suggested here, the Central Maine terrane contains source regions with non-Laurentian affinities, it is conceivable that it ultimately has a peri-Gondwanan origin resembling that of the Merrimack-Harpswell terrane collage. In this case, geochemical and isotopic differences between the granite source regions may be too small to be resolvable with the available data, even though amalgamation of the Central Maine and the Brompton-Cameron terranes to North America in the Late Cambrian (Boone and Boudette, 1989; Rankin, 1994a) implies that this composite terrane evolved separately from the Merrimack-Harpswell terrane collage for most of the Paleozoic. The results of this study do not preclude the Hackmatack Pond fault or the Norumbega fault from represent-

from peri-Gondwana terranes are distinguishable from Devonian granites from the Brompton-Cameron terrane and that their source rocks were different. In this case, there is agreement between the granite geochemical and isotopic data: different source regions are involved and at least one suture separates the two granite groups.

A fundamental question remains regarding the nature of the Central Maine terrane and its links to the Brompton-Cameron

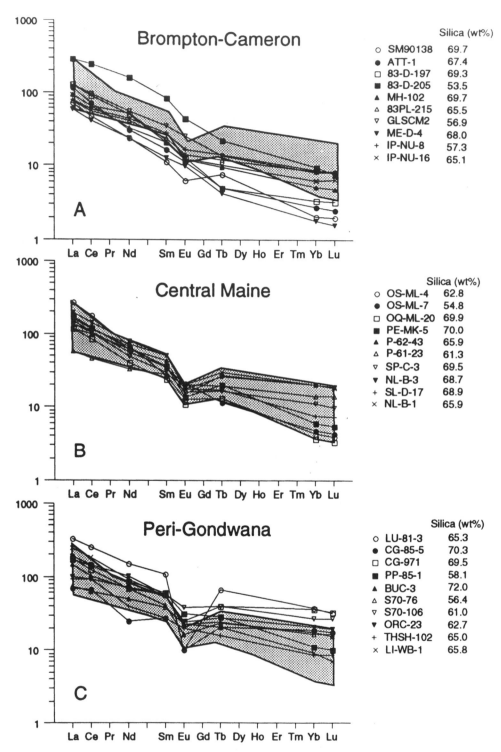

Figure 7. Rare earth element plots for representative granitic rocks (SiO$_2$ = 54–70 wt%) illustrating the range in compositions in each terrane. A: Brompton-Cameron terrane; shaded area is the field of Central Maine terrane granites; B: Central Maine terrane; C: Peri-Gondwanan terrane; shaded area is the field of Central Maine terrane granites. Samples shown as in Figure 5.

ing an Acadian suture (Ludman et al., 1993) separating the Central Maine terrane from the peri-Gondwanan terranes in south-central Maine (e.g., Stewart et al., 1995a, 1995b). Rather, because of the overlap in the geochemical data in this study, identification of unique source regions that would uniquely finger print the granites on either side of the Hackmatack Pond fault and Norumbega faults into two independent groups is not possible.

A plot of Rb-Hf-Ta (Fig. 11; Harris et al., 1986) for the least altered and most primitive portion of granites associated with porphyry Cu-Mo deposits and occurrences in the Brompton-Cameron terrane shows their volcanic arc affinities, in contrast to granites associated with Sn (U) occurrences in peri-Gondwanan terranes that plot in the late collisional and postcollisional granite fields. Mo-, Sn-, and W-associated granites from the Brompton-Cameron terrane are transitional. Devonian unmineralized granites (SiO_2 <70 wt%) from the Brompton-Cameron and Central Maine terranes, and from Silurian-Devonian granites from peri-Gondwana, overlap the fields for volcanic arc, within-plate, and late collisional and postcollisional settings, generally in agreement with results summarized here on the basis of Yb and Ta contents. This means that Ordovician granites in the Brompton-Cameron terrane point to a predominantly volcanic arc setting and that Silurian-Devonian felsic magmatism throughout this portion of New England was characterized by evolution from volcanic arc to late and postcollisional granite settings and that it included a within-plate component. It is interesting to note that regardless of terrane, granite compositions do not demand a major contribution from sources enriched in Rb and depleted in Hf, as found in syncollisional granites (Fig. 11).

Trace element variations in mafic magmas genetically linked to the generation of the felsic plutons (quartz gabbros, quartz diorites, mafic syenites, and pillow basalts containing <57 wt% SiO_2) may place further constraints on the tectonic settings during granitic magmatism if they sufficiently approximate original magmatic compositions. For example, multielement N-MORB normalized plots for Devonian Brompton-Cameron mafic rocks (gabbros, diorites, mafic syenites, and fine-grained mafic inclusions thought to represent basaltic remnants) show selected enrichments in Sr, K, Rb, Ba, and Th, as well as in Ce (probably indicative of mixing with crustal rocks or fluids), Ta, Nb, Zr, and Hf, and wide variations for Ti and Y relative to N-MORB (Fig. 12A). Most of the mafic rocks have the characteristic negative Nb anomaly relative to Th and Ce and commonly have low values of Ti and Y compared to N-MORB, consistent with a continental volcanic arc origin (calc alkaline, high K) and with inferred tectonic settings for the granites (Fig. 10). A few samples have high values of Ti/Y resembling those in collisional basalts, in agreement with the relative enrichment in Zr that points to sources available in late collisional and postcollisional collision zones.

The vast majority of mafic rocks from peri-Gondwanan terranes in this study are subalkaline, with Nb/Y values of <1 (Pearce, 1996). Moreover, Zr/Ti values are consistent with compositions ranging from basalt and basaltic andesite to andesite. Multielement plots show that the mafic rocks related to the Silu-

rian granites have been selectively enriched in large ion lithophile elements (K, Rb, Ba) relative to N-MORB, in agreement with interaction of mantle-derived rocks with crustal rocks or fluids; Th, the light REEs, incompatible high field strength elements (Ta, Nb, Hf, Zr), Ti, and Y are widely variable in comparison to N-MORB (Fig. 12B). In addition, mafic rocks from peri-Gondwanan terranes differ from those in the Brompton-Cameron terrane in that mantle-normalized plots generally show flatter patterns and lower abundances of K, Rb, Ba, and Th (Fig. 12B); the REE abundances are also lower, and REE patterns are less fractionated (Fig. 13). Many Silurian mafic rocks in peri-Gondwana terranes have N-MORB normalized values for Ti that are less than Y, a feature that eliminates an origin from within-plate type sources and is consistent with sources resembling those of volcanic arc tholeiites and calc-alkaline high-K rocks.

These general observations are corroborated by trends on a plot of Th-Hf-Ta (Wood, 1980) for quartz gabbros, quartz diorites, and pillow basalts associated with Silurian granites in peri-Gondwana terranes. The data plot for the most part in the volcanic arc field, with minor overlap with the N-MORB field (Fig. 14); Devonian mafic rocks, instead, point to a mixed source involving volcanic arc basalt (VAB) and a combination of N-MORB and within-plate basalt (N-MORB + WPB, Fig. 14). Mafic rocks associated with Devonian granites from the Brompton-Cameron terrane overlap the fields of volcanic arc basalts (VAB, plotting near the Th apex) and fields combining N-MORB and within-plate basalts (N-MORB + WPB), consistent with their generation in a setting that evolved from dominantly volcanic arc magmatism with a subduction signature, to one involving collisional magmatism (Pearce, 1996).

The main difference between the mafic rocks in the Brompton-Cameron and peri-Gondwanan terranes is that the latter show a predominant input from N-MORB–type source (relatively enriched in Hf) (Fig. 14). This means that an origin in an environment involving the closing stages of an arc is possible. More important, all of the preceding are in agreement with the idea that the Brompton-Cameron terrane contains granitic rocks having features concordant with volcanic arcs (Ordovician), and transitional to late collisional and postcollisional settings (Devonian). Few mafic intrusive rocks were analyzed from the Central Maine terrane; most are from mafic enclaves that are unlikely to represent magmas (probably cumulates or hybrids) and plot as transitional between those for volcanic arc basalts and within-plate basalts. Thus, it is not possible to further constrain the tectonic settings for the Central Maine terrane on this basis (Fig. 14). It is important to note, however, that trace element variations of Silurian to Early Devonian basaltic rocks from other portions of the Central Maine terrane point to subduction-related volcanism (Rankin, 1994b)—although an alternative suggestion is that such volcanism reflects complex, transitional tectonic regimes related to rifting environments (Fitzgerald and Hon, 1994). In peri-Gondwanan terranes, volcanic arc settings (with a contribution from within-plate sources) were first predominant (Silurian); a later (Devonian) transition from volcanic arcs to within-plate set-

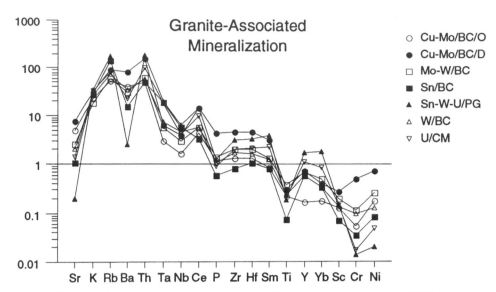

Figure 8. Normal mid-ocean ridge basalt–normalized multielement diagrams (Pearce, 1983) for average compositions of granitic rocks (SiO_2 = 54–70 wt%). Abbreviations: Cu-Mo/BC/ O, average of 12 Ordovician granites associated with Cu-Mo mineralization in Brompton-Cameron terrane (Catheart Mountain, Sally Mountain granodiorites); Cu-Mo/BC/D, average of 26 Devonian syenite samples showing Cu-Mo mineralization in the Brompton-Cameron terrane (Deboullie); MO-W/BC, average of 26 Devonian granite samples associated with Mo and W mineralization in Brompton-Cameron terrane (Priestly Lake, Deboullie granodiorites); Sn/BC, average of 18 samples showing Sn mineralization in the Brompton-Cameron terrane (Willoughby granite); Sn-W-U/PG, average of 60 Devonian granite samples associated with Sn, W (and U) mineralization in peri-Gondwanan terranes (Lucerne granite, Blue Hill granite, Deblois granite); W/BC, average of 43 Devonian granodiorite-granite samples with W mineralization in the Brompton-Cameron terrane (Averill granite); U/CM, average of 66 Devonian granite samples associated with anomalously high U contents in Central Maine terrane (Passadumkeag River granite, Whitney Cove granite). See text for explanation and data sources.

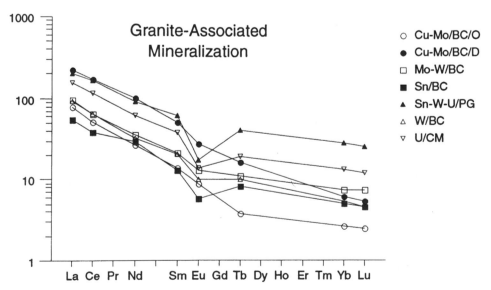

Figure 9. Rare earth element plot for average compositions of granitic rocks (SiO_2 = 54–70 wt%) in this study associated with different types of mineralization. For explanation, see Figure 8.

tings and perhaps to late collisional and postcollisional settings included juxtaposition of crustal blocks, underthrusting, strike-slip displacements, and perhaps even extensional tectonics (e.g., Uyeda, 1982; Hogan and Sinha, 1988; Stewart et al., 1995a, 1995b). Such suggestions are generally in agreement with studies of peri-Gondwanan volcanism (Gates and Moench, 1981) that point to an origin from a rifted volcanic arc or back arc basin (Fyffe et al., 1991).

The bulk of the discussion here supports the contention that various tectonic settings operated in the Paleozoic to yield the granitic rocks, and that a wide variety of possible source rocks was involved (Table 2 shows a summary). A large proportion of granitic magmatism was probably generated prior to, rather than as a result of, or during amalgamation to Laurentia, as in the peri-Gondwanan terranes. This means that geologically unrelated blocks are now adjacent and that magmatism was produced in tectonic settings far from the present location of the granites. One implication of these results is that metal zonation associated with the granitic rocks generated in a tectonic environment such as that of the Andes (Sillitoe, 1986) is unlikely to be applicable to this portion of the New England Appalachians. A more likely scenario is that granite magmatism and metallogeny reflect superposition of various tectonic settings dominated by transitional stages. Volcanic arc granites were generated in subduction environments, but magmatism also involved within-plate granites, as well as late collisional and postcollisional granites generated during block collisions—therefore, the metallogeny also reflects diverse source rocks (Table 2). Given the fact that the source regions yielding granitic magmas represent a continuum of compositions, it is not surprising that the spectrum of granitic rocks does not easily conform to rigid classifications schemes. Moreover, because trace element variations in the majority of granites point to a major contribution from mixed sources related to collisional events, ore deposits associated with these granitic rocks cannot uniquely characterize individual terranes.

CONCLUSIONS

1. Modal and major element compositions (>900 analyses) do not uniquely distinguish terranes regionally.

2. Trace element contents of granitic rocks point to chemical groups showing subtle differences, consistent with their distribution within known terrane subdivisions. Granitic rocks in the Brompton-Cameron and peri-Gondwanan terranes point to contrasting environments (volcanic arc and within-plate settings) and different mixtures of protoliths in the source, in agreement with the contention that various tectonic settings operated in the Paleozoic. Granites from the Central Maine terrane are nonunique in their trace element abundances and perhaps more closely resemble granite sources found in peri-Gondwana terranes.

3. The majority of the granitic rocks in the study were not affected systematically by processes that lead to mineralization; they commonly lack evidence for water-rock interaction, and generally indicate deep levels of erosion.

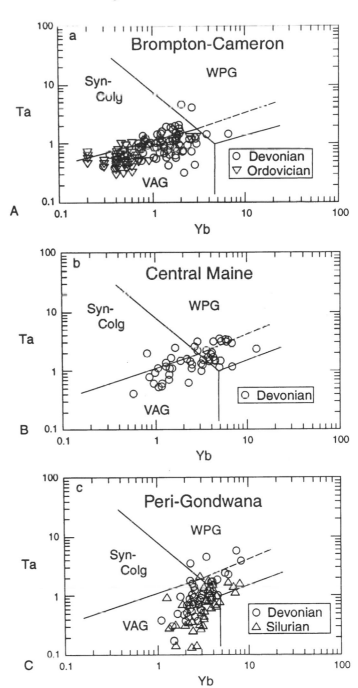

Figure 10. Ta-Yb tectonic classification diagrams (Pearce et al., 1984) for representative granitic rocks (SiO$_2$ <70 wt%) from the Brompton-Cameron terrane (A), Central Maine terrane (B), and peri-Gondwanan terranes (C). Abbreviations: Syn-Colg, syncollisional granite field including data for late collisional and postcollisional data; WPG, within-plate granite field; VAG, volcanic arc granite field.

4. Molybdenite is widely distributed in all terranes and is the most common sulfide associated with mineralized granites.

5. Important considerations for evaluating granite-related ore deposits in New England include the depth of emplacement (must be shallow enough to produce pressures <1 kbar), the pres-

148   *R. A. Ayuso*

ence of regional faults, and Fe_2O_3/FeO compositional control on
the type of associated mineralization.

6. In the Brompton-Cameron terrane, granites associated with
porphyry Cu-Mo deposits have a wide range as well as the highest
overall values of Fe_2O_3/FeO; granitic rocks hosting Sn occurrences
in the peri-Gondwanan terranes have the lowest range. Intermediate
values are found for granites associated with W and Mo mineralization. Many of the leucogranitic, most evolved, and often most aluminous rocks in the batholiths associated with mineralization have
evidence for vapor saturation in the form of abundant pegmatites,
and aplites, as in the Lucerne, Willoughby, and Averill plutons.

7. Porphyry Cu-Mo deposits are not widely distributed,
although the best-known occurrences in New England are in the
Brompton-Cameron terrane. Mo mineralization of several types
is known in all the terranes of New England. Sn occurrences are
virtually all in metaluminous to peraluminous rocks and also do
not appear to be confined to a particular terrane. No systematic
gradient or broad zonation deposit types associated with granitic
rocks can be identified in the orogen as a whole.

ACKNOWLEDGMENTS

I am grateful for perceptive and constructive reviews by D. B.
Stewart, M. Foose, N. K. Foley, H. Brueckner, and J. B. Whalen. I
also thank A. Ludman for his comments and assistance as editor.

REFERENCES CITED

Aleinikoff, J. N., Moench, R. H., and Lyons, J. B., 1985, Metamorphic and tec-
tonic implications: Carboniferous U-Pb age of the Sebago batholith, south-
western Maine: Geological Society of America Bulletin, v. 96, p. 990–996.
Allcock, J. B., 1982, Skarns and porphyry copper mineralization at Mines Gaspe,
Murdochville, Quebec: Economic Geology, v. 77, p. 971–999.
Andrew, A., Loiselle, M. C., and Wones, D. R., 1983, Granitic plutonism as an
indicator of microplates in the Paleozoic of central and eastern Maine:
Earth and Planetary Science Letters, v. 66, p. 151–166.
Arth, J. G., and Ayuso, R. A., 1993, Nd isotopic composition of Acadian plutons
from northern New England: Geological Society of America Abstracts
with Programs, v. 25, no. 6, p. A-41.
Arth, J. G., and Ayuso, R. A., 1994, Proportions of juvenile and recycled crust in
Paleozoic continental collision zone: Northern Appalachians of New
England, USA: Abstracts of the Eight International Conference on Geo-
chronology, Cosmochronology and Isotope Geology: U.S. Geological
Survey Circular 1107, p. 13.
Arth, J. G., and Ayuso, R. A., 1997, The Northeast Kingdom batholith, Vermont:
Geochronology and Nd, O, Pb, and Sr isotopic constraints on the origin of
Acadian granitic rocks, *in* Sinha, A. K., Whalen, J. B., and Hogan, J. P.,
eds., The Nature of Magmatism in the Appalachian Orogen: Geological
Society of America Memoir 191, p. 1–18.
Ayuso, R. A., 1984, Field relations, crystallization, and petrology of reversely
zoned plutons in the Bottle Lake Complex, Maine: U.S. Geological Sur-
vey Professional Paper 1320, 58 p.
Ayuso, R. A., 1986, Pb isotopic evidence for distinct sources of granite and for distinct
basements in the northern Appalachians, Maine: Geology, v. 14, p. 322–325.
Ayuso, R. A., 1988, Geochemistry of the Catheart Mountain porphyry copper
deposit, Maine, *in* Tucker, R., and Marvinney, R. G., eds., Igneous and

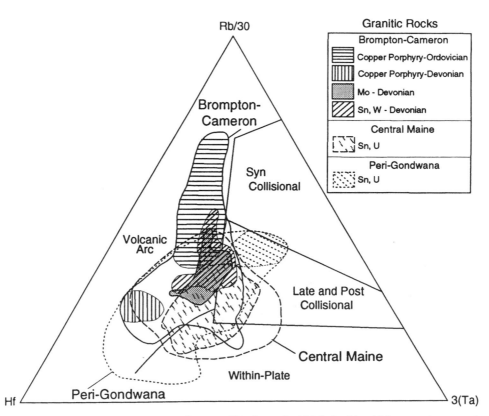

Figure 11. Hf-Rb-Ta discrimination diagram (Harris et al., 1986) for identifying granite tectonic
settings. Fields represent compositions of the least altered and most primitive samples of granites associated with Cu, Mo, Sn, W, and U occurrences used in Figure 8.

metamorphic geology Studies in Maine geology, Volume 4: Augusta, Maine Geological Survey, p. 139–162.

Ayuso, R. A., 1996, Northern Appalachians, *in* Ludington, S., and Cox, D., eds., Data base for a national mineral-resource assessment of undiscovered deposits of gold, silver, copper, lead, and zinc in the conterminous United States: U.S. Geological Survey Open-File Report 96-96, CD-ROM.

Ayuso, R. A., and Arth, J. G., 1992, The Northeast Kingdom batholith, Vermont: Magmatic evolution, and geochemical constraints on the origin of Acadian rocks: Contributions to Mineralogy and Petrology, v. 111, p. 1–23.

Ayuso, R. A., and Arth, J. G., 1997, The Spruce Head composite pluton: an example of mafic to silicic Silurian magmatism in coastal Maine, Northern Appalachians, *in* Sinha, A. K., Whalen, J. B., and Hogan, J. P., eds. The nature of magmatism in the Appalachian orogen: Geological Society of America Memoir 191, p. 19–43.

Ayuso, R. A., and Arth, J. G., 1998, Paleozoic granitic rocks from terranes in the Northern New England Appalachians: Geochemical and isotopic constraints: Geological Society of America Abstracts with Programs, v. 30, no. 1, p. 3.

Ayuso, R. A., and Bevier, M. L., 1991, Regional differences in Pb isotopic compositions of feldspars in plutonic rocks of the northern Appalachian Mountains, U.S.A. and Canada: A geochemical method of terrane correlation: Tectonics, v. 10, p. 191–212.

Ayuso, R. A., and Loferski, P. J., 1992. Trace element geochemistry of syenite and granodiorite in the Deboullie pluton, northern Maine: Geological Association of Canada–Mineralogical Association of Canada Abstracts, v. 17, p. A5.

Ayuso, R. A., and Shank, S. G., 1983, Quartz-molybdenite veins in the Priestly Lake granodiorite, north-central Maine: U.S. Geological Survey Open-File Report 83-800, 12 p.

Baedecker, P. A., 1987, Methods for geochemical analysis: U.S. Geological Survey Bulletin 1770.

Billings, M. P., 1956, The geology of New Hampshire: Part II, Bedrock geology: New Hampshire State Planning and Development Commission, 204 p.

Blevin, P. L., and Chappell, B. W., 1992, The role of magma sources, oxidation states and fractionation in determining the granite metallogeny of eastern Australia: Royal Society of Edinburgh Transactions, Earth Sciences, v. 83, p. 305–316.

Blevin, P. L., and Chappell, B. W., 1995, Chemistry, origin, and evolution of mineralized granites in the Lachlan Fold Belt, Australia; the metallogeny of I and S-type granites: Economic Geology, v. 90, p. 1604–1619.

Boone, G. M., 1962, Potassic feldspar enrichment in magma: Origin of syenite in Deboullie district, northern Maine: Geological Society of America Bulletin, v. 73, p. 1451–1476.

Boone, G. M., and Boudette, E. L., 1989, Accretion of the Boundary Mountains terrane within the northern Appalachian orthotectonic zone, *in* Horton, J. W., and Rast, N., eds., Melanges and olistostromes of the U.S. Appalachians: Geological Society of America Special Paper 228, p. 17–42.

Burnham, C. W., and Ohmoto, H, 1980, Late-stage processes of felsic magmatism, *in* Ishihara, S., and Takenouchi, S., eds., Granite magmatism and related mineralization: Mining Geology Special Issue, v. 8, p. 1–11.

Carten, R. B., Walker, B. M., Geraghty, E. P., and Gunow, A. J., 1985, Comparison of field based studies of the Henderson porphyry molybdenum deposit, Colorado, with experimental and theoretical models of porphyry systems, *in* Taylor, R. P., and Strong, D. F., eds., Recent advances in the geology of granite-related mineral deposits: Canadian Institute of Mining and Metallurgy Special Volume 39, p. 351–366.

Chappell, B. W., and White, A. J. R., 1974, Two contrasting granite types: Pacific Geology, v. 8, p. 173–174.

Chappell, B. W., and White, A. J. R., 1992, I- and S-type granites in the Lachlan fold belt: Royal Society of Edinburgh Transactions, Earth Sciences, v. 83, p 1–26.

Chappell, B. W., White, A. J. R., and Whine, R., 1988, Granite provinces and basement terranes in the Lachlan fold belt, southeastern Australia: Australian Journal of Earth Sciences, v. 35, p. 505–521.

Clarke, D. B., 1992, Granitoid rocks (Topics in the Earth Sciences 7): London, Chapman and Hall, 283 p.

Cox, D. P., and Singer, D. A., 1986, Mineral deposit models: U.S. Geological Survey Bulletin 1693, 379 p.

Feiss, G., and Slack, J. F., 1989, Mineral deposits of the U.S. Appalachians, *in* Hatcher, R. D., Thomas, W. A., and Viele, G W., eds., The Appalachian-Ouachita orogen in the United States: Boulder, Colorado, Geological Society of America, Geology of North America, v. F-2, p. 471–494.

Fitzgerald, J., and Hon, R., 1994, Mafic volcanism of the Piscataquis Volcanic belt, *in* Hanson, L., ed., Guidebook to field trips in north-central Maine (New England Intercollegiate Geological Conference, Millinocket, Maine): Dubuque, Iowa, Wm. C. Brown Publishers, p. 91–122.

Foley, N. K., and Ayuso, R. A., 1992, Character of hydrothermal fluids in the Catheart Mountain Cu-Mo deposit, Maine: Constraints on modeling a mineralizing system: Geological Association of Canada Abstracts, v. 17, p. A34.

Fyffe, L. MacLeod, M., and Ruitenberg, A., 1991, A geotraverse across the St. Croix-Avalon terrane boundary, southern New Brunswick, Part I, *In* Ludman, A., ed., Geology of the Coastal lithotectonic block and neighboring terranes, eastern Maine and southern New Brunswick (New England Intercollegiate Geological Conference, Princeton, Maine): Dubuque, Iowa, Wm. C. Brown Publishers, p. 13–54.

Gates, O., and Moench, D. H., 1981, Bimodal Silurian and Lower Devonian volcanic rock assemblages in the Machias-Eastport area, Maine: U.S. Geological Survey Professional Paper 1184, 32 p.

Gauthier, M., Chartrand, F., and Trottier, J., 1994, Metallogenic epochs and metallogenic provinces of the Estrie-Beauce region, southern Quebec Appalachians: Economic Geology, v. 89, p. 1322–1360.

Griffiths, J. R., and Godwin, C. I., 1983, Metallogeny and tectonics of porphyry copper-molybdenum deposits in British Columbia: Canadian Journal of Earth Sciences, v. 20, p. 1000–1018.

Haapala, I., 1995, Metallogeny of the rapakivi granites: Mineralogy and Petrology, v. 54, p. 149–160.

Harris, N. B. W., Pearce, J. A., and Tindle, A. G., 1986, Geochemical characteristics of collision zone magmatism *in* Coward, M. P., and Ries, A. C., eds., Collision tectonics: Geological Society of London Special Publication 19, p. 67–81.

Hermes, O. D., and Banks, P. O., 1978, Upper Ordovician peralkalic granites from the Gulf of Maine: Geological Society of America Bulletin, v. 89, p. 176–184.

Hermes, O. D. and Murray, D. P., 1988, Middle Devonian to Permian plutonism and volcanism in the North American Appalachians, *in* Harris, A. L., and Feltes, D. J., eds., The Caledonian-Appalachian orogen: Geological Society of London Special Publication 38, p. 559–571.

Hogan, J. O., and Sinha, A. K., 1988, Compositional variation of plutonism in the Coastal Maine magmatic province: Mode of origin and tectonic setting, *in* Tucker, R. D., and Marvinney, R. G., eds., Igneous and metamorphic geology (Studies in Maine geology, Volume 4): Augusta, Maine Geological Survey, p. 1–33.

Hollister, V. F., 1975, An appraisal of the nature and source of porphyry copper deposits: Mining Science Engineering, v. 7, p. 225–233.

Hollister, V. F., 1978, Geology of the porphyry copper deposits of the Western Hemisphere: New York, Society of Mining Engineers, American Institute of Mining, Metallurgical and Petroleum Engineers, 219 p.

Hollister, V. F., Potter, R. R., and Barber, A. L., 1974, Porphyry type deposits of the Appalachian orogen: Economic Geology, v. 69, p. 618–630.

Hon, R., 1980, Geology and petrology of igneous bodies within the Katahdin pluton, *in* Roy, D.C., and Naylor, R. S., eds., New England Intercollegiate Geological Conference Guidebook: Presque Isle, Maine, Boston College Press, p. 65–79.

Kooiman, G. J. A., MacLeod, M. J., and Sinclair, W. D., 1986, Porphyry tungsten-molybdenum ore bodies, polymetallic veins and replacement bodies, and tin-bearing greisen zones in the Fire Tower zone, Mt Pleasant, New Brunswick: Economic Geology, v. 81, p. 1356–1373.

Lehmann, B., 1990, Metallogeny of tin, (Lecture Notes in Earth Sciences 32): New York, Springer-Verlag, 211 p.

Leo, G., 1991, Oliverian domes, related plutonic rocks and mantling Ammonoosuc volcanics of the Bronson Hill anticlinorium, New England Appalachians: U.S. Geological Survey Professional Paper 1516, 92 p.

Loferski, P. J., and Ayuso, R. A., 1995, Petrography and mineral chemistry of the composite Deboullie pluton, northern Maine, U.S.A.: Implications for the genesis of Cu-Mo mineralization: Chemical Geology, v. 123, p. 89–105.

Loiselle, M. C., and Ayuso, R. A., 1980, Geochemical characteristics of granitoids across the Merrimack synclinorium eastern and central Maine, *in* Wones, D. R., ed., The Caledonides in the U.S.: Blacksburg, Virginia

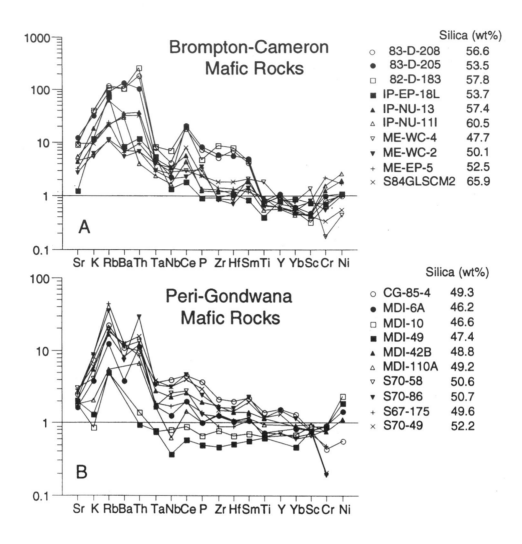

Figure 12. Normal mid-ocean ridge basalt–normalized multielement diagrams (Pearce, 1983) for representative mafic rocks (SiO$_2$ <57 wt%) associated with granitic rocks in this study: A: Brompton-Cameron terrane data shown for Devonian rocks including the Deboullie mafic syenite (Maine) (circles white square); Echo Pond gabbro (black square, plus sign); Nulhegan (triangles), West Charleston gabbro (inverted triangles); Northeast Kingdom batholith, (Vermont); Chandler Mountain gabbro (x); B: Peri-Gondwanan terranes data shown for Silurian Cadillac Mountain (circles, squares, triangles) and Silurian South Penobscot intrusive suite (Maine) (inverted triangles, plus sign, x). See text for explanation.

Polytechnic Institute and State University Memoir 2, p. 117–121.

Ludman, A., 1986, Timing of terrane accretion in eastern and east-central Maine: Geology, v. 14, p. 411–414.

Ludman, A., 1987, Pre-Silurian stratigraphy and tectonic significance of the St. Croix belt, southeastern Maine: Canadian Journal of Earth Sciences, v. 24, p. 2459–2469.

Ludman, A., 1991, The Fredericton trough and Norumbega fault zone in eastern Maine, *in* Ludman, A., ed., Geology of the Coastal lithotectonic block and neighboring terranes, eastern Maine and southern New Brunswick (New England Intercollegiate Geological Conference, Princeton, Maine): Dubuque, Iowa, Wm. C. Brown Publishers, p. 186–208.

Ludman, A., Hopeck, J. T., and Brock, P. C., 1993, Nature of the Acadian orogeny in eastern Maine, *in* Roy, D. C., and Skehan, J. W., eds., Recent studies in New England, Maritime Canada, and the autochthonous foreland: Geological Society of America Special Paper 275, p. 67–84.

Maurice, V. T., 1986, Interpretation of a reconnaissance geochemical heavy min-

eral survey in the Eastern Townships of Quebec, *in* Current research, part A: Geological Survey of Canada Paper 86-1A, p. 307–317.

Moench, R. H., 1998, Metallic mineral occurrences map of the Sherbrooke-Lewiston area, Maine, New Hampshire, and Vermont, United States, and Quebec, Canada: U.S. Geological Survey Miscellaneous Investigations Series Map I-1898-G, scale 1:250,000.

Moench, R. H., Boone, G. M., Bothner, W. A., Boudette, E. L., Hatch, N. L., Hussey, A. M., and Mavinney, R. G., 1995, Geologic map of the Sherbrooke-Lewiston area, Maine, New Hampshire, and Vermont, United States, and Quebec, Canada: U.S. Geological Survey Miscellaneous Investigations Series Map I-1898-D, scale 1:250,000.

Multschler, F. E., Wright, E. G., Ludington, S., and Abbott, J. T., 1981, Granite molybdenite systems: Economic Geology, v. 76, p. 874–887.

Neuman, R. B., Palmer, A. R., and Dutro, J. T., 1989, Paleontological contributions to Paleozoic paleogeographic reconstructions of the Appalachians, *in* Hatcher, R. D., Thomas, W. A., and Viele, G. W., eds., The Appala-

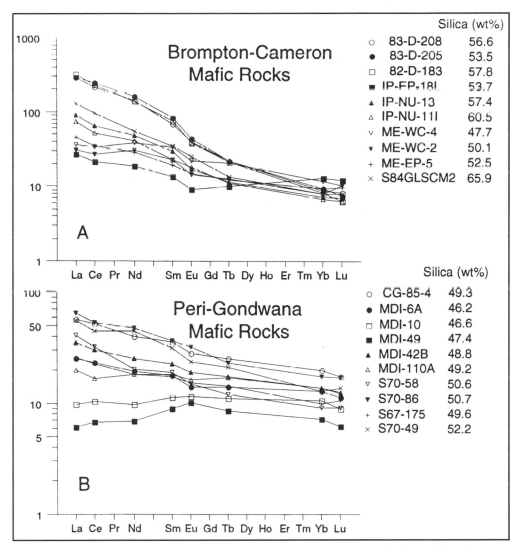

Figure 13. Chondrite-normalized rare earth element plots for representative mafic rocks (SiO_2 <57 wt%) associated with granitic rocks in this study: A: Brompton Cameron terrane. B: Peri-Gondwanan terranes. See Figure 12 and text for explanation.

chian-Ouachita orogen in the United States: Boulder, Colorado, Geological Society of America, Geology of North America, v. F-2, p. 375–384.

Nowlan, G. A., and Hessin, T. D., 1972, Molybdenum, arsenic, and other elements in stream sediments, Tomah Mountain, Topsfield, Maine: U.S. Geological Survey Open-File Report 72-1766, 18 p.

Nowlan, G. A., Howd, F. H., Canney, F. C., and Domenico, J. A., 1990a, Maps showing the distribution of chromium, molybdenum, and uranium in stream sediments, Sherbrooke and Lewiston 1 × 2 quadrangles, Maine, New Hampshire, and Vermont: U.S. Geological Survey Miscellaneous Investigations Series Map I-1898-A, scale 1:250,000.

Nowlan, G. A., Howd, F. H., Canney, F. C., and Domenico, J. A., 1990b, Maps showing the distribution of copper, lead, and zinc in stream sediments, Sherbrooke and Lewiston 1 × 2 quadrangles, Maine, New Hampshire, and Vermont: U.S. Geological Survey Miscellaneous Investigations Series Map I-1898-B, scale 1:250,000.

Nowlan, G. A., Howd, F. H., Canney, F. C., and Domenico, J. A., 1990c, Maps showing the distribution of tin, tungsten, arsenic, gold, and silver in nonmagnetic heavy-mineral concentrates derived from stream sediments, Sherbrooke and Lewiston 1 × 2 quadrangles, Maine, New Hampshire, and

Vermont: U.S. Geological Survey Miscellaneous Investigations Series Map I-1898-C, scale 1:250,000.

Osberg, P. H., Hussey, A. M., and Boone, G. M., 1985, Bedrock geologic map of Maine: Augusta, Maine Geological Survey, scale 1:500,000.

Osberg, P. H., Tull, J. F., Robinson, P., Hon, R., and Butler, J. R., 1989, The Acadian Orogen, *in* Hatcher, R. D., Thomas, W. A., and Viele, G. W., eds., The Appalachian-Ouachita orogen in the United States: Boulder, Colorado, Geological Society of America, Geology of North America, v. F-2, p. 179–232.

Otton, J. K., and Nowlan, G. A., 1980, Anomalous uranium and thorium associated with a granitic facies of the Bottle Lake Quartz Monzonite, Tomah Mountain area, eastern Maine: U.S. Geological Survey Open-File Report 80-991, 15 p.

Pankiwskyj, K. A., 1996, Structure and stratigraphy across the Hackmatack Pond fault, Kennebec and Waldo counties, Maine: Maine Geological Survey Open-File No. 96-2, 15 p., 2 maps, scale 1:24,000.

Pearce, J. A., 1983, Role of the subcontinental lithosphere in magma genesis at active continental margins, *in* Hawkesworth, C. J., and Norry, M. J., eds. Continental basalts and mantle xenoliths: Nantwich, United Kingdom, Shiva, p. 230–249.

Pearce, J. A., 1996, A user's guide to basalt discrimination diagrams: in Wyman, D. A., ed., Trace element geochemistry of volcanic rocks: Applications

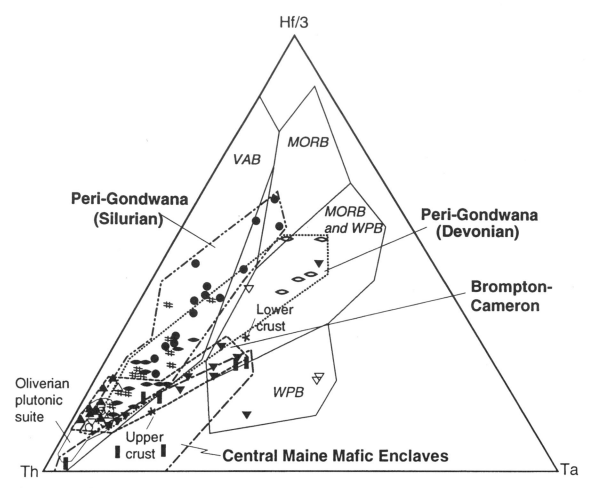

Figure 14. Th-Hf-Ta discrimination diagram for identifying tectonic settings (Wood, 1980) of representative mafic rocks (SiO$_2$ <57 wt%) associated with granitic rocks. Abbreviations: VAB, volcanic arc basalts; MORB, normal-type mid-ocean ridge basalts; WPB, within-plate basalts, upper and lower crust (Taylor and McLennan, 1985). Brompton-Cameron terrane: upright and inverted white triangles are mafic rocks in the Northeast Kingdom batholith; upright black triangles are Deboullie syenite-granodiorite; inverted black triangles are mafic enclaves in Northeast Kingdom batholith. Central Maine terrane: black rectangles are mafic enclaves in the Bottle Lake Complex, Center Pond granodiorite, and Ebeemee–Mattamiscontis–Norway Point complex. Peri-Gondwanan terranes: black circles are mafic rocks from Mt. Desert Island, white circles are Parks Pond quartz monzonite; white ovals are Spruce Head gabbro-granodiorite, pound signs are South Penobscot intrusive Suite; black ovals are Vinalhaven. Shaded field represents the Oliverian plutonic suite in New Hampshire. See text for explanation and data sources.

for massive sulfide exploration: Geological Society of Canada Short Course notes, v. 12, p. 79–113.

Pearce, J. A., Harris, N. B. W., and Tindle, A. W., 1984, Trace element discrimination diagrams for the tectonic interpretation of granitic rocks: Journal of Petrology, v. 25, p. 956–983.

Pearce, J. A., Bender, J. F., De Long, S. E., Kidd, W. S. F., Low, P. J., Güner, Y., Saroglu, F., Yilmaz, Y., Moorbath, S., and Mitchell, J. G., 1990, Genesis of collision volcanism in Eastern Anatolia: Journal of Volcanological and Geothermal Research, v. 44, p. 189–229.

Pitcher, W. S., 1993, The nature and origin of granite: London, Blackie Academic and Professional, 321 p.

Plant, J., Brown, G. C., Simpson, P. R., and Smith, R. T., 1980, Signatures of metalliferous granites in the Scottish Caledonides: Transactions of the Institute of Mining and Metallurgy, section B: Applied Earth Sciences, v. 89, p. B198–B210.

Pollard, P. J., Nakapadungrat, S., and Taylor, R. G., 1995, The Phuket supersuite, southwest Thailand: Fractionated I-type granites associated with tin-tantalum mineralization: Economic Geology, v. 90, p. 586–602.

Post, E. V., Lehmbeck, W. L., Dennen, W. H., and Nowlan, G. A., 1967, Map of south-eastern Maine showing heavy metals in stream sediments: U.S. Geological Survey, Mineral Investigations Field Studies Map MF-301, scale 1:250,000.

Rankin, D. W., 1994a, Continental margin of the eastern United States: Past and present, in Speed, R. C., ed., Phanerozoic evolution of North American continent-ocean transitions: Geological Society of America, DNAG Continent-Ocean Transect Volume, p. 129–217.

Rankin, D. W., 1994b, Early Devonian explosive silicic volcanism and associated Early and Middle Devonian clastic sedimentation that brackets the Acadian orogeny, Traveler Mountain, in Hanson, L., ed., Guidebook to field trips in north-central Maine (New England Intercollegiate Conference, Millinocket, Maine): Dubuque, Iowa, Wm. C. Brown Publishers, p. 135–146.

Robinson, G., 1990, Carbonate-hosted gold mineralization of hydrothermal-replacement origin adjacent to a syenitic stock at Cuttingville, Vermont, and the potential for other syenite-related gold deposits in New England, in Slack, J. F., ed., Summary results of the Glens Falls CUSMAP project, New York, Vermont, and New Hampshire: U.S. Geological Survey Bulletin 1887, 371 p.

Ruitenberg, A. A., and Fyffe, L. R., 1982, Mineral deposits associated with granitoid intrusions and related subvolcanic stocks in New Brunswick and

TABLE 2. SUMMARY OF TECTONIC SETTINGS AND MINERALIZATION ASSOCIATED WITH GRANITIC ROCKS
(SiO_2 = 54–70 wt%)

	Brompton-Cameron terrane	Central Maine terrane		Peri-Gondwanan terranes
Chemical Features				
Ordovician	Relatively high Sr contents compared to granites from central Maine and peri-Gondwana.		Silurian	Low Sr contents, moderate to large negative Eu anomalies.
Devonian	Relatively high Sr contents compared to granites from central Maine and peri-Gondwana, no Eu anomaly, relatively high REE contents, lower heavy REE contents than peri-Gondwanan granites, moderate contents of Th and U, and low to moderate Rb/Sr.	Low to intermediate Sr contents, small negative Eu anomalies, REE contents and patterns resemble peri-Gondwanan granites.	Devonian	Low Sr contents, moderate to large negative Eu anomalies, high Th and U contents, generally lower contents of REE than Brompton-Cameron granites, relatively high heavy REE contents, wide range in Rb/Sr.
Granite Setting (e.g., Yb-Ta, Hf-Rb-Ta plots)				
Ordovician	Volcanic-arc granite (lower in Ta and Yb than Devonian granites).		Silurian	Volcanic-arc granite and within-plate granite? (Yb contents generally higher than Brompton-Cameron granites).
Devonian	Volcanic-arc granite and collisional granite.	Volcanic arc granite, within-plate granite, and collisional granite.	Devonian	Volcanic-arc granite and within-plate granite (Yb contents generally higher than Brompton-Cameron granites).
Setting of associated mafic rocks (Th-Hf-Ta plot)				
Ordovician			Silurian	Volcanic-arc basalt and N-MORB.
Devonian	Volcanic-arc basalt and N-MORB.	Mafic enclaves: Volcanic arc, and the combined field for N-MORB and within-plate basalts?	Devonian	Volcanic-arc basalt, and the combined field for N-MORB and within-plate basalt.
Mineralization				
Ordovician	Porphyry Cu-Mo.		Silurian	Porphyry Mo?
Devonian	Porphyry Cu-Mo, Sn, W skarns and greisens	Mo and U in shear zones, porphyry Mo? Sn, W skarns and greisens?	Devonian	Porphyry Cu-Mo?: Sn and W skarns and greisens, U-Mo shear zones.

Note: Morb = mid-ocean ridge basalt; REE = rare earth element.

their relationship to Appalachian tectonic evolution: Canadian Institute of Mining and Metallurgical Bulletin, v. 75, no. 842, p. 83–97.

Ruitenberg, A. A., and Fyffe, L. R., 1992, Syn- and post-accretion granitoid related mineralization, *in* Williams, H., ed., Geology of the Appalachian-Caledonian orogen in Canada and Greenland: Geological Survey of Canada, Geology of Canada no. 6, p. 769–778.

Ruitenberg, A. A., and McCutcheon, S. R., 1993, Syn- and post-collisional mineral deposits in the Canadian Appalachians: Canadian Institute of Mining, Metallurgy and Petroleum, Third Annual Field Conference, Bathurst, N.B: New York, Pergamon Press, p. 7–9.

Scambos, T. A., Loiselle, M. C., and Wones, D. R., 1986, The Center Pond pluton: The restite of the story (phase separation and melt evolution in granitoid genesis): American Journal of Science, v. 286, p. 241–280.

Schmidt, R. G., 1974, Preliminary study of rock alteration in the Catheart Mountain molybdenum-copper deposit, Maine: U.S. Geological Survey Journal of Research, v. 2, p. 189–194.

Schmidt, R. G., 1978, The potential for porphyry copper-molybdenum deposits in the eastern United States: U.S. Geological Survey Bulletin 1401, p. 515–542.

Seal, R. R., Clark, A. H., and Morrissy, C. J., 1985, Lake George, southwestern New Brunswick: A Silurian, multi-stage, polymetallic (Sb-W-Mo-Au-base metal) hydrothermal centre, *in* Taylor, R. P., and Strong, R. P., eds., Recent advances in the geology of granite-related mineral deposits: Canadian Institute of Mining and Metallurgy Special Volume 39, p. 252–264.

Sillitoe, R. H., 1972, A plate tectonic model for the origin of porphyry copper deposits: Economic Geology, v. 67, p. 184–197.

Sillitoe, R. H., 1986, Space-time distribution, crustal setting and Cu/Mo ratios of central Andean porphyry copper deposits: Metallogenic implications, *in* Friedrich, G. H., ed., Geology and metallogeny of copper deposits: New York, Springer Verlag, p. 235–250.

Silver, L. T., and Chappell, B. W., 1988, The Peninsular Ranges batholith: An insight into the evolution of the Cordilleran batholiths of southwestern North America: Royal Society of Edinburgh Transactions, Earth Sciences, v. 70, p. 105–121.

Sinha, A. K., 1988, Plutonism in the U.S. Appalachians: American Journal of Science, v. 288-A, p. ix–xii.

Slack, J. F., ed., 1990, Summary results of the Glens Falls CUSMAP project, New York, Vermont, and New Hampshire: U.S. Geological Survey Bulletin 1887, 371 p.

Slack, J. F., Atelsek, P. J., and Whitlow, J. W., 1990, Geochemistry of stream sediments and heavy-mineral concentrates from the Orange County copper district, east-central Vermont, *in* Slack, J. F., ed., Summary results of the Glens Falls CUSMAP project, New York, Vermont, and New Hampshire: U.S. Geological Survey Bulletin 1887, p. Q1–Q21.

Stewart, D. B., 1989, Crustal processes in Maine: American Mineralogist, v. 74, p. 698–714.

Stewart, D. B., Arth, J. G., and Flohr, M. J. K., 1988, Petrogenesis of the South Penobscot Intrusive Suite, Maine: American Journal of Science, v. 288-A,

p. 74–114.

Stewart, D. B., Wright, B. E., Unger, J. D., Phillips, J. D., and Hutchinson, D. R., 1993, Global geoscience transect 8, Quebec–Maine–Gulf of Maine transect, southeastern Canada, northeastern United States of America: U.S. Geological Survey Miscellaneous Investigations Map I-2329, scale 1:1,000,000.

Stewart, D. B., Tucker, R. D., and West, D. P., 1995a, Genesis of Silurian composite terrane in northern Penobscot Bay, in Hussey, A. M. II, and Johnston, R., eds., Guidebook for field trips in southern Maine and adjacent New Hampshire (New England Intercollegiate Geological Conference, 87th Annual Meeting, Brunswick, Maine): Dubuque, Iowa, Times Mirror Company, p. A3-1–A3-21.

Stewart, D. B., Unger, J. D., and Hutchinson, D. R., 1995b, Silurian tectonic history of Penobscot Bay region, Maine: Atlantic Geology, v. 31, p. 67–79.

Streckeisen, A., 1974, Classification and nomenclature of plutonic rocks: Geologische Rundschau, v. 63, p. 773–785.

Strong, D. F., 1980, Granitoid rocks and associated mineral deposits of eastern Canada and western Europe, in Strangway, D. W., ed., The continental crust and its mineral deposits: Geological Association of Canada Special Paper 22, p. 741–769.

Strong, D. F., 1985, A review and models for granite-related mineral deposits, in Taylor, R. P., and Strong, D. F., eds., Recent advances in the geology of granite-related mineral deposits: Canadian Institute of Mining and Metallurgy Special Volume 39, p. 424–445.

Taylor, S. R., and McLennan, S. M., 1985, The continental crust: Its composition and evolution: Palo Alto, California, Blackwell Scientific Publications, 312 p.

Theodore, T. G., and Menzie, W. D., 1984, Fluorine-deficient porphyry molybdenum deposits in the western North America Cordillera, in Janelidze, T. M., and Tualchrelidze, A. G., eds., Proceedings of the Sixth Quadrennial IAGOD Symposium, p. 463–470.

Tomascak, P. B. 1995, The petrogenesis of granitic rocks in southwestern Maine [Ph.D. thesis]: College Park, University of Maryland, 137 p.

Uyeda, S., 1982, Subduction zones: An introduction to comparative subductology: Tectonophysics, v. 81, p. 133–159.

van Leeuwen, T. M., Taylor, R., Coote, A., and Longstaffe, F. J., 1994, Porphyry molybdenum mineralization in a continental collision setting at Malala, northwest Indonesia: Journal of Geochemical Exploration, v. 50, p. 279–315.

van Staal, C. R., 1994, Brunswick subduction complex in the Canadian Appalachians: Record of the Late Ordovician to Late Silurian collision between Laurentia and the Gander margin of Avalon: Tectonics, v. 13, p. 946–962.

West, D. P., Ludman, A., and Lux, D. R., 1992, Silurian age for the Pocomoonshine gabbro-diorite and its regional tectonic implications: American Journal of Science, v. 292, p. 253–273.

West, D. P., Guidotti, C. V., and Lux, D. R., 1995, Silurian orogenesis in the western Penobscot Bay region, Maine: Canadian Journal of Earth Sciences, v. 32, p. 1845–1858.

Westra, G., and Keith, S. B., 1981, Classification and genesis of stockwork molybdenum deposits: Economic Geology, v. 76, p. 844–873.

Whalen, J. B., 1993, Geology, petrography, and geochemistry of Appalachian granites in New Brunswick and Gaspesie, Quebec: Geological Survey of Canada Bulletin 436, 124 p.

Whalen, J. B., Jenner, G. A., Currie, K. L., Barr, S. M., Longstaffe, F. J., and Hegner, E., 1994a, Geochemical and isotopic characteristics of granitoids of the Avalon zone, southern New Brunswick: Possible evidence for repeated delamination events: Journal of Geology, v. 102, p. 269–282.

Whalen, J. B., Jenner, G. A., and Hegner, E., 1994b, Geochemical and isotopic (Nd, O, and Pb) constraints on granite sources in the Humber and Dunnage

zones, Gaspe, Quebec, and New Brunswick: Implications for tectonics and crustal structure: Canadian Journal of Earth Sciences, v. 33, p. 129–139.

Whalen, J. B., Fyffe, L. R., Longstaffe, F. J., and Jenner, G. A., 1996a, The position and nature of the Gander-Avalon boundary, southern New Brunswick, based on geochemical and isotopic data from granitoid rocks: Canadian Journal of Earth Sciences, v. 33, p. 129–139.

Whalen, J. B., Jenner, G. A., Longstaffe, F. J., and Hegner, E., 1996b, Nature and evolution of the eastern margin of Iapetus: Geochemical and isotopic constraints from Siluro-Devonian granitoid plutons in the New Brunswick Appalachians: Canadian Journal of Earth Sciences, v. 33, p. 140–155.

White, W. H., Bookstrom, A. A., Kamilli, R. J., Ganster, M. W., Smith, R. P., Ranta, D. E., and Steininger, R. C., 1981, Character and origin of Climax-type molybdenum deposits, in Skinner, B. J., ed., Seventy-fifth anniversary volume: Economic Geology, v. 75, p. 270–316.

Wiebe, R. A., 1993, The Pleasant Bay layered gabbro-diorite, coastal Maine: Ponding and crystallization of basaltic injections into a silicic magma chamber: Journal of Petrology, v. 34, p. 461–489.

Wiebe, R. A., and Chapman, M., 1993, Layered-gabbro-diorite intrusions of coastal Maine: Basaltic infusions into floored silicic magma chambers, in Cheney, J. T., and Hepburn, C., eds., Geological Society of America Annual Meeting Guidebook: Amherst, University of Massachusetts, p. A-1–A-29.

Wones, D. R., 1980a. Contributions of crystallography, mineralogy, and petrology to the geology of the Lucerne pluton, Hancock County, Maine: American Mineralogist, v. 65, p. 411–437.

Wones, D. R., 1980b, A comparison between granitic rocks of New England, U.S.A., and the Sierra Nevada batholith, California, in Wones, D. R., ed., The Caledonides in the U.S.A.: Blacksburg, Virginia Polytechnic Institute and State University Memoir 2, p. 123–130.

Wones, D. R., and Ayuso, R. A., 1993, Geologic map of the Lucerne granite, Hancock and Penobscot counties, Maine: U.S. Geological Survey Miscellaneous Investigations Series Map I-2360, scale 1:125,000.

Wones, D. R., and Sinha, A. K., 1988, A brief review of early Ordovician to Devonian plutonism in the North American Caledonides, in Harris, A. L., and Feltes, D. J., eds., The Caledonian-Appalachian orogen: Geological Society of London Special Publication 38, p. 381–388.

Wood, D. A., 1980, The application of a Th-Hf-Ta diagram to problems of tectonomagmatic classification and to establishing the nature of crustal contamination of basaltic lavas of the British Tertiary Volcanic Province: Earth and Planetary Science Letters, v. 50, p. 11–30.

Zartman, R. E., 1988, Three decades of geochronologic studies in the New England Appalachians: Geological Society of America Bulletin, v. 100, p. 1168–1180.

Zartman, R. E., and Hermes, O. D., 1987, Archean inheritance in zircon from late Paleozoic granites from the Avalon zone of south-eastern New England: An African connection: Earth and Planetary Science Letters, v. 82, p. 257–286.

Zen, E-an, 1983, Exotic terranes in the New England Appalachians—Limits, candidates and ages: A speculative essay, in Hatcher, R. D., Jr., Williams, H., and Zietz, I., eds., Contributions to the tectonics and geophysics of mountain chains: Geological Society of America Memoir 158, p. 55–81.

Zen, E-an, 1989, Tectonostratigraphic terranes in the northern Appalachians: Their distribution, origin, and age; evidence for their existence: International Geological Congress, 28th, Field-trip guidebook T359, Washington, D.C., American Geophysical Union, 69 p.

MANUSCRIPT ACCEPTED BY THE SOCIETY JUNE 9, 1998

Geological Society of America
Special Paper 331
1999

Norumbega fault zone:
Part of an orogen-parallel strike-slip system, northern Appalachians

Mary S. Hubbard

Department of Geology, Kansas State University, Manhattan, Kansas 66506-3201

ABSTRACT

The Norumbega fault zone has received much recent attention as a major orogen-parallel, dextral fault of late Paleozoic age in the northern Appalachians. The role of this fault in the development of the Appalachian orogen is best understood as part of a transcurrent system that was active in the northern Appalachians or, more likely, in the entire Appalachian orogen. When major fault zones of the northern Appalachians are examined it becomes clear that there are many subparallel, dextral faults that were active between Silurian and Permian time. In the Gaspé peninsula of Quebec there are several major dextral faults, some that were active in the Devonian, the displacements of which may total 150 km. In Maine and New Brunswick dextral transcurrent faults may have accumulated ~150–500 km of displacement. The Cobequid-Chedabucto fault system in Nova Scotia may have had ~540–640 km of dextral displacement. Details of exact amounts of displacement and the precise timing of movement of each fault are not well known, but there are enough data to suggest that the total of dextral transcurrent fault displacement was significant in the late Paleozoic. Data from the central and southern Appalachians also suggest that transcurrent tectonics were an important component of Appalachian orogenesis. The amounts of displacement and even the fault geometries are similar to those found at active transcurrent plate boundaries such as along the San Andreas system.

INTRODUCTION

Recent geologic and geophysical studies of mountain belts, plate boundaries, and ancient plate boundaries have provided evidence that transcurrent deformational processes are important in many plate tectonic settings (e.g., Woodcock, 1986; Sylvester, 1988; Oldow et al., 1990; Vauchez and Nicolas, 1991). Recent work in the Alps, the Himalaya, and the Appalachians has shown that transcurrent deformation may have played a significant role in the largely compressional process of collisional orogeny (e.g., Hubbard and Mancktelow, 1992; Pêcher et al., 1991; Swanson, 1992). In these three mountain belts the transcurrent fault zones parallel the trend of the orogen and are oblique or perpendicular to the inferred direction of compression during collision. Several mechanisms could be invoked to explain the presence of these orogen-parallel transcurrent zones, including (1) partition-

ing of oblique convergence, or (2) a change through time of relative plate motions. These different mechanisms could operate before, during, or after terrane accretion or continental collision, or the transcurrent deformation could span several of these events. In order to understand the role of the transcurrent deformation in collisional orogenesis it is necessary to evaluate the relation of individual faults to other regional structures in terms of geometry, kinematics, and timing.

Orogen-parallel transcurrent faulting clearly was important in the development of the Appalachian mountain belt. Transcurrent faults exist in the southern, central, and northern segments of the Appalachians (Dennis and Secor, 1987; Snoke and Frost, 1990; Vauchez et al., 1993; Hill, 1991; Valentino et al., 1994; Swanson, 1988). In the northern Appalachians the Norumbega fault zone is a major dextral fault that was active in the mid-late Paleozoic and possibly into the Mesozoic (West and Lux, 1993). Total displace-

Hubbard, M. S., 1999, Norumbega fault zone: Part of an orogen-parallel strike-slip system, northern Appalachians, *in* Ludman, A., and West, D. P., Jr., eds., Norumbega Fault System of the Northern Appalachians: Boulder, Colorado, Geological Society of America Special Paper 331.

ment along this structure is unknown, but minimum estimates are 35–50 km, on the basis of the map pattern of displaced plutons (Wones and Stewart, 1976; Ludman, 1995), and could be as high as 300 km, on the basis of extrapolation of strain measurements (Swanson, 1992). The Norumbega fault zone, however, is not the only mid-late Paleozoic dextral fault in the northern Appalachians, and it is the interaction of all of these structures as a dextral system that makes this style of deformation important to Appalachian orogenesis. Thus the purposes of this paper are to: (1) set the Norumbega fault zone in its northern Appalachian context by summarizing the structural settings of the other major dextral faults of the region; (2) compare the northern Appalachian transcurrent fault system with the southern Appalachian and San Andreas systems; and (3) discuss a plausible tectonic setting for the Norumbega fault zone and related fault zones.

NORUMBEGA-FREDERICTON FAULT ZONE

The Norumbega-Fredericton fault zone includes the Norumbega fault zone, originally identified in the state of Maine, and its northeast continuation, the Fredericton fault zone, in New Brunswick (Fig. 1). The southwest continuation of the Norumbega fault zone is a topic of debate, but may include fault zones in New Hampshire and possibly zones farther south in New England (see Goldstein and Hepburn, this volume; Bothner and Hussey, this volume). A major structural discontinuity, now known as the Norumbega fault zone, has long been recognized (Larrabee, 1964; Stoeser, 1966; Hussey, 1968), but until recently there has been some controversy regarding the sense of movement. Ubiquitous dextral kinematic indicators and a subhorizontal stretching lineation demonstrate conclusively that the Norumbega fault zone represents a locus of dominant dextral shear and/or fault movement. On the basis of differences in metamorphic grade and deformation textures, rocks exposed along the length of the Norumbega fault zone are interpreted to represent mid-crustal levels in the southwestern segment and shallow crustal levels in the northeastern segment (Hubbard et al., 1995).

At the southwestern end of the Norumbega fault zone in Maine (Fig. 1), in the Casco Bay area and in central Maine, the shear zone exhibits ductile, generally postmetamorphic, shear fabric across a wide (20–30 km) zone (Swanson, 1992; Hubbard et al., 1991; West, 1993; West and Hubbard, 1997). Within this zone metamorphic lithologies include pelite, calc-silicate rock, amphibolite, and biotite-gneiss. The regional metamorphic grade is amphibolite facies, indicating that the rocks occupied a mid-crustal position at the time of metamorphism. Granitic pods of meter to kilometer scale, are also present within the southwestern part of the Norumbega fault zone, and some have been highly deformed. Some granitic pods are pretectonic to syntectonic, and have undergone little deformation. Strain in this segment is broadly and variably partitioned across the 30 km width of the Norumbega fault zone, with narrow (1–2 km wide) zones of extremely high strain (West, 1993).

In the northeastern part of the Norumbega fault zone, from

central Maine to the New Brunswick border (Fig. 2), the shear zone first narrows to ~5 km at the northern edge of the Lucerne pluton, and then broadens to a span of 40 km within which discrete high strain zones are separated by broad areas of weak strain. In contrast to the southwest segment, deformation in this region is largely brittle, the high-strain zones being characterized by fine- to medium-grained cataclasite (Hubbard et al., 1995; Ludman, 1995; Ludman and Gibbon, this volume). Rock types within the shear zone include granitic rock of the Lucerne and Deblois plutons and the Bottle Lake complex, and lower greenschist facies metapelite and metagraywacke.

Because most lithologic contacts of stratified rocks within and adjacent to the Norumbega fault zone are parallel to the nearly vertical planar shear fabric, their displacement along the fault cannot be determined. Correlation of offset intrusive rocks led Wones and Stewart (1976) to suggest a minimum of ~25 km of displacement across the Norumbega fault zone in central Maine. Ludman (1998) has suggested 50–60 km of displacement across the Norumbega fault zone in eastern Maine, on the basis of offset intrusive rocks. Swanson (1992) calculated shear strain values of $\gamma = 2.5$, 4.7, and 10 on segments of the southwestern Norumbega fault zone using rotated quartz veins. These strain measurements translate to displacement values of 75, 141, and 300 km when extrapolated across the mapped 30 km width of the shear zone.

Timing of dextral deformation along the Norumbega fault zone is partly constrained by the ages of the intrusive rocks that are cut by the fault. The northern edge of the Lucerne granite (380 Ma, Zartman and Gallego, 1979) is clearly involved in the Norumbega fault zone deformation, thus constraining at least some of the deformation in central Maine to be post-380 Ma. Other granitic rocks that are cut by the fault zone include the Deblois pluton (393 ± 17 Ma, Loiselle et al., 1983; 383 ± 14 Ma, Ludman et al., this volume), the Wabassus Mountain granite ($^{40}Ar/^{39}Ar$ biotite cooling age, 380.3 ± 3.3, Ludman et al., this volume), and the Bottle Lake complex (380 ± 5 Ma, Ayuso et al., 1984). Along the southwestern portion of the Norumbega fault zone West and Lux (1993) directly dated fine-grained muscovite, interpreted to have formed during mylonitization in a high-strain strand of the fault zone. They interpreted low-temperature increments on a $^{40}Ar/^{39}Ar$ release spectra of ca. 293 Ma to represent the timing of recrystallization during dextral deformation. Deformation could have been continuous from ca. 380 Ma, or earlier, until ca. 293 Ma, or deformation may have been episodic, shearing at ca. 293 Ma being the last episode.

The Fredericton fault is the continuation of the Norumbega fault zone in New Brunswick. This structure has also been recognized as a dextral strike-slip fault zone (Ruitenberg and McCutcheon, 1982; McLeod et al., 1994). Although geophysical work has identified the continuity of the Fredericton fault (Haworth, 1975), limited exposure has hampered detailed structural or geochronologic study that might shed light on the amount of displacement and timing of deformation.

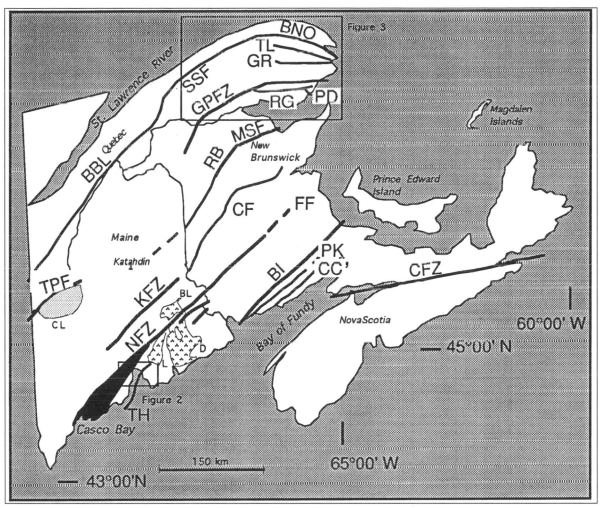

Figure 1. Generalized map of transcurrent faults of the Maine and maritime segments of the northern Appalachians. Faults shown on this map have been described as dextral faults in the literature, although for some faults movement sense has been controversial or multiphase. BBL—Baie Verte–Brompton line; SSF—Shickshock Sud fault; BNO—Bassin Nord-Ouest fault; TL—Troisième Lac fault; GR—Grand Rivière fault; GPFZ—Grand Pabos Fault zone; RG—Rivière Garin fault; PD—Port Daniel fault; TPF—Thrasher Peaks fault; RB MSF—Rocky Brook Millstream fault; KFZ—Kingman fault zone; CF—Catamaran fault; NFZ—Norumbega fault zone; FF—Fredericton fault; TH—Turtlehead–Penobscot Bay fault; BI—Belleisle fault; PK—Pocologan-Kennebecasis fault, CC—Clover Hill–Caledonia fault; CFZ—Cobequid-Chedabucto fault; CL—Chain Lakes massif–Boil Mountain complex; L—Lucerne pluton; D—Deblois pluton; BL—Bottle Lake plutonic complex.

OTHER DEXTRAL FAULTS IN MAINE

Although the structural geology of the state of Maine has traditionally been interpreted to be the product of dominantly compressive tectonics, evidence supports a transpressive or transcurrent interpretation for the shear sense of several fault zones in addition to the Norumbega (Swanson, 1988; Marvinney, 1989; Stewart et al., 1995). These transcurrent faults or shear zones strike in a northeasterly direction, subparallel to the Norumbega fault zone and the axes of the pervasive upright folds across the state (Fig. 1). Much of this evidence for strike-slip movement is new and hence few data are available to constrain the amounts of displacement and/or the timing of fault movement.

Turtlehead–Penobscot Bay fault zones

Stewart (1974) and Stewart et al. (1995) described several dextral fault zones of probable Silurian age in the Penobscot Bay region of central Maine (Fig. 2). These include the Turtlehead and Penobscot Bay fault zones as well as several other shorter fault segments. Age constraints are provided by intrusive relations with Silurian granites. These faults shuffle small lithotectonic blocks or terranes of volcanic and metasedimentary rocks. Displacement estimates of ~15–16 km for individual fault strands are based on offsets of metamorphic isograds. Stewart et al. (1995) interpreted the dextral deformation to have occurred during terrane amalgamation.

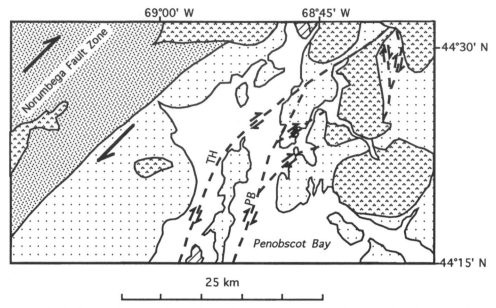

Figure 2. Fault map of the Penobscot Bay region, central coastal Maine. The Turtlehead–Penobscot Bay fault zones are interpreted as preplutonic dextral faults. Random dot pattern is the broad, ductile Norumbega fault zone; square-dot pattern includes the coastal lithotectonic terranes of Maine. Triangle pattern indicates plutonic rocks. TH—Turtlehead fault zone; PB—Penobscot Bay fault zone. After Stewart et al. (1995).

Kingman fault

The Kingman fault in central Maine is a 60-km-long, northeast-striking structure (Fig. 1). The fault marks a discontinuity in gravity measurements and is the site of minor active seismicity (Kafka and Ebel, 1989). There is also a suggested change in crustal thickness along the Kingman fault (Philips et al., 1985). Structural fabrics suggest dextral movement, and similar Silurian lithologies astride the fault suggest only minor post-Silurian displacement (Lincoln and Lincoln, 1991; Ludman 1986).

Thrasher Peaks fault

The Thrasher Peaks fault is one of the faults that form the northern boundary of the Chain Lakes massif (Fig. 1), a Middle Proterozoic complex that is overlain by rocks interpreted as lower Paleozoic ophiolites in northwestern Maine (Boudette, 1982). The steeply dipping, northeast-striking Thrasher Peaks fault is ~200 km long. Although both thrust and normal fault interpretations have been presented for this structure (e.g., Albee and Boudette, 1972; Westerman, 1979; Boone et al., 1970), Marvinney (1989) presented shear fabric evidence for a major component of dextral strike-slip displacement. Adjacent to the Chain Lakes massif, the fault juxtaposes Devonian and Silurian rocks on its northwest side with pre-Silurian rocks to the southeast. Farther northeast, Silurian and Devonian rocks are found on both sides of the fault. On the basis of offset fragments of the Ordovician Attean pluton, Marvinney estimated a displacement of 10–15 km along the fault. Timing of fault

movement is partially constrained to be younger than the 371 ± 1 Ma Spider Lake pluton, which is cut by the fault (Lux, 1983; Marvinney, 1989).

DEXTRAL FAULTS OF THE GASPE REGION

Much recent work in the Gaspé region of Quebec has led to the recognition of several faults along which there has been dextral movement (Fig. 3) (Malo and Béland, 1989). The new interpretations of dextral strike-slip deformation have been neatly meshed with the traditional interpretations and data on compressional deformation to construct a model of transpressional deformation for the Gaspé region, primarily during the Devonian, but possibly earlier as well. Faults with a history of dextral movement include the Shickshock Sud, the Bassin Nord-Ouest, the Troisième Lac, the Grand Rivière, the Grand Pabos, the Rivière Garin, and the Port Daniel faults.

Shickshock Sud fault

The Shickshock Sud fault, in the northern part of the Gaspé peninsula (Fig. 3), has a complex and protracted deformational history, and differing amounts of dextral displacement have been proposed. The northeast-striking Shickshock Sud fault approximately represents the location of the Taconian suture zone, the Baie Verte–Brompton line. Malo et al. (1992) interpreted vertical stretching lineations in Cambrian rocks to represent pre-Silurian thrust deformation and brittle fabrics in Devonian and older rocks to represent post-Middle Devonian dextral strike-slip movement.

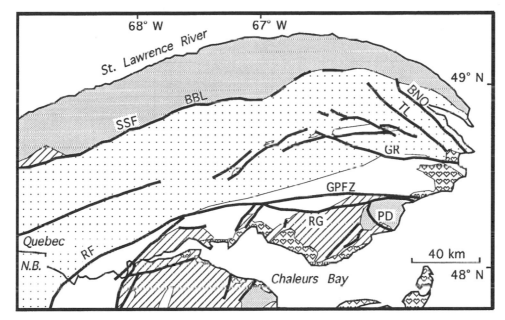

Figure 3. Major faults of the Gaspé Peninsula region, Quebec. (N.B. is New Brunswick.) Dextral faults discussed in the text are labeled. BBL—Baie Verte–Brompton line; SSF—Shickshock Sud fault; BNO—Bassin Nord-Ouest fault; TL—Troisième Lac fault; GR—Grand Rivière fault; GPFZ—Grand Pabos fault zone; RG—Rivière Garin fault; PD—Port Daniel fault; RF—Restigouche fault. After Malo and Béland (1989).

The width of the Shickshock Sud fault is no more than several tens of meters. This limited width together with the kinematic interpretation of the brittle structures support Malo et al.'s (1992) suggestion of minor strike-slip displacement on this fault. Along the Baie Verte–Brompton line from the Eastern Townships of Quebec to eastern Gaspé, however, there are several exposures of ophiolitic melange or serpentinite melange that have been correlated with one another (DeBroucker, 1987). Although this correlation does not necessitate prior juxtaposition, if there had been early dismemberment and dispersal of one ophiolitic body, the Baie Verte–Brompton line could have been the site of as much as 500 km of pre-Silurian strike-slip displacement. Sacks and Malo (1994) confirmed evidence for pre-Silurian, ductile, dextral transpressive deformation along this structure that was followed by Devonian brittle dextral transpression. Although the exact amount of displacement has not been determined for either event, M. Malo (1996, personal commun.) indicates that total dextral displacement was minor. Tremblay and Pinet (1994) suggested that much of the motion on the southwest end of the Baie Verte–Brompton line was northwest-directed, thrust-sense displacement. Due to the change in strike direction of this structure at its southwest end, a northwest-directed thrust displacement is consistent with the overall dextral transpression. Trzcienski et al. (1992) suggested a possible correlation of ophiolitic rocks of the Boil Mountain complex in the Chain Lakes area (Fig. 1) with a string of ophiolitic lithologies along the Baie Verte–Brompton line in Quebec. According to Trzcienski et al. (1992), removal of ~500 km of dextral deformation would restore the Boil Mountain complex to a position at the northeast end of the string of ophiolitic rocks in Quebec.

Bassin Nord-Ouest–Troisième Lac faults

The Bassin Nord-Ouest and Troisième Lac faults are northwest-striking structures in eastern Quebec (Fig. 3). The Bassin Nord-Ouest fault coincides with the eastern section of the Baie Verte–Brompton line and has a history of dextral movement that may have initiated during the Taconic orogeny with continued activity during sedimentation in the Gaspé belt until middle Devonian time (Béland, 1980). Offset of Lower Devonian units is less than 10 km, thus putting a limit on the post-Early Devonian displacement (Malo et al., 1992). Northwest-striking dextral faults at the eastern end of the exposed fault systems in Quebec may indicate a change in strike of the overall system or they may indicate localized, releasing-bend fault segments.

The Troisième Lac fault is located south of the Bassin Nord-Ouest fault (Fig. 3). This northwest-striking fault is entirely within Devonian rocks along much of its extent; however, the southeastern segment juxtaposes Cambrian rocks on the southwest side with Ordovician through Middle Devonian rocks on the northeast side. Fault movement is interpreted as Middle to Late Devonian. Analysis of brittle features suggests dextral movement with a displacement estimate of only a few kilometers (Kirkwood, 1989).

Grand Rivière fault

The east-west–striking Grand Rivière fault is roughly 55 km long and is located in eastern Gaspé (Fig. 3) (Malo and Béland, 1989). The Grand Rivière fault is cut by the Troisième Lac fault, so the timing of displacement is suggested to be Middle Devonian (Malo et al., 1992). The rock fabrics of this fault have been described as brittle-ductile, with dextral kinematic indicators. The intense cleavage development is attributed to high-strain deformation (Kirkwood and Malo, 1993). An offset stratigraphic contact dictates an estimate of dextral displacement of 22 km (Malo and Béland, 1989).

Grand Pabos fault

The Grand Pabos fault is a continuation of the Restigouche fault that originates in New Brunswick (Fig. 3). The entire length of the Restigouche–Grand Pabos fault system is ~225 km. Dextral shear fabrics are found across a 9-km-wide fault zone that includes the 1-km-wide Grand Pabos fault and a number of subparallel subsidiary faults. The amount of dextral displacement is 85 km and the timing is Middle Devonian (Malo and Béland, 1989).

Rivière Garin fault

Another east-west–striking dextral fault of Gaspé is the Rivière Garin fault (Fig. 3). This structure is ~88 km long and is located just south of the Grand Pabos fault. An offset lithologic contact is evidence for 10 km of dextral displacement. Shear fabrics along the fault are the product of brittle deformation (Malo and Béland, 1989). Timing of displacement, like that for the Grand Pabos fault and the Grande Rivière fault, is Middle Devonian (Malo et al., 1992).

Port Daniel fault

The Port Daniel fault is a northwest-striking fault that is cut by, and therefore predates, the Riviére Garin fault (Fig. 3). Malo et al. (1992) suggested that the Port Daniel fault may be a segment of the Baie Verte–Brompton line. Brittle and ductile shear fabrics that indicate dextral strike-slip movement are present in Late Cambrian rocks along the fault zone (DeBroucker, 1987). These strike-slip fabrics are not present in younger rocks, although normal and reverse fabrics are, thus suggesting a change in the kinematic history through time (Malo et al., 1992).

DEXTRAL FAULTS OF NEW BRUNSWICK

Dextral faults and shear zones with a northeasterly or easterly strike have been identified in several locations in New Brunswick. In some cases these steeply dipping fault zones separate different lithostratigraphic blocks and in other cases the fault zones are intraformational. Several of these faults are continuous with dextral faults in eastern Maine.

Restigouche fault

The Restigouche fault is the southwestern continuation of the Grand Pabos fault in Quebec. This fault has been most recently studied along its exposures in Quebec as discussed herein.

Rocky Brook–Millstream fault

The Rocky Brook–Millstream fault is located in northwestern New Brunswick (Fig. 1). The strike of the fault zone changes from north-northeasterly in the western segment to more east-north-easterly in the east. The fault zone separates Ordovician-Devonian ophiolitic and clastic rocks of the Miramichi Highlands region from rocks of the same age and type of the Chaleurs Uplands region. This fault boundary has been interpreted by some workers as a terrane boundary between the Dunnage and Gander terranes (Williams, 1978; Fyffe and Fricker, 1987), but more recent work favors an interpretation for the Rocky Brook–Millstream fault as a dextral fault primarily within Dunnage zone rocks (van Staal et al., 1990). Dextral kinematic indicators formed during ductile shear with possibly a brittle overprint, also during dextral movement (van Staal and Fyffe, 1991). Intrusive relationships constrain some of the fault movement to be pre–381 ± 4 Ma. There was probably also a component of Carboniferous strike-slip deformation, as suggested by localized syntectonic Carboniferous sedimentation (van Staal and Fyffe, 1991). Offset contacts suggest possible displacement along the fault of 40–80 km. This fault zone may continue in Maine as far west as the intrusive rocks of the Mount Katahdin area (Osberg et al., 1985).

Catamaran fault

The Catamaran fault, located in the southern section of the Miramichi Highlands, is nearly 250 km in length (Fig. 1). This northeast-striking fault has been recognized as a dextral strike-slip fault for more than 20 years (Anderson, 1972). Field studies and an offset anomaly on an aeromagnetic survey indicate a possible displacement of 16 km (Anderson, 1972). Timing is constrained to be Late Devonian in that the fault cuts a Middle Devonian granite (Skinner, 1970) and is overlain by undeformed Carboniferous sedimentary rocks (Anderson, 1970). The Catamaran fault is possibly the continuation of a bounding fault of the Miramichi terrane in Maine (A. Ludman, personal commun.).

Fredericton fault

The Fredericton fault in New Brunswick is the continuation of the Norumbega fault zone in Maine. The Fredericton fault has received relatively little research attention compared to the Norumbega, perhaps due to limited exposure. There is a suggestion from the Provincial geologic map (McLeod et al., 1994) that the Fredericton fault cuts Pennsylvanian rocks, thus putting some limit on the timing of fault movement. Pennsylvanian or younger displacement could be as much as 40 km, on the basis of offset of sedimentary units of that age.

Belleisle fault

The Belleisle fault in southern New Brunswick (Fig. 1) had early ductile movement with later brittle movement (Williams et al., 1995). The trace of this steeply dipping, northeast-striking structure is continuous across southern New Brunswick; exposures are also on Prince Edward Island and possibly on the Magdalen Islands. Dextral motion on the fault has long been recognized (Webb, 1969), although Belt (1968) interpreted the Belleisle fault as an extensional structure because of differences in sediment thickness across the fault. Webb (1969) estimated 45–65 km of brittle, dextral displacement on the basis of offset of Upper Devonian to Lower Carboniferous rocks. Earlier ductile displacement is undetermined.

Pocologan-Kennebecasis fault zone

The Pocologan-Kennebecasis fault zone is parallel to, and just southeast of, the Belleisle fault (Fig. 1). There have been many different interpretations of the movement sense of this zone (e.g., Rast and Dickson, 1982; Leger and Williams, 1986). Park et al. (1994) attributed the complex shear fabric geometry to reactivation of a ductile dextral zone by brittle extensional deformation. On the basis of cooling ages reported by White et al. (1990), Dallmeyer and Nance (1992), and Nance and Dallmeyer (1993), Park et al. (1994) suggested that the timing of ductile deformation was Late Silurian to Early Devonian. The amount of displacement is unknown. The width of the mylonite zone is several kilometers, which suggests measurable, although probably not appreciable, offset.

Clover Hill–Caledonia fault

The Clover Hill–Caledonia fault is another northeast-striking fault of southern New Brunswick (Fig. 1). Dextral displacement has been inferred for this structure (Webb, 1969; Nance, 1987), but because much of the fault trace is concealed there is no strong evidence for the kinematics, timing, and amount of displacement for this fault zone. The fault juxtaposes the Precambrian Caledonian Highlands on the southeast side against Carboniferous rocks on the northwest side, thus supporting Carboniferous or younger deformation.

COBEQUID-CHEDABUCTO FAULT SYSTEM OF NOVA SCOTIA

The Cobequid-Chedabucto fault system (Fig. 1) constitutes the dominant structural discontinuity in Nova Scotia and it is generally interpreted to be a strike-slip zone (Mawer and White, 1987). Evidence has been reported for other zones of strike-slip deformation in Nova Scotia, such as in the Cape Breton Highlands (Dallmeyer and Keppie, 1993), but we focus here on the Cobequid-Chedabucto system, which separates rocks of the Avalon terrane to the north from rocks of the Meguma terrane to the south. The trace of this fault system is more than 300 km long. Mawer and White (1987) examined ductile fabrics on the eastern end of the fault zone and younger, brittle fabrics on the western end of the fault. They interpreted these fabrics to represent dextral strike-slip shear. Keppie (1982) suggested that the Cobequid-Chedabucto zone was reactivated with sinistral movement during the Triassic rifting of the Bay of Fundy, but field evidence for sinistral displacement has not been documented.

The amount of displacement and the timing of dextral displacement is not well constrained for the Cobequid-Chedabucto fault system. Keppie (1982) suggested that there was 370–475 km of dextral deformation during the Early Devonian, and an additional 165 km of dextral movement between the Late Carboniferous and the Late Triassic. In general, there is agreement that the fault has been the site of major dextral movement (Mawer and White, 1987; Keppie, 1982).

OTHER TRANSCURRENT ZONES OF THE APPALACHIANS

Maine and the eastern Canadian mainland provinces were not the only locations to host orogen-parallel, strike-slip deformation during the development of the Appalachian orogen. Newfoundland geology includes many orogen-parallel tectonic boundaries, several of which are interpreted as strike-slip zones (Williams et al., 1995). Recent work in the central and southern Appalachians has revealed the presence of many major dextral zones in these regions (Fig. 4) (Hill, 1991; Valentino et al., 1994; Bobyarchick, 1988; Vauchez et al., 1993). For example, Valentino et al. presented evidence for a minimum of 150 km of late Paleozoic, dextral displacement along the Pleasant Grove–Huntingdon Valley shear system of the central Appalachians. Vauchez et al. (1993) described dextral displacements along the Western Piedmont detachment zone (Brevard zone) and the Ocmulgee fault of the southern Appalachians. The timing of these two southern Appalachian transcurrent faults is constrained by $^{40}Ar/^{39}Ar$ mylonitization ages to be ca. 350 Ma. Other workers have presented evidence for dextral systems in the central and southern Appalachians (Snoke and Frost, 1990; Tull, 1995; Gates, 1987; Hill, 1991). Generally these faults are explained either by transpression during the collision of the North American craton and Africa during the late Paleozoic or postcollisional strike-slip reactivation of compressional structures.

DISCUSSION

When estimates for displacement along the Norumbega fault zone are added to estimates for displacement along the other transcurrent zones of the northern Appalachians, a sum of ~868–1793 km of total dextral displacement is possible for the mid late Paleozoic across an ~300-km-wide zone (Table 1). These displacement values are estimates. It is also important that the faults discussed herein may not represent all of the sites of transcurrent deformation in the northern Appalachians. Nevertheless, the sum of estimates yields displacement values high enough that the transcurrent component of deformation must be considered in any tectonic analysis of the Appalachian mountains. There are several possibilities for how the transcurrent

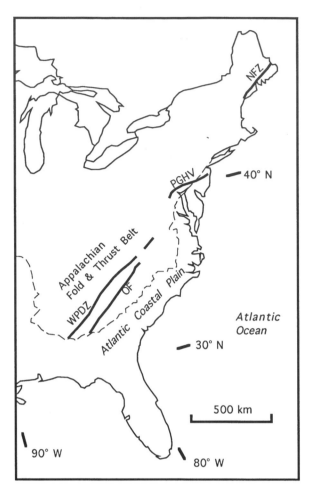

Figure 4. Map of the eastern United States showing the locations of a few transcurrent faults of the central and southern Appalachians. The Western Piedmont decollement zone (WPDZ) and the Ocmulgee fault (OF) were described by Vauchez et al. (1993) as major dextral, orogen-parallel faults. Valentino et al. (1994) interpreted the Pleasant Grove–Huntingdon Valley fault (PGHV) as a dextral fault. NFZ— Norumbega fault zone.

system for the past 30 m.y. (Atwater, 1970). Estimates for the average slip rate between the Pacific plate and the North American plate vary from about 4.8 to 6.0 cm/yr (DeMets et al., 1987; Atwater, 1970). If these rates are averaged over the past 30 m.y. one would calculate displacement amounts of 1440–1800 km for the San Andreas system. Geologic estimates of displacement based on offset units along the San Andreas fault and adjacent faults are ~315–560 km (Irwin, 1990; Hill and Dibblee, 1953). Atwater (1970) proposed that the discrepancy between the geologic estimate and the slip-rate estimate of displacement might be attributed to deformation across a zone broader than the San Andreas fault. Geodetic studies have provided direct evidence for a broad zone of deformation (~300 km) between offshore California and the western Basin and Range (Minster and Jordan, 1987; Argus and Gordan, 1991; Feigl et al., 1993). Historically active, dextral, strike-slip faults that are subparallel to the plate boundary have now been mapped across this zone (Jennings, 1992). These faults are the likely locus of the deformation that accommodates the broad transform plate boundary zone between the Pacific and North American plates.

Many similarities in fault geometry and fault movement exist between the ancient northern Appalachian system and the active San Andreas system. The most obvious similarity is that both systems compose an ~300-km-wide zone of dextral faults or fault zones. Some of the northern Appalachian faults such as the Norumbega fault zone, faults of the Baie Verte–Brompton and

TABLE 1. ESTIMATES OF DEXTRAL DISPLACEMENT AND TIMING

Fault*	Displacement		Timing
	Minimum (km)	Maximum (km)	
NFZ	25	300	Devonian-Permian
TH	15	15	Silurian-Devonian
TPF	10	15	Devonian or younger
SSF	20	500	Silurian-Devonian
BNO	10	10	Devonian
TL	5	5	Devonian
GR	22	22	Devonian
GPFZ	85	85	Devonian
RG	10	10	Devonian
RB-MSF	40	80	Devonian-Carboniferous
CF	16	16	Devonian
BI	45	65	Devonian-Carboniferous
PK	15?[†]	15?	Silurian-Devonian
CC	15?[†]	15?	Carboniferous or younger
CFZ	535	640	Devonian-Triassic
Total	868	1793	Silurian-Triassic

*NFZ = Norumbega; TH = Turtlehead–Penobscot Bay; TPF = Thrasher Peaks; SSF = Shickshock Sud; BNO = Bassin Nord-Ouest; TL = Troisième Lac; GR = Grand Rivière; GPFZ = Grand Pabos; RG = Rivière Garin; RB-MSF = Rocky Brook-Millstream; CF = Catamaran; BI = Belleisle; PK = Pocologan-Kennebecasis; CC = Clover Hill–Caledonia; CFZ = Cobequid-Chedabucto.
[†]No estimates provided in the literature.

movement could have been partitioned through the collisional history. For some zones it has been suggested that strike-slip movement occurred between terranes before they were accreted to North America (Stewart et al., 1995). For other zones authors have discussed the possibility that strike-slip movement occurred during terrane accretion or that collisional terrane boundaries were later reactivated as strike-slip zones (Mawer and White, 1987). Because geologic evidence supports the idea that the Appalachians were an active plate boundary with a component of strike-slip deformation during the middle to late Paleozoic, it is useful to look at modern analogs to see if similar fault geometries can be found at plate boundaries today. Comparisons have been made between the northern Appalachians and the San Andreas fault system (Wilson, 1962; Bobyarchick, 1988; Nance, 1987), which is perhaps the best-studied example of an active transcurrent plate boundary.

The San Andreas fault system has been active as a dextral

Grand Pabos systems, as well as several others, exhibit evidence for recurring intervals of deformation. This recurrence of deformation on single faults is also observed on faults of the active San Andreas system. Another similarity in the two systems is the localization of deformation on individual faults across a broad zone. For the San Andreas system in historic time (tens to hundreds of years) faults are active all across this broad zone. For the northern Appalachian system we are unable to resolve fault activity at the same time scale, but much evidence indicates that many of the northern Appalachian dextral faults were active in the Devonian.

Many of the differences between the transcurrent deformation in the Appalachians and the San Andreas system are due to the comparison between ancient and active systems. The exact timing and the absolute amounts of displacement for dextral faults are less well constrained for the Appalachians than for the broad zone surrounding the San Andreas system. Also, the lengths of time of active deformation are different. In the northern Appalachians, there is evidence for some episodes of strike-slip deformation as early as pre-Silurian time and as late as the Carboniferous. This time interval of ~160 m.y. is certainly much longer than the ~30 m.y. life span of the San Andreas system. It is unknown at what time period(s) the largest amounts of displacement occurred in the northern Appalachians and if they occurred at the same time for all faults. It is also unknown how much longer the San Andreas system will remain active as a transform plate boundary. For these reasons it is difficult to compare the temporal aspects of deformation between the San Andreas system and the northern Appalachians. Because the Appalachians are highly eroded, the crustal levels now exposed were deeper in the crust during the time of deformation. This difference may favor wider zones with more distributed or penetrative ductile deformation on some of the Appalachian fault zones. These differences in crustal level, however, allow the application of ancient fault systems as an aid in understanding the behavior of active systems at the inaccessible mid-crustal levels (Hubbard et al., 1995).

This chapter focused on individual transcurrent faults of the northern Appalachian mountains and their role as a once-active dextral system. Because the northern Appalachians are continuous with the central and southern Appalachians, however, and because transcurrent faulting has been important in those areas as well, a discussion of the northern Appalachians as a transcurrent or transpressional plate boundary should be extended to the entire Appalachian mountain belt. It is clear that by looking at the dextral faults of the Appalachians as a possible dextral system we may be able to better understand the role of these faults as part of a former plate boundary. The ~300 km width of this former dextral zone in the northern Appalachians is comparable to the active transcurrent Pacific–North America plate boundary. The displacement estimates of 868–1793 km for the northern Appalachians are the same order of magnitude as the estimates for the zone surrounding the San Andreas system, and the San Andreas system is likely to continue to be active for some future period of time, thus increasing its total displacement. Estimates for displacement along Appalachian transcurrent faults are, therefore, tectonically realistic and comparison with the Pacific–North American plate boundary supports an interpretation of transcurrent deformation during the mid-late Paleozoic when eastern North America was an active plate boundary. An improved understanding of the absolute timing of transcurrent tectonics and the interaction with collisional processes will be critical for a complete comprehension of Appalachian orogenesis.

CONCLUSION

In summary, the Norumbega fault zone is one of many dextral faults active during the late Paleozoic in the northern Appalachians. Taken together these faults may have operated as a broad dextral plate boundary system. This system may have been active during terrane accretion or it may have operated on previously accreted terranes. Dextral transcurrent faulting was also active in the central and southern Appalachians during the late Paleozoic, thus suggesting that transcurrent deformation truly played a critical role in the Appalachian mountain-building process. There is a need for future work to better constrain the timing of movement and the displacement on individual fault zones in order to better understand how transcurrent movements relate to the compressional and extensional processes in this classic collisional orogen.

ACKNOWLEDGMENTS

I thank Dan Lux, Charles Guidotti, Art Hussey, Allan Ludman, Phil Osberg, Dave West, Dave Stewart, Bob Marvinney, Jan Tullis, Mark Swanson, Joe White, Michel Malo, Carol Simpson, Donna Kirkwood, Mike Brown, Gary Solar, Paul Tomascak, and many others for discussions about the Norumbega fault zone and other transcurrent faults of the northern Appalachians. Constructive review comments by Mary Lou Hill, Michel Malo, and Allan Ludman greatly improved the manuscript. My work on the Norumbega fault zone was supported by National Science Foundation grant EAR-9218833.

REFERENCES CITED

Albee, A. L., and Boudette, E. L., 1972, Geology of the Attean quadrangle, Somerset County, Maine: U.S. Geological Survey Bulletin 1297, 110 p.

Anderson, F. D., 1970, Geology of McKendrick Lake map-area, New Brunswick: Geological Survey of Canada Paper 69–12, 16 p.

Anderson, F. D., 1972, The Catamaran fault, north-central New Brunswick: Canadian Journal of Earth Sciences, v. 9, p. 1278–1286.

Argus, D. F., and Gordon, R. G., 1991, Current Sierra Nevada–North America motion from very long baseline interferometry: Implications for the kinematics of the western United States: Geology, v. 19, p. 1085–1088.

Atwater, T., 1970, Implications of plate tectonics for the Cenozoic tectonic evolution of western North America: Geological Society of America Bulletin, v. 81, p. 3513–3535.

Ayuso, R. A., Arth, J. G., Sinha, A. K., Carlson, J., and Wones, D. R., 1984, Comparative geochronology in the reversely zoned plutons of the Bottle Lake complex, Maine: U-Pb on zircons and Rb-Sr on whole rocks: Contributions to Mineralogy and Petrology, v. 88, p. 113–125.

Béland, J., 1980, Faille du Bassin Nord-Ouest et faille du Troisieme Lac dans la partie est de la Gaspesie: Ministere de l'Energie et des Ressources du Québec Rapport Intérimaire, DP-740, 20 p.

Belt, E. S., 1968, Post-Acadian rifts and related facies, eastern Canada, in Zen, E., and Billings, M. P., eds., Studies of Appalachian geology, northern and Maritime: New York, Interscience Publishers, p. 95–113.

Bobyarchick, A. R., 1988, Location and geometry of Alleghanian dispersal-related strike-slip faults in the southern Appalachians: Geology, v. 16, p. 915–919.

Boone, G. M., Boudette, E. L., and Moench, R. H., 1970, Bedrock geology of the Rangeley Lakes –Dead River Basin region, western Maine, in Boone, G. M., ed., Guidebook for field trips in the Rangeley Lakes–Dead River Basin region: New England Intercollegiate Geological Conference: Syracuse, New York, Syracuse University, p. 1–24.

Boudette, E. L., 1982, Ophiolite assemblage of early Paleozoic age in central western Maine, in St-Julien, P., and Beland, J., eds., Major structural zones and faults of the northern Appalachians: Geological Association of Canada Special Paper 24, p. 209–230.

Dallmeyer, R. D., and Keppie, J. D., 1993, ^{40}Ar/^{39}Ar mineral ages from the southern Cape Breton Highlands and Crenish Hills, Cape Breton Island, Canada: Evidence for a polyphase tectonothermal evolution: Journal of Geology, v. 101, p. 467–482.

Dallmeyer, R. D., and Nance, R. D., 1992, Tectonic implications of ^{40}Ar/^{39}Ar mineral ages from late Precambrian–Cambrian plutons, Avalon composite terrane, southern New Brunswick, Canada: Canadian Journal of Earth Sciences, v. 29, p. 2445–2462.

DeBroucker, G., 1987, Stratigraphie, pétrographie et structure de la boutonniere de Maquereau-Mictaw (Région de Port Daniel, Gaspésie): Ministere de l'Energie et des Ressources du Québec Mémoire MM 86-03, 160 p.

DeMets, C., Gordon, R. G., Stein, S., and Argus, D. F., 1987, A revised estimate of Pacific–North American motion and implications for western North American plate boundary zone tectonics: Geophysical Research Letters, v. 14, p. 911–914.

Dennis, A. J., and Secor, D. T., 1987, A model for the development of crenulations in shear zones with applications from the southern Appalachian Piedmont: Journal of Structural Geology, v. 9, p. 809–817.

Feigl, K. L., Agnew, D. C., Bock, Y., Dong, D., Donnellan, A., Hager, B. H., Herring, T. A., Jackson, D. D., Jordan, T. H., King, R. W., Larsen, S., Larsen, K. M., Murray, M. H., Shen, Z., and Webb, F. A., 1993, Space geodetic measurement of crustal deformation in central and southern California, 1984–1992: Journal of Geophysical Research, v. 98, no. B12, p. 21,677–21,712.

Fyffe, L. R., and Fricker, A., 1987, Tectonostratigraphic terrane analysis of New Brunswick: Maritime Sediments and Atlantic Geology, v. 23, p. 113–123.

Gates, A. E., 1987, Transpressional dome formation in the southwest Virginia Piedmont: American Journal of Science, v. 287, p. 927–949.

Haworth, R. T., 1975, Paleozoic continental collision in the northern Appalachians in light of gravity and magnetic data in the Gulf of St. Lawrence, in Pelletier, B. R., ed., Offshore geology of eastern Canada: Geological Survey Canada Paper 74-30, p. 1–18.

Hill, M. L., 1991, Post-Taconic transpression in the Pennsylvania Piedmont, in Crawford, M. L., and Crawford, W. A., eds., Evolution and assembly of the Pennsylvania-Delaware Piedmont: Field Guide and Proceedings, Eighth Annual Meeting of the Geological Association of New Jersey, p. 8.1–8.7.

Hill, M. L., and Dibblee, T. W., Jr., 1953, San Andreas, Garlock, and Big Pine faults, California—A study of the character, history, and tectonic significance of their displacements: Geological Society of America Bulletin, v. 64, p. 443–458.

Hubbard, M. S., and Mancktelow, N. S., 1992, Lateral displacement during Neogene convergence in the western and central Alps: Geology, v. 20, p. 943–946.

Hubbard, M. S., West, D. P., Jr., Lux, D. R., Orifice, J., Guidotti, C. V., Higgins, K., and Yanasak, J., 1991, Major dextral strike-slip deformation in the northern Appalachians: The Norumbega fault zone, Maine: Geological Society of America Abstracts with Programs, v. 23, no. 5, p. A311.

Hubbard, M. S., West, D., Ludman, A., Lux, D. R., and Guidotti, C. V., 1995, The Norumbega fault zone, Maine: Crustal profile of a transcurrent boundary: Atlantic Geology, v. 31, p. 109–116.

Hussey, A. M., II, 1968, Stratigraphy and structure of southwestern Maine, in Zen, E., White, W. S., Hadley, J. B., and Thompson, J. B., Jr., eds., Studies of Appalachian geology: Northern and Maritime: New York, Interscience, p. 291–301.

Irwin, W. P., 1990, Geology and plate-tectonic development, in Wallace, R. E., ed., The San Andreas fault system, California: U.S. Geological Survey Professional Paper 1515, p. 61–80.

Jennings, C. W., 1992, Preliminary fault activity map of California: California Department of Conservation, Division of Mines and Geology Open-File Report 92-03, scale 1:750,000.

Kafka, A. L., and Ebel, J. E., 1989, Seismic structure of the Earth's crust underlying the State of Maine, in Tucker, R. D., and Marvinney, R. G., eds., Studies in Maine geology, Volume 1: Structure and stratigraphy: Augusta, Maine Geological Survey, p. 137–156.

Keppie, J. D., 1982, The Minas geofracture, in St. Julien, P., and Béland, J., eds., Major structural zones and faults of the northern Appalachians: Geological Association of Canada Special Paper 24, p. 263–280.

Kirkwood, D., 1989, Géologie structurale de la région de Percé: Ministere de l'Energie et des Ressources du Québec Etude ET 87-17, 42 p.

Kirkwood, D., and Malo, M., 1993, Across-strike geometry of the Grand Pabos fault zone: Evidence for Devonian dextral transpression in the Quebec Appalachians: Canadian Journal of Earth Sciences, v. 30, p. 1363–1373.

Larrabee, D. M., 1964, Bedrock geologic map of the Big Lake quadrangle, Washington County, Maine: U.S. Geological Survey Map MF-282, scale 1:62,500.

Leger, A., and Williams, P. F., 1986, Transcurrent faulting history of southern New Brunswick, in Current research, Part B: Geological Survey of Canada Paper 86-1B, p. 111–120.

Lincoln, B. Z., and Lincoln, T. N., 1991, Origin of compositional layering in the Kingman fault zone, Maine, in Ludman, A., ed., Geology of the Coastal lithotectonic block and neighboring terranes, eastern Maine and southern New Brunswick: New England Intercollegiate Geological Conference 83rd meeting: New York, Queens College, p. 64–79.

Loiselle, M., Eriksson, S., Wones, D. R., and Sinha, A. K., 1983, Timing and emplacement of post-Acadian plutons in central and eastern Maine: Geological Society of America Abstracts with Programs, v. 15, p. 187.

Ludman, A., 1986, Timing of terrane accretion in eastern and east-central Maine: Geology, v. 14, p. 411–414.

Ludman, A., 1998, Evolution of a transcurrent fault zone in shallow crustal metasedimentary rocks: The Norumbega fault zone, eastern Maine: Journal of Structural Geology, v. 20, p. 93–107.

Ludman, A., 1995, Strain partitioning, timing, and amount of offset in the Norumbega fault zone, eastern Maine: Geological Society of America Abstracts with Programs, v. 27, no. 1, p. 65.

Lux, D. R., 1983, ^{40}Ar/^{39}Ar mineral ages for several plutons from western Maine: Geological Society of America Abstracts with Programs, v. 15, p. 147.

Malo, M., and Béland, J., 1989, Acadian strike-slip tectonics in the Gaspé region, Quebec Appalachians: Canadian Journal of Earth Sciences, v. 26, p. 1764–1777.

Malo, M., Kirkwood, D., DeBroucker, G., and St-Julien, P., 1992, A reevaluation of the position of the Baie Verte–Brompton line in the Quebec Appalachians: The influence of Middle Devonian strike-slip faulting in Gaspé Peninsula: Canadian Journal of Earth Sciences, v. 29, p. 1265–1273.

Marvinney, R. G., 1989, Thrust and strike-slip faults near Jackman, Maine, in Tucker, R. D., and Marvinney, R. G., eds., Studies in Maine geology, Volume 2: Structure and stratigraphy: Augusta, Maine Geological Survey, p. 173–186.

Mawer, C. K., and White, J. C., 1987, Sense of displacement on the Cobequid-Chedabucto fault system, Nova Scotia, Canada: Canadian Journal of Earth Sciences, v. 24, p. 217–223.

McLeod, M. J., Johnson, S. C., and Ruitenberg, A. A., 1994, Geological map of southeastern New Brunswick: New Brunswick Department of Natural Resources and Energy Map NR-5, scale 1:250,000.

Minster, J. B., and Jordan, R. H., 1987, Vector constraints on western U.S. deformations from space geodesy, neotectonics and plate motions: Journal of Geophysical Research, v. 92, p. 4798–4804.

Nance, R. D., 1987, Model for the Precambrian evolution of the Avalon terrane in southern New Brunswick, Canada: Geology, v. 15, p. 753–756.

Nance, R. D., and Dallmeyer, R. D., 1993, $^{40}Ar/^{39}Ar$ amphibole ages from the Kingston Complex, New Brunswick: Evidence for Silurian-Devonian tectonothermal activity and implications for the accretion of the Avalon composite terrane: Journal of Geology, v. 101, p. 375–388.

Oldow, J. S., Bally, A. W., and Avé Lallemant, H. G., 1990, Transpression, orogenic float, and lithospheric balance: Geology, v. 18, p. 991–994.

Osberg, P. H., Hussey, A. M., II, and Boone, G. M., eds., 1985, Bedrock geologic map of Maine: Augusta, Maine Geological Survey, scale 1:500,000.

Park, A. F., Williams, P. F., Ralser, S., and Leger, A., 1994, Geometry and kinematics of a major crustal shear zone segment in the Appalachians of southern New Brunswick: Canadian Journal of Earth Sciences, v. 31, p. 1523–1535.

Pêcher, A., Boucher, J. L., and LeFort, P., 1991, Miocene dextral shearing between Himalaya and Tibet: Geology, v. 19, p. 683–685.

Philips, J. D., Goldsmith, R., and Stewart, D. B., 1985, The regional setting of the Quebec–Western Maine seismic reflection profile: Geological Society of America Abstracts with Programs, v. 17, p. 58.

Rast, N., and Dickson, W. L., 1982, The Pocologan mylonite zone, in St. Julien, P., and Béland, J., eds., Major structural zones and faults of the northern Appalachians: Geological Association of Canada Special Paper 24, p. 249–262.

Ruitenberg, A. A., and McCutcheon, S. R., 1982, Acadian and Hercynian structural evolution of southern New Brunswick, in St. Julien, P., and Béland, J., eds., Major structural zones and faults of the northern Appalachians: Geological Association of Canada Special Paper 24, p. 131–148.

Sacks, P., and Malo, M., 1994, Taconian and Acadian transpressional faulting, Mont Albert and Mont Logan nappes and along the Shickshock Sud fault, Gaspe Appalachians, Quebec: Geological Society of America Abstracts with Programs, v. 26, no. 7, p. A196.

Skinner, R., 1970, Tuadook Lake map-area, New Brunswick: Geological Survey of Canada Paper 70-1, Part A, p. 12–14.

Snoke, A. W., and Frost, B. R., 1990, Exhumation of high pressure pelitic schist, Lake Murray spillway, South Carolina: Evidence for crustal extension during Alleghanian strike slip faulting: American Journal of Science, v. 290, p. 853–881.

Stewart, D. B., 1974, Precambrian rocks of Seven Hundred Acre Island and development of cleavage in the Isleboro Formation, in Osberg, P. H., ed., Guidebook for field trips in east-central and north-central Maine: New England Intercollegiate Geological Conference 66th meeting: Orono, University of Maine, p. 86–98.

Stewart, D. B., Unger, J. D., and Hutchinson, D. R., 1995, Silurian tectonic history of Penobscot Bay region, Maine: Atlantic Geology, v. 31, p 67–80.

Stoeser, D. B., 1966, Geology of a portion of the Great Pond Quadrangle, Maine [M.S. thesis]: Orono, University of Maine, 88 p.

Swanson, M. T., 1988, Pseudotachylite-bearing strike-slip duplex structures in the Fort Foster brittle zone, S. Maine: Journal of Structural Geology, v. 10, p. 813–828.

Swanson, M. T., 1992, Late Acadian–Alleghenian transpressional deformation: Evidence from asymmetric boudinage in the Casco Bay area, coastal Maine: Journal of Structural Geology 14, p. 323–342.

Sylvester, A. G., 1988, Strike-slip faults: Geological Society of America Bulletin, v. 100, p. 1666–1703.

Tremblay, A., and Pinet, N., 1994, Distribution and characteristics of Taconian and Acadian deformation, southern Quebec Appalachians: Geological Society of America Bulletin, v. 106, p. 1172–1181.

Trzcienski, W. E., Jr., Rodgers, J., and Guidotti, C. V., 1992, Alternative hypotheses for the Chain Lakes "Massif," Maine and Quebec: American Journal of Science, v. 292, p. 508–532.

Tull, J. F., 1995, Southern Appalachian terrane boundary as a transpressional duplex: Geological Society of America Abstracts with Programs, v. 27, no. 6, p. A-223.

Valentino, D. W., Gates, A. E., and Glover, L., III, 1994, Late Paleozoic transcurrent tectonic assembly of the central Appalachian Piedmont: Tectonics, v. 13, p. 110–126.

Van Staal, C. R., and Fyffe, L. R., 1991, Dunnage and Gander zones, New Brunswick: Canadian Appalachian region: New Brunswick Department of Natural Resources and Energy, Mineral Resources, Geoscience Report 91-2, 39 p.

van Staal, C. R., Ravenhurst, C. E., Winchester, J. A., Roddick, J. C., and Langton, J. P., 1990, Post-Taconic blueschist suture in the northern Appalachians of northern New Brunswick, Canada: Geology, v. 18, p. 1073–1077.

Vauchez, A., and Nicolas, A., 1991, Mountain building: Strike-parallel motion and mantle anisotropy: Tectonophysics, v. 185, p. 183–201.

Vauchez, A., Babaie, H. A., and Babaie, A., 1993, Orogen-parallel tangential motion in the Late Devonian–Early Carboniferous southern Appalachians internides: Canadian Journal of Earth Sciences, v. 30, p. 1297–1305.

Webb, G. W., 1969, Paleozoic wrench faults in Canadian Appalachians, in Kay, M., ed., North Atlantic geology and continental drift: American Association of Petroleum Geologists Memoir 12, p. 754–786.

West, D. P., Jr., 1993, Nature, timing, and extent of dextral shear deformation in south-central Maine [Ph.D. thesis]: Orono, University of Maine, 228 p.

West, D. P., Jr., and Lux D. R., 1993, Dating mylonitic deformation by the ^{40}Ar-^{39}Ar method: An example from the Norumbega fault zone, Maine: Earth and Planetary Science Letters, v. 120, p. 221–237.

Westerman, D. S., 1979, Report on field mapping in the Sherbrooke 2-degree quadrangle, northwestern Maine: Maine Geological Survey Open-File Report 79-25, 8 p.

White, C. E., Barr, S. M., Bevier, M. L., and Deveau, K. A., 1990, Field relations, composition, and age of plutonic units in the Saint John area of southern New Brunswick: Maritime Sediments and Atlantic Geology, v. 26, p. 259–270.

Williams, H., 1978, Tectonolithofacies map of the Appalachian orogen: St. John's, Memorial University of Newfoundland, Map 1, scale 1:1,000,000.

Williams, P. F., Goodwin, L. B., and LaFrance, B., 1995, Brittle faulting in the Canadian Appalachians and the interpretation of reflection seismic data: Journal of Structural Geology, v. 17, p. 215–232.

Wilson, J. T., 1962, Cabot fault, an Appalachian equivalent of the San Andreas and Great Glen faults and some implications for continental displacement: Nature, v. 195, p. 135–138.

Wones, D. R., and Stewart, D. B., 1976, Middle Paleozoic regional right-lateral strike-slip faults in central coastal Maine: Geological Society of America Abstracts with Programs, v. 8, p. 304.

Woodcock, N. H., 1986, The role of strike-slip fault systems at plate boundaries: Royal Society of London Philosophical Transactions, ser. A, v. 317, p. 13–29.

Zartman, R. E., and Gallego, M. D., 1979, Radiometric ages: Compilation B, U.S. Geol. Surv., in Marvin, R. F., and Dobson, S. W., eds., Isochron/West: Bulletin of Isotopic Geochronology, no. 26, p. 18–19.

MANUSCRIPT ACCEPTED BY THE SOCIETY JUNE 9, 1998

Geological Society of America
Special Paper 331
1999

Timing of displacements along the Norumbega fault system, south-central and south-coastal Maine

David P. West, Jr.
Department of Geology, Earlham College, Richmond, Indiana 47374

ABSTRACT

Structural and geochronological data from south-central and south-coastal Maine reveal a polyphase history of movement associated with the Norumbega fault system in this region. The earliest Norumbega related dextral shear deformation began in Middle to Late Devonian time (ca. 380 Ma) after the initial accretion of a composite peri-Gondwanan terrane to North America in Late Silurian to Early Devonian time. In south-central Maine, rocks of the Central Maine and Falmouth-Brunswick sequences, the Casco Bay Group, the Fredericton belt, and the western parts of the peri-Gondwanan terrane are affected by this dextral shear deformation. A lower age limit on this broad zone of dextral shear deformation is uncertain; it may have ended in Early Carboniferous time, or alternatively, it could have continued relatively uninterrupted to earliest Permian time. This episode of dextral shear deformation is regional in extent; shear zones of this age and movement sense are present throughout the Appalachian orogenic belt.

Several relatively localized high-strain mylonite zones (Sandhill Corner, Sunny Side, Flying Point, and Rye) appear to have formed in Late Carboniferous to earliest Permian time. These zones likely reflect highly focused dextral shear strains at structural levels higher than those associated with the earlier episode of dextral deformation. The dextral strike-slip history of the Norumbega fault system appears to have ended by about 280 Ma. Thus the system seems to have had an ~100 m.y. history of dextral displacement in south-central and south-coastal Maine.

A significant thermochronological discontinuity indicates that there was a renewed period of activity along the Norumbega fault system in post-Paleozoic time. An observed time-temperature discontinuity suggests an episode of east-side-down normal fault displacement in this region. This displacement likely reflects tensional stresses associated with Mesozoic rifting, although no lower age limit exists for the timing of this late motion.

INTRODUCTION

Since its original description nearly 25 years ago (Stewart and Wones, 1974), considerable advances have been made toward understanding the extent, style, and kinematics of the Norumbega fault system in Maine. These findings have greatly improved our understanding of the role of major strike-slip fault systems in Appalachian orogenesis; however, a complete assessment awaits critical information on two very elusive aspects of the Norumbega fault system: (1) the timing of displacements and (2) the amount of displacement. These fundamental problems are not unique to the Norumbega fault system; they hinder complete evaluation of major orogen-parallel strike-slip fault zones around the world. The difficulty stems from the fact that traditional methods of evaluating fault timing and displacement amount (e.g., offsets in lithologic contacts, isograds) are not gen-

West, D. P., Jr., 1999, Timing of displacements along the Norumbega fault system, south-central and south-coastal Maine, *in* Ludman, A., and West, D. P., Jr., eds., Norumbega Fault System of the Northern Appalachians: Boulder, Colorado, Geological Society of America Special Paper 331.

erally amenable to these orogen-parallel fault systems because the faults and shear zones parallel most geologic contacts. An additional complication is that many of these structures, the Norumbega included, have undergone multiple episodes of movement over long periods of time.

It is interesting that the literature has offered little discussion of the timing of movements along the Norumbega fault system. Early discussions simply stated that the Norumbega was a "post-metamorphic structure." Since these early studies, however, our views of the Norumbega have changed radically, from a "zone 300 to 400 meters wide" (Stewart and Wones, 1974, p. 231), to a more than 400-km-long, 40-km-wide major dextral strike-slip shear zone. In addition, our views on the timing of regional metamorphism in the vicinity of the Norumbega have changed radically, from being considered all Devonian (Acadian) as late as the mid-1980s, to our present understanding of several superimposed thermal events ranging in age from Permian (West et al., 1988) to Silurian (West et al., 1995). Simply labeling the currently defined Norumbega fault system a "postmetamorphic fault" is highly unsatisfactory and offers little in the way of evaluating the tectonic significance of this important structure.

The purpose of this chapter is to discuss the timing of displacements along the Norumbega fault system in south-central and south-coastal Maine (Fig. 1). This southwestern half of the Norumbega fault system in Maine can be considered the "high-grade portion" of the fault system, because most of the structures are found within amphibolite facies regionally metamorphosed rocks (see Ludman et al., this volume, for a discussion of the timing of movements in the lower grade northeastern portion of the Norumbega fault system). Detailed structural studies (e.g., Swanson, 1992, 1995a; this volume; West, 1995; West and Hubbard, 1997) in the southwestern portion of the Norumbega fault system have revealed two very different styles of dextral shear displacement: an extremely wide zone (>30 km) of heterogeneously distributed noncoaxial ductile deformation, and relatively narrow zones (~1–2 km) of very intense high-strain mylonitization. An important goal of this chapter is to evaluate the timing of each of these episodes of dextral displacement. West et al. (1993) interpreted a profound thermochronological discontinuity along the Norumbega fault system in south-coastal Maine to be the result of significant Mesozoic normal fault displacement along a portion of this fault system. Thus, an additional goal is to evaluate the extent and significance of post-Paleozoic motion in this region dominated by Paleozoic tectonics.

REGIONAL GEOLOGIC SETTING

The southwestern high-grade half of the Norumbega fault system in Maine (Fig. 1) is located within a complex amalgamation of polydeformed, polymetamorphosed, and polyintruded tectonostratigraphic terranes. The early geologic histories of these terranes, as well as the nature of their initial accretion to the North America craton, are debated. The stratified rocks portrayed in Figures 1 and 2 are divided into several different lithostrati-

graphic belts on the basis of their internal stratigraphy (simplified from Berry and Osberg, 1989; Rankin, 1994). See Berry and Osberg (1989) for a discussion of the stratified rocks in south-central and mid-coastal Maine, and Hussey (1985, 1988) for a discussion of the rocks in southwestern Maine. A brief summary, proceeding from west to east, is provided in the following.

Tectonostratigraphic belts

The central Maine terrane (Zen, 1989) is exposed to the northwest of the Hackmatack Pond fault (Pankiwskyj, 1976, 1996) and consists of a very thick Late Ordovician(?)–Early Devonian assemblage of metamorphosed wackes, shales, and minor limestones (Osberg, 1988). The Falmouth-Brunswick sequence (Hussey, 1988), exposed immediately southeast of the central Maine terrane, represents a predominantly Ordovician metavolcanic and volcanogenic metasedimentary section (Osberg et al., 1995). The Casco Bay Group is characterized by Ordovician metasedimentary clastic rocks and minor metavolcanic rocks (Pankiwskyj, 1976; Hussey, 1985; Osberg et al., 1995). The Fredericton belt contains Late Ordovician–Early Silurian rocks of the Bucksport and Appleton Ridge Formations (metamorphosed calc-silicate and pelitic rocks, respectively). The Sennebec Pond fault (Fig. 2), located along the southeastern margin of the Fredericton belt, marks a major tectonostratigraphic boundary in the region. Rocks east of the Sennebec Pond fault include several Cambrian-Ordovician peri-Gondwanan terranes (e.g., St. Croix terrane) that were apparently amalgamated into a composite terrane prior to being accreted to ancestral North American in Late Silurian to Early Devonian time (West et al., 1992; Rankin, 1994; Stewart et al., 1995a, 1995b).

Metamorphism and plutonism

All the stratified rocks shown in Figure 2 have been metamorphosed to amphibolite facies conditions, and in many places rocks have mineral assemblages characteristic of the upper amphibolite facies (Guidotti, 1989). Rocks of the central Maine sequence preserve evidence of at least three low-pressure Devonian metamorphic events (Osberg, 1988). Rocks of the Falmouth-Brunswick sequence, Casco Bay Group, and Fredericton belt were also regionally metamorphosed to amphibolite facies conditions in Devonian time (West et al., 1988, 1993, 1995). In addition, the southern portions of the Falmouth-Brunswick sequence were subjected to a significant late Paleozoic thermal overprint (note the <300 Ma hornblende ages in Fig. 2). East of the Sennebec Pond fault, peri-Gondwanan rocks were regionally metamorphosed in Silurian time and have not been subjected to Devonian amphibolite facies metamorphism (West et al., 1995).

Intrusive rocks shown in Figures 1 and 2 are both texturally and compositionally diverse and range in age from Silurian to Permian. The relationships of these intrusions to deformational events, in particular "Norumbega-style" dextral shear deformation, are similarly variable. Several of these plu-

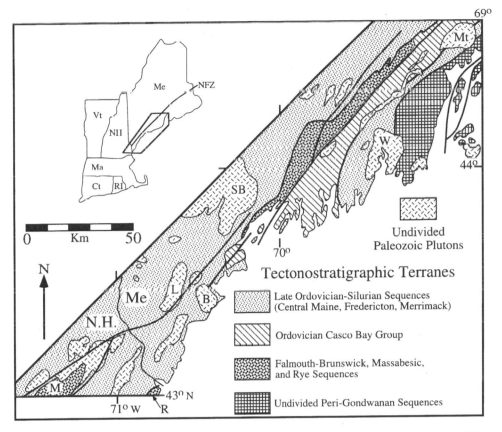

.Figure 1. Generalized geology of south-coastal Maine and southeastern New Hampshire. Modified from Osberg ct al. (1985), Rankin (1994), and Stewart et al. (1995a). B = Biddiford pluton, L = Lyman pluton, M = Massabesic Gneiss complex, Mt. = Mt. Waldo pluton, R = Rye complex, SB = Sebago batholith, W = Waldoboro pluton, NFZ = Norumbega fault zone.

tonic rock bodies are discussed in the following because they are relevant to deciphering the timing of deformational events in the region.

"Pre-Norumbega" structural features

Several important large-scale structural features are interpreted to have formed prior to the initiation of dextral shear deformation in the region. The important boundary between the central Maine and Falmouth-Brunswick sequences (Hackmatack Pond fault, Fig. 2) has been interpreted as both an early thrust fault (Pankiwskyj, 1976, 1996) and an unconformity (Osberg, 1988), and the contact appears to coincide with a prominent west-dipping seismic reflector (Stewart et al., 1993). This early structure, whether a thrust or an unconformity, has been severely overprinted by later episodes of dextral shear deformation (Orifice, 1995). The contact between the Casco Bay Group and the Fredericton sequence has been interpreted as a thrust fault (Liberty-Orrington fault, Osberg et al., 1985, 1995). This thrust is also of "pre-Norumbega" age because it was intruded by a latest Silurian pluton (R. D. Tucker, 1996, personal commun.). The contact between the Fredericton sequence and the peri-Gond-

wanan terranes exposed to the east has been interpreted to represent an early east-dipping thrust fault (Sennebec Pond fault, Fig. 2) on the basis of seismic reflection studies (Stewart et al., 1993, 1995b). This structure has also been overprinted by later dextral shear deformation. A number of Silurian, high-angle faults (e.g., Turtle Head fault, see Fig. 2) have been mapped in the Penobscot Bay region (Stewart et al., 1995a, 1995b). While most of these have been interpreted to be dextral strike-slip faults (Stewart et al., 1995b), they appear to be much older than the displacements associated with the Norumbega fault system (see following) and they are outside the zone of "Norumbega style" dextral shear deformation.

In addition to these early large scale-thrust faults, there are several pre-Norumbega regional folding events. All the stratified rocks of the Central Maine sequence, Falmouth-Brunswick sequence, Casco Bay Group, and probably the Fredericton sequence have been affected by at least two major episodes of folding (Osberg, 1988; Hussey, 1988). In these rocks, an older isoclinal recumbent phase of folding (F_1) is deformed by a dominant phase of northeast trending, upright isoclinal folding (F_2), which is responsible for the map pattern. Compositional layering and a pervasive foliation are generally axial planar to these F_2

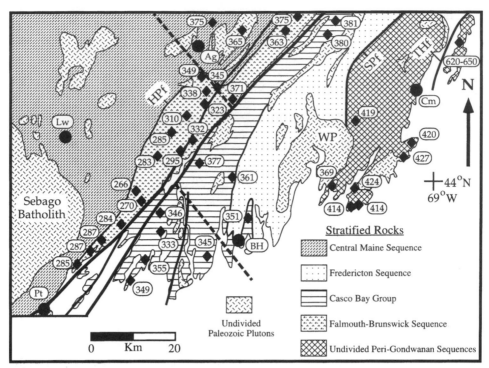

Figure 2. Distribution of $^{40}Ar/^{39}Ar$ hornblende ages from the region. Geology modified from Osberg et al. (1985), Hussey (1988), Stewart et al. (1995a). WP = Waldoboro pluton, HPf = Hackmatack Pond fault, Spf = Sennebec Pond fault, Thf = Turtle Head fault; black circles are cities: Ag = Augusta, BH = Boothbay Harbor, Cm = Camden, Lw = Lewiston, Pt = Portland. Ages (diamonds) are from West et al. (1988, 1993, 1995), and Stewart and Lux (1988). The dashed line approximates a 350 Ma hornblende chrontour and no particular amount of post-350 Ma displacement is implied by the apparent offset in this line.

folds throughout the region. Swanson (1992) and Hubbard (1992) suggested that this later episode of upright isoclinal folding and associated axial-planar foliation might be related to processes of dextral shear deformation (i.e., Norumbega related). A critical U-Pb age determination presented in Osberg et al. (1995) casts doubt on this hypothesis. R. D. Tucker (*in* Osberg et al., 1995) provided a 399 ± 1 Ma U-Pb zircon age on a metamorphosed dike that cuts upright isoclinal folds in the central Maine sequence. Both F_1 and F_2 folding events must therefore be older than about 400 Ma. Perhaps more important for the purposes of this discussion, this ca. 400 Ma dike is deformed by structures (F_3 of Osberg, 1968, 1988) associated with the wide zone of dextral shear deformation (i.e., early Norumbega deformation, discussed in the following). This dextral shear deformation must therefore be post-400 Ma, and I argue that it is significantly younger than 400 Ma.

Large-scale folding in the Peri-Gondwanan terranes exposed east of the Sennebec Pond fault is of a different style and age than the folding episodes discussed here. Rocks of the St. Croix Group have been affected by kilometer-scale northwest-directed thrusts and recumbent folds, and later northeast-trending upright folds (Osberg and Guidotti, 1974; Berry, 1987). Both of these episodes of folding are Late Ordovician to Silurian in age (Osberg et al., 1995; Stewart et al., 1995a; West et al., 1995).

DEFORMATION ASSOCIATED WITH THE NORUMBEGA FAULT SYSTEM

Noncoaxial deformational features in south-central and south-coastal Maine are here divided into two general types on the basis of style of deformation and spatial distribution of the structural features: (1) a wide zone (>30 km) of heterogeneously distributed structures consistent with dextral shear deformation, and (2) relatively narrow zones (1–2 km wide) of intense high-strain mylonitization. These are referred to as the wide zone of regional dextral shear deformation and localized zones of high-strain dextral shear, respectively. Both of these are here associated with the Norumbega fault system. The initial accretion of the various tectonostratigraphic terranes shown in Figures 1 and 2 occurred prior to the initiation of these Norumbega deformational features. The structural history of south-central and south-coastal Maine was obviously complex before Norumbega dextral shear deformation began.

Regional dextral shear deformation

Nature and extent. Detailed structural studies in south-central (West, 1995; West and Hubbard, 1997) and south-coastal Maine (Swanson et al., 1986; Swanson, 1992, 1995a, this volume) have

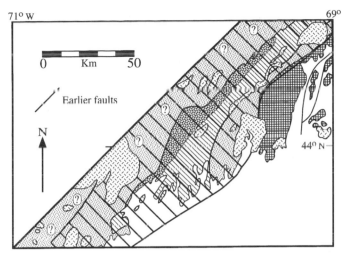

Figure 3. Approximate extent of Late Devonian–Early Carboniferous dextral shear deformation (diagonal rules). See the text for details. Geology as in Figure 1.

identified a broad region in which ductile dextral shear deformational features can be found (see Fig. 3). These deformational features affect rocks of the central Maine and Falmouth-Brunswick sequences, the Casco Bay Group, the Fredericton sequence, and the westernmost portions of the peri-Gondwanan composite terrane. Although the southeastern limit of these structures is fairly well located, the northwestern extent of this deformation is not known with certainty. Osberg (1968, 1988) and Solar (1996) described structures consistent with dextral shear deformation significantly west of the areas portrayed in Figures 1 and 2.

The structures that characterize this wide zone of dextral shear deformation include asymmetric boudinage (see Swanson, 1992), asymmetric folding, and in places pervasive shear banding (Fig. 4). The sense of asymmetry observed in all these features as well as other kinematic indicators are consistent with dextral motion. The distribution of these features varies considerably across the region, likely reflecting both variations in strain and the rheological contrasts of the various lithologies affected by the deformation. Mineral lineations, which likely approximate the dominant movement directions across the region, vary both along and across strike. In south-central Maine, these lineations (mostly hornblende and sillimanite; see Fig. 4A) are remarkably consistent; they trend northeast-southwest and plunge generally <25° (West and Hubbard, 1997). In south-coastal Maine, where the zone of deformation widens, the orientation of mineral lineations (and quartz rodding) varies considerably (Swanson, 1995a, this volume). In the western parts of south-coastal Maine, mineral lineations plunge more steeply and shear-sense indicators indicate a dextral-thrust type motion (Swanson, this volume).

Timing. As discussed herein, the parallelism of structures with lithologic contacts in these high-grade metamorphic rocks hinders timing evaluations by traditional offset methods. However, knowledge of the timing of metamorphic events and intrusions relative to the development of deformational fabrics

provides a wealth of information on the timing of the broad zone of regional dextral shear deformation.

The structures associated with the regional zone of dextral shear deformation overprint an earlier episode of upright isoclinal folding (F_1 folds of Hussey, 1988; Osberg, 1988) and the pervasive foliation throughout the region. As discussed here, the ca. 400 Ma U-Pb age on a post-F_2, but pre-dextral shear dike is critical to resolving the timing of these two important deformational events. In south-central Maine, the F_2 folding and associ-

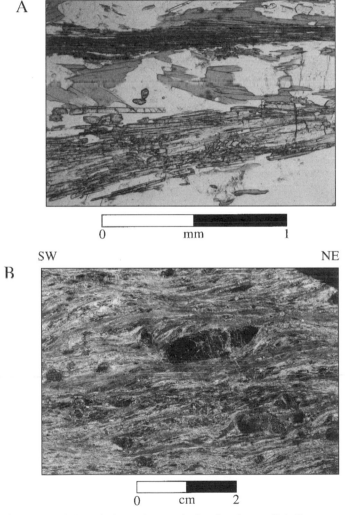

Figure 4. A: Oriented photomicrograph showing the parallel alignment of sillimanite needles in the Cape Elizabeth Formation of the Casco Bay Group, south-central Maine. This is interpreted to reflect either synmetamorphic or postmetamorphic shearing. B: Oriented hand sample from the Appleton Ridge Formation (Fredericton sequence) of south-central Maine showing the postmetamorphic nature of the wide zone of dextral shear deformation. Preexisting foliation (horizontal in the photo) is oriented ~040° and is deflected by 060° shear bands. Note the sigma-type staurolite porphyroclast in the center of the photo. This sample is from a locality ~12 km southeast of the Norumbega fault system sensu stricto (i.e., the fault line on the bedrock geologic map of Maine; Osberg et al., 1985).

ated deformational features are thus older than 400 Ma, whereas the dextral shear deformation is younger than 400 Ma.

Unfortunately, it is considerably more difficult to obtain a minimum age for the timing of this dextral shear deformation using plutonic rock bodies. It is tempting to suggest that the apparently post-tectonic Mt. Waldo granite (371 ± 2 Ma, U-Pb zircon by R. D. Tucker, *in* Stewart et al., 1995a) (see Fig. 1 for location) postdates this major episode of dextral shear deformation. Although it is clear that the Mt. Waldo granite postdates significant movement on the Sennebec Pond and Liberty-Orrington thrust faults, its relationship to the dextral shear deformation is unclear due to a lack of detailed structural study around the pluton. Paterson and Tobisch (1988) cautioned against hastily interpreting the timing of regional deformational events relative to dated plutons that have not been structurally characterized. Much the same can be said for many of the other dated plutons in this wide zone of deformation.

Detailed microstructural studies of deformed metamorphic rocks can provide important information on the timing of deformation relative to metamorphic events of known age. In south-central Maine, the timing of latest amphibolite facies metamorphism is well constrained by $^{40}Ar/^{39}Ar$ hornblende ages (see Fig. 2) to be Middle to Late Devonian (ca. 380 Ma; West et al., 1988, 1995). Coarse-grained elongate minerals such as hornblende and sillimanite that grew during this metamorphism are strongly lineated within foliation planes (Fig. 4A). In addition, porphyroblasts such as garnet, andalusite, and staurolite (Fig. 4B) that grew during this ca. 380 Ma metamorphic event are often sheared (see Fig. 4B). These relationships are interpreted to indicate that the dextral shear deformation was either synmetamorphic or postmetamorphic (≤380 Ma) in south-central Maine.

A similar relationship between deformation and metamorphism is found in south-coastal Maine. Lang and Dunn (1990) and Grover and Lang (1995) suggested that deformation (e.g., F_2 of Hussey, 1988) and metamorphism were synchronous in the Casco Bay region of south-coastal Maine. The timing of metamorphism in this region is also well constrained by $^{40}Ar/^{39}Ar$ hornblende ages (ca. 380 Ma; West et al., 1993). Because much of the dextral shear deformation in this region overprints the upright folding and associated schistosity, this shearing must also be younger than ca. 380 Ma.

A minimum age for this regional deformational event is much more difficult to ascertain and must be established indirectly. The $^{40}Ar/^{39}Ar$ muscovite cooling ages from the region that reflect the time of postmetamorphic cooling below about 320 °C (Snee et al., 1988) are summarized in Figure 5. Note that in the Casco Bay Group these ages range from about 360 to 300 Ma. Because the structures associated with the wide zone of dextral shear deformation appear to have formed in a ductile environment, they must have formed at temperatures above 320 °C, or above muscovite closure temperatures. Therefore, the broad zone of dextral shear deformation must have developed prior to regional cooling below muscovite closure temperatures. Because of the variation in muscovite cooling ages across the region, it is difficult to assign an absolute minimum age to this deformation. It can be no younger than 300 Ma, and the 360 Ma muscovite ages in south-central Maine suggest that it may be no younger than latest Devonian–earliest Carboniferous in age.

In summary, the relationships between well-dated metamorphic events and dextral shear fabrics in south-central and south-coastal Maine indicate a maximum age of about 380 Ma for the development of the wide zone of dextral shear deformation. A minimum age for this deformation, although much more difficult to establish, is likely 300 to 360 Ma.

Localized high-strain dextral shear zones

Nature and extent. In south-central Maine, all the metamorphic and deformational features discussed here, including the wide zone of dextral shear structures, are cut by a northeast-trending zone (~1 km wide) of intense high-strain mylonitization (first identified by Pankiwskyj, 1976, and termed the Sandhill Corner fault) (see Fig. 6 for location). It is this zone, and only zones like this, that prior to the 1990s were traditionally considered part of the Norumbega fault system. The Sandhill Corner fault is characterized by near-vertical mylonites and ultra-mylonites with subhorizontal mineral lineations for which microstructural kinematic indicators reveal a dextral sense of movement. These mylonites are extremely fine grained, and their textures are consistent with lower greenschist facies conditions during this deformational episode. West and Hubbard (1997) demonstrated that this indicates that deformation occurred at cooler shallower crustal levels than the deformation associated with the broad zone of dextral shear deformation.

In addition to the Sandhill Corner fault zone described here, the Sunny Side fault of Bickel (1971, 1976) in south-central Maine (Fig. 6) displays very similar characteristics. Studies by Bickel (1971) and my reconnaissance studies indicate that this is a relatively narrow zone (<1 km) of steeply dipping mylonites and ultramylonites. Kinematic analysis reveals a similar dextral sense of displacement within this zone (see Fig. 7). Because of the striking similarities in structural style between this zone and the Sandhill Corner fault zone, it is believed that the two zones developed at similar times under similar conditions.

Swanson (1995a, this volume) described zones of very high ductile shear strain (Casco Bay or Flying Point fault zone) within the much wider zone of distributed dextral shear deformation in the Casco Bay region of south-coastal Maine. These zones appear to be similar to the Sandhill Corner and Sunny Side fault zones. There are, however, some very important differences: (1) the Flying Point fault zone appears to be significantly wider than the two fault zones to the north; (2) fabrics within the Flying Point fault zone appear to be more ductile than those of the Sandhill Corner and Sunny Side fault zones; and (3) the Flying Point fault zone contains overprinting normal fault features that are not found in the northern high-strain zone. Despite these differences, it is believed that the Flying Point fault zone likely formed at the same time as the more northerly

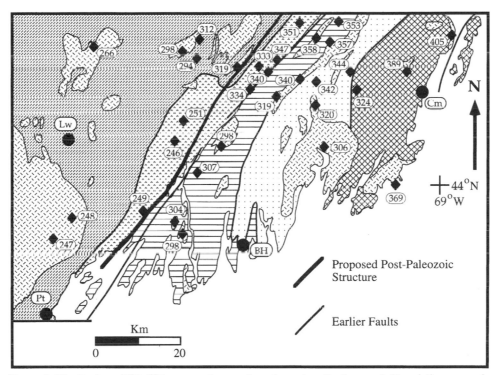

Figure 5. Distribution of $^{40}Ar/^{39}Ar$ muscovite ages from the region. Geology and abbreviations are as in Figure 3. Ages are from West and Lux (1993), West et al. (1993, 1995), and Lux (1991). Also shown is the approximate location of a post-Paleozoic normal fault (heavy dark line). See the text for details.

SW   NE

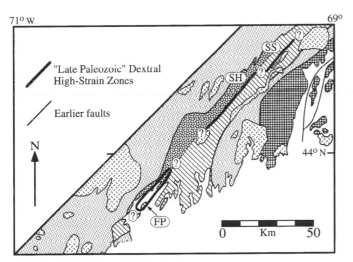

Figure 6. Distribution of late Paleozoic high-strain dextral shear zones in south-central and south-coastal Maine. FP = Flying Point fault zone (after Swanson, 1992, this volume), SH = Sandhill Corner fault zone (after Pankiwskyj, 1976; West and Lux, 1993), SS = Sunny Side fault zone (after Bickel, 1971, 1976; and my reconnaissance work). Geology as in Figure 1.

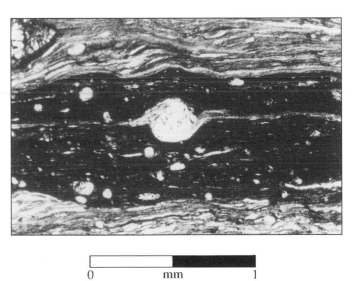

Figure 7. Oriented photomicrograph from mylonites of the Sunny Side fault zone, south-central Maine. Note the feldspar delta-type porphyroclast within a layer-parallel pseudotachylite vein—the sense of rotation is consistent with dextral shear. Also note the muscovite fish in the lower portion of the photo (also consistent with dextral shear).

Late Silurian to Early Devonian (ca. 420-390 Ma)

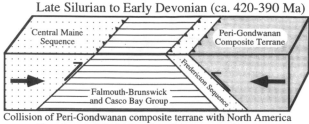

Collision of Peri-Gondwanan composite terrane with North America (thrusting, upright folding, intrusion, metamorphism)

Late Devonian to Early Carboniferous (ca. 380-320 Ma)

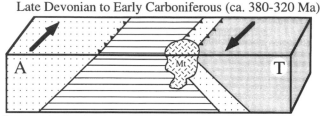

Transpressional deformation distributed over a regionally extensive area (dextral shear in south-central Maine, dextral thrusting in south-coastal Maine)

Late Carboniferous to Early Permian (ca. 300-275 Ma)

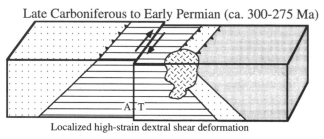

Localized high-strain dextral shear deformation

Post-Paleozoic

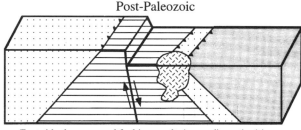

East-side-down normal faulting results in age discontinuities

Figure 8. Temporal evolution of the Norumbega fault system in south-central and south-coastal Maine. See the text for details. Mt = Mt. Waldo granite, T = toward, A = away

high-strain zones and the differences probably reflect a deeper structural environment to the south during the development of these zones (note in Fig. 5 that the younger muscovite ages to the south are consistent with this hypothesis).

Farther south, within and surrounding the Rye Formation of southernmost Maine and southeastern New Hampshire (see Fig. 1), are a number of complex brittle dextral strike-slip fault zones (Swanson, 1988, 1995b). Although these fault zones appear to be structurally different from the Flying Point fault zone (brittle versus ductile), Swanson (1995b) correlated these with the Norumbega fault system (see also the discussion in Bothner and Hussey, this volume, regarding this correlation). These zones more closely resemble the localized high-strain zones rather than the wide zone of regional dextral shear deformation.

Timing. West and Lux (1993), in a detailed $^{40}Ar/^{39}Ar$ study of muscovite porphyroclasts from the Sandhill Corner high-strain zone, obtained an age of ca. 290 Ma for the development of this mylonite zone. This age is significantly younger than the estimated age of regional dextral shear deformation in south-central Maine. Because of the structural comparisons outlined here, the Sunny Side fault zone is also believed to be of Late Carboniferous to Early Permian age.

The timing of high-strain deformation associated with the Flying Point fault zone in south-coastal Maine is constrained by U-Pb monazite ages from undeformed granites and pegmatites in the region (Tomascak et al., 1996). Crystallization ages ranging from 269 to 278 Ma for these intrusions led Tomascak et al. (1996) to conclude that ductile deformation is ≥280 Ma in this region. Because this fault zone significantly offsets metamorphic isograds in the region (Hussey, 1985), it must have developed after the wide zone of distributed shear. Thus this high-strain mylonitization is post-Late Devonian and pre-280 Ma. Because of the structural similarities outlined here and because the Flying Point fault zone is on strike with the well-dated Sandhill Corner high-strain zone, it is believed that the two zones are similar in age (i.e., latest Carboniferous–earliest Permian). Boeckeler (1994) provided a 298 ± 31 Ma Rb-Sr whole-rock age on pseudotachylytes veins within Rye Formation fault zones. While the uncertainty on this age certainly raises questions as to the appropriateness of this technique for dating pseudotachylyte, the age is consistent with the late Paleozoic ages for the other localized high-strain zones associated with the Norumbega fault system.

EVIDENCE FOR POST-PALEOZOIC NORMAL FAULTING

The Flying Point fault zone of south-coastal Maine, in addition to being a major zone of late Paleozoic dextral shear deformation, marks a major late Paleozoic–early Mesozoic thermochronological discontinuity (West et al., 1993). This time-temperature discontinuity can not be explained by dextral shear motion along the Flying Point fault zone because regional patterns of muscovite, biotite, and K-feldspar $^{40}Ar/^{39}Ar$ ages that are significantly younger than the dextral motion along the fault zone are displaced. In other words, regional cooling age patterns that are younger than the ≥280 Ma dextral motion along the Flying Point fault zone are offset. A significant discordance in $^{40}Ar/^{39}Ar$ ages suggests that in early Mesozoic time a large thermal contrast existed in the rocks now juxtaposed across the Flying Point fault. Final juxtaposition and contemporaneous cooling between rocks currently juxtaposed across the Flying Point fault did not occur until after Triassic time. West et al. (1993) interpreted this time-temperature discontinuity to reflect significant (~4 km), post-Mesozoic, east-side-down normal fault displacement along the Flying Point fault. It is interesting that Swanson (1995a, this volume) provides field evidence for late extensional features (east side down) within this fault zone.

While West et al. (1993) provided convincing evidence

for post-Paleozoic normal fault displacements along the Norumbega fault system in the immediate Casco Bay region, the nature of these displacements to the north and south of this region are not clear. The $^{40}Ar/^{39}Ar$ mica ages immediately south of the Casco Bay region (Lux and West, 1993) do not show any appreciable Mesozoic offsets in regional age patterns. It therefore seems likely that, south of the Casco Bay region, the post-Paleozoic component of movement associated with the Flying Point fault extends offshore out into the Gulf of Maine (also see Bothner and Hussey, this volume, for a discussion of southern extensions of the Norumbega fault system).

Figure 5 shows the distribution of muscovite ages from the region and provides insights as to the nature of post-Paleozoic movement north of the Casco Bay region. Mica age patterns across the central Maine sequence are remarkably consistent with chrontours (bands of equal ages) that trend slightly northwest-southeast and become systematically older to the north (see Dallmeyer, 1989; DeYoreo et al., 1989; Lux, 1991, for details). This general pattern can be seen in Figure 5, where muscovite ages from the Sebago batholith and southern portions of the Falmouth-Brunswick sequence are <250 Ma, whereas ages from the Augusta region are in the 300 Ma age range. Note, however, that this pattern does not continue into the northern portions of the Falmouth-Brunswick sequence, where muscovite ages from these rocks are 15 to 30 m.y. older than those to the west. This apparent time-temperature discontinuity can be traced to the south into the better defined Flying Point fault post-Paleozoic discontinuity. More data (both muscovite and K-feldspar) are needed from this northern region, but the data suggest that the post-Paleozoic structure can be extended to the north along the Dearborn Brook fault, a late structure in the central Maine sequence (Pankiwskyj, 1976). It is interesting that the Dearborn Brook fault is shown as an east-side-down normal fault structure on the seismic reflection profile of Stewart et al. (1993).

In summary, thermochronological discontinuities indicate a significant episode of east-side-down normal fault displacement along the Norumbega fault system in south-central and south-coastal Maine. This movement is most likely related to extensional tectonics associated with the initial openings of the North Atlantic Ocean in early Mesozoic time. Doll et al. (1996), on the basis of their interpretations of seismic reflection data, suggested that branches of the Norumbega fault system near the New Brunswick border cut the entire crust and offset the Moho. If the Moho beneath Maine formed during the Mesozoic, as suggested by Stewart (1989), then the offsets proposed by Doll et al. (1996) must be Mesozoic or younger. Both thermochronologic and seismic reflection data therefore suggest that some of the faults associated with the Norumbega were active as post-Paleozoic normal faults. A minimum age of this late motion is currently unconstrained by the data, and, in my opinion, should be the focus of continued studies.

TEMPORAL EVOLUTION OF THE NORUMBEGA FAULT SYSTEM

The structural and geochronological studies outlined herein provide significant constraints on the temporal and spatial evolution of the Norumbega fault system in south-central and south-coastal Maine. A schematic portrayal of this evolution with time is provided in Figure 8 and is outlined here. The initial accretion of a peri-Gondwanan composite terrane with ancestral North America appears to have occurred in Late Silurian to Early Devonian time (West et al., 1992, 1995; Rankin, 1994; Stewart et al., 1995a, 1995b). The nature and timing of the initial accretion of the Falmouth-Brunswick sequence and Casco Bay Group are unclear. There does not seem to be any evidence, however, of any terrane accretion in Maine after Middle Devonian time. Late Silurian to Early Devonian time seems to have dominated by compressional tectonics (e.g., thrust faulting, recumbent folding, upright isoclinal folding) in this region (Fig. 8A).

The dominant stress regime in south-central and south-coastal Maine seems to have changed beginning ca. 380 Ma, as the continued convergence of these various terranes with North America was largely accomplished through transpression (Fig. 8B). This time also marks the approximate timing of peak metamorphic conditions in rocks west of the Sennebec Pond fault. Thus the wide zone of regional dextral shear deformation reflects relatively deep level, moderate temperature dextral transpression that began in Middle to Late Devonian time. It is not clear how long this transpressional stress regime existed in this region. West (1995) and West and Hubbard (1997) argued that the region may have been under relatively continuous dextral shear strains for 80 to 100 m.y. Alternatively, dextral shear strains may have waned in Early Carboniferous time, only to be followed by intense high-strain mylonitization (the localized zones of high strain) in latest Carboniferous–earliest Permian time.

Late Devonian through Permian time in south-central and south-coastal Maine marked a prolonged period of regional uplift and exhumation. West and Hubbard (1997) suggested that dextral shear strains (i.e., Norumbega activity) were present throughout this time period and that the Norumbega fault system evolved into an increasingly narrow, but more highly focused zone of dextral deformation. Regardless as to whether dextral shear deformation continued throughout the Carboniferous, the Late Carboniferous to Early Permian localized high-strain zones (e.g., Sandhill Corner and Flying Point) reflect an episode of more highly focused dextral shear deformation at higher structural levels (Fig. 8C). The data of Tomascak et al. (1996) from south-coastal Maine seem to indicate that ductile dextral shear deformation (i.e., the Norumbega fault system as a zone of right-lateral displacement) ceased by about 280 Ma. Thus the Norumbega seems to have undergone an ~100 m.y. history of dextral displacement in south-central and south-coastal Maine.

Thermochronologic and seismic reflection studies indicate a renewed period of activity along the Norumbega in post-Paleozoic time. The observed discontinuities suggest a significant episode of east-side-down normal fault displacement within the fault zone (Fig. 8D). These displacements likely reflect tensional stresses associated with Mesozoic rifting, although no lower age limit exists for the timing of this late motion.

CONCLUSIONS

The data outlined in this chapter describe a prolonged period of dextral shear deformation in south-central and south-coastal Maine following the initial accretion of a large peri-Gondwanan composite terrane with ancestrial North America in Late Silurian to Early Devonian time. The dextral shear deformation began on a regional scale ca. 380 Ma and affected rocks of the Central Maine and Falmouth-Brunswick sequences, the Casco Bay Group, the Fredericton belt, and the western edge of the peri-Gondwanan composite terrane. Regional exhumation, perhaps accompanied by increasingly localized dextral shear deformation, occurred throughout Late Devonian and Carboniferous time. Localized, high-strain zones of intense mylonitization developed in latest Carboniferous to earliest Permian time (ca. 290 Ma), and these likely reflect dextral shear strains at higher structural levels. The dextral strike-slip history of the Norumbega fault system seems to have ended by about 280 Ma. Thermochronologic and seismic discontinuities indicate a period of significant normal faulting along the Norumbega fault system in post-Paleozoic time.

While considerable advances have been made toward the understanding of the timing of displacements along the Norumbega fault system in south-central and south-coastal Maine, several important questions remain.

1. What is the nature and exact timing of the transition between largely compressional tectonics associated with Late Silurian–Early Devonian terrane accretion and Middle to Late Devonian dextral transpression associated with the Norumbega fault system?

2. How does the wide zone of regional dextral transpression described here relate to other zones of regional transpression in the northern Appalachians (e.g., Malo and Béland, 1989; de Roo and van Staal, 1994; Langdon and Hall, 1994; Kirkwood, 1995)?

3. Was dextral shear deformation in the region relatively continuous from 380 to 280 Ma or was this time period marked by episodes of relatively static uplift and erosion?

4. How do the latest Carboniferous–earliest Permian localized high-strain zones relate to similar age terrane accretions and fault movements in southern New England (e.g., Wintsch et al., 1992; Goldstein, 1994) and Maritime Canada (e.g., Mawer and White, 1987)?

5. What are the exact timing and extent of post-Paleozoic normal faulting along the Norumbega fault system?

6. How does the timing of displacements in the southern high-grade portions of the Norumbega described here relate to the timing of displacements in the more northeasterly lower-grade portions of the fault system (Ludman, 1998; Ludman et al., this volume)?

ACKNOWLEDGMENTS

The ideas presented in this paper have evolved through discussions and field trips with numerous colleagues, in particular Spike Berry, Chuck Guidotti, Mary Hubbard, Art Hussey, Allan Ludman, Dan Lux, Phil Osberg, Dave Stewart, and Mark Swanson. Dyk Eusden and Dave Stewart provided official reviews and offered many helpful comments and suggestions for improvement of the manuscript. This paper is dedicated to the late Dave Wones, a person I unfortunately never had the opportunity to meet, but one of the original Norumbega "pioneers" who laid the foundation for studies of this and other important orogen-parallel fault zones in the Appalachians.

REFERENCES CITED

Berry, H. N., IV, 1987, Bedrock geology of the Camden Hills area, central coastal Maine: Maine Geological Survey Open-File Report 87-26, 30 p.

Berry, H. N., IV, and Osberg, P. H., 1989, A stratigraphic synthesis of eastern Maine and western New Brunswick, in Tucker, R. D., and Marvinney, R. G., eds., Studies in Maine geology: Structure and stratigraphy: Augusta, Maine Geological Survey, p. 1–32.

Bickel, C. E., 1971, Bedrock geology of the Belfast quadrangle, Maine [Ph.D. dissert.]: Cambridge, Massachusetts, Harvard University, 342 p.

Bickel, C. E., 1976, Stratigraphy of the Belfast quadrangle, Maine, in Page, L. R., ed., Contributions to the stratigraphy of New England: Geological Society of America Memoir 148, p. 97–128.

Boeckeler, A. J., 1994, Isotopic ages of pseudotachylite veins from coastal New Hampshire and SW Maine: Evidence from post-Acadian strike-slip motion: Geological Society of America Abstracts with Programs, v. 26, no. 3, p. 7.

Dallmeyer, R. D., 1989, Late Paleozoic thermal evolution of crystalline terranes within portions of the U.S. Appalachian orogen, in Hatcher, R. D., Jr., Thomas, W. A., and Viele, G. W., eds., The Appalachian-Ouachita orogen in the United States: Boulder, Colorado, Geological Society of America, Geology of North America, v. F-2, p. 179–232.

de Roo, J. A., and van Staal, C. R., 1994, Transpression and extensional collapse: Steep belts and flat belts in the Appalachian Central Mobile Belt, northern New Brunswick, Canada: Geological Society of America Bulletin, v. 106, p. 541–552.

DeYoreo, J. J., Lux, D. R., and Guidotti, C. V., 1989, A thermal model for Carboniferous metamorphism near the Sebago batholith in western Maine, in Tucker, R. D., and Marvinney, R. G., eds., Studies in Maine geology: Igneous and metamorphic geology: Augusta, Maine Geological Survey, p. 19–34.

Doll, W. E., Domoracki, W. J., Costain, J. K., Coruh, C., Ludman, A., and Hopeck, J. T., 1996, Implications of a seismic reflection profile across a part of the Norumbega fault zone, east-central Maine: Geology, v. 24, p. 251–254.

Goldstein, A. G., 1994, A shear zone origin for Alleghanian (Permian) multiple deformation in eastern Massachusetts: Tectonics, v. 13, p. 62–77.

Grover, T. W., and Lang, H. W., 1995, Examination of a well-exposed sequence of garnet through sillimanite zone metapelitic rocks in Casco Bay, in Hussey, A. M., II, and Johnson, R. A., eds., Guidebook to field trips in southern Maine and adjacent New Hampshire: New England Intercollegiate Geological Conference Guidebook, v. 87, p. 195–210.

Guidotti, C. V., 1989, Metamorphism in Maine, in Tucker, R. D., and Marvinney, R. G., eds., Studies in Maine geology: Igneous and metamorphic geology: Augusta, Maine Geological Survey, p. 1–18.

Hubbard, M. S., 1992, Fold development in a strike-slip shear zone, the Norumbega fault system, Maine: Eos (Transactions, American Geophysical Union), v. 73, p. 534.

Hussey, A. M., II, 1985, The bedrock geology of the Bath and Portland 2 degree map sheet, Maine: Augusta, Maine Geological Survey, No. 85-87, 82 p.

Hussey, A. M., II, 1988, Lithotectonic stratigraphy, deformation, plutonism, and metamorphism, greater Casco Bay region, southwestern Maine, *in* Tucker, R. D., and Marvinney, R. G., eds., Studies in Maine geology: Structure and stratigraphy: Augusta, Maine Geological Survey, p. 17–34.

Kirkwood, D., 1995, Strain partitioning and progressive deformation history in a transpressive belt, northern Appalachians: Tectonophysics, v. 241, p. 15–34.

Lang, H. M., and Dunn, G. R., 1990, Sequential porphyroblast growth during deformation in a low-pressure metamorphic terrain, Orrs Island–Harpswell Neck, Maine: Journal of Metamorphic Geology, v. 8, p. 199–216.

Langdon, G. S., and Hall, J., 1994, Devonian-Carboniferous tectonics and basin deformation in the Cabot Strait area, eastern Canada: American Association of Petroleum Geologists Bulletin, v. 78, p. 1748–1774.

Ludman, A., 1998, Evolution of a transcurrent fault system in the upper crust: The Norumbega fault zone, eastern Maine: Journal of Structural Geology, v. 20, p. 93–107.

Lux, D. R., 1991, $^{40}Ar/^{39}Ar$ mineral ages from the Kearsarge Central Maine synclinorium: Regional implications: Geological Society of America Abstracts with Programs, v. 23, no. 6, p. A136.

Lux, D. R., and West, D. P., Jr., 1993, New $^{40}Ar/^{39}Ar$ mica ages from eastern New Hampshire and southern Maine. Implications for the exhumation history of the region: Geological Society of America Abstracts with Programs, v. 25, no. , p. 35.

Malo, M., and Béland, J., 1989, Acadian strike-slip tectonics in the Gaspé region, Quebec Appalachians: Canadian Journal of Earth Sciences, v. 26, p. 1764–1777.

Mawer, C. K., and White, J. C., 1987, Sense of displacement on the Cobequid-Chedabucto fault system, Nova Scotia, Canada: Canadian Journal of Earth Sciences, v. 24, p. 217–223.

Orifice, J. J., 1995, Comparative petrologic analysis astride the Hackmatack Pond fault in East-Central Maine [Masters thesis]: Orono, University of Maine, 88 p.

Osberg, P. H., 1968, Stratigraphy, structural geology, and metamorphism of the Waterville-Vassalboro area, Maine: Maine Geological Survey Bulletin, v. 20, 64 p.

Osberg, P. H., 1988, Geologic relations within the shale-wacke sequence in south-central Maine, *in* Tucker, R. D., and Marvinney, R. G., eds., Studies in Maine geology: Structure and stratigraphy: Augusta, Maine Geological Survey, p. 51–73.

Osberg, P. H., and Guidotti, C. V., 1974, The geology of the Camden-Rockland area, *in* Osberg, P. H., ed., Geology of east-central and north-central Maine: New England Intercollegiate Geologic Conference Guidebook, v. 66, p. 48–60.

Osberg, P. H., Hussey, A. M., II, and Boone, G. M., 1985, Bedrock geologic map of Maine: Augusta, Maine Geological Survey, scale 1:500,000.

Osberg, P. H., Tucker, R. D., and Berry, H. N., IV, 1995, Is the Acadian suture lost?, *in* Hussey, A. M., II, and Johnson, R. A., eds., Guidebook to field trips in southern Maine and adjacent New Hampshire: New England Intercollegiate Geological Conference Guidebook, v. 87, p. 145–171.

Pankiwskyj, K. A., 1976, Preliminary report on the geology of the Liberty 15' quadrangle and adjoining parts of the Burnham, Brooks, Belfast, and Vassalboro quadrangles in south-central Maine: Maine Geological Survey Open File Report 76-29, 16 p.

Pankiwskyj, K. A., 1996, Structure and stratigraphy across the Hackmatack Pond fault, Kennebec and Waldo Counties, Maine: Maine Geological Survey Open File Report 96-2, 15 p.

Paterson, S. R., and Tobisch, O. T., 1988, Using pluton ages to date regional deformations; Problems with commonly used criteria: Geology, v. 16, p. 1108–1111.

Rankin, D. W., 1994, Continental margin of the eastern United States: Past and present, *in* Speed, R. C., ed., Phanerozoic evolution of North American continent-ocean transitions: Geological Society of America, DNAG Continent-Ocean Transect Volume, p. 129–218.

Snee, L. W., Sutter, J. F., and Kelly, W. C., 1988, Thermochronology of economic mineral deposits: Dating mineralization at Panasqueira, Portugal, by high-precision $^{40}Ar/^{39}Ar$ age spectrum techniques on muscovite: Economic Geology, v. 83, p. 335–354.

Solar, G. S., 1996, Relationship between ductile deformation and granite magma transfer, Tumbledown Mountain area, west-central Maine, *in* Van Baalen, M. R., ed., Guidebook to field trips in northern New Hampshire and adjacent regions of Maine and Vermont: New England Intercollegiate Geological Conference Guidebook, v. 88, p. 341–362.

Stewart, D. B., 1989, Crustal processes in Maine: American Mineralogist, v. 74, p. 698–714.

Stewart, D. B., and Lux, D. R., 1988, Lithologies and metamorphic age of the Precambrian rocks of Seven Hundred Acre Island and vicinity, Islesboro, Penobscot Bay, Maine: Geological Society of America Abstracts with Programs, v. 20, p. 73.

Stewart, D. B., and Wones, D. R., 1974, Bedrock geology of northern Penobscot Bay area, *in* Osberg, P. H., ed., Geology of east-central and north-central Maine: New England Intercollegiate Geologic Conference Guidebook, v. 66, p. 223–239.

Stewart, D. B., Wright, B. E., Unger, J. D., Phillips, J. D., and Hutchinson, D. R., 1993, Global geoscience transect 8: Quebec-Maine-gulf of Maine transect, southeastern Canada, northeastern United States of America: U.S. Geological Survey Miscellaneous Investigations Series Map I-2329, scale 1:1,000,000.

Stewart, D. B., Tucker, R. D., and West, D. P., Jr., 1995a, Genesis of Silurian composite terrane in northern Penobscot Bay, *in* Hussey, A. M., II, and Johnson, R. A., eds., Guidebook to field trips in southern Maine and adjacent New Hampshire: New England Intercollegiate Geological Conference Guidebook, v. 87, p. 29–49.

Stewart, D. B., Unger, J. D., and Hutchinson, D. R., 1995b, Silurian tectonic history of Penobscot Bay region, Maine: Atlantic Geology, v. 31, p. 67–79.

Swanson, M. T., 1988, Pseudotachylyte-bearing strike-slip duplex structures from the Fort Foster brittle zone of southernmost Maine: Journal of Structural Geology, v. 10, p. 813–828.

Swanson, M. T., 1992, Late Acadian–Alleghenian transpressional deformation: Evidence from asymmetric boudinage in the Casco Bay area, coastal Maine: Journal of Structural Geology, v. 14, p. 323–341.

Swanson, M. T., 1995a, Distributed ductile dextral shear strain throughout the Casco Bay area, *in* Hussey, A. M., II, and Johnson, R. A., eds., Guidebook to field trips in southern Maine and adjacent New Hampshire: New England Intercollegiate Geological Conference Guidebook, v. 87, p. 1–13.

Swanson, M. T., 1995b, Detailed structure of brittle strike-slip faults in coastal Maine exposures, *in* Hussey, A. M., II, and Johnson, R. A., eds., Guidebook to field trips in southern Maine and adjacent New Hampshire: New England Intercollegiate Geological Conference Guidebook, v. 87, p. 291–301.

Swanson, M. T., Pollock, S. G., and Hussey, A. M., II, 1986, The structural and stratigraphic development of the Casco Bay Group at Harpswell Neck, Maine, *in* Newberg, D. W., ed., Guidebook to field trips in southwestern Maine: New England Intercollegiate Geological Conference Guidebook, v. 78, p. 350–370.

Tomascak, P. B., Krogstad, E. J., and Walker, R. J., 1996, U-Pb monazite geochronology of granitic rocks from Maine: Implications for late Paleozoic tectonics in the northern Appalachians: Journal of Geology, v. 104, p. 185–195.

West, D. P., Jr., 1995, The Norumbega fault zone in south-central Maine: A trip through 80 million years of dextral shear deformation, *in* Hussey, A. M., II, and Johnson, R. A., eds., Guidebook to field trips in southern Maine and adjacent New Hampshire: New England Intercollegiate Geological Conference Guidebook, v. 87, p. 125–143.

West, D. P., Jr., and Hubbard, M. S., 1997, Progressive localization of deformation during exhumation of a major strike-slip shear zone: Norumbega fault zone, south-central Maine, USA: Tectonophysics, v. 273, p. 185–202.

West, D. P., Jr., and Lux, D. R., 1993, Dating mylonitic deformation by the ^{40}Ar/^{39}Ar method: An example from the Norumbega fault zone, Maine: Earth and Planetary Science Letters, v. 120, p. 221–237.

West, D. P., Jr., Lux, D. R., and Hussey, A. M., II, 1988, ^{40}Ar/^{39}Ar mineral ages from southwestern Maine: Evidence for late Paleozoic metamorphism: Maritime Sediments and Atlantic Geology, v. 24, p. 225–239.

West, D. P., Jr., Ludman, A., and Lux, D. R., 1992, Silurian age for the Pocomoonshine gabbro-diorite and its regional tectonic implications: American Journal of Science, v. 292, p. 253–273.

West, D. P., Jr., Lux, D. R., and Hussey, A. M., II, 1993, Contrasting thermal histories across the Flying Point fault, southwestern Maine: Evidence for Mesozoic displacement: Geological Society of America Bulletin, v. 105, p. 1478–1490.

West, D. P., Jr., Guidotti, C. V., and Lux, D. R., 1995, Silurian orogenesis in the western Penobscot Bay region, Maine: Canadian Journal of Earth Sciences, v. 32, p. 1845–1858.

Wintsch, R. P., Sutter, J. F., Kunk, M. J., Aleinikoff, J. N., and Dorais, M. J., 1992, Contrasting P-T-t paths: Thermochronologic evidence for a late Paleozoic final assembly of the Avalon composite terrane in the New England Appalachians: Tectonics, v. 11, p. 672–689.

Zen, E-an, 1989, Tectonostratigraphic terranes in the Northern Appalachians: Their distribution, origin, and age; evidence for their existence: International Geological Congress field trip guidebook T359: Washington, D.C., American Geophysical Union, 69 p.

MANUSCRIPT ACCEPTED BY THE SOCIETY JUNE 9, 1998

Geological Society of America
Special Paper 331
1999

Constraints on timing and displacement of multistage shearing in the Norumbega fault system, eastern Maine

Allan Ludman
Department of Geology, Queens College, City University of New York, Flushing, New York 11367-1597, and Ph.D. Program in Earth and Environmental Sciences, City University Graduate School and University Center, 365 Fifth Avenue, New York, New York 10036
Antonio Lanzirotti
Department of Earth and Space Sciences, State University of New York, Stony Brook, New York 11794
Daniel Lux
Department of Geological Sciences, University of Maine, Orono, Maine 04469
Wang Chunzeng
Department of Geology, Queens College, City University of New York, Flushing, New York 11367-1597, and Department of Geology, Guilin Institute of Technology, Guilin, Guangxi, China

ABSTRACT

Field and geochronologic evidence indicates that the shallow crustal segment of the Norumbega fault system in eastern Maine underwent sporadic deformation for at least 200 m.y., from Middle Devonian through Jurassic time. Two early episodes spaced closely around 380 Ma accounted for most of the dextral strike-slip offset along the fault system. The Deblois (ca. 384 Ma) and Bottle Lake (ca. 380 Ma) plutons bracket the first event, and the second appears to have occurred shortly after the Bottle Lake pluton intruded. These events are attributed to plate adjustments following two orogenic pulses in the region, in the Late Silurian (the Salinian event of Stewart et al.) and the Middle Devonian (Acadian). Some faults of the second event were subsequently reactivated as normal faults accompanying Jurassic (and later?) rifting and others may have undergone dextral oblique-slip motion during the Late Pennsylvanian–Early Permian Alleghanian orogeny. Additional dip-slip movement during Carboniferous transtension is possible, given the history of similar faults in the region, but is as yet unproven.

Despite its long history and broad regional extent, the Norumbega fault system appears to have caused relatively minor offset since Devonian time. Bed-parallel dextral faulting during the first episode is difficult to measure, but appears to be about 60 km. Offset of the Deblois and Bottle Lake plutons on three high-strain zones documents ~50 km of dextral motion during the second event. An additional 12–15 km dextral offset during this event is estimated by extrapolating from outcrop-scale structures to areas of diffuse strain that separate the high-strain zones. Jurassic dip-slip reactivation involved 1.5–2.5 km of vertical motion, as revealed in a seismic reflection transect across part of the fault system.

INTRODUCTION

The discovery of the Norumbega fault zone in Maine by Stewart and Wones (1974) preceded by only a few years the development of the exotic terrane concept (Coney et al., 1980; Monger and Irving, 1980), and the Norumbega was the first fault in the northern Appalachians proposed as a suture separating far-traveled terranes (Kent and Opdyke, 1978). Several similar

Ludman, A., Lanzirotti, A., Lux, D., and Wang Chunzeng, 1999, Constraints on timing and displacement of multistage shearing in the Norumbega fault system, eastern Maine, *in* Ludman, A., and West, D. P., Jr., eds., Norumbega Fault System of the Northern Appalachians: Boulder, Colorado, Geological Society of America Special Paper 331.

models for the fault zone followed (e.g., Williams and Hatcher, 1983; Zen, 1983; Keppie, 1989), but were refuted by more detailed paleomagnetic analyses (Kent and Opdyke, 1984) and field studies (Ludman, 1981, 1991). Subsequent mapping (e.g., Newberg, 1985; Swanson, this volume; West, 1993, 1995, this volume; Pankiwskyj, 1996) indicates that the 300–400-m-wide Norumbega fault zone described by Stewart and Wones is but one of several strands of a major fault system in southwestern and south-central Maine, and comparable complexity is now recognized in eastern Maine—the area discussed here. This chapter takes the broad view of Norumbega deformation, renaming the structure as the Norumbega fault system. The system is at least 400 km long and 25 to 40 km wide (Fig. 1), and was the locus of intense faulting along the northwestern margin of the Coastal lithotectonic block and southwestern margin of the Kearsarge–Central Maine synclinorium (Osberg et. al., 1985).

Although many of the early controversies concerning the Norumbega fault zone have been settled, the role of the Norumbega fault system in northern Appalachian orogenesis is still unresolved. Hubbard (this volume) suggests that the fault system was part of a 300-km-wide terrane boundary associated with perhaps as much as 1900 km of dextral displacement. Geochemical (Brock, 1993; Ayuso, this volume; Tomascak et al., 1996) and geophysical (Doll et al., 1996; Coblentz, 1988) data provide important clues to its significance as a terrane boundary, but two crucial issues remain before its role(s) in regional tectonism can be determined—the precise timing of faulting and an accurate measure of displacement.

This chapter addresses both issues. A time table for Norumbega faulting in eastern Maine is proposed, based on field relationships and new geochronologic data; events in fault zones are correlated across the 40 km width of the fault system, and then are traced along strike to the southwest to the mid-crustal segment described by West (this volume). Estimates of displacement are then discussed and tied, where possible, to individual stages of activity. Finally, these data are used to evaluate the tectonic significance of the fault system during a span encompassing early Paleozoic through at least Mesozoic time.

BACKGROUND

The Norumbega fault system is one of the largest fault systems in the Appalachian orogen, its maximum proposed length

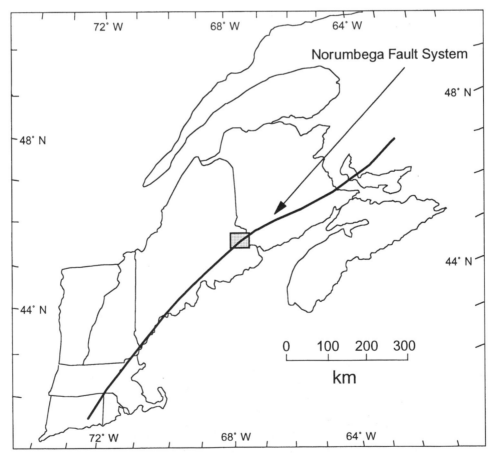

Figure 1. Possible maximum extent of the Norumbega fault system (NFS) in the northern Appalachians. Modified after Osberg et al. (1985) and Williams (1978). Solid line shows where NFS is mapped continuously: dashed lines indicate possible extensions discussed in text. No attempt is made to show full width of the system. Rectangle outlines area discussed in this paper.

exceeding that of the San Andreas system (Fig. 1). The system is mapped continuously for more than 400 km from Casco Bay in southwestern Maine to west-central New Brunswick near Fredericton. It probably extends northeastward through the New Brunswick Carboniferous basins (W. van de Poll, 1996, personal commun.), and possibly as far as the Gulf of St. Lawrence north of Prince Edward Island (Durling and Marillier, 1990). Possible connections with faults of southern New England are discussed in this volume (Goldstein and Hepburn; Bothner and Hussey), but the continuation of the system south of Casco Bay is as yet poorly understood.

Differential exhumation along the Norumbega fault system reveals middle- through shallow crustal levels during deformation (Hubbard et al., 1995; Hubbard and Wang, this volume). Most previous work focused on the deeper segment, exposed in southwestern and south-central Maine, where the Norumbega fault system comprises several fault strands (Newberg, 1985; Hussey, 1988; West, 1993; Pankiwskyj, 1996) and ranges from at least 25 km wide near Casco Bay (Swanson, 1992) to more than 30 km northwest of Penobscot Bay (West, 1993). This paper

examines the Norumbega fault system in eastern Maine, where the shallow-crustal segment of the system is best exposed and where dimensions and complexity comparable to those of southwestern Maine are now recognized.

Figure 2 is a simplified map of the Norumbega fault system in eastern Maine where it cuts low-grade metasedimentary rocks of the Fredericton belt, epizonal granites of the Deblois and Bottle Lake plutons, and post-Acadian molasse (Ludman, 1998; Ludman and Gibbons, this volume). The fault system is at least 40 km wide, consisting of three 2–5-km-wide high strain zones (Codyville, Waite, Kellyland) separated by broader areas of relatively low strain. Each high-strain zone contains numerous anastomosing faults, a geometry illustrated best by the well-exposed Waite fault zone. The intervening low-strain areas contain little evidence of shearing except for isolated brittle faults (Fig. 2).

Until recently, the timing of Norumbega fault system activity has been uncertain. Uniform orogen-parallel shear fabrics in southwestern and south-central Maine forestalled early attempts to identify individual fault episodes, and multiple events were recognized only after regional chronologic and thermochrono-

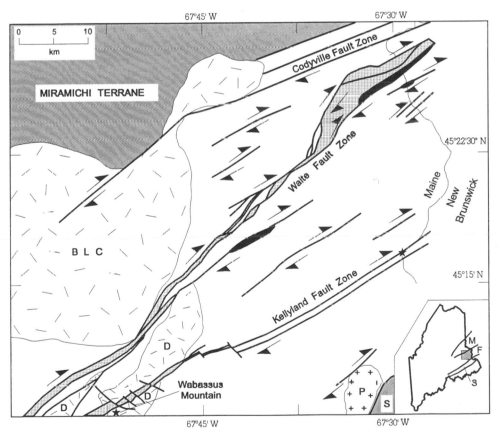

Figure 2. Simplified geologic map of eastern Maine showing relationships among the Norumbega fault system, lithotectonic terranes, and plutons. Inset shows boundaries of Miramichi (M), Fredericton (F), and St. Croix (S) terranes. Main map: white area = Fredericton belt; black fill = post-Acadian redbeds. Arrows indicate motion on faults of the Norumbega system. Stippled pattern = Norumbega fault zone mylonite and cataclasite. Random dash pattern = granitic batholiths: BLC = Bottle Lake plutonic complex, D = Deblois pluton. Plus signs denote mafic and intermediate pluton: P = Pocomoonshine gabbro-diorite.

182

A. Ludman et al.

logic studies disclosed the longevity and complexity of activity in the mid-crustal segment (see review in West, this volume). In contrast, varied fault orientations and crosscutting relationships in the shallow-crustal segment in eastern Maine reveal a multi-stage history of sporadic activity separated by strain-free intervals (Ludman, 1998; Ludman and Gibbons, this volume). Relationships of individual fault stages with dated plutons and Carboniferous molasse outline the sequence of Norumbega fault system faulting (outlined in the following), the chronology of which is discussed herein.

The absence of offset markers in the mid-crustal segment has limited the few previous estimates of Norumbega fault system displacement to approximations of cumulative offset, the sum of all faulting over the span of activity of the system. Kent and Opdyke's (1978) paleomagnetic estimate of 1500 km of sinistral post-Devonian Norumbega fault system offset was later revised to less than 150 km of dextral motion (Kent and Opdyke, 1984). Swanson (1992, 1994) estimated 150–300 km of dextral displacement by extrapolating from outcrop-scale ductile shear zones to the entire Norumbega system in southwestern Maine. In south-central Maine, Johnson and Wones (1984) inferred 35 km of dextral displacement near the southwestern margin of the epizonal segment by matching offset segments of the Lucerne pluton and Turner Mountain syenite, but this measurement was along what is now recognized as only one of the Norumbega high-strain zones.

Displacement in the shallow segment during at least some episodes of Norumbega fault system dextral shearing can be measured directly from displaced pluton–host-rock contacts and offset post-Acadian unconformities in eastern Maine and New Brunswick. In addition, the identification of distinct fault stages makes it possible to correlate some increments of these offsets with specific periods in Norumbega fault system history, and thus to evaluate models for its tectonic role during those times.

SEQUENCE OF MULTISTAGE NORUMBEGA DEFORMATION IN EASTERN MAINE

Figure 3 outlines the post-Middle Silurian deformation recorded in rocks that host the Norumbega fault system in eastern Maine. Middle to Late Silurian upright folding affected the Fredericton belt (West et al., 1993), and the postfolding, Late Silurian (ca. 424 Ma; West et al., 1992) Pocomoonshine gabbro-diorite and Devonian (see below) Deblois pluton intruded prior to initial Norumbega activity (Ludman, 1991). Four stages of shearing then occurred, each identified by its fault orientations and by crosscutting relationships with structures of the other stages. Evidence for this sequence is outlined briefly here. Readers wishing a more detailed discussion are referred to Ludman and Gibbons (this volume) and Ludman (1998).

The earliest Norumbega fault system deformation, stage 1 of Ludman (1998) and Ludman and Gibbons (this volume), produced outcrop-scale bed-parallel dextral faults in metasedimentary rocks (Fig. 4A) and a penetrative foliation in granite

Deformation		Orientation	Motion	Dateable material (New data reported here)
MULTIPLE NORUMBEGA FAULT STAGES	Stage 4	330°-350°/Steep	⇄	
	Stage 3	290°-315°/Steep	⇄	
	Reactivated Stage 2	050°-060°/Steep		Mylonite and ultramylonite in Kellyland fault zone (??)
		040°-060°/Steep	√∧	Carboniferous redbeds (preserved in Waite fault zone)
	Stage 2	040°-060°/Steep	⇄	Stage 2 mylonite: biotite, amphibole, muscovite
				Bottle Lake complex Post-Stage 1 dikes
	Stage 1	010°-020°/Steep	⇄	Stage 1 phyllonite(muscovite, biotite); Syn-stage 1 dikes
				Deblois pluton
				Pocomoonshine gabbro-diorite
Upright folding of Fredericton strata		Axial planes: 040°-060°/Steep NW		

Figure 3. Sequence of faulting events in the shallow-crustal segment of the Norumbega fault zone (after Ludman and Gibbons, this volume). Bold italics highlight new geochronologic data presented in this paper.

(Fig. 4B), with a common 010°–020° orientation in both lithologies. Stage 1 faults do not apparently offset features on a scale that would enable them to be shown in Figure 2. Stage 1 is expressed in the Deblois pluton by a penetrative foliation defined by quartz that has been converted by crystal-plastic processes to continuous ribbons that anastomose around brittlely deformed microcline megacrysts and albite crystals (see Ludman and Gibbons, this volume). Indicators of dextral motion are rare, suggesting that strain in the granite was largely coaxial—a flattening or pure shear strain. Early stage 1 fabrics in metasedimentary rocks include a weak pressure-solution cleavage in thick-bedded wackes (Fig. 4C) and phyllonitic fabrics in intercalated shales (Fig. 4D). Episodes of vein and dike emplacement were interspersed with episodes of stage 1 shearing in the metasedimentary rocks. Thick ferroan carbonate + quartz veins followed earliest folding, and thinner and less-abundant quartz veins accompanied renewed stage 1 activity (Ludman, 1998). Evidence for dextral offset on stage 1 faults in the metasedimentary rocks is abundant.

The mappable stage 2 dextral faults and high-strain zones in eastern Maine are what previous regional compilations have described as "Norumbega" faults (e.g., Williams, 1978; Osberg et al., 1985), and the stage 2 Waite and Kellyland fault zones can be traced into south-central Maine where they appear to connect with faults mapped by Higgins (1992) and West (1993). Stage 2 is expressed at outcrop scale by thin, northeast- to east-northeast–trending cataclasite zones that cut stage 1 fabrics (Fig. 5, A and B) and by similarly oriented brittle faults that dextrally offset all earlier structures and fabrics. A narrow (~100 m) unique zone of mylonite and ultramylonite crops out in the stage 2 Kellyland fault zone at the contact between the Deblois pluton and metawackes of the Fredericton belt (Fig. 6, A and B).

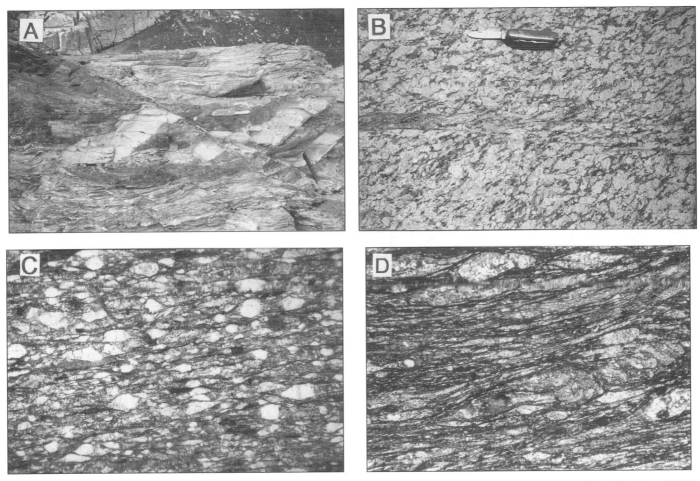

Figure 4. Effects of stage 1 faulting. A: Bed-parallel stage 1 faults (left to right) offset felsite dikes dextrally at Kellyland. Knife is 16 cm long. B: Ribbon quartz (dark) defines stage 1 foliation (lower left to upper right) in Deblois granite at Wabassus Mountain. Note late cataclasite vein parallel to knife. C: Photomicrograph showing stage 1 pressure solution cleavage in chlorite-grade metawacke (uncrossed polarizers, width of field = 6.5 mm). D: Photomicrograph showing stage 1 phyllonitic fabric in chlorite-grade pelitic layer at Kellyland (uncrossed polarizers, width of field = 8.5 mm).

Stage 2 structures are oriented 35°–50° more easterly than those of stage 1 and clearly cut stage 1 structures. Stage 1 occurred by at least partly ductile mechanisms in both metasedimentary and granitic rocks, whereas stage 2 appears to have involved almost entirely brittle processes. These relationships indicate that stages 1 and 2 should be considered as separate events in Norumbega fault system history. This conclusion is supported by euhedral carbonate crystals that grew in metasedimentary rocks and fine-grained dikes that intruded the Deblois granite during a static, strain free period separating the two stages (Fig. 7, A and B; see Ludman, 1998).

Stages 3 and 4 produced near-vertical outcrop-scale cataclasite bands oriented 290° and 340°, respectively, but map-scale displacement is restricted to a few hundred meters on a few stage 3 faults. Subhorizontal slickenlines and offset stage 1 and stage 2 structures indicate dextral motion during stage 3 and sinistral motion during stage 4. Evidence presented in the following indicates that recurrent activity on stage 1 faults over a relatively short time span and multiple reactivation of stage 2 faults over a

much longer interval caused most of the dextral displacement along the Norumbega fault system. Stages 3 and 4 do not seem to have caused significant offset and will not be discussed further.

Constraints on timing of stage 1 and 2 activity

Fault-pluton relationships broadly constrain the onset of shallow-crustal Norumbega fault system activity to post-Early Devonian time. Detailed mapping in the contact aureoles of the Pocomoonshine, Deblois, and Bottle Lake plutons reveals no evidence of Norumbega faulting prior to their emplacement. Stage 1 fabrics are observed in the Fredericton belt and Deblois pluton, but the Bottle Lake pluton shows no sign of that deformation, even though it intrudes a broad area of metasedimentary rocks sheared during stage 1. This suggests that stage 1 was bracketed between the intrusion of the Deblois and Bottle Lake bodies.

The Waite and Codyville fault zones dextrally offset the Bottle Lake complex and the Deblois pluton, so these batholiths set a maximum age for stage 2 dextral strike-slip motion. The

Figure 5 Stage 2 brittle faulting. A(above): Coarse grained cataclasite filling stage 2 fault zone in chlorite-grade metasedimentary rocks at Kellyland. Fingers at upper left give scale. B(to the right): Fine-grained cataclasite cutting foliated (stage 1) Deblois granite at Wabassus Mountain.

and correlating events in each of the three high-strain zones. The next section outlines progress toward that goal.

TIMING OF STAGE 1 AND 2 NORUMBEGA FAULTING

Our chronologic studies focused on the Kellyland fault zone at Wabassus Mountain (see Fig. 2) where relationships among coarse-grained Deblois granite, stage 1 and 2 structures, and fine-grained granitic dikes provide the best opportunity to date shallow-crustal Norumbega fault system deformation. Deformation fabrics indicate that the Deblois pluton had cooled to approximately ~275 °C before stage 1 began (Ludman and Gibbons, this volume). Because a rapid cooling rate is inferred for this epizonal pluton, its emplacement age should approximate the onset of Norumbega fault system activity. The only previously reported date for the pluton was 393±17 Ma (Rb/Sr whole-rock age; Loiselle et al., 1983) but this came from the southwestern part of the pluton, more than 60 km from the area described in this chapter.

Strategy for dating stage 1

Dating the Deblois pluton at Wabassus Mountain would provide a maximum age for stage 1, and the minimum age, as discussed herein, is constrained by emplacement of the Whitney Cove pluton of the Bottle Lake complex at 380±5 Ma (concordant Rb/Sr whole-rock and U/Pb zircon ages; Ayuso et al., 1984). In addition, fine-grained granitic dikes at Wabassus Mountain appear to bracket stage 1 deformation. Some randomly oriented dikes that display intense stage 1 foliation intruded before stage 1, whereas unfoliated dikes that cut the foliation in the host granite were postkinematic with respect to stage 1. A few dikes parallel stage 1 foliation in the granite but also exhibit that foliation. Their intrusion is inferred to have been controlled by that foliation and they may therefore have intruded during stage 1 (Ludman and Gibbons, this volume). Ages for the dikes would therefore measure the durations of stage 1 and the interval separating it from stage 2.

minimum age and duration of that motion are poorly understood because those fault zones were reactivated as dip-slip (and perhaps strike-slip) faults after their initial motion. Involvement of post-Acadian (Carboniferous?) redbeds in faulting on the Waite fault zone in eastern (Ludman, 1998) and south-central Maine (Higgins, 1992; Osberg et al., 1985) and of Pennsylvanian rocks along the Fredericton fault (the continuation of the Waite fault zone in western New Brunswick; McLeod et al., 1994) indicates late Paleozoic or younger movement on at least that strand of the Norumbega system. Map relationships yield no further constraints on the timing of this late activity.

Radiometric dating of the Bottle Lake and Deblois plutons, of dikes, and of fault-generated minerals in mylonites will eventually yield a detailed chronology of shallow-crustal Norumbega fault system activity, based on the relationships shown in Figure 3. The ultimate goal is to understand how shallow-crustal faulting was manifested through time across the fault system by dating

Figure 6. Mylonite and ultramylonite derived from Deblois granite in the Kellyland fault zone. A: Mylonite (light colored, coarse grained) sandwiched between two ultramylonite layers. Diameter of lens cap is 5.5 mm. B: Photomicrograph showing ultramylonite cut by late conjugate faults (uncrossed polarizers, width of field = 8.5 mm).

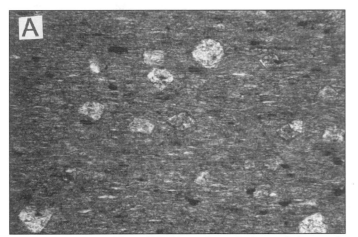

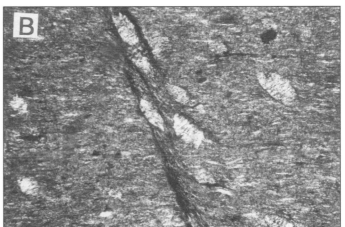

Figure 7. Evidence for strain-free period separating stages 1 and 2 in metasedimentary rocks. A: Photomicrograph showing post-stage 1 euhedral ferroan carbonate rhombs enclosing stage 1 foliation. B: Photomicrograph showing post-stage 1 carbonate rhombs deformed in stage 2 microfaults. Note dextral rotation of stage 1 inclusion trains. Both photographs: uncrossed polarizers, width of fields = 8.5 mm.

Methods

Three samples were collected in the Deblois pluton at Wabassus Mountain to pinpoint the age of stage 1 shearing: undeformed hornblende-biotite granite just south of the Kellyland high-strain zone (WAB-1); granite highly sheared during stage 1 (WAB-2); and a foliated, possibly synkinematic dike (WAB-3). Primary igneous biotites separated from samples WAB-1 and WAB-2 were dated by standard $^{40}Ar/^{39}Ar$ methods at the University of Maine at Orono (see West et al., 1992 for experimental procedures) and U-Pb zircon dating was carried out at the State University of New York at Stony Brook.

Zircons were separated from crushes, cleaned in 1N HNO_3 (30 min.), and dissolved for seven days using mixed $HF-HNO_3$ in 0.3 ml Teflon capsules in a 125 ml Parr acid digestion bomb at

215 °C (Parrish, 1987). Isotope dilution analyses of Pb and U used a mixed $^{205}Pb-^{235}U$ spike. U and Pb were separated using AG1X8 resin with an HCl eluent (after Krogh, 1973). Total analytical Pb and U blanks during the period of analysis were 20–40 pg and 3–15 pg, respectively. Pb was analyzed on a National Bureau of Standards design 12 inch, 90° sector mass spectrometer using single Re filaments with H_3PO_4-silica gel. During the period of analysis, Pb fractionation was 0.12%/amu based on equal atom SRM-982. For SRM-982 we measure Pb isotopic ratios of $^{206}Pb/^{204}Pb = 36.635(20)$, $^{207}Pb/^{206}Pb = 0.46647(16)$, and $^{208}Pb/^{206}Pb = 0.99739(34)$ (2σ external reproducibility).

U was analyzed as a metal measured statically in multiple Faraday cups on a Finnigan MAT 262 mass spectrometer using single Re filaments loaded with graphite. U analyses for this period were corrected for 0.11%/amu fractionation based on U standard U-930. During the period of analysis, we measured $^{235}U/^{238}U$ = 17.391(22) on U standard U-930 (2σ external reproducibility). The uncertainties for the U/Pb and $^{207}Pb/^{206}Pb$ ratios (2σ), ages, and corresponding uncertainties were calculated according to the method of Ludwig (1991a, 1991b) using his PBDAT and ISOPLOT regression programs.

Results

U-Pb analyses of the zircons are shown in Table 1 and Figure 8 shows concordia diagrams for WAB-1, WAB-2, and WAB-3. Common Pb corrections were made on the basis of Pb isotopic compositions of leached feldspars from the same rocks. Uranium content in all zircons was low, so that large fractions had to be analyzed rather than individual crystals in order to obtain enough lead. In addition, $^{206}Pb/^{204}Pb$ ratios for zircons from all three samples are unusually low, leading to the large uncertainties.

Undeformed Deblois granite (WAB-1) is clearly Devonian, regression yielding an upper intercept age of 383 ± 14 Ma and a lower intercept age of 87 ± 150 Ma. A more precise mean $^{207}Pb^*/^{206}Pb^*$ age of 384 ± 5 Ma was obtained for granite with a strong stage 1 foliation (WAB-2). The data allow two possible interpretations. If inheritance is negligible, the fractions dated as greater than 380 Ma require the pluton to be older than 380 Ma. However, WAB-1 has one concordant analysis at 373 Ma; this could be the true age of the body and the older ages could be the result of inheritance. That there is no evidence of stage 1 deformation in the nearby 380 Ma Bottle Lake pluton suggests that the first interpretation is more likely. The 384 Ma age of WAB-2 is therefore inferred to be the best date for intrusion of the Deblois pluton.

Preliminary $^{40}Ar/^{39}Ar$ dating of undeformed magmatic biotites from WAB-1 and deformed magmatic biotites from WAB-2 yield slightly younger ages (Table 2, Fig. 9). The release spectrum for biotites from the relatively undeformed WAB-1 granite is somewhat more disturbed than that for the highly deformed WAB-2 biotites, and may indicate partial resetting during postemplacement deformation that was not intense enough to produce typical stage 1 fabrics. The more homogeneous release spectrum of WAB-2 may reflect more complete resetting during stage 1 so that the plateau age may date the main stage 1 event.

The fine-grained dike from which WAB-3 was collected parallels stage 1 foliation in the megacrystic host granite, and also exhibits that foliation. The fabric suggests that it also preceded stage 1 deformation, but emplacement during protracted stage 1 is also possible, as already discussed. The U/Pb data support this model, although the very low $^{206}Pb/^{204}Pb$ ratios lead to large error ellipses for the lower U/Pb ratios and intercept ages of 377 ± 56 Ma and 91 ± 308 Ma. If only those fractions with high $^{206}Pb/^{204}Pb$ ratios are used, the age is 376 ± 5 Ma.

Figure 10 summarizes chronologic data currently available for stage 1. The data suggest that stage 1 deformation began around 384 Ma and continued for a few million years, ending before stage 2. As discussed earlier, the absence of stage 1 fabrics

from the Bottle Lake complex sets a minimum age of 380 ± 5 Ma for stage 1. The $^{40}Ar/^{39}Ar$ dating of hornblende and potassic feldspar from undeformed granite (WAB-1) now in progress will help construct a cooling curve for the granite to more closely constrain the maximum age of stage 1, and studies of potassic feldspar porphyroclasts in stage 2 cataclasite may provide better minimum age control.

Strategy for dating stage 2

Stage 2 faults are more difficult to date because some appear to have been reactivated during late Paleozoic and Mesozoic time (see following). In order to ascertain if Norumbega fault system activity was coeval across its entire 40 km width, the age of initial stage 2 activity must be determined separately for each of the three high-strain zones. Age constraints for early stage 2 faulting will be discussed first, followed by evidence for reactivation.

The timing of stage 2 deformation is most tightly constrained in the Codyville fault zone, where stage 2 faults cut the Whitney Cove pluton of the Bottle Lake complex but are intruded by the Passadumkeag River pluton of the same complex. Both bodies are dated as about 380 Ma (±5 m.y.). This suggests that Codyville stage 2 faulting occurred at 380 Ma, only shortly after stage 1.

The maximum age of stage 2 in the Waite fault zone, 12 km across strike to the southeast, is also 380 (±5) Ma, the emplacement age of the Whitney Cove pluton, the southeastern margin of which is cut by its faults. The actual deformation age may be determined from biotite-grade phyllonites and protomylonites exposed in fault-bounded slivers along the Waite zone between Waite and the New Brunswick border (Fig. 2). These are interpreted as the product of stage 2 dynamic metamorphism of Fredericton belt metasedimentary rocks because their fabrics are identical and locally parallel to those in adjacent chlorite-grade fault rocks that pass gradationally into typical Fredericton wackes (Ludman, 1998). Preliminary $^{40}Ar/^{39}Ar$ ages of strongly foliated metamorphic biotite and actinolitic amphibole from Waite fault zone protomylonites are shown in Figure 11 (after Ludman and West, 1994). The three specimens yielded very similar ages centering around 380 Ma, suggesting that the Waite fault zone was, like the Codyville, active at about that time. There is no evidence at this time for the minimum age of stage 2 dextral faulting, so that the duration of this episode in the Waite fault zone is unknown.

The onset of stage 2 shearing in the Kellyland fault zone had to postdate emplacement of the Deblois pluton, development of stage 1 foliation, and injection of post-stage 1 granitic dikes. Ages for the first two events presented here suggest a maximum age for stage 2 slightly greater than 380 Ma. This maximum age will be refined once the post-stage 1 dikes at Wabassus Mountain are dated. At present, the younger limit of stage 2 activity in the Kellyland zone is unknown, but two current $^{40}Ar/^{39}Ar$ studies may pinpoint the age of dextral shearing in both granitic and metasedimentary rocks. Biotite formed in the highest strain stage 2 phyllonites at Kellyland, in an area that otherwise underwent

TABLE 1. U-Pb ZIRCON ISOTOPIC DATA

Fraction	Abundance[†]			Atomic Ratios[§]					Age
	U	Pb	Pb_c	$^{206}Pb/^{204}Pb_{(m)}$	$^{208}Pb/^{206}Pb$	$^{206}Pb*/^{238}U$	$^{207}Pb*/^{235}U$	$^{207}Pb*/^{206}Pb*$	$^{207}Pb*/^{206}Pb*$ (Ma)
WAB-1c									
A	160	10.9	0.6	1060	0.1852	0.06219 (20)	0.4667 (16)	0.05443 (7)	389
B	139	8.5	0.4	1220	0.1163	0.05932 (62)	0.4419 (46)	0.05404 (6)	373
C	19	1.8	0.7	112	0.4319	0.05825 (21)	0.4338 (74)	0.05401 (86)	372
D	159	11.4	1.2	487	0.2241	0.06091 (20)	0.4580 (17)	0.05453 (11)	393
E	138	8.8	0.9	586	0.1484	0.05834 (59)	0.4345 (66)	0.05402 (57)	372
F	20	1.9	0.7	103	0.4549	0.05583 (35)	0.4152 (58)	0.05394 (64)	369
G	27	1.4	0.4	160	0.2970	0.03853 (27)	0.2859 (31)	0.05381 (41)	363
WAB-2u									
A	28	1.6	0.01	1182	0.0355	0.06095 (30)	0.4567 (24)	0.05435 (11)	386
B	24	1.4	0.04	1171	0.0394	0.06010 (23)	0.4500 (18)	0.05431 (6)	383
C	28	1.5	0.01	1249	0.0345	0.05967 (29)	0.4469 (26)	0.05432 (18)	384
WAB-3a									
A	155	10.6	1.7	361	0.1740	0.05948 (22)	0.4445 (21)	0.05420 (17)	379
B	436	27.3	2.2	760	0.1220	0.05938 (22)	0.4431 (18)	0.05412 (9)	376
C	243	14.5	0.6	1554	0.0969	0.05927 (21)	0.4420 (17)	0.05409 (6)	375
D	98	6.9	1.4	255	0.2133	0.05703 (19)	0.4263 (40)	0.05400 (45)	371
E	56	3.5	0.4	471	0.1455	0.05814 (19)	0.4340 (27)	0.05414 (27)	377
F	67	4.2	0.4	630	0.1267	0.05873 (18)	0.4381 (23)	0.05410 (22)	375

[†]Expressed in nanograms analyzed; Pb = ng total Pb, Pb_c = ng common Pb.

[§]$^{206}Pb/^{204}Pv_{(m)}$ is measured ratio corrected for fractionation; other ratios corrected for blank, fractionation, and initial common Pb errors in parentheses are 2s.

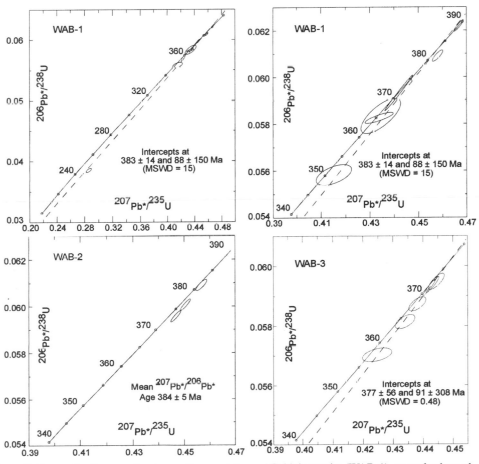

Figure 8. Concordia diagrams for zircons from undeformed Deblois granite (WAB-1), strongly sheared, foliated Deblois granite (WAB-2), and foliated dike (WAB-3).

TABLE 2. ^{40}Ar/^{39}Ar DATA FOR DEBLOIS PLUTON AT WASSABUS MOUNTAIN

WAB-1 Undeformed granite J=.007497

Temp. (°C)	^{40}Ar/^{39}Ar	^{37}Ar/^{39}Ar	^{36}Ar/^{39}Ar	moles ^{39}Ar*	% total ^{39}Ar	% ^{40}Ar rad	K/Ca	Apparent age (Ma)
760	32.614	0.01202	0.02686	26.9	6.4	75.6	40.8	306.1±3.1
900	31.743	0.00649	0.00709	70.2	16.6	93.4	75.5	361.9±3.3
1010	31.976	0.00558	0.00448	82.2	19.4	95.5	88.1	372.0±3.4
1090	31.901	0.00448	0.00456	65.2	15.4	95.7	103.4	371.9±4.0
1130	31.963	0.00799	0.00411	58.7	13.9	96.2	61.3	374.1±3.6
1310	33.217	0.01498	0.00864	32.9	7.8	92.3	32.7	373.1±3.9
FUSE	48.019	0.01715	0.05894	12.6	3.0	63.7	28.6	372.5±4.1
TOTAL				**423.9**	**100.0**			**367.1±7.1**
PLATEAU	AGE							**372.7±4.3**

WAB-2 Highly deformed (Stage 1) granite J=.007778

Temp. (°C)	^{40}Ar/^{39}Ar	^{37}Ar/^{39}Ar	^{36}Ar/^{39}Ar	moles ^{39}Ar*	% total ^{39}Ar	% ^{40}Ar rad	K/Ca	Apparent age (Ma)
760	34.362	0.01697	0.02238	24.5	6.4	80.7	28.98	352.4±4.5
900	31.899	0.00682	0.00556	76.6	20.0	94.8	71.9	381.1±3.5
1010	31.379	0.00810	0.00418	70.1	18.3	96.0	60.5	379.8±3.5
1090	31.217	0.00782	0.00360	61.6	16.1	96.5	62.6	379.9±3.5
1130	30.899	0.01051	0.00311	52.4	13.7	97.0	46.6	378.0±3.4
1230	31.286	0.01867	0.00500	43.0	11.2	95.2	26.2	376.0 3.4
1310	32.835	0.01612	0.01062	30.1	7.9	90.4	30.4	374.7±3.7
FUSE	37.950	0.02920	0.02816	24.6	6.4	78.0	16.8	374.0±6.6
TOTAL				**382.9**	**100.0**			**376.9±3.7**
PLATEAU	AGE							**380.3±3.3**

only chlorite-grade regional metamorphism (Ludman, 1998). The age of these biotites should directly date stage 2 shearing. Thermal histories of potassic feldspar porphyroclasts and microporphyroclasts preserved in stage 2 cataclasite, mylonite, and ultramylonite at Wabassus Mountain may also preserve a record of stage 2 shearing.

Field relationships and preliminary chronologic studies thus suggest that stage 2 deformation in the Codyville and Waite fault zones, spanning the northern 40% of the Norumbega fault system in eastern Maine, began simultaneously ca. 380 Ma. Coeval activity in the Kellyland fault zone cannot be definitely proven at this time, although the maximum age for the onset of stage 2 permits such timing and stage 2 deformation style in that zone is identical to that in the others. The duration of stage 2 dextral faulting in the Waite and Kellyland fault zones is unknown at this time.

POSTDEVONIAN REACTIVATION OF STAGE 2 FAULTS

Dextral strike-slip motion along the stage 2 Kellyland and Waite fault zones is well documented at outcrop scale by subhorizontal slickenlines in granitic and metasedimentary rocks, dextral separation of vertical dikes, steeply dipping beds, and stage 1 foliation, asymmetric fault lenses, and very steeply plunging drag folds adjacent to cataclasite-filled shear zones. Microscopic evidence agrees, in the form of mica fish and asymmetric potassic feldspar, albite, and biotite porphyroclasts. Map-scale dextral shear is evident in formlines of the pre-Norumbega upright folds (Ludman, 1998), confirming that dextral separation of the contacts of the Deblois and Bottle Lake plutons was the result of dextral offset. Data presented herein suggest that this deformation started in Middle Devonian time, ca. 380 Ma .

Evidence is compelling for post-Middle Devonian reactivation of at least the Waite fault zone. Post-Acadian, unmetamorphosed redbeds crop out discontinuously in fault-bounded slivers for more than 100 km along this zone, from western New Brunswick (McLeod et al., 1994) to just east of Bangor (Osberg et al., 1985; Ludman, 1991; Higgins, 1992). The redbeds are Pennsylvanian in New Brunswick (McLeod et al., 1994) and this age has been assigned in Maine without fossil confirmation, but they could be Late Devonian, like the post-Acadian Perry Formation in southeastern Maine (Osberg et al., 1985). Whether they are Pennsylvanian or Late Devonian, however, they are (1) younger than the stage 2 strike-slip faulting and (2) faulted against Fredericton belt metasedimentary rocks and stage 2 biotite-grade protomylonite. It is conceivable that this juxtaposition might have resulted from continued Middle Devonian stage 2 dextral faulting, but two lines of evidence suggest otherwise.

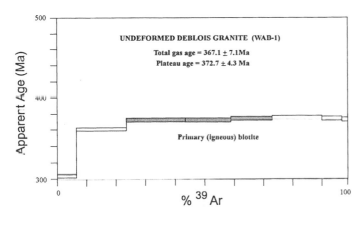

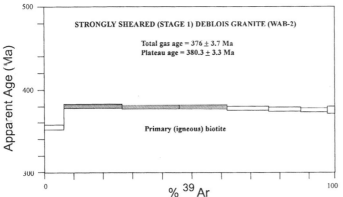

Figure 9. Argon release spectra for undeformed (WAB-1) and highly deformed (stage 1: WAB-2) Deblois granite. (MSWD – mean square of weighed deviation.)

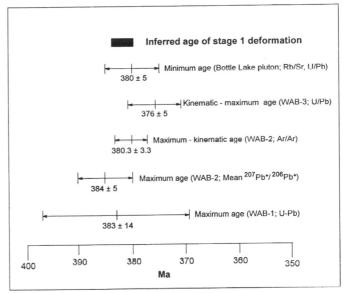

Figure 10. Constraints on timing of stage 1. See text for discussion of specimens.

Foliation in the protomylonites is deformed into a series of open, upright folds but steepens to near-vertical attitudes adjacent to the redbeds, suggesting dip-slip rather than strike-slip movement. Protomylonite is completely retrograded to chlorite or a mass of fine-grained white mica flakes and is separated from the redbeds by a zone of brittle deformation. These changes in conditions, mechanics, and sense of movement suggest a change in crustal position and the passage of time between stage 2 strike-slip movement and juxtaposition of the redbeds and protomylonite, apparently by dip-slip motion.

There is neither field nor geochronologic evidence for the age of this movement, although it was clearly post-Pennsylvanian in New Brunswick. A seismic reflection profile shows that the Waite fault zone cuts steeply through the entire crust and offsets the Moho vertically by ~1.5–2.5 km (Doll et al., 1996). Stewart's (1989) interpretation that the Moho in this region formed during Jurassic rifting led Doll et al. (1996) to propose that the late dip-slip motion on the Waite fault zone was at least late Mesozoic or, lacking any minimum age constraint, perhaps even younger.

A weaker circumstantial case can be made for post-Devonian reactivation of the Kellyland fault zone. In both south-central Maine and the Kellyland fault zone in eastern Maine, narrow bands of extremely high-strain mylonite and ultramylonite pro-

duced by dextral shear are superimposed on broader zones of less-intense shearing (West, 1995; Ludman and West, 1996). Radiometric ages of the early shearing indicate that it was coeval in both areas at ca. 380 Ma, corresponding to stage 2 in eastern Maine. The age of late dextral shearing on the Sandhill Corner fault, one of the narrow high-strain zones in the mid-crustal region, was dated as 290 Ma (Late Pennsylvanian Permian; West and Lux, 1993; West, this volume). Ludman and West (1996) showed that the high-strain mylonitization was at least partially brittle in both areas, and West and Hubbard (1997) proposed that the mylonitization took place at shallower crustal levels than the early (i.e., stage 2) deformation. If the narrow high-strain mylonite zones of the two regions formed during the same event, as appears likely based on their style, mechanics, and relationships to earlier fabrics, Pennsylvanian-Permian dextral reactivation of the Kellyland zone in eastern Maine is suggested. An ongoing study of the thermal history of potassic feldspar microporphyroclasts in the mylonite may resolve this issue. Motion at this time on the Waite fault zone can not be ruled out, although the mylonite and ultramylonite have not been discovered there.

DISPLACEMENT HISTORY

In view of a complex fault history that may span 200 m.y. (from ca. 380 to 180 Ma), the role(s) played by the Norumbega fault system in regional tectonism can be learned only by associating individual displacement increments with their appropriate fault episodes. Offset plutons and Carboniferous redbeds in eastern Maine and New Brunswick measure cumulative separation on each of the three stage 2 high-strain zones (Fig. 12). With the aid of the deformation time table presented above, each increment of stage 2 offset can be assigned to its proper

A. Ludman et al.

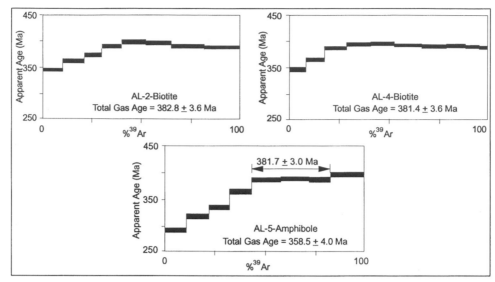

Figure 11. Argon release spectra for metamorphic biotites and actinolitic amphibole from stage 2 proto-mylonite, Waite fault zone.

place in regional accretion history by working backward and subtracting progressively older displacements from the cumulative total.

Stage 2 faults and later reactivations

Kinematic indicators mentioned earlier show that initial stage 2 motion was dominantly dextral strike slip. Most of this displacement was associated with the three high-strain zones, relatively little occurring in the broad zones of weaker strain that separate them (Ludman, 1998). Figure 12 summarizes separation on stage 2 faults in eastern Maine, on the basis of apparent displacement of plutons and their contact aureoles in the Codyville, Waite, and Kellyland fault zones. Separation on the Waite fault zone is still unknown because, although the Whitney Cove pluton is truncated by the Waite zone, the correlative body across the fault is not conclusively identified. The 35 km value used here is obtained by matching the Whitney Cove with the Lucerne pluton—a more probable geochemical and isotopic connection than with any part of the Deblois (Ayuso, 1996, personal commun.). Ludman (1998) estimated a maximum contribution of 12–15 km from the zones of weaker strain separating the three high-strain zones, suggesting total dextral separation of ~65 km for stage 2 structures throughout their evolution.

The tight age control for the Codyville fault zone suggests that the entire 8 km dextral separation of the Whitney Cove pluton and its aureole occurred in the initial stage 2 event, with no contribution from later reactivation. The relatively narrow width of the pluton's contact aureole suggests a moderately to steeply dipping contact. In the absence of evidence for significant oblique-slip movement, the observed separation is attributed to Middle Devonian dextral strike-slip offset.

The Waite fault zone is more complex because its late dip-slip reactivation potentially caused at least some of the inferred 35 km separation. For example, McLeod et al. (1994) mapped about 6 km of dextral separation of the Acadian (Carboniferous-Silurian) unconformity along the continuation of the Waite zone in western New Brunswick. The unconformity dips so gently there that all of the dextral separation probably resulted from downdip migration following vertical motion of the magnitude suggested by Doll et al. (1996). Thus, no significant post-Carboniferous dextral motion is required to explain the dextral separation of the Acadian unconformity, and significant late Paleozoic dextral strike-slip movement is unlikely for the Waite-Fredericton fault zone. Pluton–host-rock contacts dip much more steeply, however, so the dextral separation of the Bottle Lake complex cannot be explained by late dip-slip motion. Postemplacement dextral or oblique-slip motion is required. Evidence presented here again suggests that this motion began during the Middle Devonian, but its duration is not known (see following discussion).

The northeastern apophysis of the Deblois pluton indicates 12–15 km of dextral separation in the Kellyland fault zone, but the actual offset is difficult to calculate for several reasons. The metamorphic aureole at the eastern margin of the Deblois pluton is as wide as 2.2 km, suggesting that the intrusive contact dips gently eastward. Most stage 2 slickenlines are subhorizontal but some plunge as much as 25° (Ludman, 1998), indicating at least some oblique-slip movement that would have a significant effect on separation of a gently dipping contact. Unfortunately, there is no evidence for which side of the fault moved up; thus, the separation could be an underestimate of displacement (south side up) or an overestimate (north side up). Dextral strike-slip movement beginning in Middle Devonian time is certainly at least partly responsible for the offset, but there may have been some component of Permian movement, as discussed herein.

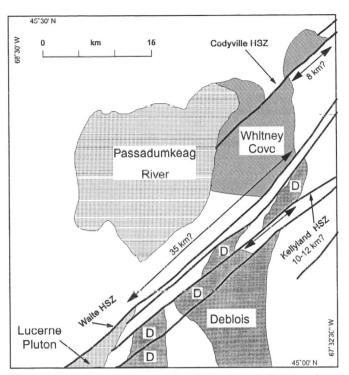

Figure 12. Map showing post-plutonism Norumbega fault system dextral separation in eastern Maine. See text for relationships between separation and actual offset. HSZ = high-strain zone.

Stage 1 displacement

The absence of offset map-scale markers and partially coaxial nature of stage 1 make it more difficult to estimate displacement during that event than during stage 2. Extrapolation from outcrop-scale offset to the full 40 km width of the Norumbega fault system is the only feasible method, but is more problematical than the approach used by Swanson (1992, 1994) in the deeper segment because stage 1 strain distribution is not fully understood and lithologic control of strain partitioning appears to have been significant in eastern Maine. Ludman (1998) estimated total stage 1 dextral offset at about 60 km, on the basis of a large exposure of sheared metasedimentary rocks at Kellyland, where strain was broadly distributed but localized within pelite beds and most offset is associated with pelite-rich horizons, little with the more abundant massive beds of wacke. Extrapolation to the entire 40 km width of the Norumbega fault system requires two assumptions: that the Kellyland exposure records average stage 1 strain and that relative amounts of displacement can be correlated with the amount of pelite in the Fredericton belt.

The first assumption is difficult to justify. The Kellyland fault zone reveals a range of stage 1 intensity in the Deblois granite, including areas that appear to have undergone greater strain than the metasedimentary rocks at Kellyland (Ludman and Gibbons, this volume). In addition, although stage 1 features are identified throughout most of the Fredericton belt, bedrock control is insufficient to confirm that strain at the baseline Kellyland outcrop is

"average" for stage 1 in metasedimentary rocks throughout the belt. The estimate of stage 1 dextral offset is thus preliminary, and will undoubtedly be modified by more detailed mapping.

DISCUSSION

Some issues concerning timing and displacement during faulting in the study area are unresolved, but a time table for deformation in the shallow-crustal Norumbega segment in eastern Maine can be constructed in light of what is already known (Fig. 13). It may never be possible to answer some of the remaining questions because even in the active San Andreas system, arguably the world's most intensely studied, the same issues of reactivation, timing of multiple fault episodes, and how much offset has occurred during each episode are debated (e.g., Dillon and Ehlig, 1993; James et al., 1993; Sims, 1993).

There is no evidence for significant faulting on northeast-trending faults in the study area prior to emplacement of the Deblois pluton at about 384 Ma. Elsewhere in the northern Appalachians, in Newfoundland (Holdsworth, 1994) and in north-central Maine (Hibbard and Hall, 1993), significant sinistral shearing accompanied an important Late Silurian accretionary event. Although Late Silurian orogenesis is well documented in and southeast of the area described in this paper (West et al., 1992; Osberg et al., 1995; Stewart et al., 1995), sinistral faulting has not been reported. Silurian sinistral shearing was either unimportant in the Coastal lithotectonic belt, or evidence for it has been obliterated by pervasive Norumbega dextral fabrics.

Data discussed herein suggest that dextral strike-slip faulting began simultaneously across the 40-km-wide Norumbega fault system in eastern Maine ca. 384 Ma, following the Acadian orogeny. Unfortunately, the overlap in current radiometric age control precludes differentiation of stages 1 and 2, even though field and petrographic evidence prove that they were separate episodes. This problem may be remedied by current $^{40}Ar/^{39}Ar$ studies of the interval between the two stages, but it is likely that stage 2 followed stage 1 too closely for the two to be distinguished. The structural relationship between stages 1 and 2 is one of the major questions concerning dextral faulting in the shallow segment of the Norumbega fault system.

Another problem is the role played by the Norumbega fault system in post-Acadian Carboniferous faulting that affected most of the Maritime Appalachians and created the Narragansett and Worcester basins in southern New England. Williams et al. (1995) showed that the large Carboniferous basins of New Brunswick, Nova Scotia, and the Gulf of St. Lawrence formed by transtensional reactivation of northeast-trending faults that had originated in the Devonian as dextral strike-slip structures. The Norumbega system, the largest component of this regional Devonian fault network, almost certainly underwent some Carboniferous motion. West (this volume) and West and Hubbard (1997) have suggested that mid-crustal activity in the Norumbega fault system spanned Carboniferous time, with possibly continuous

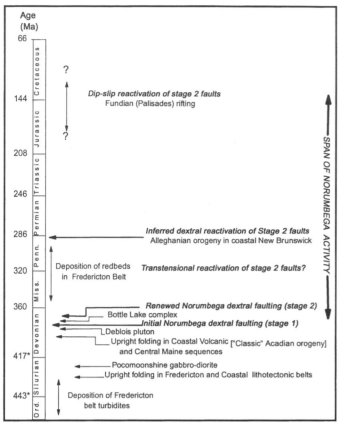

Figure 13. Time table for inferred activity along the Norumbega fault system in eastern Maine. Asterisk indicates revised ages from Tucker and McKerrow (1995).

ductile faulting from 380 to 290 Ma, but the lack of firm control for the youngest stage 2 activity makes it impossible to determine whether the shallow-crustal segment was active during this time.

Permian dextral strike-slip motion may have recurred along the Kellyland fault zone in the late Paleozoic, probably the local response to the Alleghanian orogenesis more readily observed in folded and faulted Pennsylvanian rocks in eastern New Brunswick. Even later dip-slip reactivation occurred in Mesozoic (or younger) time, at least along the Waite fault zone. The history of the Norumbega fault system faulting thus spans at least 200 m.y., more than six times that of the San Andreas system.

The time table reported by West (1993, this volume) for shearing in the mid-crustal segment of the Norumbega fault system in southwestern and south-central Maine is very similar to that summarized in Figure 13, albeit with many of the same caveats, suggesting that it may be possible to correlate some events along the length of the system in Maine. Although some deformation in the two segments was certainly coeval, different deformation mechanisms are indicated for the two crustal levels. For example, crystal-plastic processes dominated Middle-Devonian faulting across the entire Norumbega fault system in the mid-crustal segment (West, 1993; Swanson, this volume), whereas brittle comminution produced cataclasites in

narrow high-strain zones at the same time in the epizonal segment. Now that Norumbega faulting has been characterized in both middle- and shallow-crustal segments, efforts can focus on other differences between the two, such as contrasting deformation mechanisms, strain distribution, and continuous versus sporadic shearing.

Uncertainty remains about the amount of dextral offset associated with the Norumbega fault system. The maximum values given above for the shallow segment—60 km during stage 1, 65–75 km during stage 2—are within the 150 km limit for total post-Devonian dextral movement imposed by paleomagnetic data for relative paleolatitudes of easternmost Maine and cratonic North America (Kent and Opdyke, 1984). Considering its length and width, the Norumbega fault system appears to have produced remarkably little displacement.

CONCLUSIONS

Faulting in the shallow-crustal segment of the Norumbega fault system spanned the end of one Wilson cycle and the beginning of another. Devonian and possible Permian dextral shearing accompanied the Acadian and Alleghanian orogenies, collisional events in the late Precambrian through late Paleozoic Appalachian cycle that involved closing one or more ocean basins. Stage 1 and stage 2 are tentatively attributed to plate adjustments following closing of the Fredericton depositional basin and accretion to North America of terranes outboard of the Miramichi belt during the Devonian Acadian orogeny (Ludman et al., 1993). Inferred Permian dextral activity on the Kellyland fault zone is possibly the only evidence for the climactic Alleghanian orogeny in this region. This final event in the Appalachian Wilson cycle juxtaposed the Meguma terrane of Nova Scotia with ancestral North America and was one of the last steps in the amalgamation of Pangaea. The latest (Jurassic or younger) dip-slip movement along the Waite fault zone is interpreted to be a result of the Mesozoic rifting that initiated the current Atlantic cycle.

Despite its longevity and association with two major regional accretionary events, the Norumbega fault system does not appear to have been a locus of significant lateral offset. Even the most generous estimates of dextral slip during stages 1 and 2, including both Acadian and Alleghanian motion, amount to less than 150 km. The Norumbega fault system thus presents an apparent paradox. Although it is more than 400 km long and 30–40 km wide, penetrates the entire crust steeply, and contains zones of high ductile and brittle strain, it does not seem to have played a major role in regional tectonic history. It cuts the entire crust today, and has probably done so since at least Jurassic time, but was it a major tectonic boundary before then? The data presented here indicate that it was not a locus of significant transcurrent motion and thus could not have bounded exotic terranes after emplacement of the Deblois and Bottle Lake plutons in Middle Devonian time.

Nevertheless, its longevity and areal extent imply that the Norumbega fault system has been a major zone of crustal weakness, perhaps inherited from pre-Devonian tectonism. The lack of evidence for shearing along the Norumbega fault system in the Fredericton belt before pluton intrusion suggests that, in order for this hypothesis to be valid, the progenitor of the current Norumbega fault system must predate the Late Ordovician through Middle Silurian deposition of the Fredericton strata.

ACKNOWLEDGMENTS

The research reported in this paper was supported by several Public Service Congress–City University of New York grants and National Service Foundation grant EAR-9218833. Ludman is grateful to several colleagues for introducing him to the mysteries of the Norumbega fault system, sharing their data and interpretations, and contributing to the evolution of the ideas presented here. Ludman also thanks Spike Berry, Patrick Brock, John Costain, Bill Doll, Susan Gibbons, Art Hussey, Mary Hubbard, Tomas Liogys, Bob Marvinney, Dave Stewart, Mark Swanson, Jan Tullis, Terry Tullis, John Walsh, and David P. West, Jr., for their help and encouragement, and is particularly indebted to Peter Gromet and Philip Osberg for extensive comments on an earlier draft that have significantly improved this paper.

REFERENCES CITED

Ayuso, R. A., Arth, J. G., Sinha, A. K., Carlson, J., and Wones, D. R., 1984, Comparative geochronology in the reversely zoned plutons of the Bottle Lake complex, Maine: U-Pb on zircons and Rb-Sr on whole rocks: Contributions to Mineralogy and Petrology, v. 88, p. 113–125.

Brock, P. C., 1993, Geology of parts of the Peach Lake and Brewster quadrangles, southeastern New York and adjacent Connecticut, and basement blocks of the north-central Appalachians [Ph.D. thesis]: New York, City University of New York, 494 p.

Coblentz, D. D., 1988, Crustal modeling in Maine through the simultaneous inversion of gravity and magnetic data [M.A. thesis]: Chestnut Hill, Massachusetts, Boston College, 82 p.

Concy, P. J., Jones, D. L., and Monger, J. W. H., 1980, Cordilleran suspect terranes: Nature, v. 288, p. 329–333.

Dillon, J. T., and Ehlig, P. L., 1993, Displacement on the southern San Andreas fault, in Powell, R. E., Weldon, R. J., II, and Matti, J. C., eds., The San Andreas fault system: Displacement, palinspastic reconstruction, and geologic evolution: Geological Society of America Memoir 178, p. 199–218.

Doll, W. E., Domoracki, W. J., Costain, J. K., Coruh, C., Ludman, A., and Hopeck, J. T., 1996, Implications of a seismic reflection profile across a part of the Norumbega fault system, east-central Maine: Geology, v. 24, p. 251–254.

Durling, P., and Marillier, F., 1990, Structural trends and basement rock subdivisions in the western Gulf of St. Lawrence, Northern Appalachians: Atlantic Geology, v. 267, p. 79–95.

Hibbard, J., and Hall, S., 1993, Early Acadian sinistral shear in north-central Maine: Geological Society of London Journal, v. 150, p. 815–818.

Higgins, K., 1992, The Norumbega Fault Zone, Great Pond, Maine [Masters thesis]: Orono, University of Maine: 94 p.

Holdsworth, R. G., 1994, Structural evolution of the Gander-Avalon terrane boundary: A reactivated transpression zone in the NE Newfoundland Appalachians: Geological Society of London Journal, v. 151, p. 629–646.

Hubbard, M. S., West, D. P., Jr., Ludman, A., Guidotti, C. V., and Lux, D. R., 1995, The Norumbega fault zone, Maine: A mid- to shallow-level crustal section within a transcurrent shear zone: Atlantic Geology, v. 31, p. 109–116.

Hussey, A. M., II, 1988, Lithotectonic stratigraphy, deformation, plutonism, and metamorphism, greater Casco Bay region, southwestern Maine, in

Tucker, R. D., and Marvinney, R. G., eds., Studies in Maine geology: Structure and stratigraphy: Augusta, Maine Geological Survey, p. 17–34.

James, E. W., Kimbrough, D. L., and Mattinson, J. M., 1993, Evaluation of displacements of pre-Tertiary rocks on the northern San Andreas fault using U-Pb zircon dating, initial Sr, and common Pb isotopic ratios, in Powell, R. E., Weldon, R. J., II, and Matti, J. C., eds., The San Andreas fault system: Displacement, palinspastic reconstruction, and geologic evolution: Geological Society of America Memoir 178, p. 257–272.

Johnson, T. D., and Wones, D. R., 1984, Sense and mode of shearing along the Norumbega fault zone, eastern Maine: Geological Society of America Abstracts with Programs, v. 16, p. 27.

Kent, D. V., and Opdyke, N. D., 1978, Paleomagnetism of the Devonian Catskill redbeds: Evidence for motion of the coastal New England–Canadian Maritime region relative to cratonic North America: Journal of Geophysical Research, v. 83, p. 4441–4450.

Kent, D. V., and Opdyke, N. D., 1984, A revised paleopole for the Mauch Chunk Formation of the Appalachians and its tectonic implications: Eos (Transactions, American Geophysical Union), v. 65, p. 200.

Keppie, J. D., 1989, Northern Appalachian terranes and their accretionary history, in Dallmeyer, R. D., ed., Terranes in the Circum-Atlantic Paleozoic orogens: Geological Society of America Special Paper 230, p. 159–192.

Krogh, T. E., 1973, A low contamination method for the hydrothermal decomposition of zircon and extraction of U and Pb for isotopic age determinations: Geochimica et Cosmochimica Acta, v. 37, p. 485–494.

Loiselle, M., Eriksson, S., Wones, D. R., and Sinha, A. K., 1983, Timing and emplacement of post-Acadian plutons in central and eastern Maine: Geological Society of America Abstracts with Programs, v. 15, p. 187.

Ludman, A., 1981, Significance of transcurrent faulting in eastern Maine and location of the suture between Avalonia and North America: American Journal of Science, v. 281, p. 463–483.

Ludman, A., 1991, The Fredericton Trough and Norumbega fault zone in eastern Maine, in Ludman, A., ed., Geology of the Coastal Lithotectonic Block and neighboring terranes, eastern Maine and southern New Brunswick: New England Intercollegiate Geological Conference Guidebook, v. 83, p. 186–208.

Ludman, A., 1998, Evolution of a transcurrent fault system in shallow crustal metasedimentary rocks: The Norumbega fault zone, eastern Maine: Journal of Structural Geology, v. 20, p. 93–107.

Ludman, A., and West, D. P., Jr., 1994, Constraints on timing of the multiple offset history of the Norumbega fault zone, eastern Maine: Geological Society of America Abstracts with Programs, v. 26, no. 3, p. 57.

Ludman, A., and West, D. P., Jr., 1996, "Cool" shallow-crustal generation of mylonite: Examples from the Norumbega fault zone, Maine: Geological Society of America Abstracts with Programs, v. 28, no. 3, p.

Ludman, A., Hopeck, J., and Brock, P. C., 1993, Nature of the Acadian orogeny in eastern Maine: in Roy, D. C., and Skehan, J. W., eds., The Acadian orogeny: Recent studies in New England, Maritime Canada, and the autochthonous foreland: Geological Society of America Special Paper 275, p. 67–84.

Ludwig, D. R., 1991a, PDAT—A computer program for processing Pb-U-Th isotope data, Version 1.20 (revision of March, 1991): U.S. Geological Survey Open File Report 88-542, 34 p.

Ludwig, D. R., 1991b, ISOPLOT—A plotting and regression program for radiogenic isotope data: U.S. Geological Survey Open-File Report 91-445, 41 p.

McLeod, M. J., Johnson, S. C., and Ruitenberg, A. A., 1994, Geological map of southwestern New Brunswick: New Brunswick Department of Natural Resources and Energy Map NR-5, scale 1:500,000.

Monger, J. W. H., and Irving, E., 1980, Northward displacement of north-central British Columbia: Nature, v. 285, p. 289–294.

Newberg, D. W., 1985, Bedrock geology of the Palermo 7.5' quadrangle, Maine: Maine Geological Survey Open File Report 84-4; 21 p.

Osberg, P. H., Hussey, A. M. II, and Boone, G. M., 1985, Bedrock geologic map of Maine: Augusta, Maine Geological Survey, scale 1:500,000.

Osberg, P. H., Tucker, R. D., and Berry, H. N., IV, 1995, Is the Acadian suture lost?, *in* Hussey, A. M., II, and Johnson, R. A., eds., Guidebook to field trips in southern Maine and adjacent New Hampshire: New England Intercollegiate Geological Conference Guidebook, v. 87, p. 145–171.

Pankiwskyj, K. A., 1996, Structure and stratigraphy across the Hackmatack Pond fault, Kennebec and Waldo counties, Maine: Maine Geological Survey Open File Report 96-2, 15 p.

Parrish, R. R., 1987, An improved microcapsule for zircon dissolution in U-Pb geochronology: Chemical Geology, v. 66, p. 99–102.

Stewart, D. B., 1989, Crustal processes in Maine: American Mineralogist, v. 74, p. 698–714.

Stewart, D. B., and Wones, D. R., 1974, Bedrock geology of the northern Penobscot Bay area, *in* Osberg, P. H., ed., Geology of east-central and north-central Maine: New England Intercollegiate Geological Conference Guidebook, v. 66, p. 223–239.

Stewart, D. B., Tucker, R. D., and West, D. P., Jr., 1995, Genesis of Silurian composite terrane in northern Penobscot Bay, *in* Hussey, A. M., II, and Johnston, R. A., eds., Guidebook to field trips in southern Maine and adjacent New Hampshire: New England Intercollegiate Geological Conference Guidebook, v. 87, p. 29–49.

Swanson, M. T., 1992, Late Acadian–Alleghenian transpressional deformation: Evidence from asymmetric boudinage in the Casco Bay area, coastal Maine: Journal of Structural Geology, v. 14, p. 323–341.

Swanson, M. T., 1994, Minimum dextral shear strain estimates in the Casco Bay area of coastal Maine from vein reorientation and elongation: Geological Society of America Abstracts with Programs, v. 26, n. , p. 75.

Tomascak, P. B., Krogstad, E. J., and Walker, R. J., 1996, U-Pb monazite geochronology of granitic rocks from Maine: Implications for late Paleozoic tectonics in the Northern Appalachians: Journal of Geology, v. 104, p. 185–195.

Tucker, R. D., and McKerrow, W. S., 1995, Early Paleozoic chronology: A review in light of new U-Pb zircon ages from Newfoundland and Britain: Canadian Journal of Earth Sciences, v. 32, p. 368–379.

West, D. P., Jr., 1993, Nature, timing, and extent of dextral shear deformation in south-central Maine [Ph.D. thesis]: Orono, University of Maine, 228 p.

West, D. P., Jr., 1995, The Norumbega fault zone in south-central Maine: A trip through 80 million years of dextral shear deformation, *in* Hussey, A. M. II, and Johnson, R. A., eds., Guidebook to field trips in southern Maine and adjacent New Hampshire: New England Intercollegiate Geological Conference Guidebook, v. 87, p. 125–143.

West, D. P., Jr., and Hubbard, M. S., 1997, Progressive localization of deformation during exhumation of a major strike-slip shear zone: Norumbega fault zone, south-central Maine, USA: Tectonophysics, v. 273, p. 185–202.

West, D. P., Jr., and Lux, D. R., 1993, Dating mylonitic deformation by the ^{40}Ar-^{39}Ar method: an example from the Norumbega fault zone, Maine: Earth and Planetary Science Letters, v. 120, p. 221–237.

West, D. P., Jr., Ludman, A., and Lux, D. R., 1992, Silurian age for the Pocomoonshine gabbro- diorite and its regional tectonic implications: American Journal of Science, v. 292, p. 253–273.

West, D. P., Jr., Lux, D. R., and Hussey, A. M., II, 1993, Contrasting thermal histories across the Flying Point fault, southwestern Maine: Evidence for Mesozoic displacement: Geological Society of America Bulletin, v. 105, p. 1478–1490.

Williams, H. S., 1978, Tectonic lithofacies map of the Appalachian orogen: St. Johns, Memorial University of Newfoundland Map 1a, scale 1:1,000,000.

Williams, H., and Hatcher, R. D., Jr., 1983, Appalachian suspect terranes, *in* Hatcher, R. D., Williams, H., and Zietz, I., eds., Contributions to the tectonics and geophysics of mountain chains: Geological Society of America Memoir 158, p. 33–53.

Williams, P. F., Goodwin, L. B., and LaFrance, B., 1995, Brittle faulting in the Canadian Appalachians and the interpretation of reflection seismic data: Journal of Structural Geology, v. 17, p. 215–232.

Zen, E-an, 1983, Exotic terranes in the New England Appalachians: Limits, candidates, and ages: A speculative essay, *in* Hatcher, R. D., Williams, H., and Zietz, I., eds., Contributions to the tectonics and geophysics of mountain chains: Geological Society of America Memoir 158, p. 55–81.

MANUSCRIPT ACCEPTED BY THE SOCIETY JUNE 9, 1998

Geological Society of America
Special Paper 331
1999

Modern earthquake activity and the Norumbega fault zone

John E. Ebel
Weston Observatory, Boston College, Weston, Massachusetts 02493
James A. Spotila
Division of Geological Sciences, Virginia Polytechnic Institute and State University, Blacksburg, Virginia 24061

ABSTRACT

The Norumbega fault zone of New Brunswick, Maine, and New Hampshire and beyond is one of the longest fault systems in northeastern North America. Since modern seismic monitoring began in New England in 1975, there have been many earthquakes, including some of the largest recorded during this time period, that have been located near the various traces of the Norumbega fault zone. There is also much earthquake activity located away from the fault zone in eastern Maine, southern Maine, and southern New Hampshire. Only a few focal mechanisms exist for earthquakes near the Norumbega fault zone in Maine, and these are dominantly thrust mechanisms; in only one case does a fault plane strike parallel to the local strand of the Norumbega fault zone. No evidence of Holocene tectonic faulting has yet been found on any fault within the Norumbega system, and on a regional scale the geomorphic expression of the fault is weak and not suggestive of Cenozoic activity. Thus, while there is earthquake activity spatially associated with the Norumbega fault zone, the current geological and geophysical data do not demonstrate that the Norumbega is an active fault zone.

INTRODUCTION

One of the major unsolved problems in seismic hazard evaluation in the northeastern United States is the lack of an understanding where large earthquakes might occur, how large those earthquakes can be, and how likely are such earthquakes. The earthquake history of the region currently available to us hints at the answers to this problem. However, due to the short time duration of that history relative to the long repeat times of large earthquakes, it only gives us a lower bound on how strong an earthquake centered in the region might be. The strongest well-documented earthquake in the northeastern United States is the 1755 earthquake off of Cape Ann, Massachusetts, estimated to have been about magnitude 6.0 (Street and Lacroix, 1979). Ebel (1996) suggested that an earthquake in 1638 may have been centered in north-central New England and had a magnitude of about 6.5. Earthquakes as strong as magnitude 7.0 have taken place along the St. Lawrence River in Quebec (Basham et al., 1979; Ebel, 1996). Further afield

in the eastern United States are the magnitude 7 earthquake at Charleston, South Carolina, in 1886 and the magnitude 8 earthquakes at New Madrid, Missouri, in 1811–1812 (Johnston et al., 1994). Can earthquakes as large as these take place in the northeastern United States? If so, where might they be centered and how strong might they be?

Johnston and Kanter (1990) and Johnston et al. (1994) accumulated information on the largest intraplate earthquakes from around the globe. Their primary findings indicate that intraplate earthquakes as large as magnitude 8 are possible and that the largest intraplate earthquakes occur in previously rifted crust, especially crust that was rifted in Mesozoic time or later. The lithosphere of the northeastern United States has undergone several episodes of rifting during the past one billion years, the most recent rifting even having occurred in the Triassic and Jurassic at the commencement of the opening of the modern Atlantic Ocean. Thus, qualitatively, the geologic history of the northeastern United States makes this region similar to other

Ebel, J. E., and Spotila, J. A., 1999, Modern earthquake activity and the Norumbega fault zone, *in* Ludman, A., and West, D. P., Jr., eds., Norumbega Fault System of the Northern Appalachians: Boulder, Colorado, Geological Society of America Special Paper 331.

areas that have undergone the largest intraplate earthquakes during the past several hundred years.

It is well established that the larger the magnitude of the earthquake, the larger the dimensions of the fault that moves and the greater the slip on that fault (Kanamori and Anderson, 1975; Nuttli, 1983; Johnston et al., 1994). For example, according to Nuttli (1983), intraplate earthquakes of Ms 6.0, 7.0, and 8.0 have average faults lengths of 11 km, 21 km, and 40 km, respectively, and average fault slips of 26 cm, 80 cm, and 252 cm, respectively. Johnston et al. (1994) presented data showing that the average lengths of surface faulting for moment magnitude 6.0, 7.0, and 8.0 earthquakes in intraplate regions are about 10 km, 45 km, and 230 km, respectively. From these numbers it is clear that for Charleston-sized (magnitude 7) or New Madrid-sized (magnitude 8) earthquakes to be possible in an intraplate setting like the northeastern United States, they must occur on structures that range from about 20 km to greater than 200 km in length. Thus, a search for evidence of large-magnitude past earthquakes or of the potential of future large earthquakes in the northeastern United States must focus on the major geologic features such as long faults, large plutons, and regional lineaments.

This study examines the modern seismicity and geology of a segment of one of the longest fault systems in the northeastern United States, the part of the Norumbega fault zone in the state of Maine. The primary motivation for this study is to address the question of whether there is any evidence that this fault zone is a candidate for modern large earthquakes (defined here to be earthquakes of magnitude 6.5 or greater). If large earthquakes can take place, how large might they be, where on the fault system might they take place, what kind of focal mechanism might they have, and what would be the repeat times of the large earthquakes? Also, what evidence might exist for recent large earthquakes?

REGIONAL SEISMICITY OF THE NORTHEASTERN UNITED STATES AND SOUTHEASTERN CANADA

We summarize briefly here the current earthquake activity of the northeastern United States and southeastern Canada. More detailed analyses were done by Ebel and Kafka (1991) and Ebel (1987).

Earthquakes are broadly scattered throughout the region, some areas having more small earthquakes than others (Fig. 1). The most active areas in and around the northeastern United States are in central New Brunswick, along the St. Lawrence River in Quebec, along a broad northwesterly trending zone in southwestern Quebec and southeastern Ontario, along coastal and western Maine, in central and southern New Hampshire, throughout eastern Massachusetts, along south coastal New England, in southern New York and northern New Jersey, along the Hudson River around Albany, in the Adirondack Mountains of New York State, and in western New York State. The spatial distribution of earthquake epicenters as inferred from historic data closely matches that delineated by modern instrumental seismic monitoring, indicating that those areas most seismically

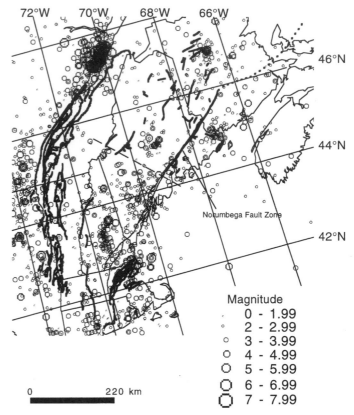

Magnitude
· 0 - 1.99
∘ 2 - 2.99
○ 3 - 3.99
○ 4 - 4.99
◯ 5 - 5.99
◯ 6 - 6.99
◯ 7 - 7.99

0   220 km

Figure 1. Map of the seismicity of New England and vicinity from 1534 to 1990. The symbol sizes are proportional to the estimated or computed magnitudes of the earthquakes. The bold lines show the locations of faults from the map of Williams (1978), and the lighter lines through southern Maine and New Hampshire and into Massachusetts show the Norumbega fault system from Osberg et al. (1989). The heavy dotted line starting at the northeastern end of the Norumbega fault system is a possible projection of the Norumbega system through Prince Edward Island (from Doll et al.,1996). The position of the cross section in Figure 3 is shown by the northwest-southeast dashed line from Quebec to the Maine coast.

active in the historic past continue to be active today (Ebel and Kafka, 1991).

The largest earthquakes in this region in the past few hundred years have generally been centered in one of these more active areas. The largest earthquakes have taken place in the Charlevoix seismic zone along the St. Lawrence River in Quebec. Other areas that have had large earthquakes this century are western Quebec at Timiskaming in 1935 (body wave magnitude, mb 6.2) and in central New Brunswick in 1982 (m_b 5.8). In New England the strong earthquakes were the 1638 and 1755 events, the 1904 earthquake centered near Eastport in downeast Maine (Lg wave magnitude, M_{Lg} 5.9; Leblanc and Burke, 1985), and a pair of M_L 5.5 (M_L = Richter magnitude) earthquakes at Ossipee, New Hampshire, in 1940 (Ebel et al., 1986).

The occurrence rates of the smaller earthquakes in the region have been used to estimate the average repeat times of earthquakes in New England. The most recent such estimates are that earthquakes of magnitude 5.0 and 6.0 have average repeat times of

60–94 yr and 447–1,035 yr, respectively (Williams et al., 1995). If magnitude 7.0 earthquakes are possible in New England, a linear extrapolation of the Gutenberg-Richter recurrence relation (Gutenberg and Richter, 1959; Richter, 1958) indicates that events of this size might average one every 4,300–11,000 yr.

Earthquake focal mechanisms and near-surface borehole stress measurements have been used to infer the modern regional stress directions in the northeastern United States (Ebel and Bouck, 1988; Ebel and Kafka, 1991). The crust of New England is under regional compression, the maximum stress direction being ~east-west. Whereas most of the earthquakes in New England have thrust mechanisms, the focal mechanisms of individual earthquakes in New England show great variation around this average. In southeastern Canada and northern and western New York State, the regional compression has a maximum stress direction oriented ~northeast-southwest. Most of the earthquakes in that area are also thrust events, although a few with predominant strike-slip movement have also been observed.

There have been no cases of surface faulting observed from modern earthquakes in the northeastern United States or southeastern Canada, although surface faulting was found from the 1989 Ungava earthquake of northern Quebec province. Most of the earthquakes have been so small that no surface faulting would be expected. Of the largest earthquakes during the past few decades, the 1988 mb 5.9 Saguenay earthquake was much too deep to cause surface faulting. The m_b 5.8 earthquake and accompanying events at Miramichi, New Brunswick, in 1982 caused some minor surface offsets of joints, but no primary tectonic faulting was found at the surface from the events at that locality (Wetmiller et al., 1984). No surface faulting has been discovered from earlier strong earthquakes known from the historic record in northeastern North America. Neither has there been any geologic study that has found definitive evidence for earthquake faulting in postglacial time.

HISTORY AND CURRENT STRUCTURE OF THE NORUMBEGA FAULT ZONE

The Norumbega fault zone is a system of primarily steeply dipping faults most clearly recognized in the Coastal lithotectonic block in Maine. It was first described as a single fault trace by Stewart and Wones (1974). Later work in Maine demonstrated that the Norumbega consists of zone of faulting that is at least 25 km wide in southwest Maine (West, this volume) to greater than 40 km in width in easternmost Maine (Ludman et al., this volume). The mapped extent of the Norumbega fault zone is mapped to Fredericton, New Brunswick, on the northeast, although the reflection results of Marillier et al. (1989) suggest that the Norumbega system may extend to north of Prince Edward Island. On the southwest the fault zone can be traced into southern New Hampshire, where it connects with some major faults in eastern Massachusetts and possibly into Connecticut and Rhode Island (Godstein and Hepburn, this volume; Bothner and Hussey, this volume). The Norumbega fault zone may extend more than 1,200 km if the interpretations from Prince Edward Island to Connecti-

cut are correct. In Maine where it has been most intensively studied and where it is the subject of this study, the Norumbega system has an extent of about 400 km (Fig. 2). It is one of the longest fault zones preserved in the crust of New England.

As described in previous studies and in the papers in this volume, the faults that compose the Norumbega fault system evidence a long history of motion and a variety of types of fault slip (Ludman, 1991). The fault probably formed as a dextral strike-slip fault during the later part of the Acadian orogeny in Devonian time, with a maximum offset of at least 125–150 km (Ludman, 1991; Ludman et al., this volume) and perhaps as much as 300 km (Swanson, this volume). The fault later underwent dip-slip motion in a tensional environment during the Mesozoic (Roberts and Williams, 1993; Ludman, this volume), followed by Permian dextral shearing (West, 1993, West, this volume; Ludman et al., this volume), and Jurassic and/or younger dip-slip faulting (Doll et al., 1996; West, this volume; Ludman et al., this volume). West et al. (1993) argued that the cooling history of rocks on either side of the fault in Maine requires ~4 km of dip-slip displacement (west side up) across one strand of the Norumbega fault zone, the Flying Point fault, during early Mesozoic time. Thus, even though the

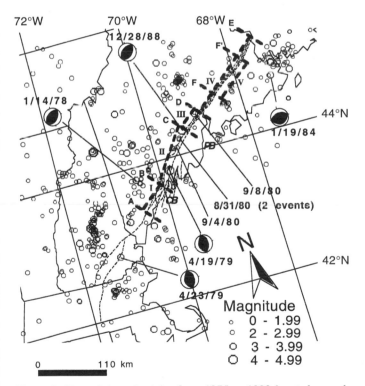

Figure 2. Map of the seismicity from 1975 to 1992 located near the Norumbega fault zone (light dashed lines). The traces of the Norumbega fault system are from Osberg et al. (1989). Also shown are the lower hemisphere focal mechanisms for those events on or near the Norumbega fault zone for which fault-plane solutions have been computed, as well as the locations of other earthquakes mentioned in the text. The heavy dashed lines and corresponding letters and numerals delineate segments of the fault zone with different topographic expressions, as described in the text. PB is Penobscot Bay and CB is Casco Bay.

fault zone is not currently considered to bound a major terrane, the evidence is strong that it underwent significant lateral and vertical displacements during at least 200 m.y. of activity.

At the Earth's surface the Norumbega fault zone is dominantly parallel to the structural grain of the regional geology. The fault zone changes exposure levels along trend in Maine. It is exposed in high-grade (amphibolite facies) rocks in southwest Maine, although the exposures are low grade (greenschist facies) along the northeastern part of the fault in eastern Maine (A. Ludman, 1996, personal commun.). There is geophysical evidence that the fault has a noticeable signature in the crust and into the upper mantle, at least along its eastern extent in Maine. Zhang (1992) analyzed data from the 1984 Maine Seismic Refraction Experiment (Murphy and Luetgert, 1986) cross-strike profile to determine the Poisson's ratio for the upper crust across Maine. According to this work the Norumbega fault zone just west of Penobscot Bay exhibits a high Poisson's ratio at least several kilometers into the crust (Fig. 3). This high Poisson's ratio is consistent with a highly fractured fault zone extending to these depths.

The Norumbega fault zone also has a signature at deeper crustal depths. Reflection profiling in the vicinity of the Bottle Lake Pluton showed that the Norumbega fault zone dips moderately to steeply to the northwest and offsets the Moho at that locality (Doll et al., 1996). Farther southwest, just northwest of Penobscot Bay, Unger et al. (1987) found a zone of disturbed Moho reflections beneath the trace of the Norumbega. The results from these reflection surveys coupled with the evidence of a highly fractured zone in the upper crust indicate that the Norumbega fault zone extends through the entire crust.

SEISMICITY IN THE VICINITY OF THE NORUMBEGA FAULT ZONE

One important indicator that a fault is active today is an alignment of earthquake hypocenters along the fault. Some active faults show high levels of earthquake activity at small and moderate magnitudes (e.g., the San Andreas fault in central California), and others show little or no minor magnitude seismicity (e.g., parts of the San Andreas fault near Los Angeles and San Francisco, California). Thus, although an alignment of epicenters of small earthquakes is evidence that a fault might be active, the absence of such seismicity does not, by itself, rule out the possibility that a fault can have a significant earthquake.

As is clear from Figures 1 and 2 and from an analysis of Ebel and Spotila (1992, 1993), since 1975, when modern instrumental monitoring became widely active in the region, there have been many earthquakes located near the various traces of the Norumbega fault zone. Since 1975 there have been five earthquakes of magnitude 4.0 or greater centered in New England; two of these five events are associated with the Norumbega fault zone. Much of the modern seismic activity has occurred along the Norumbega fault zone in central and southern Maine, along with some earthquakes along possible strands of the fault in southern New Hampshire. For example, from 1975 to 1991 there were 445 events in

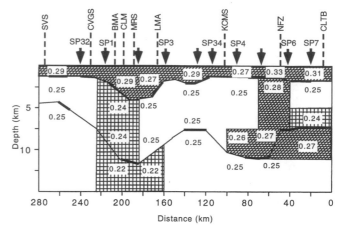

Figure 3. Variation of Poisson's ratio along the cross-strike refraction line from the 1984 Maine seismic refraction experiment conducted by the U.S. Geological Survey. Diagonally hachured areas have the high values of Poisson's ratio, square hachured areas have low values of Poisson's ratio, and unshaded areas have a Poisson's ratio of 0.25. The northwestern end of the line is on the left, and the southeastern end of the line is on the right (see Fig. 1) (from Zhang, 1992).

New England that released 7.0×10^{18} erg of energy. Of these, 35 events that released 7.4×10^{17} erg of energy were located near surficial strands of the Norumbega fault zone, with the following spatial distribution: 23 events (7.1×10^{17} erg) within 5 km of the surficial fault strands, an additional 7 events (1.4×10^{16} erg) between 5 and 10 km from the surficial fault strands, and an additional 5 events (1.6×10^{16} erg) between 10 and 15 km from the surficial fault strands. About 8% of all the earthquakes in New England and about 10% of the seismic energy release between 1975 and 1993 came from earthquakes within 15 km of one of the fault traces of the Norumbega fault zone. It is evident that most of the earthquakes associated with the Norumbega system took place within 5 km of one of the surficial fault strands, with fewer events out to 10 km and 15 km from the fault traces on the surface. However, there is also much earthquake activity located away from fault zone in eastern Maine, southern Maine, and southern New Hampshire, and it would be difficult to delineate the Norumbega fault zone from a map of the epicenters without knowing a priori where the fault is found. There are no unusual concentrations of epicenters observed along the fault. Thus, the spatial pattern of modern earthquake activity does not support the idea that the Norumbega is an active fault.

However, on closer inspection of the modern earthquake data there are some intriguing hints of associations of some particular earthquakes with the Norumbega fault system. In April 1979, there was a coda-wave magnitude (M_c) 4.0 earthquake near Bath, Maine.

The main shock was located several kilometers from mapped traces of the fault and had a thrust mechanism on a north-south–striking fault plane. However, several small aftershocks following this event were recorded on portable seismographs, and all of these aftershocks were located at 7 km depth directly beneath the surface trace of the Cape Elizabeth fault strand of the Norumbega system (Ebel, 1983). Although it is not clear if this mainshock took place on a fault of the Norumbega system, the aftershocks did. One interpretation of the data is that the mainshock was mislocated and it was centered where the aftershocks were located. Another interpretation is that the mainshock did not take place on the Norumbega fault zone but that it triggered some minor seismicity on the fault. In either case, the well-located aftershocks demonstrate that there was earthquake activity in 1979 that was located directly in the Norumbega fault zone.

An unusual sequence of earthquakes, seemingly associated with the Norumbega fault zone, was observed in Maine in 1980. Over nine days, four earthquakes were recorded at different locations along the fault. These earthquakes spanned a total distance of about 60 km (Fig. 2). This temporal-spatial pattern of earthquakes has a very low chance of occurring randomly, and it suggests that these earthquakes were somehow causally related. No other such pattern of several earthquakes occurring on a single geologic feature over a short time span has been detected from anywhere in northeastern North America. This burst of minor earthquake activity along a 60 km segment of the fault hints that a significant stretch of the fault could be related mechanically. If this part of the fault zone failed in a single event, that event would be larger than magnitude 7.0.

None of these observations show that the Norumbega fault zone is currently active. However, they can be taken as indications that the association of the local earthquakes and the fault is worthy of continued study.

FOCAL MECHANISMS OF EARTHQUAKES ALONG THE NORUMBEGA FAULT ZONE

Another clue that a mapped fault is seismically active is the demonstration that earthquakes on the fault are associated with slip on the fault contact at depth. In this case, if the fault is active, one would expect that the focal mechanisms of the earthquakes along the fault should have one nodal plane with an orientation approximately parallel to the fault surface, the direction of slip on that fault plane being driven by the regional stress field. Clearly, the more seismicity with this characteristic that is recorded along a fault, the more convincing the evidence that the fault is currently active. Because a focal mechanism solution for an earthquake determines two possible, mutually orthogonal fault planes for the event, there is always some ambiguity as to which of the two planes is the possible fault plane unless independent evidence on this issue can be found. Thus, even with well-determined focal mechanism solutions, it can be difficult to demonstrate that local earthquake focal mechanisms are consistent with movement on a mapped fault.

Earthquake focal mechanisms and borehole stress measurements have been used by several investigators (e.g., Ebel and Kafka, 1991; Zoback and Zoback, 1991) to show that New England is currently in a horizontal compressive stress regime, the maximum compressive stress direction being very close to east-west. Most of the earthquakes in the region have thrust focal mechanisms, although a few strike-slip mechanisms have been observed. Normal faulting mechanisms are almost completely absent in the region. Although the average maximum stress direction is east-west, some individual focal mechanisms have a P-axis that deviates significantly from this average direction (Ebel and Kafka, 1991; Ebel and Bouck, 1988).

On or near the Norumbega fault zone there have been only a few earthquakes for which sufficient instrumental data exist that focal mechanism solutions can been computed. These mechanisms are shown in Figure 2. The focal mechanism for the April 18, 1979, earthquake in Bath, Maine, shows that the fault plane for that main shock was not parallel to the local strike of the mapped traces of the Norumbega fault zone, but rather that the fault-plane trend is very close to a north-striking feature (the Phippsburg fault) inferred from the local topography (Ebel, 1983). The December 28, 1988, earthquake in Albion, Maine, had moderately dipping nodal planes with strikes parallel to the Norumbega fault zone. That earthquake could have been associated with some moderately dipping fault that crops out within the Norumbega system. The Hackmatack Pond fault could be such a feature (Stewart et al., 1995). In New Hampshire there is one thrust focal mechanism with north-south–striking nodal planes near a possible trace of the Norumbega fault zone.

There are two focal mechanisms in Maine for earthquakes that were not along the Norumbega fault zone directly but were located relatively near the fault zone. Near Passamaquoddy Bay in eastern Maine there is an earthquake focal mechanism showing movement associated with north-south maximum compression. The nodal planes for that event are moderately dipping and strike east-west. In southwestern Maine there is an event focal mechanism that is similar to that for the 1988 Albion earthquake, which took place about 125 km to the southwest.

The current stress field in New England favors thrust earthquakes on northwest-southeast– to north-south–striking fault planes. Strike-slip events with northeast-southwest–striking fault planes (with right-lateral movement) or northwest-southeast–striking fault planes (with left-lateral movement) are also possible. Thus, if the near-vertical parts of the Norumbega fault zone can have a large earthquake, that event would most likely be a right-lateral strike-slip event along the fault. If a large thrust earthquake can take place near the Norumbega fault system, it would most likely take place on one of the thrust faults that are subparallel to or within the Norumbega system. The Norumbega fault zone is composed of a complicated system of anastomosing strands and secondary thrusts that could have been produced while the fault zone was undergoing its major strike-slip motion. The Norumbega system probably has a multitude of different strands and fault planes of different orientations, so that some are bound to be favorable for reactivation as thrust events in the present-day stress field. A third possibility is that a large, modern earthquake could nucleate in the existing fault zone but rupture in a new direction (e.g., as a northwest over southeast thrust event). The 1988 Albion event is the only one located on the Norumbega fault system with a fault plane parallel to the strike of the Norumbega fault zone. This thrust event is inconsistent with the strike-slip scenario described here, but it supports the idea that a thrust fault within or near the Norumbega could be activated or that rupture in a new direction could take place. In general, the available focal mechanism data cannot be used to argue that the Norumbega fault zone is currently seismically active.

NEOTECTONIC HISTORY OF THE NORUMBEGA FAULT ZONE

The most important clues that a fault is currently active are indications of neotectonic deformations along the fault. Evidence of Holocene slip on a fault is the most convincing evidence that a fault is active. However, neotectonic indications that a fault is active do not constrain the largest magnitude that might occur on that fault. The minimum largest magnitude is constrained by the size of the largest Holocene earthquake that is known to have taken place on the fault. The fault length would constrain the maximum earthquake size of which the fault is capable. Generally, for any fault the largest earthquake that might take place on that fault is somewhere between these two extremes.

For the Norumbega fault zone the neotectonic information is ambiguous as to whether the fault might be active and capable of a large earthquake. Some minor postglacial offsets have been discovered in the vicinity of the Norumbega fault zone in eastern Maine (Thompson, 1981). All were bedding-plane faults found in a single formation in Maine (the Vassalboro) and were confined to surfaces only a few meters in length. The cause of these offsets is unknown, and they cannot be clearly identified as being of tectonic origin. No other offsets that might be indicative of geologically recent active faulting have been reported.

An examination of the 7 1/2 minute topographic maps of the Norumbega fault zone in Maine has also failed to identify any landforms that may have been caused by multiple episodes of significant fault movement. These 1:24,000 scale maps show topography with 10 or 20 ft contours, so that only landforms greater than a few tens of meters in dimension can be identified by this kind of analysis. The southwestern part of the fault examined this study (section I, A to B in Fig. 2) has no topographic expression. For a long distance to the northeast (section II, B to C in Fig. 2) the fault zone is expressed as a number of north-northeast– to northeast–trending lineaments. These lineaments were probably produced by the differential erosion of bedrock types juxtaposed by the fault zone, but they also represent a more regional geologic fabric. Farther to the northeast (section III, C to D in Fig. 2) these lineaments are crossed by a number of northwest-trending drainages and glacial features that likely overprinted the geologic fabric during the last glaciation. This northwest-trending overprint continues to the New Brunswick border (section IV, D to E in Fig. 2), and in places the fault zone has no topographic expression. For a significant length of this stretch (section V, F to F', Fig. 2), however, the fault zone is expressed by a prominent lineament and discontinuous bedrock escarpment that is more than 50 m high in places. This feature corresponds to lithologic juxtapositions across the fault strands and has clearly been modified by the northwest-trending erosional overprint. Near the New Brunswick border (F' to E, Fig. 2) the fault strands are marked by irregular topographic deflections and small northwest-facing knobs, which cannot be explained by lithologic juxtapositions. These irregularities seem to perturb the course of the Saint Croix River and may indicate relict surficial displacement that has not yet been eroded down.

Nowhere along the fault are there surface features that might have been formed by postglacial tectonic activity, and none of the topographic disruptions of cross-fault glacial features can be shown as specific offsets across the fault. The sense of vertical separation along the various northeast lineaments that make up the surface trace of the Norumbega is inconsistent along much of the length of the fault zone. The majority of the fault is in flat or mountainous regions in which there is no vertical separation, but one-third of the fault zone has escarpments that are evenly split between northwest and southeast side up. An exception to this is the northeastern stretch of the fault zone near the New Brunswick border, where the majority of northeast-trending escarpments show southeast side up vertical separation. Although most of these escarpments can be explained by differential erosion and lithologic contrasts across the fault, some of them may represent relict surficial displacement. Because the dominant drainage direction along this extent is northwest to southeast, the northwest-facing features along the fault are counter that which would be expected for erosion. This suggests that dip-slip motion along the fault produced uplift on the southeast that has not been fully eroded down. This apparent vertical topographic separation corresponds to the sense of offset on the Moho resolved in a seismic line across this stretch of the fault zone (Doll et al., 1996). Although it is difficult to judge how long such uplift could survive erosion, the subdued topographic expression could easily be pre-Quaternary. It is even possible that normal faulting in the Mesozoic produced topographic uplift that has been retained despite erosion throughout the Cenozoic.

This topographic examination of the Norumbega fault zone thus shows no evidence for modern strike-slip or reverse reactivation of the fault at the 1:24,000 scale. In general, the entire trace of the zone could not be identified on the basis of topography alone (a priori), suggesting that the Norumbega is not a major active fault. All of the geomorphic features we identified can be explained by differential erosion, glacial processes, or relict topography associated with pre-Cenozoic faulting.

DISCUSSION

The purpose of this study is to examine critically the hypothesis that the Norumbega fault zone might be an active fault, potentially capable of a significant earthquake. The evidence to support such a hypothesis is not totally lacking, but it is sparse. Whereas there is some seismicity that has located very near or on the fault, the activity rate is only slightly elevated relative to the average for the region. One burst of earthquake activity along a 60 km extent of the Norumbega fault zone may indicate that earthquakes above magnitude 7.0 are possible on the fault. The few earthquake focal mechanisms that are available are unable to confirm that slip has occurred on the preexisting fault surface. No definitive geologic indicators of significant surface slip in Holocene time have been found. Thus, at this time the Norumbega fault zone cannot be argued to be an active fault. Future geologic work and the continued accumulation of earthquake data will undoubtedly add new evidence to this question in the future.

If future evidence does come to light supporting the idea that the Norumbega fault zone is capable of significant earthquakes, many new questions will need to be addressed. A fault as long as the Norumbega system usually does not rupture along its entirety in a single earthquake, but rather it has a number of earthquakes along different segments of the fault. If the Norumbega is active, then the segmentation of possible ruptures along the fault would need to be determined. Another question that would need to be addressed is that of determining the repeat times of the large earthquakes on the fault. A determination of the largest possible earthquake along different segments of the fault would need to be made.

The ambiguity concerning the potential seismic activity of the Norumbega fault zone, as documented in this study, is typical of that for most major faults and other structures in central and eastern North America. This is due to the relatively low seismicity rates in the region, because the earthquake data that are most important for determining which geologic structures are capable of generating the largest earthquakes inherently accumulate very slowly. Relatively rapid erosion rates and dense vegetation quickly mask many of the geologic indicators of neotectonic movements, also making new advances difficult. Persistence and continued vigilance of the earthquake activity are needed to advance our understanding of these important issues of seismic hazard.

REFERENCES CITED

Basham, P. W., Weichert, D. H., and Berry, M. J., 1979, Regional assessment of seismic risk in eastern Canada: Seismological Society of America Bulletin, v. 69, p. 1567–1602.

Doll, W. E., Domoracki, W. J., Costain, J. K., Çoruh, C., Ludman, A., and Hopeck, J. T., 1996, Seismic reflection evidence for the evolution of a transcurrent fault system: The Norumbega fault zone, Maine: Geology, v. 24, p. 251–254.

Ebel, J. E., 1983, A detailed study of the aftershocks of the 1979 earthquake near Bath, Maine: Earthquake Notes, v. 54, p. 27–40.

Ebel, J. E., 1987, The seismicity of the northeastern United States, seismic hazards, ground motions, soil-liquefaction and engineering practice in eastern North America: National Center for Earthquake Engineering Research, NCEER-87-0025, p. 178–188.

Ebel, J. E., 1996, The seventeenth century seismicity of northeastern North America: Seismological Research Letters, v. 67, p. 51–68.

Ebel, J. E., and Bouck, B. R., 1988, New focal mechanisms for the New England region: Constraints for the regional stress regime: Seismological Research Letters, v. 59, p. 183–187.

Ebel, J. E., and Kafka, A. L., 1991, Earthquake activity in the northeastern United States, *in* Slemmons, D. B., Engdal, E. R., Zoback, M. D., and Blackwell, D. D., eds., Neotectonics of North America: Boulder, Colorado, Geological Society of America, Map Volume 1, p. 277–290.

Ebel, J. E., and Spotila, J. A., 1992, Seismicity along the Norumbega Fault in New England: Implications for seismic hazard in the northeast United States: Geological Society of America Abstracts with Programs, p. 17.

Ebel, J. E., and Spotila, J. A., 1993, The relationship between earthquakes and regional geology in New England: EOS, Transactions of the American Geophysical Union, v. 74, no. 16, p. 288, Supplement.

Ebel, J. E., Somerville, P. G., and McIver, J. D., 1986, A study of the source parameters of some large earthquakes of northeastern North America: Journal of Geophysical Research, v. 91, p. 8231–8247.

Gutenberg, B., and Richter, C. F., 1959, Seismicity of the Earth and associated phenomena (second edition): Princeton, New Jersey, Princeton University Press, 310 p.

Johnston, A. C., and Kanter, L. R., 1990, Earthquakes in stable continental crust: Scientific American, v. 262, p. 68–75.

Johnston, A.C., Coppersmith, K. J., Kanter, L. R., and Cornell, C. A., 1994, The earthquakes of stable continental regions: Palo Alto, California, Electric Power Research Institute Report TR-102261-V1, 342 p.

Kanamori, H., and Anderson, D. L., 1975, Theoretical basis of some empirical relations in seismology: Seismological Society of America Bulletin, v. 65, p. 1073–1095.

Leblanc, G., and Burke, K. B. S., 1985, Re-evaluation of the 1817, 1855, 1869 and 1904 Maine–New Brunswick area earthquakes: Earthquake Notes, v. 56, p. 107–124.

Ludman, A., 1991, The Fredericton trough and Norumbega fault in eastern Maine, *in* Ludman, A., ed., Geology of the Coastal lithotectonic block and neighboring terranes, eastern Maine and southern New Brunswick: New England Intercollegiate Geological Conference Guidebook, v. 83, p. 186–208.

Marillier, F., Keen, C. E., Stockmal, G. S., Quinlan, G., Williams, H., Colman-Sadd, S. P., and O'Brien, S. J., 1989, Crustal structure and surface zonation of the Canadian Appalachians: Implication of the deep seismic reflection data: Canadian Journal of Earth Sciences, v. 26, p. 305–321.

Murphy, J. M., and Luetgert, J. H., 1986, Data report for the Maine-Quebec cross-strike seismic-refraction profile: U.S. Geological Survey Open-File Report 86–47, 71 p.

Nuttli, O. W., 1983, Average seismic source-parameter relations for mid-plate earthquakes: Seismological Society of America Bulletin, v. 73, p. 519–536.

Osberg, P. H., Tull, J. F., Robinson, P., Hon, R., and Butler, J. R., 1989, The Acadian orogen, *in* Hatcher, R. D., Jr., Thomas, W. A., and Viele, G. W., eds., The Appalachian-Ouachita orogen in the United States: Boulder, Colorado, Geological Society of America, Geology of North America, v. F-2, p. 179–232.

Richter, C. F., 1958, Elementary seismology: San Francisco, California, W. H. Freeman and Company, 768 p.

Roberts, W., and Williams, P. F., 1993, Evidence for early Mesozoic extensional faulting in Carboniferous rocks, southern New Brunswick, Canada: Canadian Journal of Earth Sciences, v. 30, p. 1324–1331.

Stewart, D. B., and Wones, D. R., 1974, Bedrock geology of northern Penobscot Bay area, *in* Osberg, P. H., ed., Geology of east-central and north-central Maine: New England Intercollegiate Geological Conference Guidebook, v. 64, p. 223–239.

Stewart, D. B., Unger, J. D., and Hutchinson, D. R., 1995, Silurian tectonic history of Penobscot Bay region, Maine: Atlantic Geology, v. 31, p. 67–79.

Street, R., and LaCroix, A., 1979, An empirical study of New England seismicity: 1727–1977: Seismological Society of America Bulletin, v. 69, p. 159–175.

Thompson, W. B., 1981, Postglacial faulting in the vicinity of the Norumbega fault zone, eastern Maine: U.S. Geological Survey Open-File Report

No. 81-1039, 22 p.

Unger, J. D., Stewart, D. B., and Phillips, J. D., 1987, Interpretation of migrated seismic reflection profiles across the northern Appalachians in Maine: Royal Astronomical Society Geophysical Journal, v. 89, p. 171–176.

West, D. P., Jr., 1993, Nature, timing, and extent of dextral shear deformation in south-central Maine [Ph.D. thesis]: Orono, University of Maine, 228 p.

West, D. P., Jr., , Lux, D. R., and Hussey, A. M., II, 1993, Contrasting thermal histories across the Flying Point fault, southwestern Maine: Evidence for Mesozoic displacement: Geological Society of America Bulletin, v. 105, p. 1478–1490.

Wetmiller, R. J., Adams, J., Anglin, F. M., Hasegawa, H. S., and Stevens, A. E., 1984, Aftershock sequences of the 1982 Miramichi, New Brunswick, earthquake: Seismological Society of America Bulletin, v. 74, p. 621–654.

Williams, H., 1978, Tectonic lithofacies map of the Appalachian orogen: St. Johns, Memorial University of Newfoundland, Map no. 1a, scale 1:1,000,000.

Williams, M. E., Nishenko, S. P., and Ebel, J. E., 1995, Proceedings of the Working Group Meeting on Northeast United States Earthquake Probability: U.S. Geological Survey Open-File Report 94–643, 24 p.

Zhang, W., 1992, Variation of shear wave velocity and Poisson's ratio across the northern Appalachian orogen in Maine and Quebec [M. S. thesis]: Chestnut Hill, Massachusetts, Boston College, 115 p.

Zoback, M. D., and Zoback, M. L., 1991, Tectonic stress field of North America and relative plate motions, *in* Slemmons, D. B., Engdahl, E. R., Zoback, M. D., and Blackwell, D. D., eds., Neotectonics of North America: Boulder, Colorado, Geological Society of America, Map Volume 1, p. 339–366.

MANUSCRIPT ACCEPTED BY THE SOCIETY JUNE 9, 1998